THE
PRACTICAL
BUILDER

A COMPREHENSIVE AND AUTHORITATIVE GUIDE
TO THE LATEST METHODS OF MODERN
BUILDING PRACTICE

Edited by

R. GREENHALGH, *A.I.Struct.E.*

ODHAMS PRESS LIMITED, LONG ACRE, LONDON, W.C.2

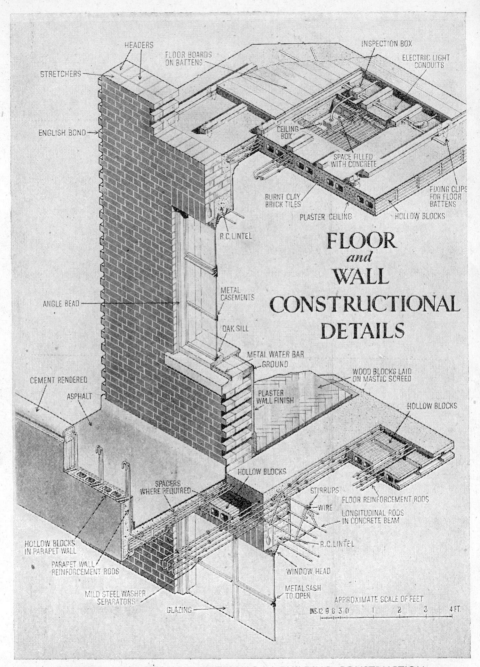

FLOOR *and* WALL CONSTRUCTIONAL DETAILS

Labels within the illustration:

HEADERS
FLOOR BOARDS ON BATTENS
INSPECTION BOX
ELECTRIC LIGHT CONDUITS
STRETCHERS
ENGLISH BOND
CEILING BOX
SPACE FILLED WITH CONCRETE
BURNT CLAY BRICK TILES
FIXING CLIPS FOR FLOOR BATTENS
PLASTER CEILING
HOLLOW BLOCKS
R.C. LINTEL
METAL CASEMENTS
ANGLE BEAD
OAK SILL
METAL WATER BAR
GROUND
WOOD BLOCKS LAID ON MASTIC SCREED
PLASTER WALL FINISH
HOLLOW BLOCKS
CEMENT RENDERED
ASPHALT
HOLLOW BLOCKS
STIRRUPS
WIRE
FLOOR REINFORCEMENT RODS
LONGITUDINAL RODS IN CONCRETE BEAM
SPACERS WHERE REQUIRED
R.C. LINTEL
HOLLOW BLOCKS IN PARAPET WALL
PARAPET WALL REINFORCEMENT RODS
WINDOW HEAD
MILD STEEL WASHER SEPARATORS
METAL SASH TO OPEN
GLAZING
APPROXIMATE SCALE OF FEET
INS 12 9 6 3 0   1   2   3   4 FT.

MODERN METHODS AND MATERIALS IN BUILDING CONSTRUCTION

Isometric drawing showing construction of wall, floor and balcony for a block of flats. The wall is in English bond. The floor is of reinforced-concrete ribs supporting hollow floor blocks. Floor clips are embedded in concrete to fix the floor battens. The balcony is of cantilever construction with vertical reinforcement. The windows are metal casements.

CONTENTS

STEEL-FRAME CONSTRUCTION

Construction of a large steel-frame building. Bricklayers are at work on the walls, which are faced with glazed bricks. The shuttering for the concrete floors is supported from the floor level. Note how the raking shores are used to support the old building on the right.

CHAPTER 1

PREPARATORY WORK

Choice of site. Freehold and leasehold terms. Functions of architect. Plans. Specifications. Quantities. Foundations. Shoring. Builders' plant. Use of concrete. Time schedules : Stonework. Brickwork. Carpentry and joinery. Plumbing. Heating and ventilating. Electrical work. Painting.

BEFORE a start is made on actual building work, many preliminary steps have to be taken. The site has to be decided, the land purchased or leased; the building has to be designed to suit the client, plans have to be prepared, and passed by the local authority. Usually the quantities of building materials and labour to erect the building are calculated, and a builder who will do the job for a satisfactory price is selected. The site has then to be surveyed, and the lines of the plan set out so that the trenches for the walls can be dug. Possibly demolition of previous premises has to take place.

Building Sites

Street hoardings may have to be erected, huts built for workmen and stores. Forethought has to be displayed to ensure that work will run smoothly, and time-charts are very often made which give the dates on which the various sections of the work must be completed, so that the numerous operations and material supplies will work in harmony without hold-up in the building routine. Illustrations to show how these preliminaries operate will follow later, in items such as a job time-chart and preliminaries to tradesmen's work.

For a start let us suppose that a person, firm or public body is desirous of investing in the erection of a dwelling-house, a factory or warehouse block, or business or public offices, on either a city, town, or country site.

A plot of land is the first requirement for any building project, and the choice and method by which it is secured vary with each scheme: the public or private office block is required near the hub of the business section or community; the block of flats is wanted in a desirable residential area; steel smelting and rolling works in the vicinity of coal and iron ore supplies. The site for each building scheme has to be treated on its merits.

Land may be purchased outright as freehold, which includes complete ownership, and carries with it deeds of title giving claim to absolute possession. On the other hand, land may be purchased for a period of years, during which time it is held under a lease, and is then known as leasehold land.

Securing the Land

The term of a lease may be any agreed length of time, as 999 years, 99 years, 75 years, one or all of which are common to some parts of England, or down to the indefinite period of one or two lives in years. Freehold land is free from ground rents; leasehold land is subject to a yearly ground-rent charge. The "feu" term is common in Scotland, where land is owned by the laird; tenure conditions include in some cases the performance of some services by the tenant, or a stipulated annual rental.

Building land, whether obtained free-hold, leasehold, or by any other method, requires that the title to land ownership must be proved to the purchaser; and to negotiate this matter, it is necessary to engage the services of a solicitor.

It will be appreciated that city and town dwelling-house building sites have the advantage of public services, such as main drainage, water supply, gas, and electricity; such services are not always available for a country site.

The introduction of these services where not obtainable needs considera-tion, otherwise the cost figure of a com-pleted block may be excessive; sinking a well, installing an electric generating set, or forming a septic tank with service and outfall drains, add heavy costs.

Nature of Subsoil

A building plot which is suitable in position may not be desirable for other reasons. Given the choice, it would be foolish to turn down a chalk-gravel or rock foundation for one of waterlogged, boggy earth or moving sand. The chalk foundation has splendid weight-bearing values, besides being dry and free from ground mists and damp conditions.

Gravel also ensures a dry and sound foundation for a building site, while rock provides maximum stability, but may prove costly if parts of the building site have to be removed.

Waterlogged earth is treacherous for carrying the loads of a building during a dry-weather spell, and it is humid, damp and cold at other times. Boggy earth has the same drawbacks as water-logged foundations with the added dis-advantage of its being liable to lateral movement.

Loose, moving or quicksand soils are extremely difficult grounds on which to erect any type of building, involving costly operations in labour and materials. There are standards of building loads, laid down by the local and county authorities, fixing the maximum weights which the ground may carry. Those for the London area will be found on p. 16.

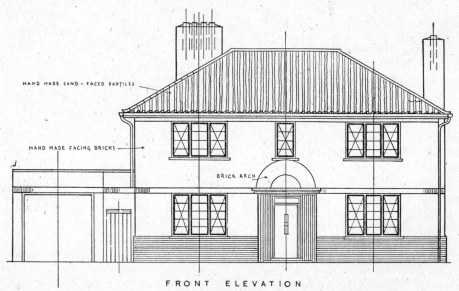

HAND MADE SAND - FACED PANTILES

HAND MADE FACING BRICKS

BRICK ARCH

FRONT ELEVATION

Fig. I. Front elevation, drawn to scale, showing general treatment and main features of design. Typical examples of architect's drawings for a dwelling-house are shown in Figs. I to 9.

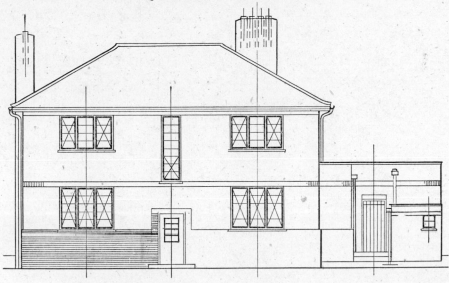

ELEVATION TO GARDEN.

Fig. 2. Back elevation to garden with open access to yard area offices and garage. The garage is set back in order to clear the scullery windows as shown in Fig. 6.

Assuming that the project is a dwelling-house in a town suburb it is first of all necessary to consider the main features and sizes and types of rooms required; and if the client is wise he will appoint a qualified architect to look after his interests.

The architect takes the specified particulars of his client, and proceeds to plot them to scale on paper, arranging his plan with a view to obtaining the maximum of sunshine and seclusion for home and garden. The placing of the pantry in a northerly position, and similar minor but vital arrangements, are matters in which the architect's fund of experience may be of great benefit to the client.

A bathroom having a north aspect, with water service pipes attached to the inside of an external wall—which may freeze when a wintry north wind blows —can become very costly in maintenance. Foresight and care in initial decisions are paying business propositions for every type of building project.

The client who invites an architect to serve him in a building scheme is required to conform to standard terms and conditions; and when agreement is reached the architect practically becomes proxy for the client in the execution of the building project. He reviews the main general features, and submits plans and elevations after surveying the site area; and he links up with the local council regarding by-law conditions, such as building line, set-backs for street improvements, drains, thickness of walls for height of building, and similar matters.

Choice of Materials

The architect also considers and recommends suitable building materials and labour which are available in the district, and decides whether brick, stone or timber supplies predominate in quantities sufficiently to influence the character of the building shell and internal finishings.

When particulars are tentatively

THREE TYPICAL MODERN BUILDING OPERATIONS

Above: View of underside of floor with all centring struck; the steel floor and stanchions to right have been concreted in; note the Ang-Kary racks for supporting form-work still in position under main beam.   Compare with illustrations Fig. 34 and Fig. 35 for speed in fixing and dismantling.

On opposite page (top): A $\frac{1}{2}$-cubic yard concrete mixer, with gauge and elevator; the revolving drum in which the cement, sand, coarse aggregate and water are mixed is shown to the left.   The filling process is shown proceeding during mixing and discharge operation.

On opposite page (bottom): Type of bench in common use by plumbers during preliminary assembly of parts by jointing; connections of waste pipes and traps are shown.   Preassembling has the advantages of freedom for wiping, soldering, and finishing branch joints, and for fixing economy.

settled between the architect and client, the rough-dimensioned sketches which have been prepared provide a medium for obtaining cubical contents from which an approximate cost figure, based on work executed of a similar character, is obtainable; and thus the stage for preparing final and working drawings is reached.

For a straightforward dwelling-house the drawings generally include:—

1. *Block Plan.* Drawn to a small scale, showing the location of the site in relation to the surrounding or adjoining properties or roadways.

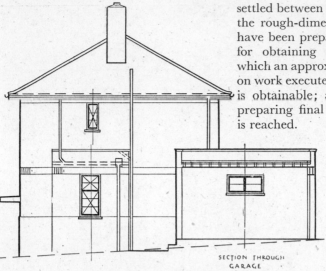

Fig. 3. Side elevation of dwelling-house with section through garage showing the method of roof construction.

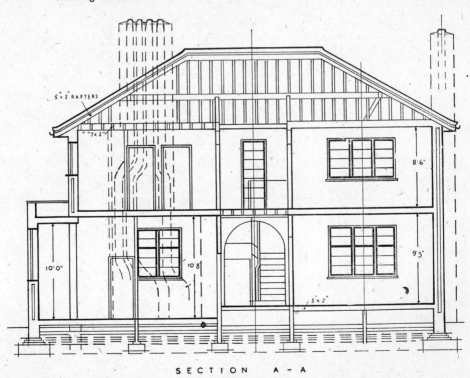

SECTION A — A

Fig. 4. Main section on the line A—A through dwelling-house, showing constructional details from footings to ridge. Refer also to the ground-floor plan in Fig. 6, and first-floor plan in Fig. 7.

2. *Foundation Plan.* Usually drawn to $\frac{1}{8}$-in. or $\frac{1}{4}$-in. scale, showing the lay-out of trenches, concrete and brick foundations and footings of external, internal and ground-floor dwarf walls.

3. *Ground-Floor Plan.* Showing the arrangement and sizes of all the ground-floor rooms with the internal walls supporting the floor over, as well as partitions built later to divide up the ground-floor areas into the requisite rooms and accommodation.

4. *First-Floor Plan and any upper separate floors.* Details of the arca spacing of the landing, bath and other rooms, with the positions of internal walls carried up to support the roof timbers. Position of fireplaces, window and door openings and the like.

Roof Plan. Shows the roof lay-out—whether simple span or pitched roof

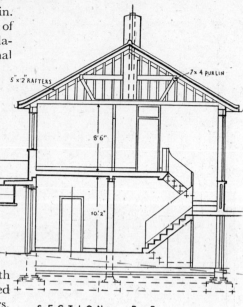

S E C T I O N   B.- B.

Fig. 5. Section on the line B—B showing constructional features at right-angles to those detailed in section A—A. *See also* **Figs. 4 and 6**

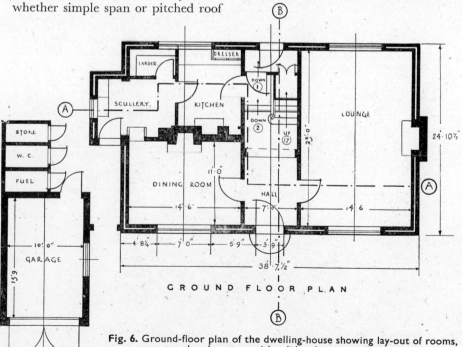

G R O U N D   F L O O R   P L A N

Fig. 6. Ground-floor plan of the dwelling-house showing lay-out of rooms, courtyard and garage, with solid and cavity walls depicted.

Fig. 7. First-floor plan showing lay-out of upper-storey rooms and roof finish of the one-storey block.

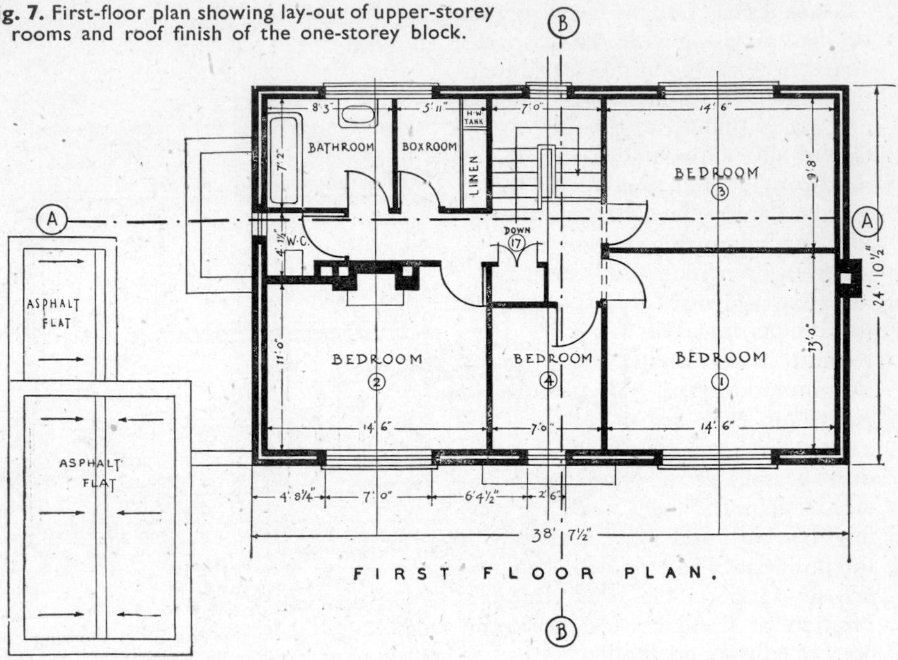

FIRST FLOOR PLAN.

with gables, hipped to retain level eaves round the house, or a combination of both features.

6. *Elevation Designs.* May be described as drawings showing semi-pictures of the four or more frontages.

7. *Longitudinal Section.* Comprises a constructional sectional drawing of all supports, framing and features that could be seen by slicing the building lengthways on a given line A–A or other denoting letters, which are marked on all the plans affected.

8. *Cross-section.* Shows similar treatment on a line slicing the building through from top and bottom across the width of the building as at B–B.

9. *Perspective.* A perspective view of the proposed block set in its surroundings is sometimes added to the foregoing.

The number of drawings required varies according to the size and type of the building, but a typical set of drawings of a house, designed by H. Ingham Ashworth, M.A., F.R.I.B.A., is shown in Figs. 1 to 9. These drawings have been simplified somewhat so as to give clarity in the reproduction.

In addition to preparing the drawings the architect collects all notes of the client's and building requirements into a text form known as a *Specification*, which describes in detail the work and materials required to execute the proposed building. This is mainly for the guidance of the quantity surveyor, who, from the plans and specification notes supplied by the architect, prepares a set of *Quantities*. Descriptive notes, when indicated on the architect's drawings, assist the surveyor and the builder.

Quantities and Surveyor

The quantity surveyor is skilled in visualizing, measuring, and scheduling all the labours and materials that are required to erect any given building for which an architect has prepared a set of drawings. The bill of quantities prepared by the surveyor aims at describing the nature of all the trade or craft labours that will have to be employed, as well as the character of the materials to be obtained for the proposed building.

The set of quantities thus prepared, with the aid of the plans, provides a groundwork for the builder and sub-contractors to estimate item by item the labour and materials described in detail, and in that way arrive at a contract cost figure for the fully described and grouped labours and materials necessary to execute the work.

If competition is introduced the quantities are supplied to a selected number of builders, who are also invited to examine the architect's drawings at his office or other stated place, for the purpose of obtaining any other information to help them in estimating.

Reference Documents

The plans and quantities, with descriptive notes, become the reference documents on which the terms of the agreement to erect the building for the client, by the builder under the direction of the architect, are drawn up and signed.

Drawings and quantities are signed by both parties to the agreement and, of course, become the documents referred to in the text of the agreement. The Royal Institute of British Architects and the Master Builders' Association have mutually agreed working conditions for common use in agreements.

Where the builder accepts responsibility for all the trades and labours, and desires to sublet some trades, separate agreements are drawn up between the builder and sub-contractors for special sections with the knowledge and approval of the architect.

The architect's services are often supplemented, on important steel-framed and other buildings, by consultants who function in team with the architect, as for instance, structural steel, heating and ventilating, and electrical engineering consultants; these professional men direct and supervise the highly technical features of such buildings for the client through the architect.

On large buildings of this character it is customary also to employ the whole-time services of a clerk of works, whose practical building knowledge qualifies him to keep a watchful eye on the work in progress throughout the building period; he also serves as a clearing-house on the site between all interested parties engaged on the undertaking, in reporting and conveying information regarding building progress.

The salary of the whole-time clerk of works, though serving under the architect, is usually paid by the client, but a part-time or visiting clerk of works is directly employed by the architect.

Apart from erecting temporary store, mess and office sheds, the initial start with building operations is that of clearing and levelling the area of the building plot. Soil and vegetable matters are dug

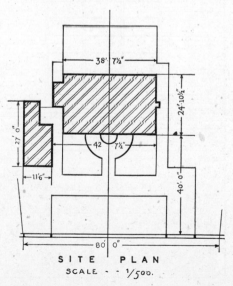

Fig. 8. Site block plan denoting the position of the dwelling-house shown in the preceding diagrams, on the dimensioned building plot.

8'6"

9'5"
8'5"

9 1/2

DINING ROOM ←— 3'6" —→ ←— 3'9" —→ HALL ←—— 7'0" ——→

←—— 7'0" ——→ ←—— 5'9" ——→ ←— 3'9" —→ |← 1'10½"

PART PLAN OF GROUND FLOOR WINDOW,
FRONT DOOR. ETC.

PART PLA

| BRICK (PLAN) | BRICK (SECTION) | CONCRETE | HARD CORE | PLASTER | WOOD (WROT) | WOOD (UNWROT) |

TYPICAL DETAIL DRAWING OF A DWELLING-HOUSE SHOWING

Fig. 9. Reduced reproduction of ½-in. scale drawing, part elevation, part section, which more clearly
defines the finishings required in the sectional features embodied in the scheme. The diagrams for

8'6"

3'3"

10'2"

6'8"

6" SURFACE CONCRETE.
4" HARD CORE.

LL, STAIRS, ETC. UP

CUPBᴰ   LOBBY

3¾"   3'.5¼"   3'.0"   3'.0"

LOUNGE ——— 23'.0"

CROSS-SECTION AND PARTS OF FRONT AND REAR ELEVATIONS
Figs. 1 to 9, which are reproduced from plans designed by H. Ingham Ashworth, M.A., F.R.I.B.A.,
have been somewhat simplified as regards details for the purpose of giving clarity in the reproduction.

up and either dumped for re-use, or carted away to tip. When the subsoil is uncovered it discloses the nature of the ground and indicates the weight loads which it is equal to carrying.

In the London area, the L.C.C. By-laws allow foundation ground bearing areas to be loaded to the following limits.

Natural bed of soft clay or wet or loose sand .	1 ton per super foot
Natural bed of ordinary clay or confined sand .	2 tons per super foot
Natural bed of compact gravel—London blue clay or chalk . .	4 tons per super foot

It will be appreciated that widths of trench excavations for foundations are governed by the loads they will have to carry, and this in turn indicates that particulars of all superimposed loads on foundations have to be calculated and mutually agreed with the local authority to obtain the requisite building permit.

Setting Out

Two governing conditions must be settled before the marking out of the building outline can proceed: (*a*) the building line; (*b*) the ground floor or other datum level. The building line is much more readily obtained in built-up areas than in country districts, the property front line being fixed by a line between existing properties or at a given distance from the centre of a roadway.

When the front building base line has been defined and fixed, it is a comparatively easy matter to erect perpendicular lines to the base line (with two steel tapes or other simple methods), and measure the parallel lines acquired, and in this manner secure true boundary site lines. To extend straight long lines the workman uses a simple sighting frame as shown in Fig. 10. The same workman excavating in a dark tunnel would use three candles. Internal room spaces can be pegged out and readily tested for regularity and squareness by checking the diagonals.

The datum level may either be a Government Ordnance bench mark in the vicinity or an up-or-down fixed dimension from some nearby permanent level marking. The Government Ordnance land survey maps indicate datum marks thus: $\overline{\Lambda}$; these maps also show positions in which they may be found and state the height of the level line above or below a fixed tidal water line.

Unlike the building line, which must be drawn on the spot, the datum level may be transferred from any fixed horizontal plane. The common methods used by the excavators to transfer a level from one point to another may be either by the use of a straight-edge and level, or by using three boning (or T-square) rods (Fig. 11). The latter method is a good one, and is carried out as follows:

Two level points are at A and B; C peg can be driven in until the top of the boning rod resting on the peg at C sinks

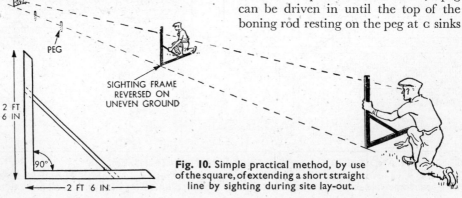

PEG

SIGHTING FRAME
REVERSED ON
UNEVEN GROUND

2 FT
6 IN

90°

← 2 FT 6 IN →

Fig. 10. Simple practical method, by use of the square, of extending a short straight line by sighting during site lay-out.

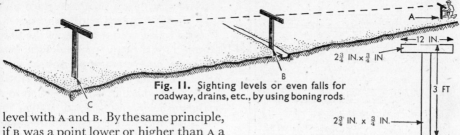

Fig. II. Sighting levels or even falls for roadway, drains, etc., by using boning rods.

12 IN.

$2\frac{3}{4}$ IN. x $\frac{3}{4}$ IN

3 FT

$2\frac{3}{4}$ IN. x $\frac{3}{4}$ IN.

level with A and B. By the same principle, if B was a point lower or higher than A a regular rising or falling line could be equally well produced and extended, as in the case of setting drain pipes to a regular fall.

The method shown in Fig. 12 is similar in principle, but in this case the sighting boards are set level on top edge and fixed on three posts triangular in plan, thereby providing sighting facilities in all directions from the sighting frame as centre site unit, or outside the area as in Fig. 12.

The civil engineer uses for surveys the theodolite for sighting, and the dumpy level for general levels, combined with the use of sighting poles and rod. The intelligent use of these instruments, especially the dumpy level on a building site, is invaluable on steel-framed and works buildings, and proves at all times a short cut to accuracy.

Digging for building plots must be executed to accommodate the requirements peculiar to each scheme. The bungalow or small dwelling-house plot of land without cellar requires little besides soil-stripping over the site, and digging shallow trenches for the weight-distributing footings of the outside walls.

Larger buildings such as office blocks and factories, with lower floors and sub-basements, naturally require their foundations much deeper, with boundary walls strong enough to carry the loads of the superstructure and resist the lateral earth pressures. Excavated trenches of this character require well timbering with face sheeting, poling timbers, and strut framings assembled *in situ* and inserted stage by stage as the excavating proceeds.

The face-sheeting timbers support the earth sides of the trench and in turn get their support from the poling timbers, while the latter are firmly fixed by tightly driven struts. Fig. 13 is a simple illustration of this type of assembled framing timber for trench excavation.

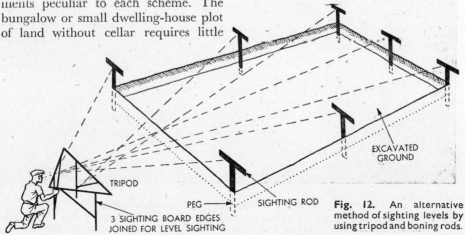

EXCAVATED GROUND

TRIPOD

PEG

SIGHTING ROD

3 SIGHTING BOARD EDGES JOINED FOR LEVEL SIGHTING

Fig. 12. An alternative method of sighting levels by using tripod and boning rods.

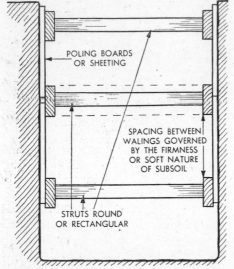

Fig. 13. Timbering used for the purpose of retaining earthwork during trench excavations.

An example of trench excavating and timbering is shown in Fig. 14. In this case a retaining boundary wall was required on a new building line; the trench to receive it is shown on the surface and sunk to the required width and depth. The old wall served throughout the time required for the construction of the new boundary and retaining wall. When the new retaining wall was sufficiently matured it was allowed to function in a manner shown by illustration Fig. 15, which shows the building plot or inside face of the retaining wall being opened up by the removal of the old wall face and the earthwork between the latter and the new wall.

Supports inside the boundary walls, like stanchion, column or pier foundations, are separately excavated to required depths, the earthwork being retained at the sides of the excavation by the same methods of timbering, with the exception that the hole being square or rectangular, the poling timbers are employed on the ends as well as sides of the excavation (Fig. 14). It must be appreciated that timbering as described above

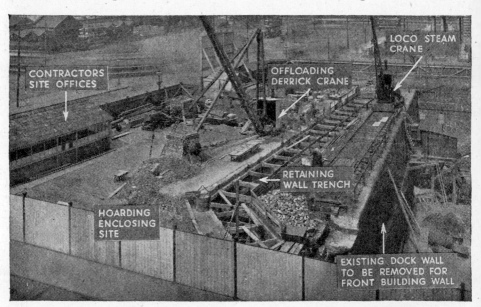

PRELIMINARY WORK ON A BUILDING SITE

Fig. 14. The illustration shows the use of trench timbers for an area retaining wall. Contractors' offices, licensed hoarding over footpaths and off-loading derrick crane also shown.

ANOTHER VIEW AT LATER STAGE OF BASEMENT IN FIG. 14

Fig. 15. The trench timbers have been removed, showing one end of the new concrete retaining wall.

is only adapted to subsoils that are firm enough to resist the tightening pressure which is applied to the timber framing by means of the width-spacing struts which are driven between the poling boards.

Piling

Building plots are often chosen on the banks of rivers or near tidal waters where deposits of soft waterlogged black silt (or bungam) have collected over many years; treatment in these cases makes it necessary to adopt other methods than those of timbers or trenches. In these cases, the plot may be enclosed by driving interlocking steel sheeting piles on the boundary line through the black spongy deposit into firm ground beneath, thus leaving the earth inside the piles free for removal.

The removal of soft earths in bulk to a firm foundation is not always possible. Pile driving into such sites is often adopted. The piles may be either baulks

of timber, or cast in concrete which is reinforced with steel rods throughout its length. Both types are provided with a pointed shoe to ease the driving process, which is undertaken by rearing the pile vertically for driving alongside a high pile-driving frame supplied with winch and suitable trip and ram.

This trip, or "monkey," is a hook which slides up and down the frame and picks up the ram. The winch is employed to hoist the heavy ram until the trip supporting hook is disengaged, thus freeing the weight and allowing it to fall on the pile with a ramming blow. This operation is repeated until the pile reaches a firm foundation, or is so tight that skin friction prevents it from being driven farther; after that stage has been reached repeated blows will show a tendency to destroy or shatter the pile top.

Caisson sinking is employed in soft earths for central or isolated supporting piers that require a firm foundation. The

FIXING CAISSONS FOR PIER FOUNDATIONS

Fig. 16. View of excavations in spongy earth showing the use of self-supporting cast-iron caisson sections instead of timber framing for the excavations to the pier foundations.

caisson consists of a self-supporting shield, and a useful type of shield is a cast-iron section of the kind used for lining circular tunnels.

Fig. 16 illustrates the fixing process, which consists of fixing by bolts one or two top rings of sections together and digging out the centre earth until external skin friction supports the rings; followed later by centre sinking and assembling the sections to the underside flanges of the fixed upper shield as the subsoil is cleared for the process.

Foundations required at a depth below the foundation of an adjoining building introduce other features necessary to retain the stability of the existing properties. In such cases underpinning the party or gable walls is undertaken, by excavating staggered pockets of earth in short lengths to the depth of new building foundations, and building piers of thickness and height to support the existing building from a lower level.

By undertaking the underpinning in short lengths the risk of settlement to the existing block is more reasonably avoided, although shoring to the existing buildings is often a vital necessity. The method is clearly illustrated in Fig. 17.

Examples of raking shoring to party walls during a reconstruction stage are also shown in Figs. 17 and 18; those in Fig. 18 show the rider shores laced together with battens.

Flying shores (Fig. 19) are often used

for staying the upper reaches of party walls which are temporarily without the stiffening floor slabs at the various levels in the height of the building. They consist of storey-height vertical members attached to the party walls on each side of the gap, with a centre member wedged in horizontally as a stiffening beam at an upper floor level. Struts are fixed under and over the beam at the end of the beam for the purpose of supporting the top and bottom ends of the wall member, as well as bridging the horizontal tie beam against whip and sagging.

The reinforced-concrete raft foundation (Fig. 20) is another method commonly employed for light earths, blown sand, or other groundwork in which appearances suggest possible settlement. In this type of foundation a concrete raft, reinforced with steel, is laid over the whole site in order to spread the building loads evenly over the area.

PRELIMINARY WORK ON A CONFINED SITE

Fig. 17. Working conditions of excavating in a confined pocket for underpinning adjoining buildings, including support of existing block by raking shores, and with steel framing fixing in progress.

GANTRY AND RAKING SHORES

Fig. 18. Grubbing out old foundations, with the method of shoring adopted for high adjoining buildings. The horizontal boards lace the struts together to ensure unison in action against the wall.

Pile driving is another method that lends itself for adoption in soft spongy earth, and Fig. 21 is an illustration showing a building site on which several hundred concrete piles were driven.

Hoists

The simplest form of hoisting is by the cat-head (Fig. 22), gin wheel, and hemp fall rope, hoisting a basket or bucket by the hand-over-hand method. Another method is by barrow hoists hugging the outside face of a building; these are operated by power winches, which have long ago displaced the old method of using a horse to draw up the loads through a snatch block fixed near the ground-floor level.

The "Exe" barrow hoist now commonly seen attached to the face of building scaffolding in the London area shows real progress in lifting plant for light loads. The guides are of light angle-iron construction, with a platform service cage, equal to lifting a barrow, box, bag or other container; this hoist works very speedily and smoothly.

The "Lidgerwood" barrow hoist cage (Fig. 23) is formed of a roughly framed square platform, hung by two side triangles of framed angle-iron; the two vertical cage guides are fixed centrally with the platform of the cage, and pick up the U-shaped brackets fixed at the platform and apex sides of the triangular frame. The hoisting process is by a

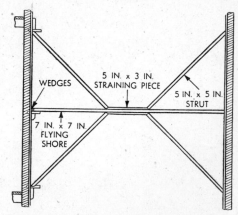

Fig. 19. Flying shore for use in auxiliary support to two walls over building space, functioning until the new building front and back and division walls and intermediate floors are inserted.

geared winch, driven by motor or engine. The twin Lidgerwood hoist, for lifting $\frac{1}{2}$-yd. or $\frac{3}{4}$-yd. wagons of concrete, worked stone, or brick supplies to upper floors, consists of stronger units of the single type.

The raising of one cage must synchronize with the lowering of the other, and that operation demands a double-instead of a single-action winch ; that is, one wire rope drum giving out and the other winding in on the drum.

Ordinary buildings do not warrant the inclusion on a building site of saw-mill and joinery machinery, stone saw-

ing and planing, and other building plant, but occasionally circumstances demand their installation. Stone-planing machines are shown in the stage of being set up on the site in Fig. 23; these machines are equal to planing and moulding (exclusive of sawing) 1,000 cub. ft. of Portland stone per week.

A similar lay-out is shown on the building site illustrated in Fig. 24, the gantry for the travelling crane being erected to serve stone to the several sawing and planing machines which are generally housed in the sheds on each side of the open stone yard.

PREPARATIONS FOR REINFORCED CONCRETE OVER SITE

Fig. 20. Steel rods set to reinforce concrete which is to cover the whole site area, so as to ensure the soft loose sand foundation being evenly loaded when the superstructure is raised.

Fig. 21. Concrete piles stacked ready for hoisting and driving. The pile-driving frame, guy derrick crane and hand derrick crane are also shown. Several hundred piles were driven on this site.

Fig. 22. Simple form of cat-head hoist for lifting light loads, with gin wheel and hemp fall rope.

TWO ILLUSTRATIONS SHOWING LIFTING AND PILE-DRIVING EQUIPMENT

Compressed air plants with percussion drills are hardly worth the builder's while to purchase, owing to the occasions for use being intermittent for long periods; they are always available for hire. During demolition periods for the work of grubbing out old concrete beds and foundations they are an invaluable site-clearing medium, and in addition they are specially serviceable for steel-plate riveting on skeleton steel-framed buildings. This operation is well illustrated in Fig. 25. A compressed air plant unit—engine and air vessels—is shown

in Fig. 18, the compressed air used by the driller being conveyed by strong rubber tubing from the compressor to the operating drill.

All types of scaffolding are controlled by Home Office regulations, which specify widths of working platforms for heights and weights to be carried, so as to ensure safety for the workmen employed upon them. Among the first training essentials taught to young men employed on building construction work are: how important it is to keep a sharp look-out as to where their feet are

SCAFFOLDING AND CRANES FOR ERECTION OF A LARGE BUILDING

Fig. 23. A Lidgerwood double hoist is shown, and the illustration includes a view of gantry for travelling crane over stone-sawing and planing machines; also stonemason's banker shed.

placed; to watch head room; and to correct defective footholds everywhere which might trap a fellow workman.

The Government Home Office Building Regulations require scaffolding to be examined by a qualified workman before use, but the Regulations are broad enough to accept certain customs and practices that are common to particular districts. For instance, in some of the northern counties the bricklayers lay the outside facing brickwork of a building from an inside scaffold; this scaffold is of a simple character, the floor joists of each floor level being sheeted with planking to provide a sound working platform.

The northern bricklayers are trained in this method, and being accustomed to overlook their work from varying heights, quickly become skilful in erecting tall factory chimneys; the working scaffolds in such cases are supported on *putlogs* which in turn have a direct bearing on the shell brickwork itself.

In southern districts the workmen grow up with the practice of using external scaffolding, anchored for support to the wall in course of construction, and on that account do not take kindly to overhand work. The two chief types of scaffolding are those required for brick-faced buildings (Fig. 26), and for stone-faced buildings (Fig. 27).

Stone-faced construction does not lend itself to supporting putlogs directly on to the wall (as in the case of bricks), and on that account requires extra standards, ledgers and parts of the tying-members duplicated on the wall face, and anchored to the wall by ties through window openings.

The parts of a scaffold include *standards*, which are vertical members transferring the working platform loads to the ground level. The standards are made stable by framing members called *ledgers*, which are fixed at right angles to the standards at about 5 ft. 6 in. height spacings; the ledgers and the

CONSTRUCTION OF REINFORCED-CONCRETE BUILDING FACED WITH STONE
Fig. 24. Stone-planing machines for site-worked stone facings; coil reinforcement for reinforced-concrete columns; main beam and floor slab centring for concrete; assembling electric crane.

standards are firmly secured at intersections. Resting at intervals on the ledgers are cross members named putlogs, which are spaced and attached to ledgers or wall at spacings to accommodate the lengths of the working platform timbers.

Long frontages require, in addition, *diagonal braces* fixed at angles and centre to prevent lateral movement; to give more even distribution of platform material weights; and to prevent swaying by wind or loads, as illustrated in Fig. 28.

Scaffolding with hemp and wire lashings is still employed for scaffolding erection in many parts of the country. Before the introduction of tubular steel scaffolding the scaffixer chain as used in Fig. 28 superseded the earlier wire and rope lashings.

RIVETING STANCHION ON STEEL-FRAMED BUILDING
Fig. 25. Steelwork is first fixed together by temporary bolts, and then riveted with compressor riveter and dolly.

A great deal of valuable pioneer work with scaffoldings has been carried out and many difficult problems have been solved. The steel coupler has been invented for connecting steel tubes. The supplying of tubular scaffolding as a special sub-contracting business has been developed, and also the hiring out of the continuous suspended scaffold for the use of builders (Figs. 29 and 32). This type of scaffold is specially adapted as a working platform; it can be raised and lowered at will, giving the building craftsman the benefit of working at a convenient bench height. When the work is completed the same scaffold facilitates washing down the wall face, fixing of window frames, and painting.

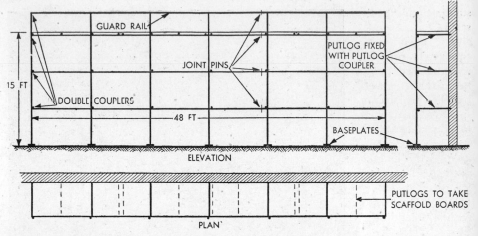

Fig. 26. Type of scaffolding used for brick-faced buildings, with the members of the framing named.

This scaffolding is independent of opening ties, and leaves the internal finishings free for progress immediately the building is clothed in by the shell walls. The suspended or swinging boat unit is in common use for high and occupied buildings; its usefulness for building maintenance, as cleaning down glazed brickwork, painting, pointing or renewing stack pipes, is obvious from Fig. 30 without further comment. A modern type of floor scaffold which has many points in its favour for inside platform work is that formed of telescopic folding standards.

Concrete Centring

Aggregates like broken bricks, ballast, and chippings, when mixed with the correct proportions of sand, water and cement to form a liquid mixture, require container support until the concrete has reached a firm and self-supporting set. Beams require bottom and side supports

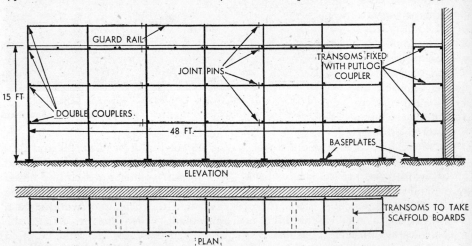

Fig. 27. Similar scaffolding to Fig. 26 but including inner and outer standards for stone-faced buildings, which only allow anchorage of the scaffolding through window or other wall voids.

TIMBER POLE SCAFFOLDING TO STONE BUILDING ASSEMBLED WITH SCAFFIXERS
Fig. 28. Note generous window openings that allow of working levels being served by putlogs anchored through the openings, and method of bracing standards to save racking or lateral motion.

(Fig. 31), while floor areas require plain surface form-work. The boards and scantlings for both types are costly in labour, materials, waste, and accidents, the latter being due to the exposed or projecting nails of dismantled loose-lying form-work timbers.

Steel forms to supersede the general use of wood have been introduced on the market for hire to builders. For large floor or wall areas this type of form-work (which can be bolted together), is very economical and the forms can be obtained in varying sizes of flanged plates. The steel form-work shown assembled in Figs. 32 and 33 is known on the market as "Conforms," and the illustrations reveal its free and easy adaptability for horizontal or vertical positions.

The former practice of propping the form-work for a concrete upper floor from a lower floor level is being modified today in favour of hanging "Ang-Kary" plant units directly from the rolled-steel beams and joists of a steel-framed building (Fig. 35 and page 8). Advantages due to this method are clear floor spaces; freedom in spreading concrete mix (Fig. 34); fewer void pockets; no floor slab weeping perforations after casting; minimum of making-good operations when striking centring or form-work.

Reinforced-concrete floors having a hollow earthenware tile filling between the joist ribs need not be fully sheeted; and the same conditions apply to the Truscon hollow floor, which, though cast *in situ*, employs a corrugated tile to span the space between the concrete ribs or joists of the floor areas as shown in Fig. 36.

Precast concrete beam specialities span the bay spaces between the floor skeleton supporting beams, and call only for working scaffolds to use during the fixing process.

Mixing concrete by hand is slow and laborious work, and the present demand

SCAFFOLDING SUSPENDED FROM TOP OF BUILDING

Fig. 29. Building brickwork from a suspended scaffold which, when provided with overhead cover, allows work to proceed in wet weather.

the full batch of mixed concrete into a waiting tipping bucket or wagon. The divided unit of mixer and power provides a better chance of protection for the power factor. The builder aims at efficiency in output, with the minimum of heavy labour, and, when possible, uses gravity to assist in the mixing of the concrete.

A job where the practice is demonstrated is shown in Fig. 38. Here the granite chippings and sand were delivered by tipping a motor lorry on to the roadway level; the sand was tipped on the east side and the chippings on the west side; the cement shed is on the hoarding line near the mixer providing receipt of cement on the roadway side and the withdrawal on the mixer side.

for speed in construction work accounts for the many and varied types of power-driven concrete mixers in use at the present time.

Capacity sizes of $\frac{1}{3}$-yd. (Fig. 37), $\frac{1}{2}$-yd. (page 9), $\frac{3}{4}$-yd. (Fig. 38) and 1-yd. mixing machines accommodate small, medium, or bulk demands. They can be obtained as direct-driven units with either gas, electricity or oil; they are fed by hopper or elevator, and can be controlled to deliver part, or discharge

The gauge for stone chippings and sand aggregates had a divisional board in the truncated-shaped receiving hopper, the top edges of which were level with the working stage; while the small square delivery mouth of the hopper was immediately over the open top of the mixer. This was the Swiss pattern shaped container, having arm paddles that churned up the matrix before delivering it into the narrow-gauge railway wagons which conveyed the mixture to the placing position.

Gauge railways, tipping wagons and bogies are efficient units for employing on site-clearing and levelling, and for transporting excavated earthwork from building site to a dump or tip.

When the track and wagons are required on a building site for excavating work, they are just as valuable as a transport medium for distributing supplies of concrete, brick, stone, and steel, from the roadway receiving position to work in progress positions (Fig. 38).

Tipping wagons receive their load at one point and, after transporting the load, by a tipping action they discharge it at the delivery end. Flat-topped bogies receive their skip load of bricks or other material within range of a roadway receiving and off-loading crane (Fig. 14), and after transporting it to a desired position they are either off-loaded and the material stacked by hand, or rehoisted intact for deposit by another crane.

The general foreman in charge endeavours to lay all railway track with a falling run for full loads, and when a double track with turntables (Fig. 38) is used, a short incline on the return empty line is introduced to ensure a slight fall in the track back to the

roadway receiving station, much labour being eliminated by this arrangement. A brick skip is illustrated in Fig. 31 and tipping buckets in Figs. 14, 17 and 18.

For hoisting and slewing from a stationary position the derrick type of crane is a favourite with the builder; its parts, whether hand or power driven, comprise a geared mast, set and kept vertical by horizontal sleeper members set at right-angles to each other; and back stays inclined at 45 degrees to the sleepers and linking the ends of the sleepers with the mast head, thus forming two triangular frames for supporting a jib member that can be hoisted or slewed at will (Figs. 14 and 15).

PAINTERS AT WORK ON SUSPENDED SCAFFOLD

Fig. 30. Painters' boat scaffold hung from outriggers anchored to specially prepared lugs on roof flat. On left, a typical casement window pivoted to open inwards for easy cleaning from inside.

STEEL REINFORCEMENT AND FORM-WORK IN POSITION BEFORE POURING CONCRETE
Fig. 31. Note the brick skip for hoisting bricks, stone, cement, or other loose building materials. Beams require bottom and side supports, while floor areas require plain surface form-work.

Stability is guaranteed by the mast sleepers and back stays which are framed to act as a triangular frame, weighted with the brick or other type of load bearing on the tail end of the sleepers and bottom joint of the back stays, as in Fig. 14.

The off-loading derrick crane shown in Fig. 14 is set so as to pick up loads from the roadway and deposit them on to the building site. The cranes, elevated on king and queen post stages as in Fig. 39, are placed so as to command the building site floor by floor during progress, and for receiving and placing for fixing the large Portland stone blocks used in all four fronts of this island building.

The guy derrick crane shown in Fig. 21 operates practically the full circle, but the jib of the crane requires to be lowered to pass under the guy ropes of the derrick, which is free for raising to any desired height in any of the sections between the guy ropes.

Plant and scaffolding units used by trades other than those undertaking the work of erecting the shell of a building are much simpler in character, as instanced in the slaters' scaffold (Fig. 41). Other scaffolding, used for internal finishings, is free from heavy loading and wind pressures, and is easily stayed to prevent lateral and collapsing movements by being erected between the shell walls of the block. Fig. 42 shows such scaffolding erected for the use of plasterers engaged on hanging and attaching decorative plaster mouldings to walls and ceilings.

Fig. 43 illustrates the nature of plasterers' plant employed as ground work for plaster finishings to circular walls and dome ceiling, and includes the plasterers' board and stand. Fig. 44 illustrates the use of the moulding horse, used vertically for forming raised panels on pilaster projections.

Preparatory work for many trades required in building fittings and furnishings

PREPARATORY WORK BEFORE CONCRETING

Fig. 32. Concrete walling executed with steel "Conform" centring from a suspended scaffold. Steel forms have largely superseded wooden forms.

is executed on working-height benches. The casting of fibrous plaster mouldings, as being fixed in Fig. 42, is shown in process of manufacture on benches in Fig. 45.

The plumber's bench in common use requires a rough skeleton frame to secure the lead members prior to the jointings being either soldered or wiped, (page 9). Scaffolding for fixing *in situ*, prior to its being built in, is illustrated in Fig. 46.

In addition to the general preliminaries described, there are other initial matters which develop when the builder

receives the contract to undertake the actual building erection. Especially is this the case when the conditions of the contract stipulate that the proposed building must be erected complete by a fixed date.

Contract conditions of this nature suggest that the only wise course to adopt is for the builder to plot, in chart form, his estimate of the periods required to obtain materials, labour and plant, in order to accomplish the task within the specified time allowed.

A simple example of charted time plotting is shown in Fig. 40. A forecast

Fig. 33. Scaffolding supports with "Conforms" assembled for casting a stairway in concrete.

progress chart of this nature has many all-round advantages in its favour, and it can become a definite business asset if all interested parties work together as a team to accomplish the end in view.

A time schedule is of advantage to a client in that it: (a) provides an expert's estimate of the time necessary to obtain possession; (b) fixes a period of unproductive capital expense for purchase or rent of land and outlay on building; (c) provides an approximate date for engaging the control and working staff, and for furniture and stocks to be negotiated on a forward market.

Through its medium the architect is assisted in arranging his drawing-office programme of work, arranging for specialists' supplies to fit in, and where necessary anticipating the requirements of the interested consecutive crafts and labour engaged on the building site.

The advantages that accrue to the builder, quite apart from financial gain,

include: steady and regular employment of labour and better building progress; saving the delays that are responsible for increasing the job overhead costs; shorter retention of unnecessary plant; smaller establishment charges; and generally creating conditions favourable to retaining valuable workmen who have grown with the work, and whose displacement would mean introducing at a later stage fresh workers who are not conversant with the ruling conditions. The disturbance to material deliveries, and to workmen who lose wages and spend their time between leaving one building site and obtaining employment on some other building, are all sources of expense and delay.

A schedule of specified forward dates for supply of labour and material products by sub-contractors and others is a valuable business procedure; it allows all and sundry to be accommodated, and assists the interested firms in maintaining regular and steady supplies to meet commitments in a reliable manner.

Examined in detail Fig. 40 illustrates a convenient method of plotting graphically the times estimated to execute the work of the chief trades and labours over, say, a nine months' period. Experience in building procedure, with calculations of time, enable the builder to gauge approximately not only the full time necessary, but the stage at which it is possible to introduce other process trades and labours without interfering with those in progress.

Excavating

Apart from soil-stripping, setting-out, fencing in the site, and lay-out of temporary offices, stores and mess-rooms, excavating is the first process labour for which a time estimate is required.

Factors known to the builder at this stage include among others: (a) the nature of the subsoil to be excavated;

(b) the capacity of available labour or plant output in yards cube; (c) the transport facilities for removing the earth, with the distance to tip; (d) whether bulk excavation precedes a start with trench work; (e) the summer or winter working conditions; (f) the men and timbers for retaining wall or trenching, strutting and timbering; (g) road access to site; (h) availability of water, gas or electricity supply.

On the other hand unknown factors and risks have to be considered, for example: (1) a spell of inclement weather involving heavy pumping charges; (2) a period of hard frost with the resultant ground hardening and swelling; (3) a pocket of running sand, shale, chalk or rock, foreign to soil disclosed by site trial holes; (4) for building in city and township areas the builder must budget against damage, and allow for maintenance of public services like electricity mains, gas, water, hydraulic and similar conduits, postoffice telephone and telegraph cables buried under the road footways.

The time chart assumes that all the foregoing factors have been considered and it allocates: (1) seven weeks as a fair estimate of time that can be allowed for bulk excavating; (2) nine weeks for trench and stanchion base excavating; (3) seven weeks for inserting drains with manholes.

The introduction of drains at this early stage may be questioned, but advantages do accrue when comparing

SUSPENDING FORM-WORK

Fig. 34. Modern method of supporting form-work from bottom flange of steel beam—to ensure strength, fewer voids, pockets, freedom from floor slab weeping perforations, and a clear floor surface.

LAYING CONCRETE FLOORING

Fig. 35. The clear-space method of spreading concrete to floor and upper supports of form-work. Compare ease of working by this method with the difficult form-work seen in the background.

a drained with a waterlogged building site. Trenches for sewer connections, drains and manholes, executed in the early stages, benefit in solidity of the returned earth to trenches.

Good organization on a building site adopts the common business procedure of raw materials at one end of the factory site, with gradual process of movement towards the dispatch station, thereby allowing the processes to operate without crossing or overlapping. An early start with concrete work benefits by excavating being started at one end, or corner, of a building site, with movement towards the extreme angle, besides assuring clean firm excavated trench bottoms and sides for concrete deposit.

It is reasonable to assume that the builder will endeavour to keep pace with

FORM-WORK FOR PIERS AND FLOORS

Fig. 36. Open form-work for concrete hollow tile flooring. This method employs a corrugated tile to span the space between the concrete ribs or joists of the floor areas.

CONCRETE MIXER IN USE

Fig. 37. A ½-cubic yard hand-fed concrete mixer. Concrete mixers can also be obtained as direct driven units, with gas, electricity or oil, and fed by hopper elevator, fitted for discharging contents

digging operations, hence the finishing as well as the starting date following closely after that of excavating, subject to the concrete aggregate and cement supplies, together with mixing plant and labour, being equal to requirements.

Suspended or upper concrete floors are not included as a charted item, but, where employed, time allocations would follow immediately after the erection of the lower part of the steel skeleton has been set vertical, level, square and bolted or riveted up. Progress charting for reinforced-concrete structures is timed according to the predominating factors of centring, reinforcing steel supplies, concrete mixing and placing labours, and the interim times necessary for the concrete setting process to mature before applying a further casting load to the newly placed concrete and steel members.

Steel frames form an important part of many modern buildings, and when employed must be considered in the preliminary stage, for they invariably introduce specialists' work outside the lay-out of the builder; and while the latter may calculate and specify a definite period of time for the supply and erection of the steel frame, it does not always follow that it will or can mature.

Steel Supplies

In this item the builder usually relies on the time required being supplied by the constructional steelwork firm whose business routine keeps them conversant with the manufacturers' periodic sectional steel rollings and stocks. In advance of designing the building, the structural steel firm will supply an approximate steel tonnage as soon as they know the loads which the floors are expected to carry plus the cubical contents of the proposed block.

With the tonnage of steel a known factor, the time estimated for the progress chart is based on the fabricating capacity of the hoisting, cutting, turning, drilling and planing machinery equipment at the works.

LEVEL TIP FEEDING AND GAUGING HOPPER

DATUM LEVEL 3 FT. ABOVE FLOOR FOR GENERAL USE

MIXER ON PLATFORM

POCKET TO HOUSE THE ¾ TIPPING WAGGON

NARROW GAUGE RAILS

RETURN TURNTABLES

LARGE BUILDING SITE SHOWING METHOD OF CONVEYING MATERIALS

Fig. 38. A ¾-cubic yard concrete mixer set to work by gravity and showing narrow-gauge railway waggons and track in collecting and distributing service. Gauge railways, tipping waggons, and bogies are invaluable for site clearing, levelling and excavation work, and many other purposes.

The vital calculation required by the builder is the time necessary to supply and erect a steel frame up to the first or second floor level. Steelwork supplies control progress in a similar manner, for a start cannot be made on the wall fabric until part of the steel frame is finished.

By the time the builder has got all the clothing process trades and labours at work on a routine basis, the steelwork firm supplies can be budgeted for, being well ahead of all other trades.

The actual stages to be visualized for a progress chart estimate include: (a) the design of the framework—executed in the drawing office of the engineering firm; (b) submitting design and calculations to consultant and to the local authority—to allow of check for comply-

ing with by-laws regarding strengths and wind pressure; (c) the ordering of steel supplies from the rolling mill; (d) the preparation of working, fixing and key plan drawings; (e) the cutting, setting out, drilling and fabricating work; (f) the site delivery, hoisting, assembly, setting, bolting and riveting.

Charting for Trades

Masonry is scheduled before brickwork for the reason that preparatory work for stonework should be in advance of brickwork because the latter is always executed from standard units on the site. Stone is a natural product that has to be obtained by quarrying operations, and then converted into requisite sizes and shapes by cleaving, sawing and planing.

Stone block is purchased from the

quarry in random sizes of an average cubic capacity, and it is economical to select blocks of sizes required to minimise waste in conversion from random block to worked stone. The builder should arrange to commence masonry supplies immediately the contract is signed, the chief steps in this procedure being: (a) preparation of scale drawings of stone façades, defining height, length and depth on bed, with vertical jointings; and in due course submission for architect's approval; (b) lettering and numbering courses and ashlar; (c) separately scheduling every block of each stone course.

Time is saved by undertaking these preparatory stages, it being the builder's policy to receive and set stonework in the building in the sequence of general progress to save unnecessary stacking and handling of worked stone.

The governing factor for stone supplies to a building site is the output capacity of the machinery and labour of the masonry works yard in worked stone cubic feet; the approximate quantity required being known to the builder, who calculates the amount by cubing the dimensions of length, height and depth.

An early start in preparing masonry allows stocks of marked stone courses to be stacked in advance of requirements, the value of which is specially evident when the stage of setting and fixing is undertaken; this is a further demonstration of the advantage of reviewing and plotting the findings in progress chart methods.

Reviewed in advance, brickwork in its correct building sequence can usually be estimated as ready for process labours

ELECTRIC DERRICK CRANE

Fig. 39. I, Back stays anchored to weighted queen-post; 2, crane mast supported on king-post; 3, crane stage or access working platform; 4 and 5, queen-post serving one back stay of two cranes; 6, head gear of double Lidgerwood hoist; 7, framing and guides of hoist; 8, queen-post; 9, first-floor level; 10, stanchion form-work horizontal stays; 11 and 12, crane king-post; 13, underside of platform staging; 14, 95-ft. hoisting jib of crane; 15, crane cab, housing gear; 16, pilot attendant stage; 17, crane mast. Note the combination of strength and lightness.

FEATURES OF BUILDER'S TIME PROGRE

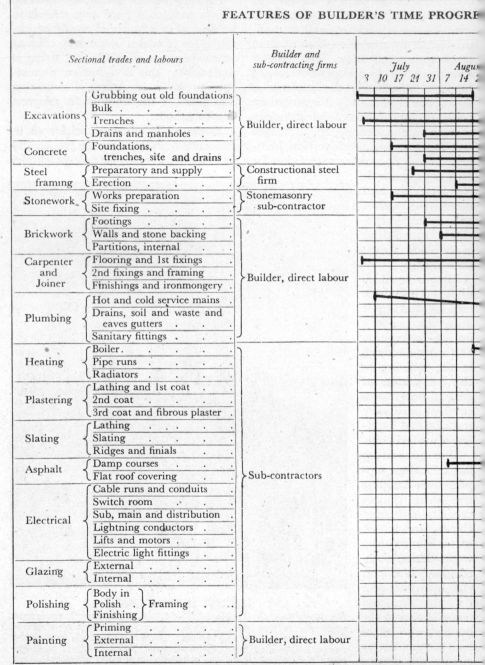

Sectional trades and labours		Builder and sub-contracting firms	July					Augus		
			3	10	17	24	31	7	14	2
Excavations	Grubbing out old foundations	Builder, direct labour								
	Bulk . . .									
	Trenches . . .									
	Drains and manholes .									
Concrete	Foundations, trenches, site and drains .									
Steel framing	Preparatory and supply .	Constructional steel firm								
	Erection . . .									
Stonework	Works preparation . .	Stonemasonry sub-contractor								
	Site fixing . . .									
Brickwork	Footings . . .	Builder, direct labour								
	Walls and stone backing .									
	Partitions, internal .									
Carpenter and Joiner	Flooring and 1st fixings .									
	2nd fixings and framing .									
	Finishings and ironmongery .									
Plumbing	Hot and cold service mains .	Sub-contractors								
	Drains, soil and waste and eaves gutters . .									
	Sanitary fittings . .									
Heating	Boiler									
	Pipe runs . . .									
	Radiators . . .									
Plastering	Lathing and 1st coat .									
	2nd coat . . .									
	3rd coat and fibrous plaster .									
Slating	Lathing . . .									
	Slating . . .									
	Ridges and finials .									
Asphalt	Damp courses . .									
	Flat roof covering .									
Electrical	Cable runs and conduits .									
	Switch room . .									
	Sub, main and distribution .									
	Lightning conductors .									
	Lifts and motors . .									
	Electric light fittings .									
Glazing	External . . .									
	Internal . . .									
Polishing	Body in Polish . Finishing } Framing . .									
Painting	Priming . . .	Builder, direct labour								
	External . . .									
	Internal . . .									

Fig. 40. The above charting illustrates a method of plotting graphically the times estimated to execute the work of the chief trades over a period of nine months, and combines labour and material supplies for a typical complete building. The same principles apply when charting is required separ-

IEDULE FOR UNIT BUILDING

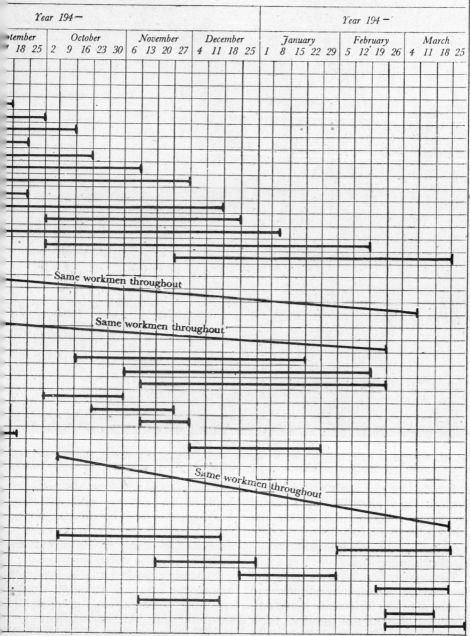

Year 194—   *Year 194—*

| tember | October | November | December | January | February | March |
| 18 25 | 2 9 16 23 30 | 6 13 20 27 | 4 11 18 25 | 1 8 15 22 29 | 5 12 19 26 | 4 11 18 25 |

Same workmen throughout

Same workmen throughout

Same workmen throughout

ately for: (1) Necessary labour demands which are calculated by the known average output of
workers in the various trades; (2) necessary material supplies, such as steel for framings, which depend
on the rolling-mill programmes, and stones for facings which are subject to quarrying conditions

SCAFFOLDING FOR SLATERS

Fig. 41. Stillages to scaffolding as used by slaters during roofing operations. Slates are shown centre nailed; the method of counter-lathing under slates is used for good-class work.

in foundations and walls within ten to fourteen days after the insertion of foundation concrete; the thicker the concrete foundations the longer the time lag to insure a concrete set equal to resisting the accruing loads.

The regular sizes of brick units and the relative working conditions are factors allowing brickwork time estimates for quantities of specified yards or rods in bulk to be estimated with more ease than some other building crafts. The builder in this section finds it necessary to gauge time that will be required for erecting and changing working scaffolds and platforms, and for waiting periods for other trade attendance such as damp course and stone fixing in advance of backing work.

Inclement weather, rain or frost, are among the risks and unknown factors requiring consideration, especially in this trade; but because bricklayers are usually in great demand for erecting internal partitions and services to other trades (in such matters as perforations

Fig. 42. Type of internal scaffolding required by plasterers when fixing precast fibrous plaster.

TWO EXAMPLES OF PLASTER WORK ON A LARGE BUILDING

Fig. 43. Scaffolding and roughly framed trammel used for circular moulding and flat dome in plaster.

through floors and walls by plumbers, heating and ventilation engineers, and electricians), stoppages for weather conditions can largely be curtailed to the period required for erection to ground floor, if the building has a lower or basement floor; and to first-floor level in other cases.

Charting for the carpentry and joinery is required to be almost continuous through the building period, subject to varying labour to the job requirements. This is due to the very general services that are undertaken by the carpenter and joiner, which for many types of buildings include floor joist and roofing timbers. The first fixings start at an early stage on labours preparatory to the first plastering coat.

MOULDING HORSE USED VERTICALLY

Fig. 44. Plasterers' tool known as a "horse," which is used for forming even and regular plaster mouldings on the solid.

The second fixings (skirtings, architraves, etc.) follow on to allow of plaster finishing being undertaken. The third stage includes fixing panelling, hanging doors, windows, fixing door and window furniture and other ironmongery.

, When manufactured joinery is introduced into buildings a fourth section should be added to this group.

Wood staircases, panelling, bookcases, tables and other fixed furnishings mean the provision of detail drawings; also the conversion of baulk, plank or board timbers; planing, mortising and tenoning and loosely assembling the framings for storage and seasoning in the early stages; to be followed later by wedging up and cleaning off.

The foresight of the builder in plotting chart dates of labour and materials for plumbing is expressed by keeping regular and steady labour throughout rather than in starting and stopping sections. Regular service with a minimum labour group has advantages such as that of a plumber being on the spot for service to the trades and labour employed on the building during construction.

Concrete mixing requires a water supply, and is often operated by two or more portable concrete mixers. Brickwork, masonry, and plastering are trades that need similar accommodation.

Heating flow-and-return pipes as well as drains require testing, and mess-room and workmen's conveniences must be maintained; they all require convenient water services. In Fig. 40 is a typical illustration of good progress charting that provides for plumbing bench work to be executed on the lines suggested.

The method of assembling and setting work up on the bench gives the plumber fair working conditions for plying his craft (page 9 and Fig. 46).

The assembling as shown, fixed in advance of building glazed brickwork, is a guarantee that : (*a*) all joints will be properly made and equal to later test; (*b*) by building *in situ* the costly making good to brickwork voids will not be necessary, and damage to lead pipes will be prevented; (*c*) brickwork perpends will be maintained; (*d*) the cutting-away and making-good charges, with material approximately worth sixpence per brick, will be avoided.

These are matters of organization which the builder considers when estimating time-chart periods. Buildings

NEGATIVE SHAPED MOULDING "HORSE" FOR SHAPING SOLIDS

PLASTER MOULD

ENRICHMENT CAST FROM GELATINE MOULD

PLASTER STOP

GELATINE ENRICHMENT NEGATIVE

PREPARING FIBROUS PLASTER FOR FIXING LATER IN BUILDING

Fig. 45. Plasterers' benches and method of casting and finishing fibrous mouldings in the workshop.

having internal cast-iron drain services or sanitary arrangements in the lower floors, with discharges direct into the manholes, require plumbing services to be charted for proceeding as soon as the floor immediately over the lowest sanitary block has been inserted; while at the other end plumbing services are required to apply finishing touches to the sanitary fittings already installed.

Heating and Ventilating

Charting and estimating useful times for arranging sub-contracting labour and plant for heating and ventilating suggest a date when a complete floor over the lowest one has been inserted, always assuming that the site has been drained. The boiler seating occupying space at the lowest level; the receipt and erection of the boiler; pipe fitting; preparing and hanging the basement horizontal circulating mains—all these are processes that can be done while the

fitters are on the site ready to insert vertical flow-and-return branches.

Heating coils or panels specified to be embedded in the concrete require to be set while the steel framing of the building is in the skeleton stage (Figs. 47 and 48). The question of providing temporary heating facilities to maintain process trades during winter periods has to be reviewed on merit, in either the client's or builder's interest. An early start, and keeping pace with progress generally, are advantageous to both sides if they can be arranged.

This sectional trade is not always controlled by the builder; in some districts the work is linked with the plumbing trade for domestic buildings, while works and other blocks employing steam generating units like the Lancashire, Cornish, Economic or Loco-type boilers, usually stipulate that the work is to be executed by a sub-contracting heating and ventilating firm; in which case

CAULKING AND FIXING WASTE PIPES (see also page 9)
Fig. 46. Scaffolding and working conditions required by the plumber during building operations.

EMBEDDED PANEL HEATING

Fig. 47. Typical light temporary scaffolding as used by heating engineers while engaged in fixing embedded heating panels with flow-and-return pipes during building construction.

advance dates are negotiated between the builder and this sub-contractor.

Plastering

Plastering work dates must of necessity follow on after ceilings have been protected from dampness and frost; in short, after the roof covering has been applied. But this practice is not always carried out, for in a few important London and provincial buildings owners have met the extra expense of having an upper floor covered with an asphalt coating to allow of plastering and other finishing trades being employed on lower floors while the upper floors and roof were in construction.

The introduction of precast fibrous plaster mouldings and slabs has played a large part in speeding up progress.

Figs. 42 and 45 are indications of the procedure in such cases. Fibrous plaster, cast and dried out at the plastering firm's depot, is ready for fixing in the form of decorative treatment when waterproofed ceilings are provided, and very readily follow on with directly applied wall and ceiling coatings.

The maturing of specified dates and access of follow-on trades (which require removal of the plasterer's scaffolding), is more accurate when hanging provision of the type shown in Fig. 34 (or similar attachment to that shown) is provided during the casting of the concrete floor. Estimates of time for applying two- or three-coat plaster to walls and ceilings are based on specified yardage supplied as a quantity item.

Slating is safe to chart as following on the erection of the building shell, together with internal wall supports and the fixing of the roof timbers.

Fig. 41 illustrates a concrete roof fully lathed with slating in progress.

In charting a proposed starting date, the builder has to visualize the steps, and compare the plotted times required by the controlling trades in order to arrive at a reasonable advance date, for the slating sub-contractor's work.

The fixing of the date for the roof covering finish is an important period in all building contracts, and when it is accomplished within the scheduled time, appearances are very favourable to completion being up to date also.

Asphalting is included as another of the sub-contracting trades to the builder, because of the specialist nature of the work. In practice, the builder's business policy is to maintain trade sections that can be employed for regular periods, rather than at long intervals.

VIEW FROM UPPER-FLOOR LEVEL OF HEATING PANEL IN CEILING OF LOWER ROOM
Fig. 48. Embedding a heating panel in concrete, showing wire anchorage until the concrete sets.

Charting asphalt advance times involves dates for executing horizontal damp-course work, just above ground level, or with vertical damp course when the horizontal damp course is set at a lower level in foundation walls; and then not until roof flats or parapet damp courses under copings are ready for laying damp courses.

Electrical Services

The reliable charting for electrical work is vital because it is necessary to: (a) leave voids for the reception of power and lighting cables, meters provision, main services to sub-main and distribution boards; (b) provide sleeves through and chases in walls for housing vertical and horizontal conduit runs, fuse boxes, and sunk switches, in advance of the insertion of concrete to floors and stanchion casings; (c) provide hanging or attachment provision for pendant and bracket fittings.

Electric hoists, passenger lifts and power units have to be considered on merit, and agreed as to approximate insertion dates with the lift manufacturers and suppliers; the information is vital at the initial stages for steel framing or wall-carrying foundation loads.

Glazing

Glazing comprises another sectional intermittent process trade that requires to be charted on a time schedule to suit the season of the year.

The drying-out process of a new building project is often obtained naturally by wind and warm air currents, and when the builder knows these will be available the glazing of sashes or casements would be deferred to a later stage; alternatively, if artificial drying is to be employed, glazing should be plotted in the early stages of the work.

In very exposed places, builders of house property have frequently found it necessary to insert the window panes in advance of slating the roof, so as to save the risk of the roof being blown away. Internal glazing, whatever the season or drying conditions, is an item usually charted during the finishing stages, with material orders for leaded lights, or other special glass, ordered well in advance of insertion date.

When hardwood joinery framing and panelling are employed for doors, partitions or wall finishings, it is necessary to provide two or more stages for execution.

Panels housed in grooved framings are free to expand and shrink without splitting, and this freedom requires the whole of the wood panel to be bodied in with polish before it is housed in its framing, to avoid showing unpolished panel edges. In this case the builder plots dates to accommodate polishing of panels in an early stage, followed by a seasoning void; then a period for bodying-in and polishing the framed and cleaned-off joinery—both undertaken at the joinery works; and finally the cleaning, touching up, and finishing process on the joinery when completed.

Painting

Conditions in the painting trade are general in character. The builder's experience guides him, when charting dates, as to the requirements of other trades upon which painters attend, for example: (a) priming coats of paint to all framed-up woodwork or steel casements and frames that will finally be finished by painting; (b) spirit-coat painting with lead-base paint to Keene's wall-plaster finishings, in preparation for later decorations, following the trowelled finish by the plasterer; (c) decorative internal finishings in order to provide accommodation for the client, who not infrequently desires to occupy sectional parts of the premises in advance of the final completion of the building.

CHAPTER 2

WALL CONSTRUCTION

Types of walls. Brickwork terms. English and Flemish bonds. Foundations and footings. Junctions and crossings. Cavity walls. Arches. Reinforced brickwork. Fireplaces and flues. Masonry. Rubble walls. Ashlar. Moulded work. Lintels. Cast stone. Concrete aggregates. Shuttering. Surface treatment. Renderings. Hollow blocks. Partition walls. Terra-cotta. Plastering.

MODERN manufacturing methods and structural systems have in many ways revolutionized the uses of brick and stone. New materials have been introduced which enable us to use entirely new methods of wall construction. Chief of these new materials are concrete, reinforced concrete, steel, hollow blocks and metal lathing.

Modern walls may be divided into the following types:—

(1) Brick, load bearing; (2) stone, load bearing; (3) precast concrete blocks; (4) terra-cotta blocks; (5) hollow blocks of various materials; (6) cement rendering on metal lathing; (7) panel walls in steel and reinforced-concrete framed buildings.

Walls serve the purpose of bearing floor, roof and other loads, and/or of enclosing, screening and partitioning.

LOAD-BEARING WALLS serve all of the above purposes. This is the traditional form of wall function. Such walls support floors, beams, roofs and other loads. Their strength must be considered in relation to these loads.

PANEL OR SCREEN WALLS are non-load bearing. They are the walls used in steel or reinforced-concrete frame buildings. They are supported on beams and stiffened by columns. Their function is to enclose the building and they need only sufficient strength to support their own weight. For this reason hollow blocks or other light-weight materials are often used.

COMPOSITE WALLS consist of a substantial backing material faced with stone, facing bricks, glazed tiles, glass, metal, cement rendering or other suitable material. The facing material may be secured to the backing by either (*a*) bonding or (*b*) metal cramps or ties. Cement rendering, of course, is an exception—this adheres to the backing.

BRICKWORK

BRICK is one of the best walling materials. Brickwork has good strength, durability, weather resistance, fire resistance, heat and sound insulation and good appearance, and it is moderate in cost. Traditional methods are still largely used in construction, though there are many modern developments.

Brickwork depends for its strength and durability on the mortar which cements the brick units together, and the bond which enables one brick to be overlapped by a number of adjoining bricks. Good bond results in a wide distribution of loads throughout the wall. Poor bond tends to concentrate loads on

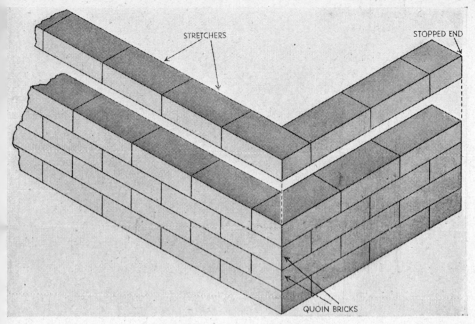

STRETCHER BOND 4½-IN. WALL

Fig. 1. Stretcher bond consists of all the bricks laid lengthways, and is generally only used for half-brick walls or cavity walls. The vertical joints are staggered by 4½ in.

small areas, which may result in unequal settlement and cracking. The brick-layer should always practise a sound method of laying, filling all mortar joints, and adopting correct bonding.

Bricks laid with a long side showing on the wall face are called *stretchers*, and those laid with an end showing are called *headers*. Bonds consist of various arrangements of stretchers and headers overlapping one another.

STRETCHER BOND consists of stretchers in every course, each vertical joint being over the middle of the bricks above and below as in Fig. 1. Thus the vertical joints are staggered by 4½ in. This bond is used for walls 4½ in. thick. It is not generally suitable for thicker walls as it does not provide cross bond, so that in a 9-in. wall there would be no bond between the inner and outer leaves.

HEADER BOND consists of headers in every course. They overlap 2¼ in., as in

Fig. 2. The transverse strength is excellent, but longitudinally the bond is not so good as stretcher bond. Header bond is used for walls curved on plan to a small radius, as it enables the curve to be more easily followed than with any other bond, and also for footings, but it is not ordinarily used for straight walling.

Before describing other bonds we must understand some of the technical terms which are used in the description of brickwork.

TERMS. There are three *standard sizes* of bricks: The length of all three is 8¾ in. and the width 4 3/16 in. The three standard thicknesses are 2 in., 2⅝ in., and 2⅞ in.

Each row of bricks is called a *course*. The edge or angle of a brick is called the *arris*. A *bat* is a portion of a brick; thus a half-brick is called a *half-bat*. A *frog* is a panel recess in the bed of a brick. A machine-made brick may have one frog

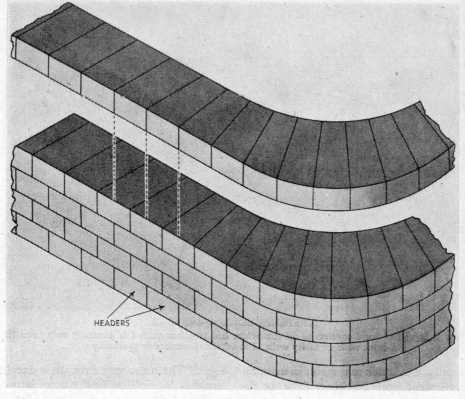

HEADER BOND 9-IN. WALL

Fig. 2. Header bond has all headers, and is chiefly used for walls curved on plan. At the curved parts the bricks have to be cut or laid with wedge-shaped joints. The headers overlap $2\frac{1}{4}$ in.

or two frogs, but wire-cut bricks have no frog.

The *bed* of a brick is the bottom surface. The horizontal mortar joints are called *bed joints*. The vertical joints on the wall face are called *perpends*. A vertical joint continuing through two or more courses is called a *straight joint*. Straight joints should be avoided as far as possible as they weaken the bond. A *quoin* is a corner brick. A *squint quoin* is a corner brick with an exterior angle greater or less than a right angle.

A *corner* or *returned end* to a wall is usually a right angle, but may be an acute or obtuse angle—that is, a squint. A *stopped end* of a wall is an end which is

finished and does not turn a corner. A *jamb* is a vertical side of an opening in a wall. A *reveal* is the portion of the jamb which can be seen—usually the portion of brickwork between the frame and the face of the wall. *Footings* are projecting courses at the base of a wall; they serve to spread the load over the foundation. A *plinth* is sometimes formed from ground level rising a few courses—it is distinguished from the upper wall by a slight projection or by some difference in colour or material.

ENGLISH BOND consists of alternate courses of headers and stretchers, as in Figs. 3A and 3B, known as the header course and the stretcher course. The perpends are staggered by $2\frac{1}{4}$ in. Headers are placed above and below the middle of each stretcher and adjoining headers are above and below perpends in the stretcher course. There are no straight joints in English bond, except a width of about $\frac{3}{8}$ in. where vertical joints intersect, and for this reason it is considered the strongest of all bonds.

A square corner and a stopped end in English bond are illustrated in Figs. 3A and 3B. Correct bonding at these points is of great importance. Here we must use a brick of less than standard width— a closer which is only $2\frac{1}{4}$ in. wide. This enables the end of the wall to be brought to a flush face. This particular closer is called a *queen closer*. There are two others: the *bevelled closer*, illustrated in Fig. 4 and the *king closer* illustrated in Fig. 5. They all serve a similar purpose and all show only $2\frac{1}{4}$-in. width on the face. They are cut by the bricklayer from standard bricks, though occasionally they are specially made. The queen closer is usually cut in two portions, as the full 9-in. length is not easy to cut.

The closer is placed next the quoin header. This is an important rule of bonding. In English bond there is no closer in the stretcher course. But as the course turns a corner it changes from a stretcher to a header course, and vice versa. The reason is clear when it is seen that a quoin stretcher on one wall face changes to a header round the corner.

It will be noticed that the bonding varies with the thickness of the wall. In a $13\frac{1}{2}$ in. thick wall in English bond there are headers backing stretchers in one course. In an 18-in. wall one course consists of stretchers on the faces with headers in the interior of the wall.

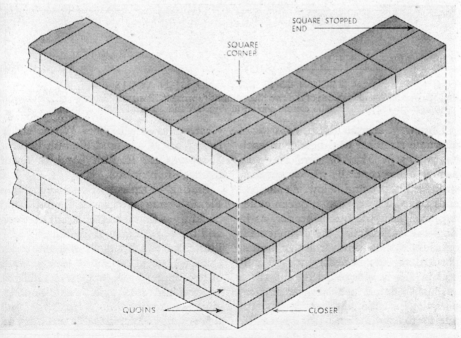

ENGLISH BOND 9-IN. WALL

Fig. 3A. English bond is the strongest bond, and consists of alternate courses of headers and stretchers. Correct bonding is of great importance. The perpends are staggered by $2\frac{1}{4}$ in.

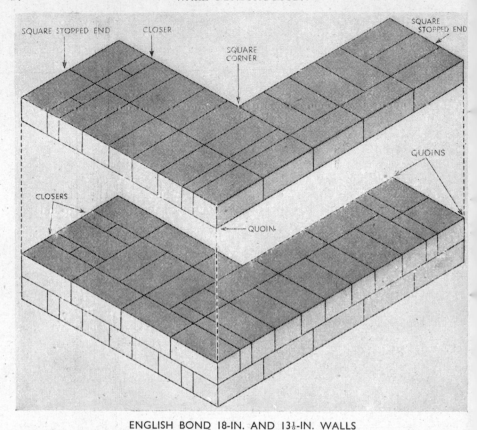

ENGLISH BOND 18-IN. AND 13½-IN. WALLS

Fig. 3B. The left-hand portions of the two illustrations represent 18-in. wall; the right-hand portions represent 13½-in. wall. The closers shown in Figs. 3A and 3B are known as queen closers.

DOUBLE FLEMISH BOND consists of alternate stretcher and header in each course, as in Figs. 6A and 6B, each header being centrally placed between stretchers above and below. At stopped ends and square corners a queen closer is placed next the quoin header, as in English bond. Notice the arrangement of bricks in the various wall thicknesses, particularly the necessary use of half-bats in the interior of a 13½-in. wall.

Flemish bond has straight vertical joints 2¼ in. wide, and in this respect is inferior to English bond. But it is usually considered to be a better looking bond. If the headers are of darker colour than the stretchers a pronounced pattern is given to the wall face. Where costly facing bricks are used Flemish bond is cheaper than English bond as fewer facings are required.

SINGLE FLEMISH BOND combines Flemish bond facings with English bond backing, so that it has the strength of one and the appearance of the other. Fig. 7 illustrates this bond. It is suitable for thick walls and cannot be used in walls of less than 13½-in. thickness. Half-bat headers are used in alternate courses, giving straight joints 9 in. wide, but this results in considerable economy in facing bricks. The strength of transverse bond can be improved by using three-quarter bats as headers, thus reducing the straight joints to $2\frac{1}{4}$-in. width, but, of course, it increases the number of facing bricks required.

THREE-AND-ONE BOND, illustrated in Fig. 8, is also called English garden-wall bond and by various other names, but many bricklayers call it "three-and-one bond" because there are three courses of stretchers to one course of headers.

This bond is often used with thin facing bricks and thick common backing bricks. Each header course of the facings should bond into the backing, as in Fig. 9, and the rise of the courses must be arranged to enable this to be done.

FLEMISH GARDEN-WALL BOND consists of three stretchers to one header in each course, each header being placed centrally over the middle stretcher of the group of three above and below, as in Fig. 10. This bond is economical in facing bricks and is a better-looking bond than "three-and-one." The transverse bond is strong enough for ordinary wall loads up to moderate heights. If the headers are of darker colour than the stretchers a pleasant pattern in the wall is introduced.

Minor Bonds

There are a number of minor bonds. One modern bond which is used fairly widely is a variation of Flemish garden-wall bond, consisting of two stretchers to one header in each course. A weaker modification of "three-and-one bond" consists of a header-stretcher course to three-stretcher courses—this is sometimes used for garden walls. But the bonds illustrated are those in general use.

FOUNDATIONS. The purpose of a foundation is to spread the wall load over an adequate area of ground so that the wall will not sink, crack or lean over. This may be achieved by laying brick footings, the lowest course of which should be twice the thickness of the wall. Thus

footings spread the load over double the area of the wall base. The area may be further increased by placing concrete before commencing the footings. Fig. 11 shows a typical foundation section and indicates how the width and depth of foundations are found by simple graphical means.

Foundations must be deep enough in the ground to be out of reach of soil disturbance due to atmospheric and other causes. They must also be built on firm soil and never on surface soil or recently made-up ground. On unreliable ground reinforced-concrete rafts are sometimes laid over the whole site. The depth of the foundation bottom should not be less than 2 ft. In clay it should not be less than 3 ft.

FOOTINGS. As far as possible footings should be bonded with headers only. If

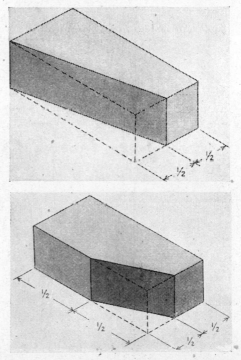

Figs. 4 and 5. A closer is a brick of less than standard width. Fig. 4 (above) is a bevelled closer, and Fig. 5 (below) is a king closer.

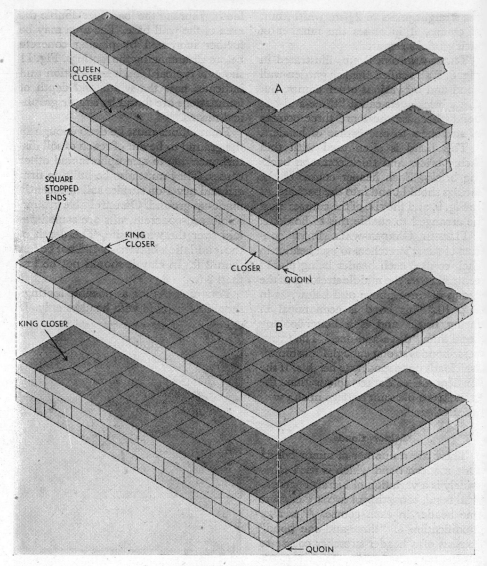

QUEEN CLOSER

SQUARE STOPPED ENDS

KING CLOSER

CLOSER

QUOIN

KING CLOSER

B

QUOIN

DOUBLE FLEMISH BOND

Fig. 6. At A is shown a 9-in. wall; at B a 13½-in. wall. In Flemish bond headers alternate with stretchers on each course. Double Flemish bond means Flemish bond on both sides of the wall.

stretchers must be used to make up the correct width they should, if possible, be placed in the interior. Stretchers on the edge of footings tend to tip under load, especially if laid direct on the ground. Fig. 12 illustrates these points. The four footings courses necessary for an 18-in.

wall are illustrated in Fig. 13, which shows a square corner. Care should be taken to avoid straight joints.

Sleeper-walls (Fig. 14) are necessary to support timber floor joists in hollow ground floors. They are usually 4½ in. or 9 in. thick and are built on the surface concrete. They should be honeycombed by leaving a gap between stretchers, in the case of a 4½-in. wall, so that air can circulate under the timber floor.

Air bricks, 9 in. × 3 in. or 9 in. × 6 in., are built into walls so that air can be admitted into hollow timber floors (for the prevention of dry rot), and also to admit air into certain rooms. If the wall is more than 4½-in. thick it is necessary to lay a slate over the opening at the rear of the air brick to provide support for the mortar bed of the course above.

BRICKLAYING. Having described the various types of wall and the bonds used, a brief description of the practical operation of bricklaying is now necessary. Bricklaying cannot be taught by the printed word, but a description of good practice will be useful to the beginner.

Almost all bricks are absorbent. If they are dry when laid they will rapidly absorb the water in the mortar, reduce the plasticity of the mortar and cause poor adhesion. The bricks should, therefore, be well wetted either by spraying from a hose or immersion in water for about five minutes. It is not desirable that bricks should be completely soaked, but momentary immersion is not enough.

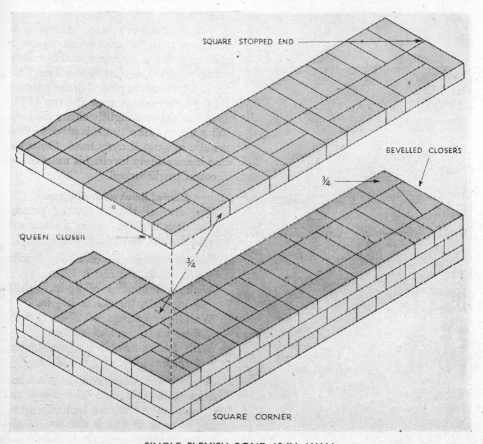

SINGLE FLEMISH BOND 18-IN. WALL

Fig. 7. This bond shows Flemish bond on the outside of the wall and English bond on the inner face. Single Flemish bond combines Flemish bond facings with English bond backing.

Bricks which are almost impervious, such as Staffordshire blue bricks, tend to slide on the mortar. The reason is that they have no suction and do not "grip" the mortar. A rather porous brick with a rough texture sucks in the mortar and so takes a good "grip." Bricks must be clean and free from dust when laid. It is important to soak them in clean water. Bricks should not be stacked on the ground.

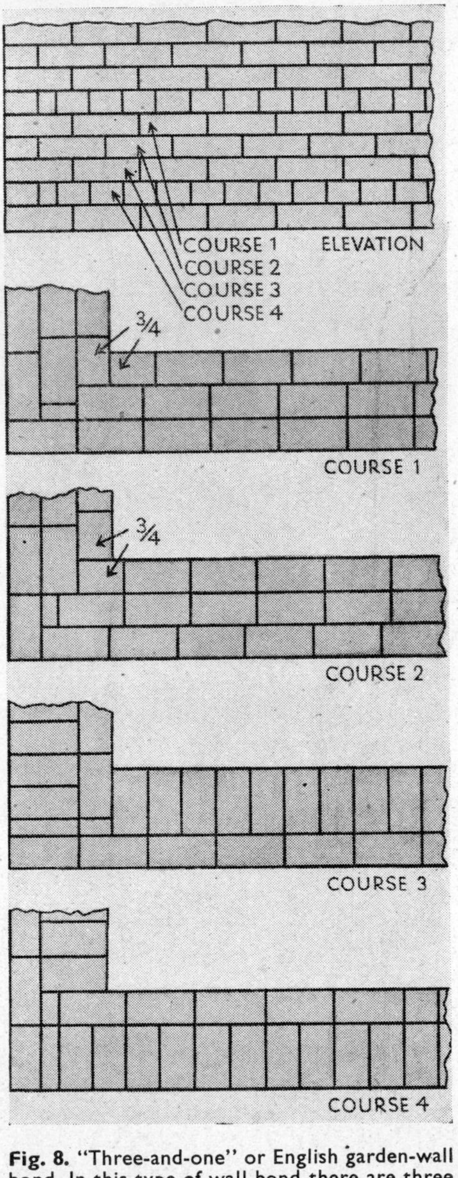

In commencing a wall the quoins are built up for a few courses. The brick-layer's square is used to set out a right-angled quoin. The plumb rule is used to test the faces for verticality, holding the edge against the wall so that the plumb line hangs free and central. The beds are tested by placing the spirit-level on a straight-edge on the horizontal bed. With the quoins built up, as in Fig. 15, the straight runs of walling can be proceeded with.

The bricklayer's line, which is a length of string wound on steel pins, is used to give a truly horizontal line from quoin to quoin, so that the beds are kept level. The pins are placed in the joints so that the line comes over the top of the quoin bricks and slightly clears the face. With a long line a tingle is placed in the middle to keep it truly level. Once the line is accurately levelled it must on no account be disturbed.

Rise of Brickwork Courses

The rise of the brickwork courses varies. It is decided by the thickness of the bricks and bed joints. For example:

With four courses of $2\frac{5}{8}$-in. bricks, $\frac{3}{8}$-in. beds, the rise is 12 in.

With four courses of $2\frac{5}{8}$-in. bricks, $\frac{1}{2}$-in. beds, the rise is $12\frac{1}{2}$ in.

With four courses of $2\frac{7}{8}$-in. bricks, $\frac{3}{8}$-in. beds, the rise is 13 in.

With four courses of $2\frac{7}{8}$-in. bricks, $\frac{1}{2}$-in. beds, the rise is $13\frac{1}{2}$ in.

A gauge rod, which consists of a wood batten with saw cuts indicating the thickness of a course including bed joint, is used to check the rise of the courses. It is held against the face of the wall so that the marks are in line with the top of the bricks.

Fig. 8. "Three-and-one" or English garden-wall bond. In this type of wall bond there are three courses of stretchers to one course of headers.

The bricklayer must take care to keep the perpends in correct position. Where the perpends in alternate courses lie on a vertical line, this line must be carefully worked to. Nothing spoils the appearance of the bond more than perpends which are allowed to wander all over the wall in an irregular zigzag. A small steel square is used to help in keeping the bricks square with the wall and the perpends in vertical line.

Cement-Lime-Sand Mortar

Mortars are described elsewhere, but the merits of cement-lime-sand mortar may be commended here. A 1-1-4 mix makes a strong mortar. The sand-lime coarse stuff should be prepared first, the cement being added immediately before use. If dry hydrated lime is used the whole mix may be made up at once. Whatever method of mixing is employed the mortar should be used within three hours of its final preparation. Retempering by adding water to mortar which has stood for some hours is not recommended, though within a twelve-hour period the consequent weakening may not be serious.

A cement-lime mortar works easily off the trowel and is much less liable to shrinkage and expansion cracks than a strong cement mortar. For all ordinary purposes a cement-lime mix has adequate strength.

Damp walls are more often caused by suction of water through the fine cracks between mortar and brick than through the brick itself. The addition of lime to cement mortar prevents such admission of damp by avoiding shrinkage and cracks.

TOOTHING. If, instead of finishing the end of a wall flush, alternate projections and recesses are left, this is called toothing. This is useful if we have to continue the wall later on, as it allows continuity of bond. If a wall has to be

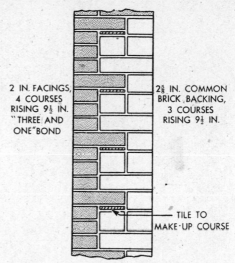

2 IN. FACINGS, 4 COURSES RISING 9½ IN. "THREE AND ONE" BOND

2⅜ IN. COMMON BRICK BACKING, 3 COURSES RISING 9½ IN.

TILE TO MAKE-UP COURSE

Fig. 9. Cross-section of 13½-in. wall with thin facings and 2⅝-in. common brick backing.

added later at right angles to the wall which is being built a toothing may be left in the face of the wall so that a properly bonded junction can be made later. For English and Flemish bonds this toothing will consist of 2¼-in. recesses in alternate courses the width of the wall to be added (Fig. 16).

If a vertical toothing is left at the end of a rather high wall it may be found, if we later build on to that toothing, that, as the later work settles, cracks appear down the line of toothing. This is because of the pressure exerted as the new work begins to settle. A strong cement mortar should be used in the new wall and it should be built up slowly to avoid excessive settlement. But it is better to build the wall junction in one and allow the joining wall to be racked back so that it can be completed later. With care unequal settlement and cracking can be avoided by this method.

RACKING. To avoid the cracking referred to above, the end of a high wall which must be added to later should be racked back. This consists of stepping back the end of the wall, as in Fig. 15.

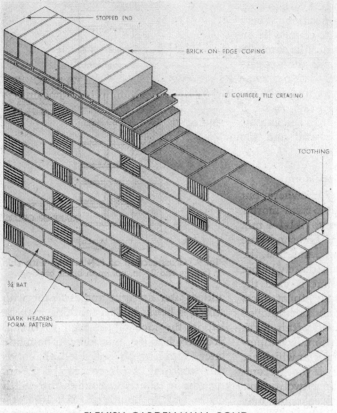

STOPPED END

BRICK-ON-EDGE COPING

2 COURSES, TILE CREASING

TOOTHING

¾ BAT

DARK HEADERS
FORM PATTERN

FLEMISH GARDEN-WALL BOND

Fig. 10. Note that all courses are alike, except at the end, and consist of one header to three stretchers. If the headers are of darker colour than the stretchers, a pleasant pattern is introduced.

WALL JUNCTIONS. Proper bonding is essential in building wall junctions. It is usual to bond alternate courses $2\frac{1}{4}$ in., as shown in Fig. 16. In most cases in English bond it is convenient to bond $2\frac{1}{4}$ in. into the stretcher course, so that to do this the joining wall must coincide in thickness with the joints of the main wall. The header course will then butt against the header course of the main wall. The isometric views in Fig. 17 will make this point clear. The alternative is to bond in the header courses, in which case the joining wall must coincide with joints in the header course of the main wall. This is illustrated in the plans in Fig. 17.

The bonding of junctions in $13\frac{1}{2}$-in. English bond is illustrated in Fig. 18. It is necessary to place a three-quarter bat at the side of the closer and one header. This illustration also shows the bonding of a $4\frac{1}{2}$-in. partition wall where it joins the main wall. As the partition wall is in stretcher bond it is convenient to bond in $4\frac{1}{2}$ in., as the perpends of stretcher bond are staggered by $4\frac{1}{2}$ in. In the junctions illustrated it will be seen that by following the correct principles cutting is avoided. A junction in Flemish bond is shown in Fig. 19.

CROSSINGS. Where one wall crosses another it is usual to pass alternate courses of one wall through the other, as shown in Fig. 17. The header course of one wall can be passed through the stretcher course of the other, and vice versa.

The choice of positions for junctions and crossings may be taken at $2\frac{1}{4}$-in. intervals, but the joints of one course of the main wall must coincide with the thickness of the joining or crossing wall. Room dimensions must be worked out to suit this rule, otherwise awkward cutting is necessary and the bond will be weakened.

SQUINT QUOINS. Corners forming less than a right angle are called acute

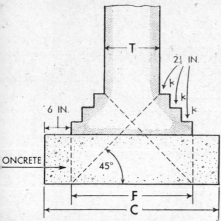

Fig. 11. The diagram shows the method of finding width and depth of wall foundation. T= thickness of wall; $F = T \times 2$; $C = T \times 2 + 12$ in.

angles. Corners forming more than a right angle are called obtuse angles. Examples of both types are illustrated in Figs. 20 and 21. With an acute angle it is necessary to use a wedge-shaped closer next to the quoin header. With an obtuse angle a special squint quoin brick of appropriate angle should be used, as shown, and the interior angle is best formed with a special interior angle brick. The method of bonding of squint quoins varies with the angle.

CAVITY WALLS. A cavity wall consists of two thin walls or leaves of brickwork separated by a cavity. The object of the cavity is to prevent the passage of moisture from the outside to the inside of the wall. Typical details are illustrated in Fig. 22.

A very important rule in building cavity walls is that the ability of moisture to creep by capillary movement must be guarded against. The two leaves of a cavity wall must be tied together for strength, and metal ties of various patterns are used for this purpose. A twisted metal tie is shown in Fig. 22. The object of this twist is to form a drip for the water; the twist is, in fact, a barrier across which the water cannot creep.

Precautions must be taken to prevent

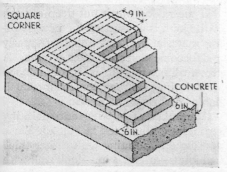

Fig. 12. Footings and concrete foundation for 9-in. wall. Headers are best for footing bonds.

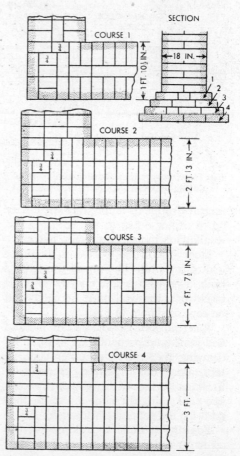

Fig. 13. Footings courses for an 18-in. wall with square corner. Straight joints must be avoided.

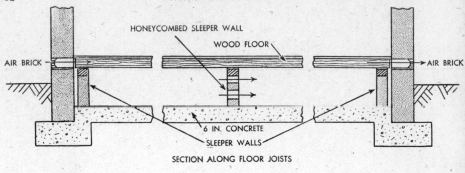

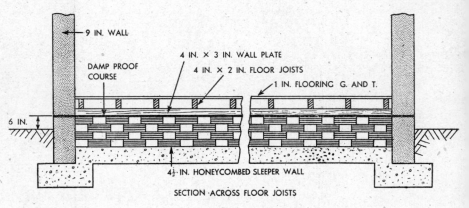

SLEEPER WALLS

Fig. 14. Cross-sections showing construction of sleeper walls. Note the arrangement of honey-combing between stretchers to allow for a through current of air so as to prevent dry rot.

mortar droppings falling into the cavity on to ties or down to the bottom, and so allowing moisture to creep across.

Floor joists are supported on the inner leaf of the wall. The top of the wall is built over with a few courses of solid brickwork, the wall plate being placed on top, as shown in Fig. 22.

JOINTING AND POINTING. The faces of bed joints and perpends are finished by drawing the trowel, or other suitable tool, along them. Jointing is done by finishing the face of the joint as the work proceeds, using the same mortar as that used for the general bricklaying.

Pointing is done by raking out the joints to a depth of $\frac{1}{2}$ in. to $\frac{3}{4}$ in. and filling and finishing the joint with a specially prepared mortar. A special

mortar with an admixture of colouring matter or special sand is often used for this purpose. When raked out the joint should be brushed clean and well wetted before inserting the pointing. The pointing mortar should be well worked in.

If the raking out is not deep enough or the joint is not wetted the new pointing material will not adhere properly and become defective after a time. A cement-lime mortar is recommended for pointing; a strong cement mortar is liable to shrink and crack.

A number of jointing and pointing finishes are illustrated in Fig. 23. Flush jointing and pointing with rather thick bed joints—about $\frac{1}{2}$ in.—look well with bricks of rough texture. Weathered pointing throws off rain-water and is considered to be the most durable. Struck jointing should not be used for exterior facing as it leaves the upper edge of the bricks exposed to the weather.

The hollow-keyed joint is formed by shaping with a suitably shaped piece of wood or metal. Tuck point consists of making up the face of the joint with a mortar coloured to the same tint as the bricks and then inserting a thin putty pointing, working along a straight-edge.

LINTELS. A lintel is a beam placed over an opening in a wall, with sufficient bearing at each end, so that it forms a support for the wall above. Some examples are illustrated in Fig. 24. Wood lintels may be built up, using two or more timbers side by side. It is usually sufficient to have two timber members separated by blocks of wood, the whole being nailed or bolted together, as at A (Fig. 24). A useful rule for finding the depth of fir lintels is to allow $1\frac{1}{4}$ in.

depth for every foot of clear span, using lintels the full thickness of the wall.

If a third of the thickness consists of blocking pieces, as at A, $1\frac{1}{2}$ in. depth for every foot of span should be allowed. The minimum bearing at each end of a lintel should be 4 in., with a bearing equal to the depth of the lintel for lintels more than 4 in. deep.

Where a wood door or window frame is placed at the front of the opening, as at B (Fig. 24), a brick-on-edge course may rest direct on the head of the frame, provided that the mullions or posts are spaced no more than 2 ft. from centre to centre. A wood lintel is placed at the back, as shown, and the depth of this should be calculated as described above.

Brick-on-end as well as brick-on-edge courses may be placed over door and window frames. If steel windows are used the brickwork must not be allowed to rest on the frame. A rolled-steel angle

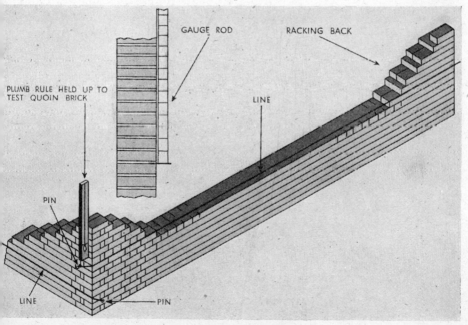

BRICKLAYING OPERATIONS

Fig. I5. The illustration shows how corners are built up and a line stretched to keep courses level. Once the line is levelled it must not be disturbed. With a long line, a tingle is placed in the centre.

Fig. 16. Method of constructing toothing to receive a cross wall.

section may be used to provide support for the brick head, as shown at c (Fig. 24). This illustration shows a wall 13½ in. thick with a reinforced concrete lintel behind a brick-on-end course.

Rolled steel sections, usually **I** sections, may be used as lintels, but if they are to be plastered, expanded metal on wood grounds must be attached to them. They are suitable for wide spans and heavy loads. At Fig. 24 a steel lintel, consisting of two **I** sections bolted together through tubular separators, is shown. For heavy loads such lintels should bear on large stone or precast concrete templets, which distribute the loads over the brickwork and so prevent excessive settlement and fracture of the wall.

Cavity walls must have lintels so designed that water cannot creep or soak across from outside to inside. An example of good practice in this matter is shown in Fig. 25. On the outside wall the head of the window opening consists of a brick-on-edge course while the inside wall has a reinforced-concrete lintel. The wood frame covers the cavity. It is necessary to give temporary support to the brick-on-edge course until the mortar has set.

SOLDIER ARCHES. A brick-on-edge or brick-on-end course over an opening is often supported on a steel bar, as in Fig. 26. When the

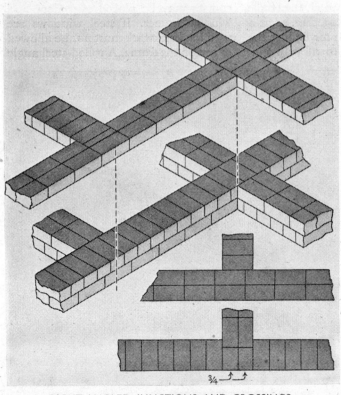

¾

RIGHT-ANGLED JUNCTIONS AND CROSSINGS
Fig. 17. Isometric views and plans showing right-angled junctions and crossings in 9-in. English bond.

mortar joints have set, this bar is in tension, while the brickwork takes the compression. Soldier arches can also be supported in other ways.

A soldier arch is not a true arch; in most cases it is a lintel. If the bricks are arranged to a slight camber, so that the underside is slightly curved and the centre lines of the bricks radiate from a common centre, it is a true arch.

Reinforced brick lintels are formed by placing mild steel rods, usually in a mortar bed joint, in the brickwork immediately over the opening, as shown in Fig. 26. A soldier arch may be formed in reinforced brick-

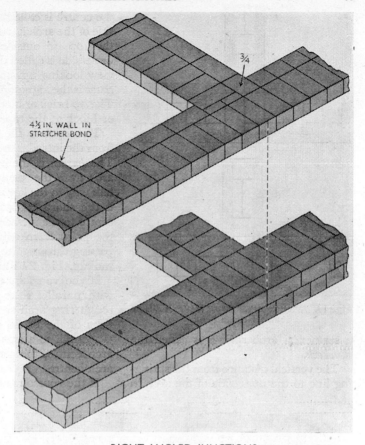

4½ IN. WALL IN STRETCHER BOND

¾

RIGHT-ANGLED JUNCTIONS

Fig. 18. Isometric views showing two courses of right-angled junctions in 13½-in. and 4½-in. walls laid in English bond.

work, the rods being passed through holes in the brick-on-edge or brick-on-end, but in this case the description "soldier arch" is a contradiction—the member being a reinforced brick lintel.

Load Transmission

ARCHES. An arch consists of a number of blocks arranged on a curve so that the blocks are wedge-shaped. As each block transmits a load to the next block until the load on the arch is brought to bear on the wall at each side of the opening, the arch is mainly in compression, though tension and shear stresses occur as well.

Referring to Fig. 27, the segmental arch transmits a diagonal thrust to the wall on each side, but the semicircular arch transmits a thrust more nearly vertical.

A rough ring arch consists of standard bricks, so that the bed joints between must be wedge shaped, as in the rough ring segmental arch in Fig. 27.

Here the learner should study the various terms used in describing the parts of an arch. Each brick or block is called a *voussoir*; the first brick or block on each side is called the *springer*. The inclined bearing on each side from which

P.B.—C

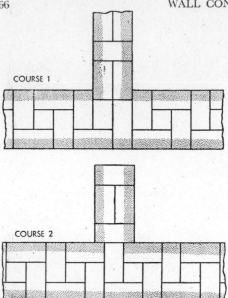

COURSE 1

COURSE 2

Fig. 19. Junction of 9-in. to 13½-in. walls in double Flemish bond.

a segmental arch springs is called the *skewback*.

The vertical distance from the springing line to the underside of the arch in the centre is called the *rise*. The underside of the arch is called the *intrados*, and the top or outside the *extrados*. The underside is called the *soffit* if the surface view looking upwards is intended. The *crown* is the highest point of the extrados. The *key* brick or block is the centre brick or block at the top of the arch.

The *depth* is the shortest dimension from the intrados to the extrados curves. The *haunch* is the outer portion of the arch from the springing line to a point half way to the key or crown. The *radius* is the shortest distance from the arch centre to the intrados. The arch *centre* is the point from which the radial lines passing through the bricks or bed joints radiate. Fig. 27 illustrates these terms.

If the voussoirs are standard bricks with parallel sides or beds, as in the rough ring arch shown in Fig. 27, the sides of the bricks are on lines drawn tangential to a small circle around the arch centre, the centre of which is the arch centre.

If the voussoirs are wedge shaped, as

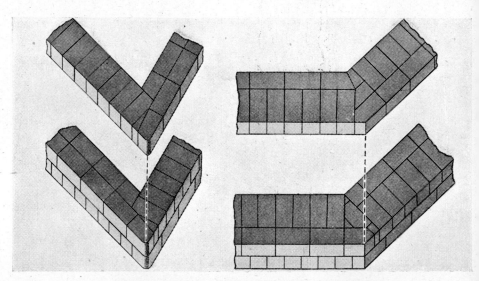

SQUINT QUOINS—ACUTE AND OBTUSE ANGLES

Figs. 20 and 21. Isometric views showing the use of acute-angled squint quoins in 9-in. English bond (left), and obtuse-angled squint quoins in 13½-in. English bond (right).

in the axed semi-circular arch shown in Fig. 27, the axis lines drawn through the centre of the bricks radiate from a common centre, as shown. In this case the bed joints between the voussoirs are of regular thickness throughout.

Rough ring arches are built in half-brick rings (4½ in.), as the wedge-shaped joints resulting from a whole brick arch would be inconveniently wide at the extrados. But the springer should be a whole brick, as shown in Fig. 27, because this spreads the load on the skewback or springing.

Axed arches consist of voussoirs formed to the correct wedge shape

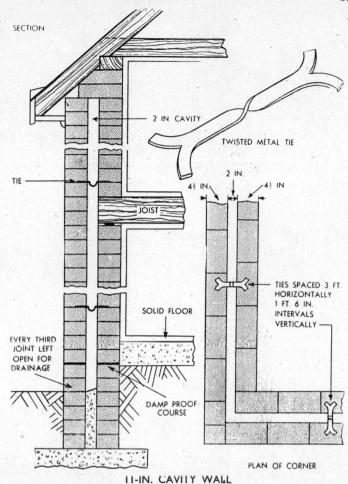

Fig. 22. Broken vertical section showing construction from foundations to eaves, and plan of 11-in. cavity wall, with inset sketch of metal wall tie.

from standard bricks by cutting with a bricklayer's axe, scutch, or bolster and hammer. A wood templet should be made to the correct wedge shape of the voussoir, setting out the templet according to the radius and clear span of the arch and using a piece of thin board. The templet is placed on the brick face and the wedge shape marked along the edges.

A small tin saw is used to cut this outline about ⅛ in. deep into the brick. This process is repeated on the reverse face of the brick and the ends squared.

The cutting can be done with bolster and hammer, finishing with the scutch.

Moulded brick arches are built of voussoirs which are specially moulded to the correct wedge shape, according to the radius and span of the particular arch. No cutting is required and the shapes are more regular than those of axed bricks. The semicircular arch illustrated in Fig. 27, though shown in axed work, may be taken as an example of moulded work.

Bonding arches transversely is of

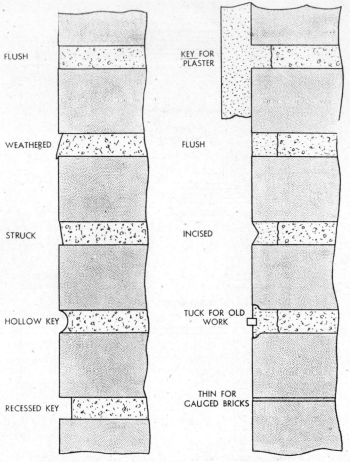

FLUSH

WEATHERED

STRUCK

HOLLOW KEY

RECESSED KEY

KEY FOR
PLASTER

FLUSH

INCISED

TUCK FOR OLD
WORK

THIN FOR
GAUGED BRICKS

JOINTING AND POINTING TO BRICKWORK

Fig. 23. Methods of jointing (left), and pointing (right). Wide joints look well with bricks of rough texture, and weathered pointing throws off rain.

and faces true, whereas the size and shape of moulded bricks vary slightly.

The flat arch, or camber arch, illustrated in Fig. 28, is a gauged brick arch, the joints of lime putty being only about $\frac{1}{16}$ in. thick. The soffit of a flat arch should be set out to a camber or curve, the rise in the centre being 1 in 30. The voussoirs should be set out to have equal thickness along the curve set out from the radius, as shown.

Relieving arches are arches built over lintels. An example is illustrated in Fig. 29, the relieving arch consisting of a two-ring rough arch. The space between lintel and arch

importance in a wide or deep arch. The voussoirs may consist of headers and stretchers, as in the semicircular axed arch in Fig. 27.

Gauged brick arches have wedge-shaped voussoirs with very thin bed joints. The bricks have a fine texture and are soft enough to be cut and rubbed to shape. Gauged bricks are often used to form arches of such shapes as would be awkward to form in axed or moulded work. The size of the voussoirs can be kept absolutely regular and the beds

soffit is filled with brickwork and this is called the *core*. A relieving arch is used where it is required to square the head of the opening in an interior wall, using a lintel of small section which would not be strong enough to carry the load. A relieving arch may also be used over a stone mullion or other window to relieve the frame of load.

Pointed arches, or Gothic arches, as illustrated in Fig. 30, are struck from two or more centres and the two sides or halves of the arch meet at a point or intersection in the centre. The methods of setting out shown in Fig. 30 are self-explanatory.

REINFORCED BRICKWORK. Brickwork is relatively strong in compression but weak in tension and shear, which means that it is strong under a vertical load but comparatively weak against a diagonal or side thrust. By reinforcing brickwork with mild steel rods and wires considerable strength in tension and shear may be gained. With proper design this may result in considerable economy of material and cost.

Vertical and horizontal reinforcement may be placed in ordinary brick walls, as shown in Fig. 31. The horizontal reinforcement is placed in the bed joints and the vertical reinforcement in the intersecting or straight joints. Bricks can also be cut or holed to take vertical reinforcement. A reinforced brick lintel has already been illustrated in Fig. 26.

PIERS. These take two distinct forms: *detached* columns, as in Fig. 32; and pilasters projecting from the wall face—

called *attached* piers, as in Fig. 33. The principles of bonding should be followed, straight joints being avoided as far as possible, alternate courses bonded in English bond and headers in Flemish bond. Proper closers should be used as necessary and small pieces avoided. As piers are usually placed to take a specific load or to stiffen a wall the workmanship and materials should be of the best.

JAMBS AND REVEALS. Openings for windows and doorways need careful consideration if the bonding of the walls or piers between the openings is to be satisfactory. The aim should be to preserve the regular pattern of the bond used. Fig. 34 illustrates some examples in English bond. The sides of the openings are called *jambs* and that portion of the jamb which can be seen in front of the frame is called the *reveal*.

Ordinary square jambs are formed like square stopped ends. Rebated jambs are formed by using a special closer, usually a king closer, as in Fig. 34. Jambs suitable for cavity walls are illustrated in

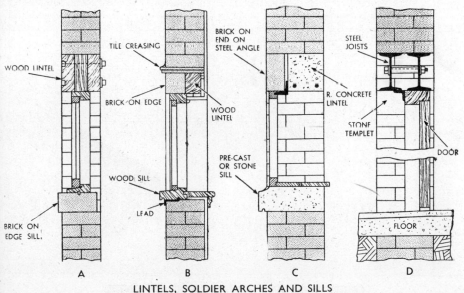

LINTELS, SOLDIER ARCHES AND SILLS

Fig. 24. A lintel is a beam placed over a wall opening. The illustration gives four vertical sections showing alternative constructions at lintels and sills to openings in brick walls.

Fig. 35. In two of them slates in cement are used as vertical damp-proof courses to prevent moisture passing across the jamb. In the third example a special steel sub-frame is used.

STEPS, SILLS AND COPINGS. Steps and sills may be formed by using brick-on-edge or brick-on-end. They should be set in strong cement or cement-lime mortar. Stone and precast concrete can also be used. Specially moulded bricks are very often used for sills. Similar materials are frequently used for copings.

A sill should be proof against saturation by rain water. It is desirable to weather the top surface—that is to have it sloping outwards, and also to project the front edge and to have a groove or throating under the projection.

Steps should have a slight weathering or slope outwards and it is desirable to have a slight bullnose or rounded angle to the front edge.

FIREPLACES AND FLUES. Fireplaces

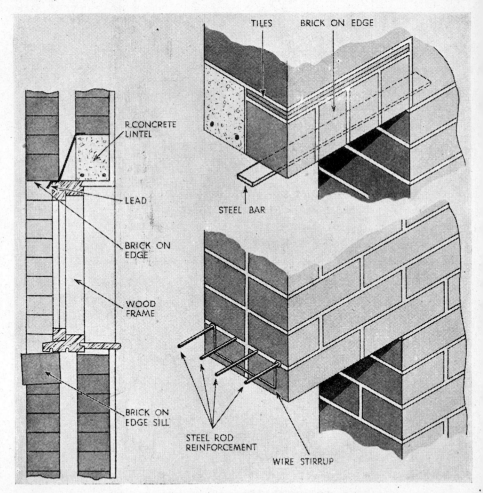

CAVITY WALL AND REINFORCED BRICK LINTEL

Fig. 25 (left) shows cavity wall with sheet-lead apron to protect the wooden frame against weather conditions. **Fig. 26** (right) illustrates two modern methods of forming lintels to brick openings.

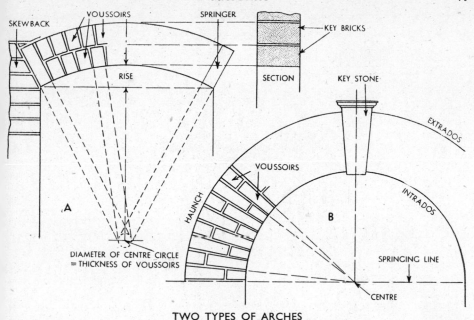

TWO TYPES OF ARCHES

Fig. 27. A shows a rough ring segmental arch—two ring; and B illustrates the construction of an axed semicircular arch. The various terms used in arch work are indicated in the diagram.

may project into the room, or project outwards, or project both into the room and outwards. They may also be placed cornerwise.

An example of a projecting fireplace and flue is illustrated in Fig. 36. The solid brickwork is gathered over the opening into a 9 in. × 9 in. flue, and this passes upwards at the side of the upstairs fireplace.

The fireplace opening may be spanned either by an arch or a reinforced concrete lintel, as shown. If the chimney breasts at the sides are less than 13½ in. wide an iron chimney bar must be placed to support and tie in the arch, the ends being turned up and built into the brickwork.

Gas-fire flues are usually 9 in. × 4½ in., but smaller flues may be used in cases where concrete flue blocks are built into the walling.

MASONRY

THE general principles of load bearing and non-load bearing walls have been described at the beginning of this chapter. Structurally, masonry walls consist of three distinct types:—

(1) Solid masonry walls, load bearing: usually consisting either of rough blocks or pieces of stone throughout, or stone more or less cut to a fair face for facing the wall and rough rubble for backing.

(2) Composite masonry walls, load bearing: usually consisting of blocks or pieces of stone bonded to a brick or concrete backing.

(3) Stone facing slabs to panel walls, non-load bearing: used in framed buildings, the stone facing usually consisting of thin stone slabs secured by cramps to the brick or hollow block backing and steel or reinforced concrete framing.

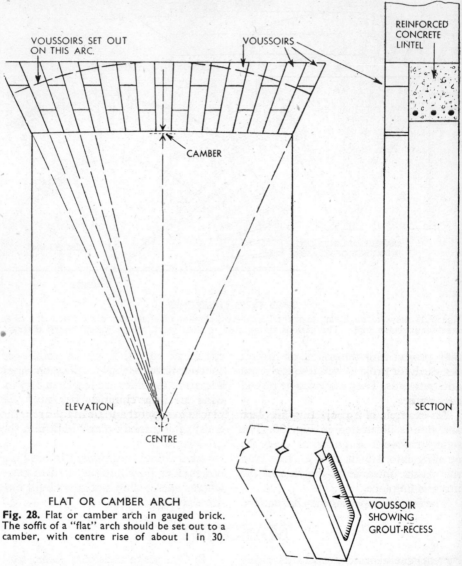

FLAT OR CAMBER ARCH
Fig. 28. Flat or camber arch in gauged brick. The soffit of a "flat" arch should be set out to a camber, with centre rise of about 1 in 30.

The materials used in masonry walls are: natural stone either worked into rectangular blocks or used in roughly dressed pieces; artificial stone which is really concrete made with certain aggregates and coloured cements to resemble natural stone; reconstructed stone which is a special concrete made with a stone aggregate and surfaced to reveal the aggregate, resulting in a very close resemblance to natural stone. In addition, ordinary concrete blocks may be considered as a branch of masonry.

Natural stone may be used in many forms, as follows:—

UNCOURSED RANDOM RUBBLE consists of stones of all sizes, roughly rectangular but used as they are quarried with little or no tooling. The sizes vary with the kind of stone, but the principle of use in walls is the same. Figs. 37A and 37B illustrate this. The stones are not laid to horizontal courses but a fairly regular bed is selected for each stone. The smaller stones are used to fill up between the larger. One large stone to about every yard superficial should bond through the wall.

For boundary walls random rubble is often built dry, the coping or top course being set in mortar. For the walls of buildings great care should be taken to fill all joints with mortar. If slurry is used to fill interior joints, care must be taken that it does not "run out." At corners and openings it is best to use roughly squared stones as quoins. Uncoursed rubble walls are seldom less than 18 in.

RANDOM RUBBLE IN COURSES. Stones are roughly squared by knocking off projections with a hammer and the work is laid to rough courses from 12 in. to 18 in. thick according to the sizes of stones. Fig. 37c shows a typical example. This work is rather stronger and neater than uncoursed work.

SQUARED RUBBLE IN COURSES. The larger stones are squared up as truly as possible with the mason's hammer and chisel, excepting the back. In building the wall the work is brought to horizontal courses from 12 in. to 18 in. deep, as in Figs. 37D and 37E. Properly done this makes a sound

P.B.—C*

wall which has a very good appearance.

SQUARE SNECKED RUBBLE. Some stone breaks when quarried into strata of convenient thicknesses and with very little tooling can be squared into various sizes. It is built in a wall as shown in Fig. 37F. It is not laid to courses, but small stones called *snecks* are placed in the wall to prevent continuous straight joints.

REGULAR RUBBLE IN COURSES. The stones are squared with hammer and chisel, making the corners true right angles, though the back is left rough. Stones of regular thickness are then sorted so that they can be laid in straight courses as shown in Fig. 38A, though the courses vary in thickness one from another. The interior or heart of the wall is filled with rough rubble and grout.

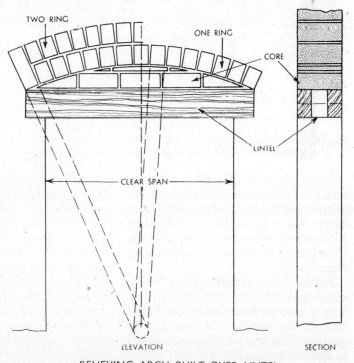

RELIEVING ARCH BUILT OVER LINTEL
Fig. 29. Relieving arch consisting of a two-ring rough arch. The space between the lintel and arch soffit (the core) is filled with brickwork.

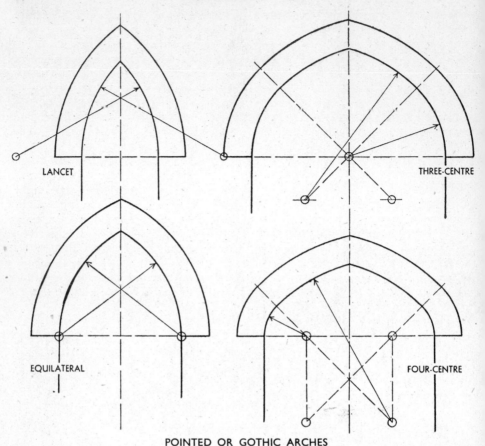

LANCET

THREE-CENTRE

EQUILATERAL

FOUR-CENTRE

POINTED OR GOTHIC ARCHES

Fig. 30. The methods of setting out four different types of pointed or Gothic arches are clearly shown in the above diagram. The arches are struck from two or more centres.

FLINT WALLING. The flints are small and hard. They are dressed with the hammer, or *knapped* to a roughly square shape. Flints are used in combination with courses of squared stone or brick. Flint panels are often formed by using stone "posts."

BRICK-BACKED RUBBLE. Stone rubble of the various kinds described above is largely used for house and other buildings in the districts in which it is quarried. But it is generally economical to build a composite wall with rubble facing and brick backing, as shown in Fig. 52. The thickness of the wall

should be from 11 in. to 15 in., with a 4½-in. brick backing. Small rubble and grout should be used as "heart filling." The brick backing should be bonded into the stone by placing a header course every six courses, and the bond can be strengthened by placing a through bond stone the full thickness of the wall to about each square yard.

Select a hard stone for this purpose, as soft stone is too absorbent. If the stone is rather soft and porous it is advisable to fill the hearting with a waterproofed cement concrete or grout.

ASHLAR is stone accurately worked to

plane surfaces and sharp right-angled corners. The courses are truly horizontal and level, though they may vary in thickness. Joints are rarely more than $\frac{1}{8}$ in. thick. Ashlar is prepared for facing only, the backing being either brick or rubble (Fig. 38B). The backing should be built in a stronger mortar than the ashlar, as the backing has more bed joints and therefore tends to settle more than the ashlar. The use of a stronger mortar in the backing prevents cracking through unequal settlement. A hydraulic lime mortar is suitable for the stone facing.

PREPARATION OF STONE. The first operation after the stone is quarried is the rough preparation. The scabbling hammer is used for this purpose and the stone so treated is called *quarry pitched* or *hammer faced* and also *rock* or *rustic* work. Such stone is ready for use in rubble walling.

Further preparation consists of bringing the stone to a roughly rectangular shape. The waller's hammer is used for this purpose—projecting corners and angles being knocked off. This tool is used by the waller to shape the stones.

PREPARING ASHLAR. The saw or chisel is used to prepare a plain or half-plain face; the saw being used for soft or small stones. The first treatment with these tools gives a *half-plain* face. Further treatment is needed to give a *plain* face.

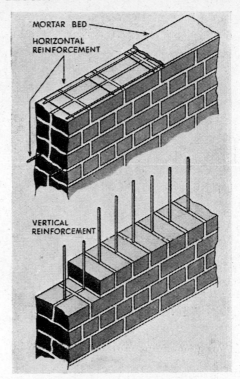

Fig. 31. Methods of reinforcing brickwork by means of mild-steel rods. Both vertical and horizontal reinforcements are shown.

Ashlar blocks are often prepared with a plain face and sawn or chiselled bed and side joints. In large quarries this work is done by machinery, but hand sawing is done with a large frame saw suspended from pulleys. Small work is sawn with a small hand saw. A double

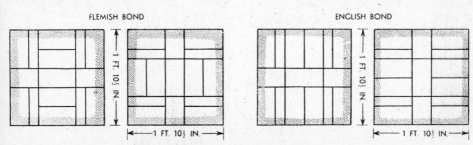

ALTERNATE COURSES FOR BRICK PIERS

Fig. 32. Alternate courses for two-and-a-half brick detached piers in Flemish bond and English bond. Note that the alternate courses are identical, but turned through 90 degrees.

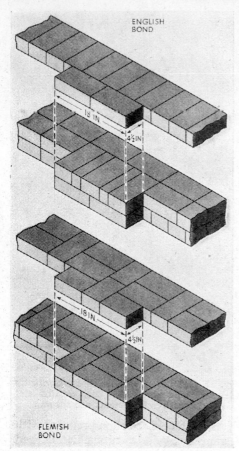

Fig. 33. Attached piers, or pilasters, showing the arrangement of brickwork of alternate courses in English bond and Flemish bond.

handed saw may be used to cut large soft stones. Sand and water are used as a lubricant in sawing. Sawing through a large stone to make two is termed *half-sawing*.

Chiselling to bring a rough surface to a half-plain face is carried out as follows. A margin is first draughted round the edges. Two opposite ends are first draughted and tested for alignment with a straight-edge. The remaining two edges are then draughted. The central mass is then chiselled off level with the margins.

To finish a surface after the prelimi-

nary preparation just described a comb or drag is used. The comb is worked across the surface in all directions, thus producing a pleasing texture. The chisel can be used to produce a number of face finishes. In cases where the chisel is worked obliquely in parallel lines across the face the work is termed *boasted* or *droved*.

Parallel chisel lines worked with the chisel is termed a *tooled* finish (Fig. 39). Ornamental treatment of the face is sometimes done within a chisel-draughted margin, as in Fig. 40. Reticulated work and pointed work (Fig. 40) are special ornamental treatments, chiefly used for quoin stones.

The mason's axe, or a patent multi-bladed axe, is used to finish the face of a hard stone, a series of cross cuts being made across the surface from chisel-draughted margins.

A perfectly smooth face is produced by rubbing with a piece of stone, using sand and water as a lubricant and gradually reducing the quantity of sand as the work proceeds. Machine polishing with revolving iron disks is used in the stone yards.

Moulding Machinery

MOULDED WORK. In large stone yards most moulded work is done by machinery, but for small jobs in the country hand-work is still common. The hand-work is carried out as follows: a zinc profile of the moulding section is first made and the profile is scribed on the ends of the stone with a steel point. A draught (Fig. 41) is then sunk at each end with the chisel; the mass of material is carefully cut away, using the straight-edge to test the line and an external zinc profile to test the shape.

Circular work such as arch voussoirs is carried out by hand as follows: The arch is carefully set out to a large scale. A suitable stone is selected from which

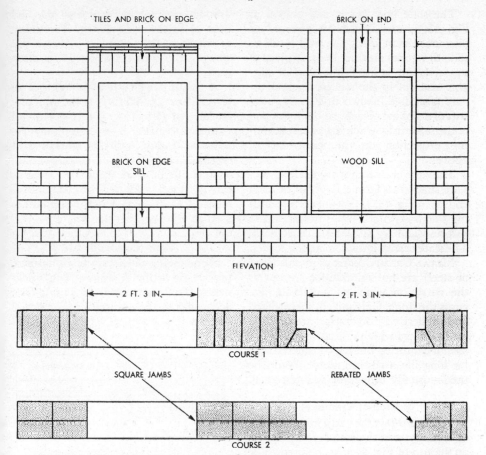

TILES AND BRICK ON EDGE

BRICK ON END

BRICK ON EDGE
SILL

WOOD SILL

ELEVATION

◄── 2 FT. 3 IN. ──►

◄── 2 FT. 3 IN. ──►

COURSE 1

SQUARE JAMBS

REBATED JAMBS

COURSE 2

TYPES OF WINDOW OPENINGS IN BRICK WALL

Fig. 34. Two openings in a brick wall in English bond showing different arrangements. A king closer is generally used for rebated jambs, as shown. The regular pattern of the bond should be preserved.

to cut the voussoir. The side intended for the intrados is worked to a plain face and the rectangle set out, as in Fig. 53. One end or face is then square and the face mould taken from the drawing is applied. The other end is also squared and the face mould applied, scribing the shape round the edges. The intrados is then hollowed out and the voussoir faces carefully and smoothly finished.

JOINTS. Bed joints for stone walls are shown in vertical section in Fig. 42, but in various parts of masonry certain special joints are used to prevent stones

moving laterally if subjected to side thrust or other stresses which tend to strain the mortar joints.

The cement joggle illustrated in Fig. 43 is formed by making a groove of V section in the side surfaces of two stones which meet in a side joint. The groove is grouted with cement after the stones have been set in position. In the case of cornice stones the grooves are cut to form an inverted Y and it is easy to see how this shape of joggle secures the cornice stones against movement backwards or forwards.

The slate bed joggle, also shown in Fig. 43, is useful where horizontal or diagonal thrust along the wall tends to slide the stones on their beds. A piece of squared slate is fitted into slots of suitable size cut in the stones, as shown.

A table bed, shown in Fig. 43, consists of a sinking or depression in the bed of the stone into which fits a corresponding projection on the stone surface above.

The slate cramp consists of a length of slate shaped to form a dovetail at each end, as in Fig. 43. It fits into corresponding slots in two adjoining stones and so secures them against lateral movement. The slate cramp is used in coping stones.

METAL CRAMPS. Ferrous metals (iron or steel) are not suitable for cramps as the corrosion which is inevitable disrupts the stone. Galvanized, sherardized and parkerized iron cramps are suitable for buildings which are not intended to last for centuries, but it is considered that for long life a rustless metal should be used—usually bronze or stainless steel.

Method of Cramping

To cramp together adjoining cornice or coping stones the metal cramp shown at the top of Fig. 44 may be used. The ends of the cramp are cranked downwards and roughened. A suitable slot is cut in the stones, the end depressions being slightly dovetailed, and the metal cramp is caulked in lead. The lead plug, as shown in Fig. 44, is formed by pouring the hot liquid metal into a plug hole of the shape shown.

FIXING FACING SLABS. Stone slabs fixed to brick or concrete hollow-block backing by cramps (not by bonding) depend solely upon the metal cramps for security. Fig. 44 illustrates various types of metal cramps in common use. One type consists of thick bent wire and another of a short metal bar cranked at one or both ends, and in some cases

split at one end to bond into the bed joint of brickwork backing. For fixing to concrete, the patent continuous slot system, also shown in Fig. 44, is often used.

A continuous vertical metal slot of dovetail section is built into the concrete backing as shown. Into this slot metal cramps are fixed. The cramps can be adjusted to any level. All cramps with cranked ends must have a corresponding slot cut in the stone bed. The stone is thus secured against outward movement. Cement joggles are sometimes used in the vertical joints.

Stone Facing Slabs

Stone facing slabs may be of natural, precast or artificial stone. The thickness of the slabs varies from 3 in. to 5 in. according to the nature of the material and the job. A typical panel wall detail

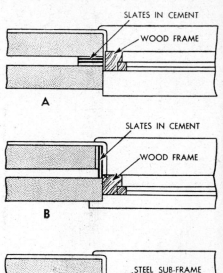

Fig. 35. Three methods of forming window jambs in cavity walls. In A and B slates in cement are used as vertical damp-proof courses. In C a special steel sub-frame is used.

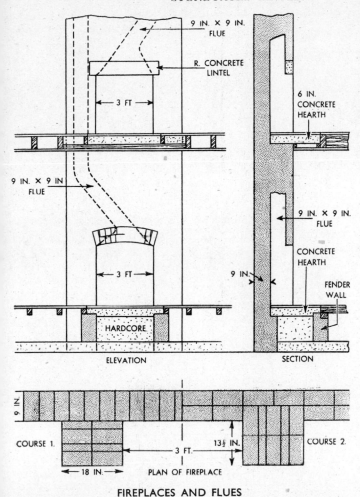

FIREPLACES AND FLUES

Fig. 36. Elevation and section illustrating alternative methods of supporting brickwork above fireplaces, and methods of forming hearths.

showing stone slab facing flush over the stanchion casing, the stanchion projecting inside the building (Plan A), and the other showing at Plan B a stanchion projecting outside with bonded stone block pilasters and brick walls.

STONE-FACED LINTELS. In modern building the old type of stone lintel is not often used. Even if the building has load-bearing walls it is desirable to use steel or reinforced concrete for lintels. Fig. 46 illustrates two typical details. The stone lintel blocks are cut to fit against a r.s.j. lintel and are secured to it by bolt, nut and plate in the manner shown. A slot is cut in the side joints of the stones so that one plate secures two stones. The lintel blocks are screeded at the back against the steel.

The detail of a precast stone facing to a reinforced concrete lintel shows how the lintel blocks are specially reinforced and reinforcing rods are left projecting so that they can be bonded into the concrete lintel at the back.

BONDED ASHLAR. The traditional method of building masonry walls, as already explained, is to overlap stones

is illustrated in Fig. 45. The structure is a steel-framed building with concrete floors and concrete casing to the steelwork, but the same principles apply to a building which is framed in reinforced concrete.

The wall load is transmitted through the beams and stanchions to the stanchion foundations. Cornices are usually supported on projecting concrete lips. Details of typical stanchion casings to outside walls are shown in Fig. 45; one

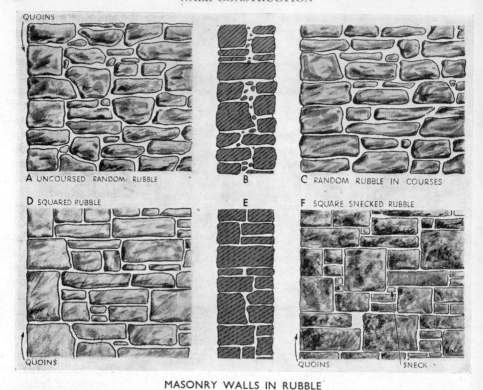

MASONRY WALLS IN RUBBLE

Fig. 37. Four types of masonry walls, arranged in order of quality from cheap to fairly expensive work.

and bricks or blocks to form a bond. Metal and other cramps are only required where side stress is developed at certain points.

Typical bonding details are illustrated in Figs. 47 and 48. The walls consist of ashlar facing with brick backing, the face being bonded to the backing. Foundation, plinth, sill, jambs and quoins are shown in Fig. 47, and window head, cornice and parapet are shown in Fig. 48. The details shown in these two illustrations are designed on Renaissance lines—a style of architecture which follows the formal classic style of ancient Greece and Rome. This style is now being displaced by the plainer modernist style which is better suited to panel walling in framed buildings.

Another traditional style of architec-

ture which is still used is the Gothic style, with its many variations. The pointed arches already illustrated (Fig. 30) belong to this style. A simple doorway with a dripstone moulding over a solid stone lintel is shown in Fig. 49. The dripstone is a Gothic moulding which serves the practical purpose of throwing off rain-water.

Gothic Windows

A window detail of Gothic type is illustrated in Fig. 50. This has stone mullions, pointed heads and a dripstone moulding. Notice the slate dowels securing the beds of the stone mullions and the cement joggles to the pointed heads. Typical mullion sections are illustrated in Fig. 51.

A casement window set in a rubble

wall is illustrated in Fig. 52. Notice the stone arch set on a fixed turning piece, with a projecting dripstone course above and a reinforced concrete lintel at the back. The quoins and sill stones are larger than the walling stones and are roughly squared. This detail is typical of modern cottage and house building in the stone districts.

SELECTING THE BED. By this is meant the direction of the grain or strata of the stone in relation to the bed. Natural stone blocks in walls should be laid so that the natural strata is horizontal. If the block is laid so that the strata is vertical, trouble will follow through disruption and spalling of the surface.

Stone arch voussoirs should be so cut that the strata is parallel to a radius line passing through the centre of the voussoir. Thus, the strata will be approximately in the same direction as the bed joint—bearing in mind that the bed joints are between arch voussoirs and on radius lines. The direction of strata will thus be at right angles to the arch load (Fig. 53).

Mullions must have the strata horizontal. This means that the stones from which they are cut must be taken from a deep bed.

MORTAR. There is some variation of practice in the selection of a suitable mortar for natural stone. The Building Research Station at Garston, near Watford, recommends that the permeability of the mortar should be considered in relation to that of the stone. Thus, a rather dense mortar may be used with a dense, impervious stone, "but there is every reason to avoid the use of a dense mortar with stones of fair permeability."

Of three specifications quoted by the Building Research Station, the following is No. 2, a moderately strong mix: 12 parts fine crushed stone (by volume);

A SQUARED REGULAR COURSED RUBBLE

B PLAIN ASHLAR

MORE EXPENSIVE TYPES OF WALLING

Fig. 38. Two more expensive types of walling in which all the stones are worked to regular courses in contrast to those in Fig. 37.

STONE WALLS WITH SQUARED RUBBLE
A West country cottage showing a good example of stone wall built with squared rubble.

3 parts lime putty or hydrated lime;
1 part Portland cement.

The materials should contain very little free salts. These are present in Portland cement, so that a strong cement mortar used either with the stone or with the brick backing is likely to produce efflorescence—the unsightly white deposit which disfigures the surface of so much good work.

FIXING. Large ashlar blocks are fixed with joints of about ⅛-in. thickness. It is important to see that the bed joints are of consistent thickness throughout. Screeding irons (strips of metal of the bed joint thickness) are laid on top of the

stones already fixed and temporarily secured by placing a little mortar on each edge. The mortar bed is then spread and screeded by working a straight-edge over the irons. The bed is left for a very short time and the irons are then removed and the stone lowered.

The plumb rule is used to test the face, as in bricklaying. In rough rubble work the plumb rule cannot be conveniently used. Profile boards should be set up at suitable intervals and a line can then be stretched between the boards.

CAST STONE is the name by which is now meant precast, reconstructed or artificial stone, made to imitate the

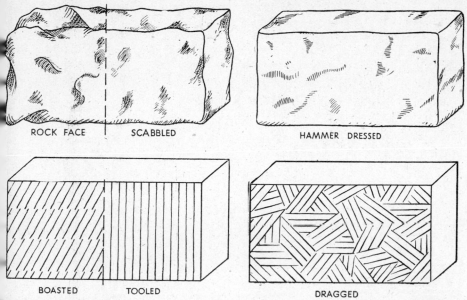

ROCK FACE   SCABBLED   HAMMER DRESSED

BOASTED   TOOLED   DRAGGED

Fig. 39. Various finishes to stonework. Note that the difference between the boasted and tooled finishes is that in tooled work the chisel or "bat" marks run vertically across the face of the stone.

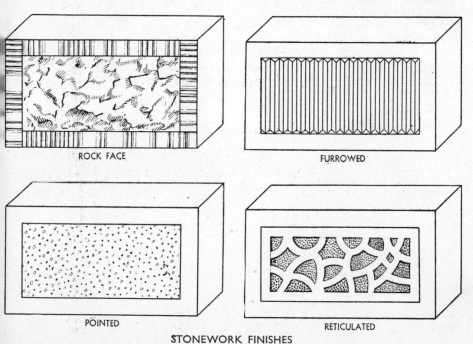

ROCK FACE   FURROWED

POINTED   RETICULATED

STONEWORK FINISHES

Fig. 40. Various finishes with chisel-draughted margins. Vermiculated ashlar is very similar to reticulated ashlar, but the sinkings are more irregular and the bands between them vary in width.

colour and texture of various natural stones, and with crushed stone as the principal aggregate. This distinguishes the material from precast concrete blocks made with gravel and sand and included in the general description of precast concrete products.

The following is a specification for cast Portland stone: $1\frac{1}{2}$ parts crushed Portland stone $\frac{1}{4}$ in. to $\frac{1}{8}$ in.; $1\frac{1}{2}$ parts crushed Portland stone $\frac{1}{8}$ in. down; 1 part white Portland cement.

The special mix which gives the appearance of the natural stone is rather costly and is applied in the mould to the surface only, to a thickness of about 1 in. Mechanical tamping and vibration is used thoroughly to consolidate the material and to give a dense hard and uniform texture. The surface is usually rubbed smooth while the concrete is still "green," and the material may be surface worked by the mason, using ordinary mason's tools.

Cast stone is not usually reinforced but reinforcing steel is incorporated for special purposes, such as in lintels and beam casings.

CONCRETE

WALLS may be built of: (1) plain mass concrete; (2) reinforced concrete; (3) concrete panels either in poured work or in slabs as filling in framed buildings.

Plain mass concrete walls may be compared with ordinary brickwork. The strength varies according to the mix used. The following is a mix of moderate strength, about equal to the best quality "common" brickwork in cement mortar: 112 lb. Portland cement; $2\frac{1}{2}$ to $3\frac{1}{4}$ cub. ft. sand (depending on the degree to which it has bulked or swollen according to moisture content); 5 cub. ft. clean, hard, coarse aggregate.

Qualities of Aggregate

AGGREGATE. This is of two kinds: fine aggregate, which in most concretes is sand; and coarse aggregate, which may be broken brick, stone or gravel.

All aggregates should be clean, free from loam and vegetable matter. Sand should not be too fine and the grains should vary in size. The coarse aggregate too should vary in size. This size variation if perfectly "graded" gives a dense uniform concrete, as all the voids are filled.

The aggregate for walling in the above specification should pass through a $\frac{3}{4}$-in mesh sieve and be retained upon a $\frac{3}{16}$-in mesh sieve, and should consist of approximately equal parts of material between $\frac{3}{4}$ in. and $\frac{3}{8}$ in., and $\frac{3}{8}$ in. and $\frac{3}{16}$ in. For thick walls the maximum size might be slightly increased.

MIXING. Sufficient water should be used to make the concrete sufficiently workable for the particular job. If too much water is used the concrete will be weakened and difficulty may be caused by the tendency to excessive flow when placed. If not enough water is used it will be difficult to mix thoroughly and to place the concrete properly.

Thorough mixing is essential. This is now usually done in a concrete mixing machine, the time required being from one and a half minutes upwards. Usually about three minutes is sufficient to give good results.

Ordinary Portland cement has what is called an "initial" set of about thirty minutes. The concrete must be placed in position in rather less time than this from the commencement of wet mixing, and it should on no account be disturbed thereafter. Mixed concrete which cannot

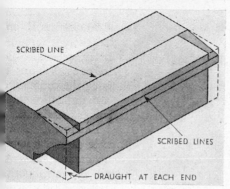

SCRIBED LINE

SCRIBED LINES

DRAUGHT AT EACH END

Fig. 41. Method of cutting a moulding.

e used within twenty-five minutes
hould be scrapped, or used for site
lling under floors.

SHUTTERING. The shuttering or form-
ork consists of a built-up shell, usually
f timber, into which the concrete is
oured and tamped into position.

Fig. 54 illustrates timber shuttering
or a concrete wall. The size of timbers
nd sheeting largely depend upon the
eight and thickness of the wall. The
huttering must, of course, be a rigid job
hich will not move
s the concrete is
oured and tamped
ito it. Wall sheeting
aries from 1 in. to
in. Edges may be
ongued and grooved,
evelled or square.
heeting timber
ould not be too dry
hen fixed. If too dry
will swell when the
et concrete is poured
nd may give trouble
y buckling.

If the concrete is
ot to be plastered
ie sheeting should
e oiled or greased so
aat it will strip away
asily. For concrete
be plastered a non-

staining oil or soft soap and water may
be used.

There are various proprietary systems
of steel shuttering. One system is illustrated in Fig. 54. This consists of tee-
bars separated by distance bars which
are secured by wedges. Wood sheeting
is placed inside the tee-bar framing.

PERMANENT SHUTTERING. The cost of
concrete walls can be reduced by using
some form of permanent sheeting which
remains in place as a lining or facing to
the wall. Certain water-repellent fibre
boards and building boards can be used
inside, flat-head nails being partly
driven in the back to bond in the concrete as in Fig. 55. On the outside, precast slabs about 2 in. thick may be used.
These slabs may be lightly reinforced
and the reinforcing wires turned out at
the back so that they bond into the
concrete. Cramps may be used with
stone slabs.

STRIPPING SHUTTERING. The shuttering must not be removed until the
concrete has attained sufficient strength

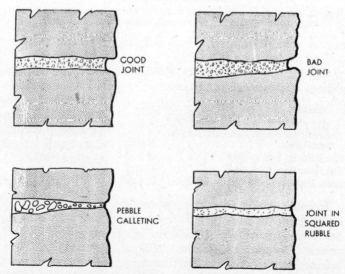

GOOD
JOINT

BAD
JOINT

PEBBLE
GALLETING

JOINT IN
SQUARED
RUBBLE

BED JOINTS FOR STONE WALLS

Fig. 42. The joints should always be made so that the water will run
off them. Examples of good and bad joints are shown.

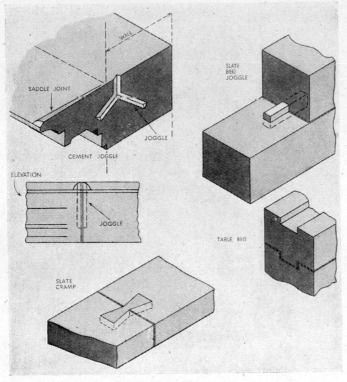

JOINTING MASONRY

Fig. 43. Methods of constructing masonry joints in order to prevent, by means of joggles, any lateral displacement of stones.

take a temperature of 36 degrees F. on a falling thermometer, or below 34 degrees F. on a rising thermometer, as an indication that frost is imminent.

TAMPING. Concrete should not be too rapidly poured into the form-work. It should be poured in long layers about 12 in. thick, and the slower the "rate of rise" the less will be the pressure on the form-work. If a high thick wall is poured at a rapid rate the shuttering may collapse. The more water that is used and the smaller the aggregate, the greater the pressure. Thorough consolidation is essential. The concrete should be tamped into position with an iron bar or hardwood piece of a size and shape suitable to the particular position. In narrow work and between reinforcement the tamping is a most important operation on which the strength of the job largely depends, but care should be taken not to disturb the reinforcement.

not to require support. Data on the subject varies. The following are suggested periods for ordinary Portland cement and average conditions:—

MINIMUM SHUTTERING PERIODS (Normal weather about 55 degrees F.)

Vertical wall sides, column boxes, beam sides	4 days
Flat slabs up to 3 ft. span. . .	4 days
Flat slabs above 3 ft. span . .	7 days
Beam bottoms and props up to 12 ft. .	16 days

In cold weather these periods should be increased by one-third, as low temperatures retard the setting of the cement. Concreting should not be done in frosty weather or when frost threatens. Light covering with sacks is not sufficient protection. A good rule for frost prediction is to watch the thermometer, and to

Consolidation Vibrator

Consolidation by vibration is coming into increasing practice. The vibrator may be driven by electricity or compressed air. The device is attached to the shuttering.

Vibration probably results in better consolidation, less honeycombing, a more uniformly dense concrete and a better surface than can be achieved by hand tamping. The mix may be stiffer if a vibrator is used, with a consequent gain in strength. Extra care is necessary to ensure strong, rigid shuttering, as the vibration may cause movement in defective shuttering.

REINFORCEMENT. Reinforced concrete consists of a combination of concrete and steel. Concrete is relatively strong in compression and steel in tension, as previously explained in the case of reinforced brickwork. The design of reinforced concrete is such that both

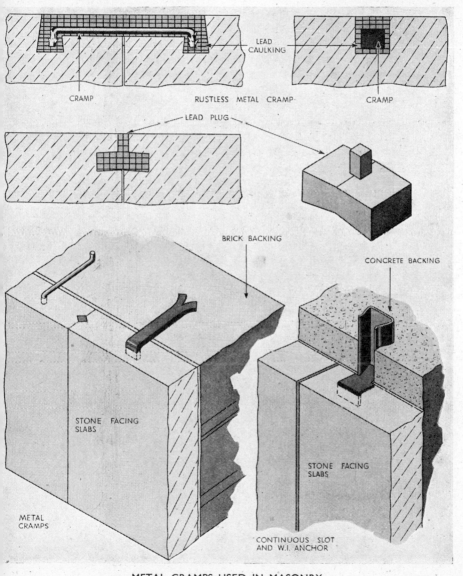

METAL CRAMPS USED IN MASONRY

Fig. 44. Metal cramps for copings and wall facings. They have only been used in recent years.

materials are economically used. In a reinforced-concrete beam the steel is placed at the bottom to take the tension stress which results from the bending tendency, and steel stirrups are placed to take the shear stress which occur near the supports.

Although walls are usually in direc compression they tend to buckle, just a a sheet of plywood buckles if it is stoo

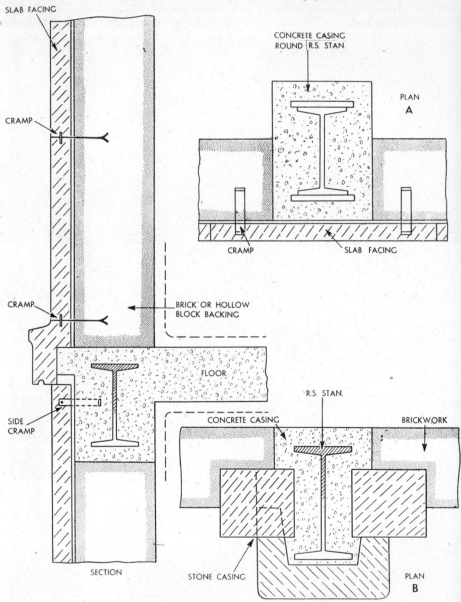

PANEL WALLS AND STANCHION CASINGS
Fig. 45. Vertical and alternative horizontal sections. Note method of cramping facing stones.

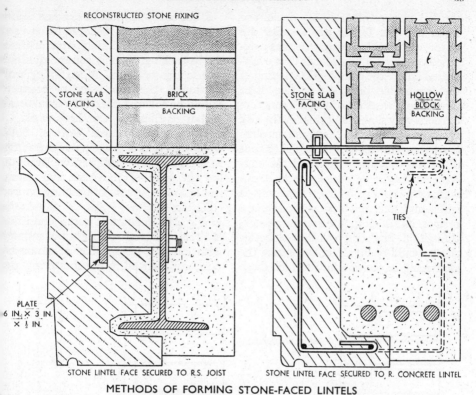

RECONSTRUCTED STONE FIXING

STONE SLAB FACING   BRICK   BACKING

STONE SLAB FACING   HOLLOW BLOCK BACKING

TIES

PLATE
6 IN. × 3 IN.
× ½ IN.

STONE LINTEL FACE SECURED TO R.S. JOIST   STONE LINTEL FACE SECURED TO R. CONCRETE LINTEL

METHODS OF FORMING STONE-FACED LINTELS

Fig. 46. Vertical sections showing stone lintel face secured, by means of bolt, nut and plate, to rolled-steel joist (left) and to reinforced-concrete lintel (right).

upright and heavy pressure applied to it at the top; wind pressure also causes a bending stress. Comparatively thin concrete walls can be made buckle resisting, by incorporating steel reinforcement on both sides, about 1 in. or 1¼ in. from the face. Whichever way the wall tends to buckle, the steel takes the resulting tension. Steel reinforcement in a wall also resists the tension and shear stresses produced by shrinkage and temperature movements and so does much to get over the chief defect in concrete construction.

For this purpose the Building Research Station recommend a minimum percentage of steel to whole concrete section in each direction at each face of approximately ·1 per cent. In the case of a con-

crete wall 4 in. thick this would be fulfilled by placing $\frac{3}{16}$-in. diameter steel bars vertically and horizontally at 6 in. centres (forming 6-in. squares) on each side of the wall (Fig. 55).

Just as reinforcement may provide against the buckling tendency of a wall under load, so it may be used to provide against the buckling tendency of a column under load. Usually four vertical mild steel rods are used in a column, one at each corner, wrapped round with wire.

Reinforcing rods should be hooked at the ends. Joints should be made by hooking, overlapping and tying with iron wire.

CURING. Many cases of crazing and cracking occur in concrete construction through uncontrolled drying out of the water content. In hot, dry weather the water will rapidly evaporate from exposed concrete. The water is thus evaporated before the complete hardening of the cement has taken place. The effect of very cold weather is that the concrete hardens very slowly and there is the risk of frost setting in before complete hardening has taken place. The object of curing concrete is to allow the concrete to harden gradually in a damp warm atmosphere. Timber shuttering is sufficient protection against rapid evaporation if it is left in position for a week, though in hot, dry weather a better result would be obtained by leaving the shuttering in position for fourteen days.

If the concrete must be exposed before it has hardened off it should be covered with waterproof building paper or clean damp sacking. This is commonly done with concrete floors. When filling wall shuttering the top layer of concrete should be covered if left for a meal break and when finishing the day's work.

HOLLOW CONCRETE WALLS. Solid walls are often of greater thickness than is necessary for compressive strength for the sake of the heat and sound insulation. A system of building poured concrete hollow walls is illustrated in Fig. 56. Pneumatic cores, consisting of fabric-covered rubber tubes inflated with an air pump like a motor-car tyre, are inserted in the shuttering and

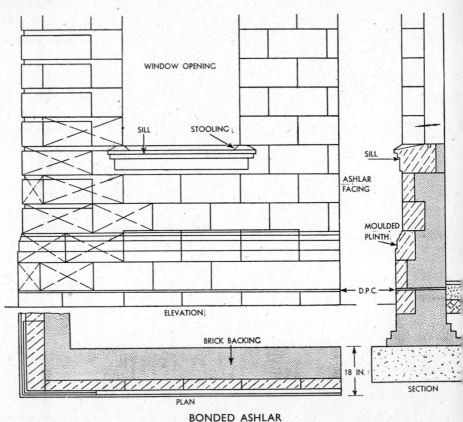

BONDED ASHLAR

Fig. 47. Details of ashlar facing with brick backing, showing also plinth and sill to window opening

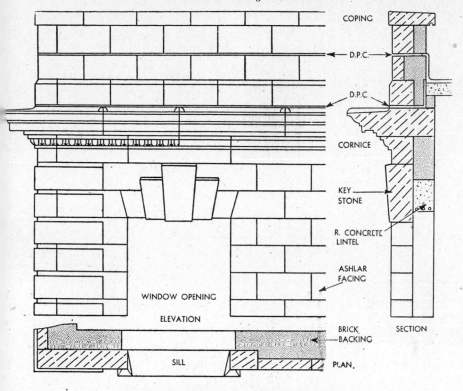

COPING

D.P.C.

D.P.C.

CORNICE

KEY
STONE

R. CONCRETE
LINTEL

ASHLAR
FACING

WINDOW OPENING

ELEVATION

BRICK
BACKING

SECTION

SILL

PLAN.

ANOTHER EXAMPLE OF BONDED ASHLAR

Fig. 48. Masonry details in Renaissance style of the upper portion of the wall shown in Fig. 47.

secured in the correct position. The concrete mix is then placed between cores and shuttering, and after the concrete has sufficiently set the cores are deflated and withdrawn. A similar system is used in making poured concrete hollow floors.

CONSTRUCTION JOINTS. This description is applied to joints in monolithic concrete which must occur when the work is interrupted and later resumed. If more than twenty-four hours elapse before resumption of pouring, a scum is formed on the concrete which will be a source of weakness and will not allow of proper bonding with the next section of concrete.

This scum must be cleaned off by brushing with a wire brush and then well wetted and covered with a 1 : 1 cement-sand mortar. The concreting can then proceed. These construction joints appear on the face when the shuttering is removed. As they are rather unsightly a sunk joint line is sometimes made by fixing a bevelled wood fillet inside the shuttering.

In long walls considerable expansion and contraction takes place with temperature variations. This movement may crack the wall; to prevent this, vertical expansion joints are sometimes made. This is done by leaving a gap of about $\frac{3}{4}$ in. vertically through the wall and closing it with a corrugated metal filler strip.

SURFACE TREATMENT. Concrete wall surfaces may be left as they are when the

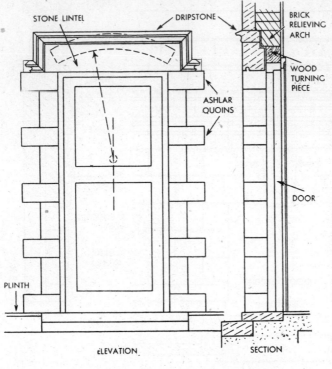

STONE LINTEL DRIPSTONE BRICK RELIEVING ARCH WOOD TURNING PIECE ASHLAR QUOINS DOOR PLINTH

ELEVATION SECTION

DOORWAY WITH DRIPSTONE MOULDING

Fig. 49. Simple doorway with dripstone moulding over solid stone lintel. The dripstone serves the purpose of throwing off rain-water.

then applied with a brush, keeping the wash well stirred and using each wet batch in less than thirty minutes.

On small surface the shuttering may be safely stripped while the concrete i still green. The sur face can then b brushed with a wir brush to expose the aggregate. Specia aggregates can b used to give desire colours and textures Tooling, bush ham mering and sand blasting can also b used in dressing th surface.

RENDERING. Th covering of the ex terior surface with rendering of Portlan cement mortar i often adopted, as i gives a good regular surface and any colour desired can be obtained by using coloured cements.

The conditions for sound rendering are by no means universally agreed upon. The following can, however, b safely termed good practice: The wall surface must be rough to provide a goo key. If necessary it should be hacked t improve the key. The wall surface mus be sprinkled with clean water so that i will not rapidly absorb the water in th rendering. The wall surface must, o course, be clean and free from efflores cence. The mix should not be too strong or shrinkage cracks may occur. Th Building Research Station recommend the following mixes: Undercoat (part by volume): 3 parts white hydrated lim

shuttering is stripped. The surface appearance will then depend upon the care with which the material was tamped or vibrated, and on the nature of the shuttering surface and the care with which it was erected. Shuttering is now often lined with waterproof ply-wood, or other suitable sheeting, so that board lines will not appear on the surface of the concrete.

Cement Wash

Cement wash is sometimes applied to the concrete wall surface. Ordinary Portland cement or white or coloured cement may be used as desired. This improves the colour and to some extent the texture. The wash should be mixed to the consistency of stiff oil paint and

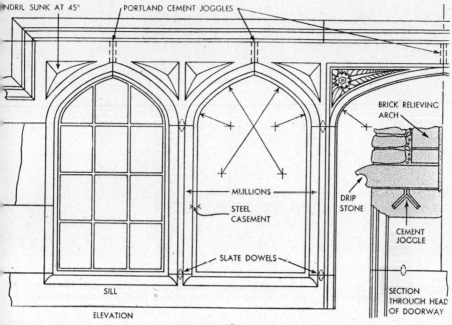

GOTHIC WINDOW

g. 50. A good example of a Gothic type of window with stone mullions and steel casements

stiff lime putty; 1 part Portland ment; 10 parts clean sand or crushed one aggregate. Finishing coat: 3 parts ne as above; 1 part Portland cement; parts sand or crushed stone according colour and texture required.

If lime putty is used this may be ocked up into lime-sand coarse stuff, d the cement added before use. All aterial should be used up within about two hours from the time when the cement is added.

This is stated to be satisfactory for the average inland site, but for severe exposure a cement-sand mix is recommended for the undercoat, finishing in a cement-lime-sand mix.

Renderings should not be highly worked with the trowel. It is better to finish with a wood float. Excessive

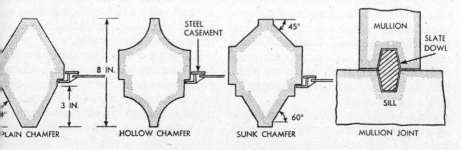

MULLIONS OF VARIOUS TYPES

g. 51. Alternative sections of stone mullions to windows and vertical section showing joint at sill

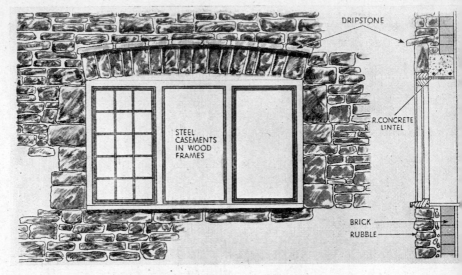

DRIPSTONE

R.CONCRETE LINTEL

STEEL CASEMENTS IN WOOD FRAMES

BRICK

RUBBLE

CASEMENT WINDOW SET IN RUBBLE WALL

Fig. 52. Elevation and vertical section of casement window set in rubble wall. The stone arch set on a fixed turning piece. Note the brick backing and reinforced-concrete lintel.

working up of the surface produces a rich skin which tends to crack and flake off. Various rough-textured finishes are produced by scratching and scraping, wiping with sacking and other devices. This has a beneficial effect as it removes, or partly removes, the rich skin.

Rough Cast

Rough cast, consisting of pebbles or gravel thrown on the rendering, seems to be less liable to cracking and other faults than smooth-finished rendering. This is probably because the impact, when the material is thrown on, improves the adhesion to the wall by removing air pockets. In some countries it is the custom to throw on the rendering instead of working it off trowel or float, and the former method is thought to give a better result.

SLAB AND POST WALLS. This is a system of wall construction, primarily intended for offices, canteens, small factory buildings, garages and dwellings which are urgently required. The build-

ings can be rapidly erected by semi-skilled labour. There are a number of proprietary systems. The units are standardized and wall lengths and heights should be arranged to suit the standard dimensions. The general principle is illustrated in Fig. 57. The pre-cast concrete posts are reinforced. These are grooved so that precast concrete slabs can be fitted into the grooves.

The large number of buildings of the precast slab and post type erected to meet urgent war needs has proved the merits of this type of construction and the ease with which such buildings can be put up, and also taken down and removed to another site.

RENDERING ON EXPANDED METAL. In framed structures the panel walls are sometimes constructed of expanded metal, or a special form of expanded metal stiffened with ribs, rendered with several coats of Portland cement rendering to form a reinforced monolithic panel 2 in. to 3 in. thick, as illustrated in Fig. 58. Expanded metal is also sed to wrap round steel stanchions and beams to form a key for plaster or concrete. This forms a sound weatherproof wall which is also durable. The use of expanded metal enables awkward shapes and curves of short radius to be easily negotiated (Fig. 58).

Small buildings are sometimes constructed in this system. A light framing of timber or steel is erected to support the roof and stiffen the walls, and the expanded metal is fixed to the framing by tying it with iron wire or clips. The inside and outside are then rendered as just described.

False piers, duct casings and suspended ceilings are also often erected, using expanded metal as a combined lathing and reinforcement. With plain expanded metal, mild steel rods are used as stiffeners. With ribbed expanded metal, the ribs provide the required stiffening.

HOLLOW BLOCKS. These are made of precast concrete, clay, terra-cotta and diatomaceous earth. Some blocks are made for outer walls and some for partition walls.

Blocks may have a smooth face for facing work which is not to be rendered,

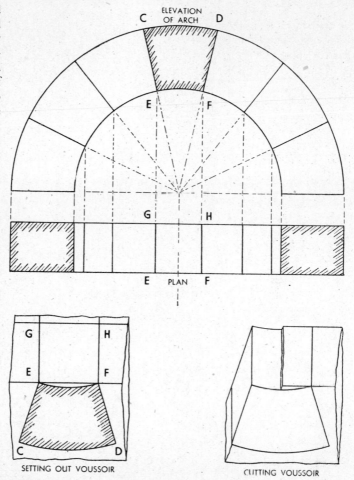

STONE ARCH VOUSSOIR

Fig. 53. Elevation and plan of simple arch, with method of setting out and cutting a voussoir. The direction of strata is at right angles to arch load

or a rough or keyed face for rendering. Rendering or plastering should not be practised on smooth-faced blocks. Blocks are larger than bricks and the joints do not provide sufficient key for plaster.

Concrete blocks are obtainable in a variety of sizes. For exterior work some blocks are faced with a special fine concrete to a depth of about 1 in. A popular size for outside walls is $17\frac{3}{4}$ in. $\times$ 9 in. $\times$ $8\frac{3}{4}$ in. An example of this size is shown

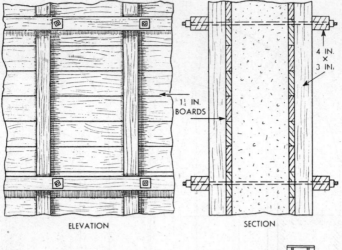

ELEVATION   SECTION

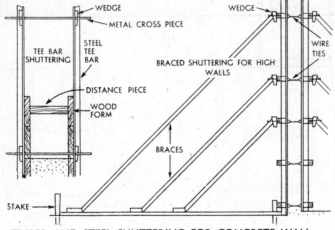

TIMBER AND STEEL SHUTTERING FOR CONCRETE WALL

Fig. 54. Three types of shuttering for concrete walls, showing also alternative methods of supporting the sheeting.

loads from beam and trusses can thu be constructed o filled reinforce blocks, no shutte ing being require

Solid concret blocks are als made. Light-weigl breeze and pumi and plaster block are produced for tl construction of pa titions. These a much used in ta framed building where they effe considerable redu tion in dead loa Thicknesses are in., $2\frac{1}{2}$ in., 3 in. an 4 in.

Where the sla butt against walls triangular fillet fixed to secure tl junction. The sla are keyed to inte lock and may l laid dry if they a skew nailed at th angles. They shoul also be secured timber framing wit nails. These slal are 3 ft. × 1 ft. The may also be obtained sized to 1 ft. 6 i × 1 ft.

Hollow Clay Blocks

Hollow clay blocks are made in variety of types and sizes. The use such blocks as backing in panel walls h already been described. Fig. 60 show hollow clay blocks with keyed beds an faces suitable for external wall constru tion for light buildings. The keyed fac enable the blocks to be rendered i

in Fig. 59. This particular type of block has been largely used in the construction of air-raid shelters and traverse walls. The hollows can be filled with concrete or with sand. For light buildings they could be left empty. The plan in Fig. 59 shows the arrangement and bonding of these blocks in air-raid surface shelters.

It should be noticed that the through cavities in the blocks enable vertical reinforcement to be introduced with concrete filling. Piers for bearing

Portland cement outside and plastered inside.

Hollow clay partition blocks vary in thickness from 2 in. to 4 in. An example with interlocking beds is illustrated in Fig. 60. These blocks are of light weight, and, like the breeze and plaster blocks just described, may stand direct on upper floors without beam support. Most hollow clay blocks are 12 in. × 9 in. They are laid to stretcher bond.

PARTITION WALLS. Load-bearing partition walls are of ordinary brickwork, concrete or solid concrete blocks. Fig. 61 illustrates a 4½-in. thick brickwork partition wall and foundation with a solid floor one side and a timber floor on the other. Such a wall may rest direct on the surface concrete, but unless the bearing value of the ground is very high an extra depth of concrete should be provided for the foundation. Alternatively the concrete may be reinforced.

Cellular bricks (bricks of standard size but hollow within) are often used for partitions, as they save weight.

SOUND-PROOF PARTITIONS. The blocks just described are often used in the construction of sound-proof partitions. The term sound-proof is used in a relative sense to mean proof against the moderate noise sound in houses, offices and similar buildings. Block partitions are not in themselves sound-proof, but in con-

junction with other materials they have very high sound resistance.

Sound is transmitted through a structure by vibrations. The harder the materials and the more rigid the connections between one part of the structure and another, the greater is the amount of sound transmitted. Sound-absorbent materials are usually soft and have a cellular structure.

If the material is of a loose fibrous nature it is made up into quilting enclosed in building paper. Sound-absorbing boards are thick fibre boards or cork slabs. Sound-absorbing pads on which stanchions, beams and partitions rest may be of any suitable material, but thick cork, asbestos and rubber are usually used. Thick sheet lead is sometimes used for heavy loads.

The problem of sound-proofing

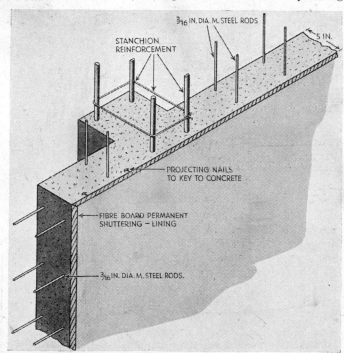

PERMANENT SHUTTERING

Fig. 55. Permanent fibre-board shuttering to one side of reinforced-concrete wall, with steel bars forming 6-in. squares, and stanchion.

.B.—D

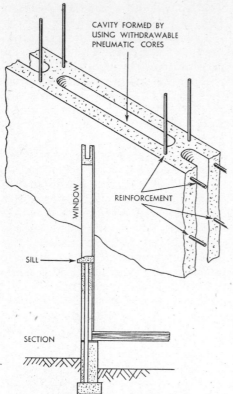

CAVITY FORMED BY USING WITHDRAWABLE PNEUMATIC CORES

WINDOW

SILL

REINFORCEMENT

SECTION

Fig. 56. Vertical section and isometric sketch of hollow reinforced-concrete wall formed by the use of pneumatic or other cores.

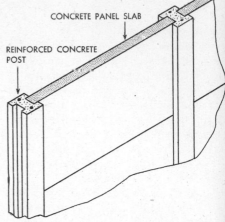

CONCRETE PANEL SLAB

REINFORCED CONCRETE POST

Fig. 57. Post and panel wall. Sometimes the post have another groove or rebate in which inner slabs are fixed, thus giving cavity construction

partitions and walls should be studied in two parts. First, the wall or partition should be insulated from the surrounding structure (floor, ceiling, beams and stanchions) by interposing resilient pads. Second, the partition or wall itself should be highly sound absorbent. These points are illustrated in Fig. 62. At A, a partition wall of ordinary bricks or building blocks is shown. This rests on a sound-absorbent pad which damps out vibrations transmitted through the solid floor. The partition is lined by sides with 2-in. thick thatchboard. Corkboard and other materials are made equally suitable for this purpose.

The partition at B is a cavity or double partition. Thin blocks or slabs would be used for this purpose with a cavity $1\frac{1}{2}$ in. to 3 in. thick between. The blocks or slabs rest on a resilient pad thus insulating the partition from the floor, as before described. The plaster face is applied direct to the partition. As there is no rigid connection between the two portions of the partition, sound vibrations are not readily transmitted through it.

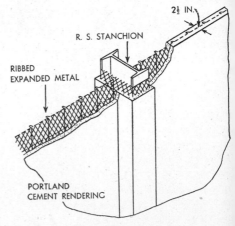

$2\frac{1}{2}$ IN.

R. S. STANCHION

RIBBED EXPANDED METAL

PORTLAND CEMENT RENDERING

Fig. 58. Ribbed expanded metal and rendering Sometimes the cement rendering is shot on from a cement gun.

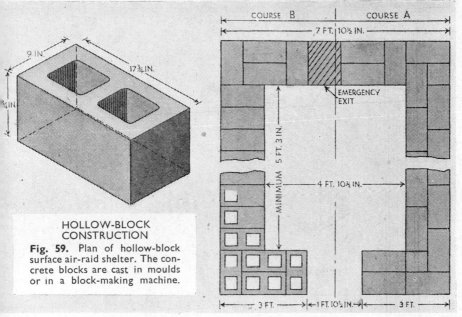

HOLLOW-BLOCK
CONSTRUCTION
Fig. 59. Plan of hollow-block
surface air-raid shelter. The concrete blocks are cast in moulds
or in a block-making machine.

Sound-proof partitions should not be rigidly connected to the floor above. An air gap may be left or a resilient pad may be fixed to close the gap. Doors should be of a sound-absorbent type or the object of sound-proofing the partition may be defeated.

The sound resistance of outer solid walls may be improved by similar means, the sheeting materials described being used between the plaster or sheeted face and the solid wall. Floors should rest on resilient pads. Much noise is transmitted through floors—this point is therefore very important.

TERRA-COTTA. Moulded-clay products embracing blocks for walls and for facing work are included in the description terra-cotta. Terra-cotta may be glazed, but the description used alone refers to moulded blocks used as a facing material. The natural colours of terra-cotta depend on the clay used. Red, buff and grey are the usually natural tints. The material is dense and durable.

Glazed terra-cotta has a matt-glazed surface. Polished glazed terra-cotta is usually called *faience*. It is produced in a range of brilliant colours.

Terra-cotta facing material consists of hollow blocks specially produced for the particular building. It may be regarded as a substitute for stone, but the material has characteristics of its own which should be developed in design and taken account of in construction. As a clay product it shrinks in firing and also distorts the moulded shape to some extent. The blocks must therefore be small compared with stone masonry or the distortion will be so great as to prevent accurate fixing.

Terra-cotta blocks are filled with concrete on the site. The concrete should not be too strong, or the expansion may crack the blocks. One part Portland cement to seven of mixed ballast is usual, the maximum size of aggregate being $\frac{3}{4}$ in.

Joints are usually $\frac{1}{4}$ in. thick and weathered. Mortar must be cleaned off as the work proceeds. The blocks must

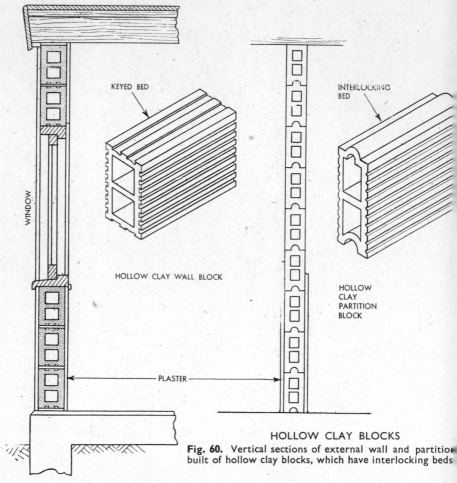

KEYED BED

INTERLOCKING BED

WINDOW

HOLLOW CLAY WALL BLOCK

HOLLOW CLAY PARTITION BLOCK

PLASTER

HOLLOW CLAY BLOCKS

Fig. 60. Vertical sections of external wall and partition built of hollow clay blocks, which have interlocking beds

be a good fit and if the distortion is too great the block should be rejected. Terra-cotta blocks should not be cut or holed. All required holes and chases should be moulded in the blocks.

Rustless metal dowels and cramps should be used, but as the blocks are open at the back they may be filled as fixed and so bond into a concrete backing, as in Fig. 63. Dovetail grooves can be made to provide a keyed joint—the dovetail being moulded in the block. Projecting cornices should be filled with concrete at the back. The front part is left hollow, thus keeping the

overhanging portion of light weight, as shown in Fig. 63.

DAMP-PROOF COURSES. These have already been mentioned and some uses have been illustrated. The material used for a damp-proof course must be durable and impermeable. Non-absorbent slates laid in cement, using two courses and laying the slates so that the side joints in one course are positioned over the centre of the slates above or below, as in Fig. 64, are often used. The total thickness of the course so formed is about $1\frac{1}{2}$ in. Slates are specially produced for various wall thicknesses.

Hard, close-textured bricks, such as Staffordshire blue bricks, laid in cement mortar can be used to form damp-proof course. The whole of the plinth of a building may be built in such bricks, so that the walls rest on a damp-proof plinth.

Flexible damp-proof course materials are produced in rolls to standard wall widths. Bituminized felt, sheet bitumen, asphalt poured and screeded over the wall, sheet lead and sheet copper are suitable materials. A typical flexible damp-proof course is shown in Fig. 64.

The position of a horizontal damp-proof course is of great importance. This should be at least 6 in. above the finished ground or paving level, as shown in Fig. 65. Wall plates or floor joists should be placed above the d.p.c.

Vertical damp-proof courses are necessary in basement walls. An example is shown in Fig. 65. If the ground is very damp it may be necessary to continue the d.p.c. through the concrete floor, as

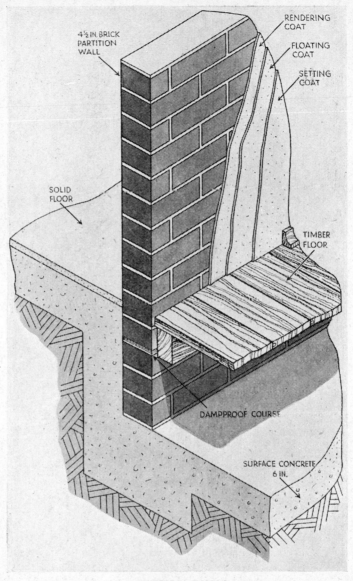

PARTITION WALLS

Fig. 61. Sketch of half-brick partition wall and foundation. The floor joists are supported on sleeper walls. The foundation has a solid floor on one side and a timber floor on the other.

shown. Waterproofed cement and sand are sometimes used for this purpose.

Note the position of the d.p.c. in the partition wall in Fig. 61; a solid floor one side and a timber floor on the other.

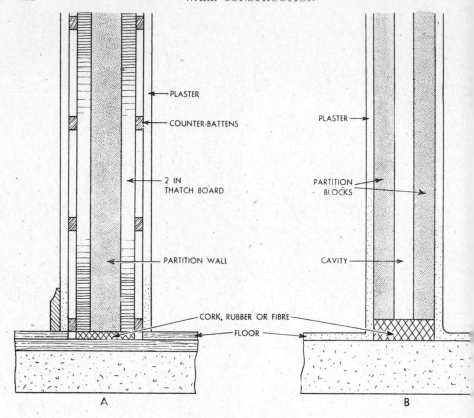

INSULATED PARTITIONS

Fig. 62. Vertical sections of two sound-resisting walls between rooms: A shows a half-brick wa?
sound-insulated on both sides, and B a cavity wall built of partition blocks. Note the methods
disconnection at junction with floor. The problems of sound-proofing partitions and walls that
all probability will confront the learner are fully discussed in the text.

PLASTERING

THE plasterer's craft has been modified by the introduction of new plasters, but it is still a handicraft depending for success upon the skill and experience of the craftsman. Failures of plaster are nearly always due to some avoidable cause. The speed of modern building operates against sound methods in plastering. Where sufficient time for drying out cannot be allowed, it is better to use building board rather than to rush the plasterwork.

Laths of wood applied to timber jois: ceilings should be arranged so that th: butted ends are nailed to a joist and d: not overhang. Laths should break joint that is, all of the ends should not b: nailed to one joist, nor should adjoin: ing laths be nailed to one joist. If end: are nailed to one joist so that the butt line up, the plaster will certainly crac: along this line.

The space between the sides of th: laths should be $\frac{3}{8}$ in. Great care shoul:

expanded metal, 22 gauge, weighing $3\frac{3}{4}$ lb. per yd. super. For internal work expanded metal 24 or 26 gauge may be used—the light 26 gauge on partitions and the medium 24 gauge on ceilings. Studs, joists or battens should not be more than 13 in. apart in the clear.

Internal plastering is usually carried out in three coats, sometimes described as render, float and set. The first rendering and the second or floated coat consist of coarse stuff made up of 1 part lime to 2 or 3 parts sharp sand, and on lathing 1 lb. of clean cowhair should be added to each 3 cub. ft. of mix.

Gauged stuff consists of 3 to 4 parts of fine stuff to 1 part plaster of Paris. For moulded work equal parts are used.

Modern plasters, such as Portland cement, Sirapite, Selenitic lime, Keene's cement, Martin's cement, and Parian cement have two advantages over the

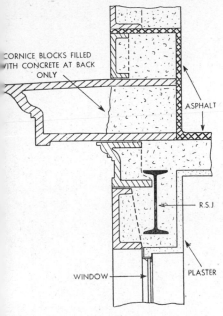

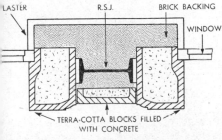

Fig. 63. Plan of pier and vertical section of cornice showing methods of fixing terra-cotta. Note that the cornice is only filled with concrete at the back in order to avoid undue weight in the overhanging portion.

be taken to keep this key gap constant. Faulty lathing leads to cracks and in bad cases to the falling of the plaster.

The joists or studs to which the laths are fixed should not be more than 2 in. wide. Wider joists should have the edges chamfered, or narrow battens should be nailed to them. A greater width than 2 in. against the lathing weakens the key to such an extent that the plaster cannot take a proper grip.

For external lathing (for Portland cement renderings) it is better to use

Fig. 64. Two methods of forming damp-proof courses, the lower example being flexible.

traditional lime mixes: rapidity of setting and hardness. In modern rush jobs the rapidity of setting is certainly an advantage provided that the work is smartly done.

DRYING CONDITIONS. The success of plastering largely depends upon drying conditions. Each coat should be almost dry before the next is applied. Much depends upon the weather, but drying out may be assisted by placing portable heating stoves in the building. The time allowed for the drying out is no criterion in this matter. In damp weather the plaster may retain practically all its moisture for several weeks.

SCREEDING. The first coat of coarse stuff should be $\frac{1}{2}$ in. thick. The second or floating coat should be $\frac{1}{4}$ in. to $\frac{3}{8}$ in. thick, and the finishing or setting coat about $\frac{1}{8}$ in. thick. The second coat must be screeded to bring the surface level. The screeds are narrow strips of plaster plumbed and lined up. An inferior screeding method is to use wood lath as temporary screeds, but this is not recommended. When the floating coat is applied it is levelled off by passing the floating rule over the screeds. If the work is not screeded the surface will be irregular, owing to the fact that walls are not perfectly even on the face.

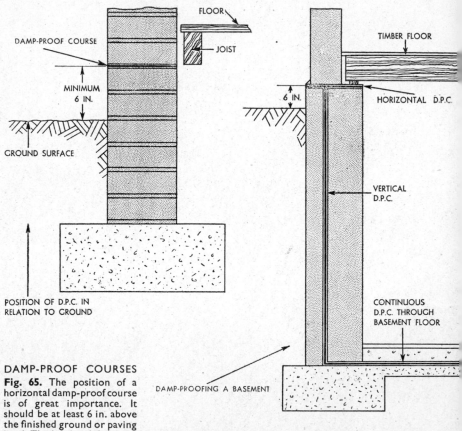

DAMP-PROOF COURSE

MINIMUM 6 IN.

GROUND SURFACE

FLOOR

JOIST

TIMBER FLOOR

6 IN.

HORIZONTAL D.P.C.

VERTICAL D.P.C.

POSITION OF D.P.C. IN RELATION TO GROUND

CONTINUOUS D.P.C. THROUGH BASEMENT FLOOR

DAMP-PROOF COURSES

Fig. 65. The position of a horizontal damp-proof course is of great importance. It should be at least 6 in. above the finished ground or paving level. The left-hand drawing shows the usual position in an external wall. In the right-hand drawing the basement is sealed from the earth. Vertical damp-proof courses are necessary in basement walls.

DAMP-PROOFING A BASEMENT

CHAPTER 3

FLOORS AND FLOOR FINISHINGS

Suspended and unsuspended floors. Loading on floors. Weights of materials. Length of bearings. Supports. Strutting. Trimming methods. Sleeper walls and piers. Concrete floors. Floor finishings. Strip floorings. Cement and sand, and granolithic pavings. Wood block floorings. Quarry-tile pavings. Terrazzo and mosaic pavings. Avoiding cracking. Parquet floorings. Composition, asphalt, rubber and other special floorings.

FLOORS, of whatever material they may be constructed, are essentially structural and must, as such, be capable of supporting safely the various loads on them as well as their own weight.

FLOOR FINISHINGS OR FLOORINGS come under a distinct heading as compared with "Floors." They are supported by the structural and load-supporting floors, and are the actual surfaces used for pedestrian or other forms of traffic, for furniture, goods, etc., and, being almost invariably exposed to view, they are often subject to consideration or treatment to make them pleasing or artistic in appearance.

The simplest example to show the difference between a floor and a floor finishing is the ordinary timber floor of a house; the floor joists form the structural floor and they support all the main loads of and on the floor and transmit them to walls and other parts of the main structure. The flooring boards are the floor finishings.

FLOORS

PRACTICAL AND TECHNICAL KNOWLEDGE APPLIED TO FLOORS. To ensure compliance with the best principles and details of floor construction it is essential to appreciate that there are many aspects, both practical and technical, which really must be considered together. It is quite wrong, as it is unfair to all parties, whether they be designers or craftsmen, or both, to cloak technical work with such ambiguous specification clauses as "Construct the floor in a proper and workmanlike manner."

This at once causes what may be aptly termed an interpretation clash of minds between the designer and crafts-man. From the simplest type of timber floor—which has very many points to be considered, as will be understood later—to the more complicated reinforced concrete floor, the following matters all have to receive attention to ensure the best results both practically and technically:

(1) Structural mechanics, which deal with stresses and strains and their computation; by no means a difficult subject for designers and also for many able craftsmen who can soon become interested and proficient in this matter.

(2) The use of modern tabular information and data, which eliminate many

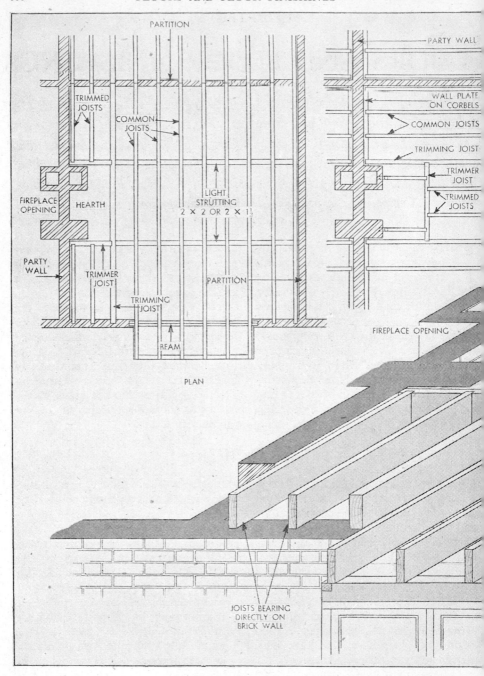

TYPICAL TIMBER SUSPENDED

Fig. I. Note the method of trimming round the hearth and the names of the different joists. The ceiling to the bay window below and the floor to the bay window above are carried by cantilevering

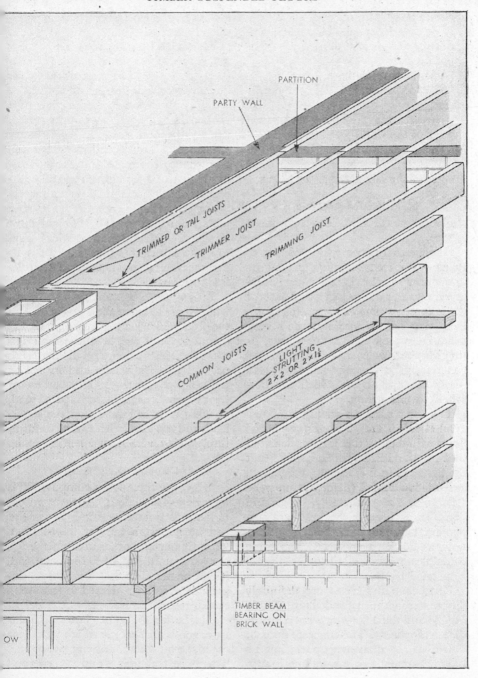

PARTITION

PARTY WALL

TRIMMED OR TAIL JOISTS

TRIMMER JOIST

TRIMMING JOIST

COMMON JOISTS

LIGHT STRUTTING 2 × 2 OR 2 × 1½

TIMBER BEAM
BEARING ON
BRICK WALL

OW

FLOOR TO AN UPPER STOREY

the common joists over a beam spanning the window opening. The illustration also gives an alternative plan showing the arrangement of joists which are at right angles to the party wall.

of the computations mentioned in (1).

(3) The economical and commercial aspects having regard to the purpose of the floors.

(4) The building by-laws

(5) The "following" trades and finishings.

(6) The designing, detailing and specifying of the work.

(7) The execution of the work by the carpenter, the concretor, the steel erector, the labourer and/or others.

Main Groups of Floors

Floors are divided into two main groups, viz.:—

SUSPENDED FLOORS which consist of structural members which extend or span over space, having, of course, bearings on walls, steelwork or other parts of the main structure. The spanning members may be the ordinary and very extensively used timber floor joists, or they may be of slabs, such as of reinforced concrete, plain concrete and steel, and many other materials which are described in this section.

The most common examples of suspended floors are the ordinary house floors with their timber joists as depicted by Figs. 1 and 2. It will be noticed that the floor in Fig. 1 is to an upper storey, and that in Fig. 2 (described on page 125) to the ground storey, or ground floor. In both cases the joists are suspended between their bearings; they span as beams over space. The same principle applies to all the other types of suspended floors.

UNSUSPENDED FLOORS are definitely different from the suspended type. Study Fig. 26 and the difference will be immediately apparent. The concrete floor or slab does not span over space, has no bearings at ends or edges, but is supported throughout its area by the ground; there are no beam or slab members which are, or should be, subject to bending stresses which are described later.

TIMBER-FRAMED FLOORS are almost invariably of the suspended type, more used than any other, particularly for housing work, and are economical.

Fig. 1 shows an isometric view of a timber-framed floor to an upper storey, usually the first storey in an ordinary two-storeyed house, and its design and construction represent a fund of interesting knowledge for craftsmen and technicians alike. The floor does not merely mean throwing a number of timber joists from wall to wall; thought must be given to all the matters which tend to make this simple floor a credit to its designer and constructor and trouble-free to its user.

Timber joists are essentially beams which have to carry the loads of and on the floor. The load *of* the floor is the actual or dead weight of the materials comprised in the floor and the materials used in floor finishings and in ceiling finishings or coverings. The load *on* the floor is known as the superimposed load, or what is sometimes called the superload, and this load is that caused by furniture, goods, and the movement of people.

Computation of Loads

"How are these loads computed?" it may be asked. The dead loads are not difficult to ascertain, as it is known, or can be got from tabular information, what timber and other materials weigh per given unit. But, as to the superload, it will be manifest that it would be impossible even for a wizard to state with any degree of accuracy what the weight would be for different classes of furniture, goods and people which would, or could, be on the floor at any given time. Therefore, technicians and scientists and building acts assist in this problem by telling us how many pounds per super foot shall be allowed as superload to

TABLE I	SUPERIMPOSED LOADING ON FLOORS (including note on dead loading) MINISTRY OF HEALTH MODEL BY-LAWS

For the purpose of calculating the superimposed loading on beams, pillars, piers and walls the minimum superimposed load on each floor of a building shall be estimated as equivalent to the dead load specified below.

Description of building	Pounds per square foot of floor area
Rooms of dwelling-houses, flats, hotel buildings and similar residential buildings; hospital rooms and wards; corridors, staircases and landings of dwelling-houses and flats	40
Offices—floors above entrance floor	50
Offices—entrance floor and floors below entrance floor	80
Churches, schools, reading-rooms, art galleries, and similar buildings . .	70
Retail shops and garages for cars of not more than 2 tons dead weight . .	80
Assembly halls; drill halls; dance halls; gymnasiums; light workshops; public spaces in hotels and hospitals; corridors, staircases and landings for the buildings mentioned in this table excepting those to dwelling-houses, flats, etc.; cinemas; restaurants; and grandstands	100
Warehouses, book stores, stationery stores and buildings similarly used and garages for motor vehicles exceeding 2 tons dead weight. *Actual load to be calculated but not less than*	200

NOTE ON DEAD LOADING. For the purpose of calculating the dead loading of a building or any part of a building, the weights of the materials shall be assumed to be those set out in British Standard Specification, *No. 648, 1935—Schedule of Unit Weights of Building Materials*, or if not set out in that Specification shall be determined by test (*see* Table III).

Table I. Ministry of Health Model By-laws for superloads for buildings outside the London area.

cover all reasonable conditions and contingencies.

Table I gives the superloads to allow in accordance with the Ministry of Health Model By-laws for buildings outside the London area. Table II applies to London where the L.C.C. by-laws operate. Table III gives the weights of various materials used in floors, such weights being extracts from the British Standard Specification No. 648, 1935—Schedule of Unit Weights of Building Materials.

Therefore, by using the appropriate Table I or II, together with III, we obtain not only reasonable but the legal

minimum dead and superloads to allow in our calculations (if made) to ascertain the loads on each of the floor joists and to compute the size of such joists.

To compute the loads on floors, and the sizes of joists, to combat bending stresses, deflection, bearing, etc. (all explained fully in Chapter 7) while being very interesting and by no means difficult, is considered by many busy technicians, architects and craftsmen as being a little laborious and time-taking. To meet these conditions tabular information is available, which saves time.

A study of Tables IV and V will make it clear that the correct size of

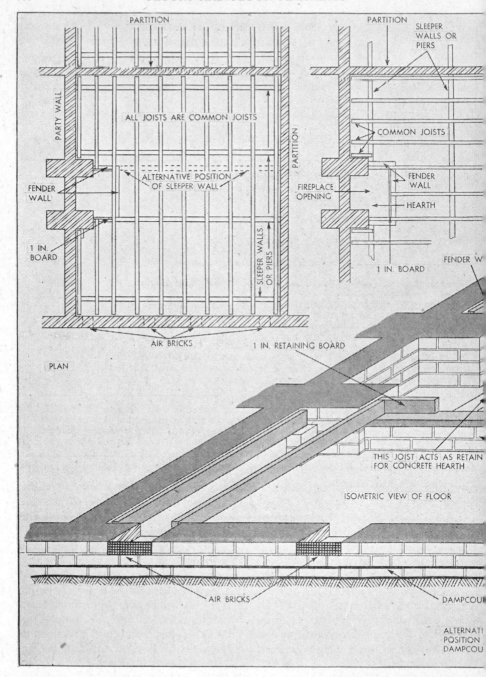

TYPICAL TIMBER SUSPENDED

Fig. 2. Note that the joists at the hearth are supported on sleeper walls and require no trimming. The floor should be adequately ventilated underneath, as indicated, to prevent dry rot. The same

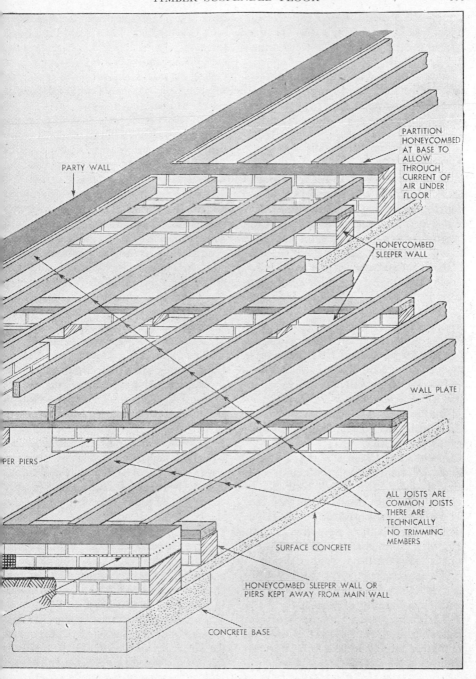

FLOOR TO A GROUND STOREY

principle applies in a general sense to all types of suspended floors. The illustration also gives an alternative plan showing the arrangement of joists which are at right angles to the party wall.

timber floor joists to use for housing work can be settled in a few seconds, whereas calculations take very much longer.

It will be assumed that the sizes of joists will be obtained from tables, and that the following general structural and other subjects must be given attention.

Structural Details

Depths of Joists. It is more economical, in the use of timber, to use a deep and reasonably thin joist than a joist of less depth and greater thickness or width; this rule is true as regards the provision of greater strength and greater resistance to deflection; but it should not be overlooked that an extra inch or so added to the depth of a joist may add an extra inch or so to the general height of a building.

The strength of a joist varies as the square of its depth and directly as its width. As examples: a 9-in. × 2-in. joist has a strength value of $9 \times 9 \times 2 = 162$, and a 7-in. × 3-in. joist equals $7 \times 7 \times 3 = 147$. It will be noted that 9 in. × 2 in. has 18 in. in section and 7 in. × 3 in. has 21 in. Not only is the latter joist weaker than the former; but it has nearly 17 per cent more timber.

Proportion of Depth to Width. To avoid buckling or winding, the depth of a timber floor joist should not exceed about $5\frac{1}{2}$ times its width; therefore, 11 in. × 2 in. is permissible; but 11-in. × 2-in. *scant* which may finish about $10\frac{3}{4}$ in. × $1\frac{3}{4}$ in. is not particularly good but is often used.

The least width of joists should be $1\frac{3}{4}$ in. to provide sufficient width for nailing without a liability of splitting.

The distance apart of joists is of considerable importance and should be regulated largely by the following considerations:—

(1) and the most important—is to make the distance apart to suit the flooring and ceiling covering which is used. The ceiling material usually regulates the distance. Joists should not be so far apart as to cause flooring boards, etc., to unduly sag or be springy, or ceiling boards, lath and plaster, etc., to sag or crack. Table VI will be found of practical use.

(2) The distance apart should be the maximum so that the best strength value may be obtained from the timber. In old times 12 in. or 14 in. centres was the rule; during the past decade or two the centres have been increased to about 16 in. In these modern times with the use of various kinds of flooring and ceiling materials it may be sound economy to use much greater centres.

Deflection in floor joists should not exceed $\frac{1}{360}$ of span. This rule is not only good but will comply with the L.C.C. by-laws, and the British Standard Specification. The author's Tables of Sizes of Timbers for Floors, examples as Tables IV and V, allow for $\frac{1}{360}$ deflection. Any greater deflection may cause too much springiness in floors.

Bearings. The bearings of the ends of timber joists on walls, partitions, steel beams and other structural parts of a building necessitate particular attention to ensure consistent strength.

It should be manifest that any weakness at the bearings will almost assuredly cause the strength value of the joists to be reduced to the value of the strength at the bearings; in other words, if a joist is designed to carry a combined dead and superload of, say 10 cwt., the bearings must also be capable of supporting safely that proportion of the loads which calculations show is necessary.

This important matter can be advanced one stage further by stating that the structural part on which the bearings occur must also be of sufficient strength.

The simplest and most common type of bearing is where the end of a joist or timber beam rests on a timber wall plate,

TABLE II	SUPERIMPOSED LOADING ON FLOORS (including note on dead loading) L.C.C. BY-LAWS		
Class No.	Use of floor	Superimposed loading in lb. per square foot of floor area	
		Slabs	Beams
	SECTION 1. FLOORS OTHER THAN OF TIMBER CONSTRUCTION		
1	Rooms used for residential purposes, and corridors, stairs and landings within the curtilage of a flat or residence	50	40
2	Offices—floors above entrance floor . . .	80	50
3	Offices—entrance floor and floors below entrance floor; retail shops, and garages for private cars of not more than 2¼ tons net weight . . .	80	80
4	Corridors, stairs and landings not provided for in Class 1	Loading to be provided for to be ascertained to the satisfaction of the district surveyor, but not less than:— 100	100
	SECTION 2. FLOORS OF TIMBER CONSTRUCTION		
5	Rooms used for residential purposes . . .	40	40
6	Offices—floors above entrance floor . . .	80	50
7	Offices—entrance floor and floors below entrance floor; retail shops and garages for cars of not more than 2¼ tons net weight	90	80
8	Corridors, stairs and landings	100	100
	SECTION 3. FLOORS OF ANY PERMITTED CONSTRUCTION, SUCH AS TIMBER, REINFORCED CONCRETE, ETC.		
9	Workshops and factories, garages for motor vehicles other than private cars of not more than 2¼ tons net weight	Loading to be provided for to be ascertained to the satisfaction of the district surveyor, but not less than:— 150	120
10	Warehouses, book stores, stationery stores and the like.	Ditto; but not less than:— 200	200
11	Any purpose not herein specified	Loading to be provided for to be ascertained to the satisfaction of the district surveyor	
	Note on dead loading. Same as stated in Table I.		

Table II. L.C.C. by-laws for superloads on floors for buildings within the London area.

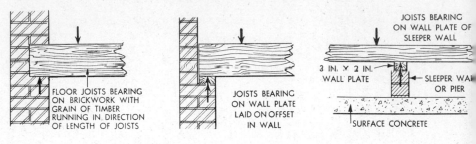

FLOOR JOISTS BEARING ON BRICKWORK WITH GRAIN OF TIMBER RUNNING IN DIRECTION OF LENGTH OF JOISTS

JOISTS BEARING ON WALL PLATE LAID ON OFFSET IN WALL

JOISTS BEARING ON WALL PLATE OF SLEEPER WALL

3 IN. × 2 IN. WALL PLATE

SLEEPER WALL OR PIER

SURFACE CONCRETE

PLAIN BEARINGS OF TIMBER JOISTS

Fig. 3. The diagrams show the simplest and most common types of bearings. The thick arrows depict the direction of the downward and upward forces.

brick wall, etc., as shown by Fig. 3. It is often specified that the length of bearing shall be 4 in., which, it must be admitted, is usually ample. But, how often is this 4 in. governed by a simple examination of facts, and calculations made to ascertain the accuracy of the length of bearing? Very seldom.

Timber has not the same resistance to crushing of its fibres by a force acting at right angles to the direction of the fibres or grain as it has if the force is acting parallel to or in the direction of the fibres. As one example, the permissible stresses on non-graded redwood according to L.C.C. by-laws for timber construction are as follows:—

Compression in the direction of the grain in posts, etc., having a slenderness ratio not exceeding 10, is 800 lb. per sq. in. Compression perpendicular to grain is 165 lb. per sq. in. Most joists and timber beams have the grain running in the direction of the length of the timber, as depicted by Fig. 3, and consequently the upward force at the bearings acts perpendicularly or at right angles to the grain as shown, and there is only, with the timber specified above, a resistance of 165 lb., or say $1\frac{1}{2}$ cwt., per sq. in.

Now it is possible to give a very good reason why the length of bearing should be considered with great care. Refer to Table IV and it will be seen that an 11 in. × 2 in. joist may span 17 ft. 5 in. at 15-in.

centres. The superload is 40 lb., and it may be allowed that the dead load is 16 lb., making a total of 56 lb. or $\frac{1}{2}$ cwt. super foot. As the span is 17 ft. 5 in. and the centres of joists 1 ft. 3 in. each joist has a load area of say $17 \cdot 50 \times 1 \cdot 25$, equals $21 \cdot 875$, or say 22 super ft., which, multiplied by $\frac{1}{2}$ cwt., equals 11 cwt. over the whole beam. Only half of this load goes to each bearing, viz. $5\frac{1}{2}$ cwt.

Safe Resistance in Timber

As there is a safe resistance of $1\frac{1}{2}$ cwt. per sq. in. in the timber it should be clear that the area of bearing must not be less than $5\frac{1}{2}$ divided by $1\frac{1}{2}$, equals say $3\frac{1}{2}$ sq. in. As the joist is 2 in. wide a length of bearing of 4 in. gives an area of 8 in., which is more than ample. This does not infer that the bearing should be much less than 4 in. long; as a matter of fact it is advisable in most cases to maintain this length as it gives good nailing space when joists bear on timber wall plates and gives a little margin to allow the maintenance of sufficient bearing in case a wall may develop any bulging.

Notches in timber joists may be made at bearings and elsewhere, subject to rules which ensure that no weakness is caused. It is often good practice to notch the end of joists over plates; Fig. 4 gives two examples. To show the possible danger of too-deep notching a ridiculous notch is depicted at A. It is quite obvious that

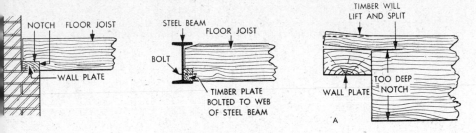

NOTCHES IN TIMBER JOISTS

Fig. 4. Notches may be made at bearings and elsewhere, provided that no weakness is caused. An example showing the possible danger of too-deep notching is shown at A.

the little depth of timber left over the notch would promptly break and split somewhat as shown.

This extreme case proves that there must be some limit to the depth of notching, and the limit is governed by the resistance of timber to shear, a safe practical rule being: Notches at bearings should not be more than half, and preferably two-fifths, of depth of joist.

Another form of notch which can greatly weaken a joist is that cut either at the top or bottom for service pipes or conduits as Fig. 5. These notches are very often cut in wrong positions which prove ignorance or carelessness in connection with one of the simplest laws of mechanics of structures.

Plumbers and electricians require watching by architects, builders, and their staff as to positions of any notching, which should not be made to cause shorter runs of pipes, etc., if by doing so

the joists are improperly weakened. When really necessary, these notches are made as near the supports as possible.

Maximum Bending Moment

The maximum bending moment usually occurs at the centre of the span of a timber floor joist, and consequently the maximum cross-section of timber is required at such centre for resistance. If a notch is cut at, or near the centre, the depth of the joist is reduced by the depth of the notch. As the strength of a joist varies directly as the *square of its depth*, it can be proved to what extent strength-damage is done by indiscriminate notching.

Take an example: a joist is 8 in. deep (width does not matter) and it is notched 1 in. deep at centre of span thereby reducing its effective depth to 7 in. The strength value of 8 in. depth is 8 squared which equals 64, and 7 in. depth which

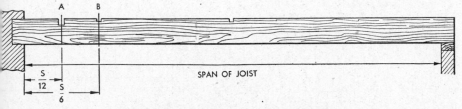

NOTCHING JOISTS FOR SERVICE PIPES

Fig. 5. Notches which do *not* weaken joists are as A and B, provided that the depth of A does not exceed one-quarter depth of joist, and B one-sixth. A notch near centre is specially weakening.

TABLE III	WEIGHTS OF VARIOUS MATERIALS USED IN FLOORS Extracts from British Standard Specification No. 648, 1935— Schedule of Unit Weights of Building Materials

Material	Weight
ASBESTOS-CEMENT SHEETING, flat ¼ in. thick	2·3 lb./sq. ft.
BOARDS	
Fibre, ½ in. thick	0·75 ,,
Fibre, compressed (hardboard), ¼ in. thick	0·65 ,,
Plaster-cored, ⅜ in. thick	2 ,,
Plaster-cored, ⅜ in. thick, plus setting coat	3 ,,
PAVING with granite aggregate	150 lb./cub. ft.
CONCRETE .	
Ballast or stone	140 ,,
Brick	115 ,,
Clinker	90 ,,
Pumice	70 ,,
Reinforced (about 2% steel)	150 ,,
CORRUGATED STEEL SHEETING, galvanized unfixed, 18 B G (add 20% for laps)	2·27 lb./sq. ft.
FLOORING	
Magnesium oxychloride, normal type per 1 in. of thickness with sawdust filler	7·5 ,,
Heavy-duty type per 1 in. of thickness with mineral filler . . .	11·5 ,,
Rubber, ¼ in. thick	2·3 ,,
Hardwood, e.g., oak, maple { ⅞ in. finished thickness . . .	3·3 ,,
1⅛ in. finished thickness . . .	4·3 ,,
Pitchpine (longleaf dense) { ⅞ in. finished thickness . . .	3·0 ,,
1⅛ in. finished thickness . . .	3·8 ,,
Softwood, e.g., redwood, whitewood, Douglas fir { ⅞ in. finished thickness .	2·3 ,,
1⅛ in. finished thickness .	2·8 ,,
PLASTER	
Fibrous, ⅝ in. thick	3 ,,
Gypsum or lime, ½ in. thick	5 ,,
Hydraulic lime or Portland cement, ½ in. thick	6 ,,
Wood or metal lathing add to above weights	1·25 ,,
PLYWOOD, per mm. of thickness	0·14 ,,
ROOF BOARDING, SOFTWOOD ROUGH SAWN	
¾ in. thick	2 ,,
1 in. thick	2·5 ,,
1¼ in. thick	3 ,,
SCREEDING, PORTLAND CEMENT, 1 to 3 per ½ in. of thickness . . .	6 ,,
TERRAZZO PAVING, ⅝ in. thick as laid	7 ,,
TIMBER	
Hardwoods, e.g., teak, oak, maple, etc.	45 lb./cub. ft.
Pitchpine (longleaf dense)	41 ,,
Softwoods, e.g., pine, spruce, Douglas fir, etc.	30 ,,

NOTES. The above weights have been agreed for the purposes of calculation and are not necessarily the actual weights of any particular sample. Detailed information is given in British Standard Specification, *No. 648, 1935—Schedule of Unit Weights of Building Materials.*

Table III. British Standard Specification Schedule of Unit Weights of Building Materials.

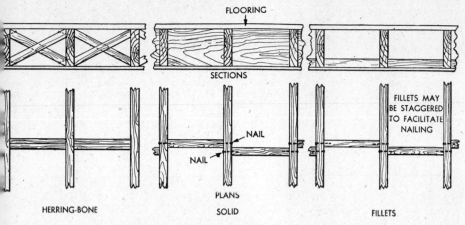

FLOORING

SECTIONS

NAIL

NAIL

FILLETS MAY
BE STAGGERED
TO FACILITATE
NAILING

PLANS

HERRING-BONE   SOLID   FILLETS

TYPES OF STRUTTING TO FLOOR JOISTS

Fig. 6. The advantages and disadvantages of these types of strutting are fully discussed in the text.

quals only 49, a very considerable reduction of about 23 per cent.

Of course, the farther away from the centre of span, and nearer the bearing, a notch is cut, the less is its weakening effect because the bending moment becomes less and less at different points which are farther away from the centre of span. A good rule for notching timber joists is: a notch not exceeding one-eighth of depth of joist may be made not more than a distance from bearing equal to one-sixth of span, i.e., 2 ft. in the case of a joist spanning 12 ft., and not exceeding one-quarter depth of joist if occurring one-twelfth of span from bearing. If there is any question as to this rule then use deeper joists to compensate for the depth of notch; this is usually very uneconomical.)

Strutting, either herring-bone or solid, as Fig. 6, has hitherto been considered as good practice. Nowadays there is reverse opinion, which the author shares with his colleagues who were responsible for the framing of the British Standard Specification 1018: Part I: 1942—Timber in Building Construction: Floors of Ordinary Board and Joist Construction. This B.S.S. states: "Lateral restraint of beam. Any beams having a depth exceeding three times its breadth and a length exceeding fifty times its breadth shall be laterally restrained from winding or buckling and the distance between such restraints shall not exceed fifty times the breadth."

"NOTE.—In the case of ordinary floors, floor boards fixed in accordance with this specification afford adequate lateral support, but strutting may be required in order to prevent excessive vibration."

Vibration and Shrinkage

To meet the above vibration condition, and to prevent side movement of the joists by shrinkage or swelling of the timber, which may affect ceiling coverings, it is a good principle to strut the lower part of the joists with small timber members as in Fig. 6. Normally the distance apart of the members should not exceed 50 times the breadth of the joist; about 40 should be aimed at. The members can often be utilized for bearers to fix ceiling boards.

The disposition of joists in a building is a matter to which enough thought is not always given. It should be borne in mind that floors are very important parts of

TABLE IV	FLOOR JOISTS OF REDWOOD to Residential Floors in London Area — ACCORDING TO L.C.C. BY-LAWS

FOR BUILDINGS OUTSIDE LONDON this table is also recommended for rooms of dwelling-houses, flats, hotel buildings, and similar residential buildings; hospital rooms and wards; corridors, stairs, and landings of dwelling-houses and flats.

Clear spans for various scantlings at different centres in non-graded redwood, yellow deal, etc. (800 lb. extreme fibre stress in bending).

40 lb. per sup. ft. superload

In accordance with the L.C.C. by-laws for timber construction.

Scantling in inches	Maximum CLEAR Spans with Joists at following CENTRES				
	14 in.	15 in.	17 in.	20 in.	22 in.
3 × 2	5' 0"	4' 9"	4' 6"	4' 3"	4' 0"
3½ × 2	5' 10"	5' 6½"	5' 3"	4' 11½"	4' 8"
4 × 2	6' 8"	6' 4"	6' 0"	5' 8"	5' 4"
4½ × 2	7' 6"	7' 1½"	6' 9"	6' 4½"	6' 0"
5 × 2	8' 4"	7' 11"	7' 6"	7' 1"	6' 8"
6 × 2	10' 0"	9' 6"	9' 0"	8' 6"	8' 0"
7 × 2	11' 8"	11' 1"	10' 6"	9' 11"	9' 4"
8 × 2	13' 4"	12' 8"	12' 0"	11' 4"	10' 8"
9 × 2	15' 0"	14' 3"	13' 6"	12' 9"	12' 0"
11 × 2	18' 4"	17' 5"	16' 6"	15' 7"	14' 8"
		15 in.	17½ in.	21 in.	25 in.
6 × 2½		10' 6"	10' 0"	9' 0"	8' 6"
7 × 2½		12' 3"	11' 8"	10' 6"	9' 11"
8 × 2½		14' 0"	13' 4"	12' 0"	11' 4"
9 × 2½		15' 9"	15' 0"	13' 6"	12' 9"
11 × 2½		19' 3"	18' 4"	16' 6"	15' 7"
		15 in.	18 in.	21 in.	22½ in.
6 × 3		11' 0"	10' 6"	10' 0"	9' 6"
7 × 3		12' 10"	12' 3"	11' 8"	11' 1"
8 × 3		14' 8"	14' 0"	13' 4"	12' 8"
9 × 3		16' 6"	15' 9"	15' 0"	14' 3"
11 × 3		20' 2"	19' 3"	18' 4"	17' 5"

This simple, practical table gives information that allows the almost instant choice of scantlings, spans, and centres of floor joists. As an instance, for 12-ft. clear span of floor joists, 8 in. × 2 in. at 17-in. centres, 8 in. × 2½ in. at 21-in. centres, 7 in. × 2½ in. at 15-in. centres, or 7 in. by 3 in. at 18-in. centres may be used.

Table IV. Although this Table of Floor Joists gives measurements in accordance with L.C.C. by-laws it can also be usefully applied to buildings outside the London area.

the general structure of a building, and, apart from their primary function as floors, they can perform a most important second duty by greatly assisting in binding together walls and floors.

Examine Fig. 7 and it will be noted that all the floor joists (except some of the trimming members) run in one direction, between the rear and front main walls, and consequently such walls are bound, or can be bound, to the floors while the flank wall is left unbound. This subject requires a little explanation to avoid misunderstanding as to relative strength values of what may be termed short-height walls (with a low slenderness ratio), which are fairly heavily loaded, and long-height walls

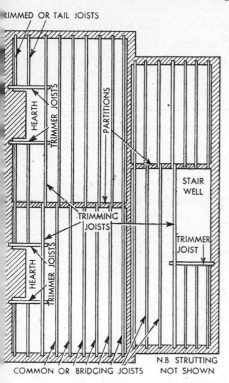

RIMMED OR TAIL JOISTS

HEARTH

TRIMMER JOISTS

PARTITIONS

STAIR WELL

TRIMMING JOISTS

TRIMMER JOIST

HEARTH

TRIMMER JOISTS

COMMON OR BRIDGING JOISTS

N.B STRUTTING NOT SHOWN

g. 7. The customary but not very good dis-sition of floor joists to the first floor of an ordinary semi-detached house.

Legally, modern by-laws demand that walls shall be limited in height in relation to thickness (slenderness ratio), the height being measured between points of lateral support. Such support is given by floor joists if connected adequately to walls.

The connection of floor joists to walls to provide lateral support needs consideration to ensure adequacy coupled with economy. Although the weight of a joist bearing directly on brick, stone or concrete work, with the binding between the materials, does cause a certain amount of resistance to lateral movement in a wall, such amount is not enough, and other, or auxiliary methods, should be adopted.

Fig. 9 shows a wall plate bedded on the offset of a wall with the joists nailed

with a high slenderness ratio) without uch load on them.

It is a structural fact that a one-brick-ick wall about 20 ft. high which is not terally supported at about the centre its height is weaker than a similar wall at is laterally supported even if such pport is by a floor which transmits a nsiderable load on to the wall.

Fig. 8 shows a good disposition of ists which causes the rear and front alls to be well tied in laterally for a od proportion of their length, and the nk wall also well supported laterally. n advantage is also gained by the poss-le use of smaller-sized joists over the ort span between the partition and nk wall, than the size of joists neces-ry elsewhere.

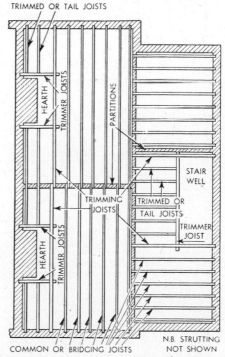

TRIMMED OR TAIL JOISTS

HEARTH

TRIMMER JOISTS

PARTITIONS

STAIR WELL

TRIMMING JOISTS

TRIMMED OR TAIL JOISTS

TRIMMER JOIST

HEARTH

TRIMMER JOISTS

COMMON OR BRIDGING JOISTS

N.B. STRUTTING NOT SHOWN

Fig. 8. A much better disposition which ensures that the rear and front walls are well tied in and the flank wall supported laterally.

TABLE V	FLOOR JOISTS OF DOUGLAS FIR to Residential Floors in London Area ACCORDING TO L.C.C. BY-LAWS

FOR BUILDINGS OUTSIDE LONDON this Table is also recommended for rooms of dwelling-houses, flats, hotel buildings, and similar residential buildings; hospital rooms and wards; corridors, stairs, and landings of dwelling houses and flats.

Clear spans for various scantlings at different centres in Douglas fir and 1,200 lb. f. (extreme fibre stress in bending) timbers.

40 lb. per sup. ft. superload

In accordance with the L.C.C. by-laws for timber construction.

Scantlings in inches	Maximum CLEAR Spans with Joist at following CENTRES				
	14 in.	16 in.	19 in.	22 in.	26 in.
3 × 2	5' 6"	5' 3"	5' 0"	4' 9"	4' 6"
3½ × 2	6' 5"	6' 1½"	5' 10"	5' 6½"	5' 3"
4 × 2	7' 4"	7' 0"	6' 8"	6' 4"	6' 0"
4½ × 2	8' 3"	7' 10½"	7' 6"	7' 1½"	6' 9"
5 × 2	9' 2"	8' 9"	8' 4"	7' 11"	7' 6"
6 × 2	11' 0"	10' 6"	10' 0"	9' 6"	9' 0"
7 × 2	12' 10"	12' 3"	11' 8"	11' 1"	10' 6"
8 × 2	14' 8"	14' 0"	13' 4"	12' 8"	12' 0"
9 × 2	16' 6"	15' 9"	15' 0"	14' 3"	13' 6"
10 × 2	18' 4"	17' 6"	16' 8"	15' 10"	15' 0"
11 × 2	20' 2"	19' 3"	18' 4"	17' 5"	16' 6"
	15 in.	17½ in.	20 in.	23¾ in.	27½ in.
6 × 2½	11' 6"	11' 0"	10' 6"	10' 0"	9' 6"
7 × 2½	13' 5"	12' 10"	12' 3"	11' 8"	11' 1"
8 × 2½	15' 4"	14' 8"	14' 0"	13' 4"	12' 8"
9 × 2½	17' 3"	16' 6"	15' 9"	15' 0"	14' 3"
10 × 2½	19' 2"	18' 4"	17' 6"	16' 8"	15' 10"
11 × 2½	21' 1"	20' 2"	19' 3"	18' 4"	17' 5"
	16½ in.	18 in.	21 in.	24 in.	28½ in.
6 × 3	12' 0"	11' 6"	11' 0"	10' 6"	10' 0"
7 × 3	14' 0"	13' 5"	12' 10"	12' 3"	11' 8"
8 × 3	16' 0"	15' 4"	14' 8"	14' 0"	13' 4"
9 × 3	18' 0"	17' 3"	16' 6"	15' 9"	15' 0"
10 × 3	20' 0"	19' 2"	18' 4"	17' 6"	16' 8"
11 × 3	22' 0"	21' 1"	20' 2"	19' 3"	18' 4"

Table V. The floor joist measurements given in this Table of L.C.C. by-laws may also be use with advantage for buildings outside the London area.

to the plate; this may be allowed as giving fairly good lateral support to the wall; but a better method is to tie the plate into the wall with 1-in. × ⅛-in. cramps as shown by Fig. 10. Hoop iron is liable to corrode too quickly and should not be used.

Fig. 11 depicts at A an old method of supporting a wall plate on iron corbel It will be noted that any lateral (or side movement in the wall may cause th corbel to pull through the mortar join If the back of the corbel is turned up o down as B a much better job results.

Fig. 12 depicts a very bad method of construction by building a timber wall plate *into* a wall (timber is much softer than brick, etc., and thereby weakens a wall), but it definitely gives good lateral support to the wall because the plate is well secured in wall, and the joists being nailed down to the plate obviate movement.

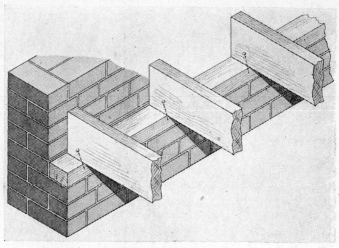

LATERAL WALL SUPPORT

Fig. 9. The lateral support to a wall depends on the weight of the floor and the adhesion of the plate to the mortar bed joint. This is fairly good support, but a much better method is to tie the plate into the wall by means of metal cramps, as shown in Fig. 10 below.

Connecting timber joists to steel beams is quite a common practice. The simplest and a very strong joint is shown by Fig. 13. The timber bears squarely on the top flange of the steel beam. Beam filling or timber separators and the general structure of the flooring and ceiling will hold the joists against side movement. If deemed necessary a timber plate may be bolted to the flange and the joists nailed down. Fig. 14 shows another simple method of construction.

To save height of building, or to prevent beams showing too deeply below a ceiling it is often advisable to let timber

joists be supported directly or indirectly on the bottom flange of a steel beam, as examples depicted by Fig. 15. Very great care is necessary in designing strong joints between timber and steel.

As explained previously the length of bearing must be sufficient; often, 2 in. is enough. The bearing must be "dead" throughout its length, and, as steel flanges are not at right angles to web

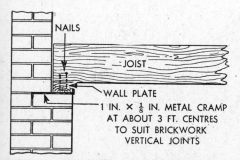

Fig. 10. Binding a wall plate to wall by means of small metal cramps at about 3 ft. centres.

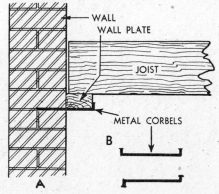

Fig. 11. A shows an old method and B an improved method of using iron corbels.

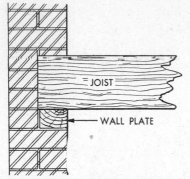

Fig. 12. Timber is softer than brick, and it is bad practice to build a timber wall plate into a wall.

(98 degrees or so) the bottom of a timber joist, which rests directly on a flange as A, Fig. 15, must be shaped to the angle. If a plate rests on the flange, and is

bolted to the steelwork, the underside of the plate must be cut to the correct angle as shown at B.

A very doubtful method is shown at C. A plate is used which does not rest on the bottom flange. It will be noticed that the plate is bolted to web of steel beam, and a common specification often calls for $\frac{1}{2}$-in. bolts at such centres as 2 ft. to 3 ft. It can soon be proved that such a specification is ridiculous; allow, for example, that the bolts are 2 ft. apart, and the plate is even 3 in. (and not 2 in.) thick.

Firstly, consider one bolt. Its bearing area on timber (ignoring circular bearing) is 3 in. $\times \frac{1}{2}$ in., equals $1\frac{1}{2}$ in., and allowing $1\frac{1}{2}$ cwt. sq. in. safe stress at right angles to grain, a total resistance of

TABLE VI	DISTANCE APART OF BEARINGS, JOISTS, STUDS, ETC. FOR CEILING AND WALL COVERINGS	
	Description of covering	*Centres apart in inches of joists, studs, etc.*
Plastering with $\frac{3}{16}$-in. laths		14
Plastering with $\frac{1}{4}$-in. laths		16
Plastering with 24-g. expanded metal lathing		14
Plastering with 22-g. expanded metal lathing		16
Plaster, plaster lath and similar boards about $\frac{3}{8}$ in. thick		16
Thin tough fibre boards $\frac{3}{16}$ in. thick		12 to 14
Thin tough fibre boards $\frac{1}{4}$ in. thick		16
Thick loose fibre insulation boards $\frac{3}{8}$ in. thick		14 to 16
Thick loose fibre insulation boards $\frac{1}{2}$ in. thick		16 to 18
Hardboards, $\frac{1}{8}$ in. thick		12 to 14
Hardboards $\frac{3}{16}$ in. thick		14 to 16
Super-hardboards $\frac{1}{8}$ in. thick		14 to 16
Super-hardboards $\frac{3}{16}$ in. thick		16 to 18
Plywood, asbestos-cement sheets about $\frac{3}{16}$ in. thick		16
Plywood, asbestos-cement sheets $\frac{1}{4}$ in. thick		18 to 20
Timber matchboarding, etc., $\frac{1}{2}$ nominal thickness		24
Timber matchboarding, etc., $\frac{3}{4}$ nominal thickness		30
Timber matchboarding, etc., 1 nominal thickness		36

NOTES. Stock lengths and widths of boards and sheets can usually be obtained to suit specified centres without much cutting and waste. Centres may be modified slightly to suit particular stock sizes; such modification should not, as a rule, be greater than would result if *centres apart* be read as *clear distance apart* of joists, studs, etc.

Table VI. This Table gives practical information which will save much time in making calculations.

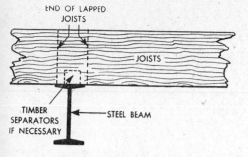

Fig. 13. Floor joists bearing squarely on steel beam, a simple and very strong joint.

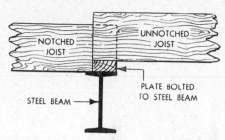

Fig. 14. Another simple method of connecting joists to the top of steel beam.

$2\frac{1}{4}$ cwt. is given. As the bolts are 2 ft. apart this means that there is only $1\frac{1}{8}$ cwt. resistance per linear foot of floor bearing on the plate, which is very inadequate except for exceptionally short span floor joists.

Another weakness is that the bolts can be subject to cantilevering stresses unless there is a balancing plate on the other side of the web. The correct method of construction is to use the bolts only as a means of tying the plate to the steelwork and to rely entirely on packing blocks to support the loads as shown at D, Fig. 15. These insignificant-looking members require much thought to ensure them being of correct size. The area of all the blocks in contact with the underside of the plate must, at least, equal the required bearing area of all the joists which rest on top of the plate.

It is necessary to make this quite clear: if a certain area of joist is necessary to prevent the grain in the joist and plate being crushed at right angles to the grain, then it is manifest that as the packing blocks exert an upward resistance to the underside of the plate, it is essential to have at least the same bearing area in both cases.

Trimming members and their joints. Openings have to be formed in many timber floors for stairwells, hearths, chimney breasts, etc., and these make trimming necessary, as shown by Fig. 16, which indicates the difference between trimming, trimmer and trimmed joists. Trimming and trimmed joists are made thicker than common joists; the rules compiled by the writer and included in the new by-laws of many local authorities should be used.

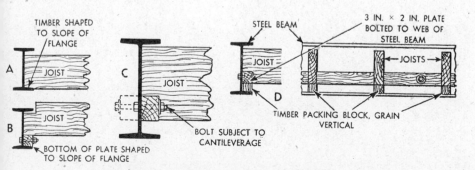

CONNECTING TIMBER FLOOR JOISTS TO STEEL BEAM

Fig. 15. Various methods of supporting timber joists on the bottom flange of a steel beam.

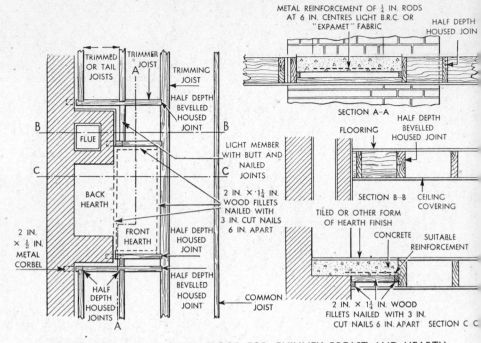

CONSTRUCTION OF TIMBER FLOOR FOR CHIMNEY BREAST AND HEARTH

Fig. 16. Detailed sections and plan showing the trimming which is necessary for openings in timber floors for chimney breast and hearth. Note the trimming, trimmer and trimmed joists.

Joints. It will assist if two very unsound joints are considered before those that are perfectly sound if used in correct positions. Refer to Figs. 17 and 18. The former depicts a butted and nailed joint, which, although suitable for very lightly loaded and stressed members, is quite unsuitable for ordinary floor work. The only strength lies in nailing, owing to the resistance of nails driven through timber. Fig. 18 shows a joint which may be worse or better than the joint in Fig. 17, according to the number of nails used to connect the various members.

Obviously this joint also relies entirely on nailing. Good types of joints are as Figs. 19 to 22, but they must be used with care. Fig. 19 is the *half-depth housed joint* which provides a little, but very useful, dead bearing for the supported on the supporting member. It causes a little loss of sectional area in the

Fig. 17 (left). A butt joint nailed with a few nails is a very bad joint.

Fig. 18 (right). A butt joint resting on a fillet and the whole lot nailed is also a bad joint, as it relies upon the nails for its strength.

supporting member which must, if necessary, be made up by increasing the width of such member. Fig. 20 is the *half-depth bevelled housed joint* and is stronger than the last described joint as it provides a greater bearing area, and reduces the sectional area of the supporting member mostly near the neutral axis and less elsewhere.

Fig. 21 illustrates the *bevelled haunched mortised and tenoned joint* which is a strong joint inasmuch as it gives a considerable bearing area. Fig. 22 is the well-known *tusk-tenoned joint* and is one of the strongest structural joints, but costly. In the future it will probably be superseded by metal stirrups.

GROUND-STOREY FLOORS. Now refer back to Fig. 2 which illustrates typical timber ground-floor construction incorporating modern principles and details. The following are the chief differences to those explained previously for upper storey methods of construction:—

The joists may be of small scantling owing to the use of sleeper walls or piers. Hitherto it has been common practice to use 4-in. $\times$ 2-in. joists and to use sleeper walls at distances apart to suit these joists; it is, however, much more prudent to study the cost of sleepers in relation to the additional cost of 4½-in. $\times$ 2-in. or 5-in. $\times$ 2-in. joists and design accordingly. It is often possible to use a sleeper wall less and save money even after allowing for an extra ½ in. on depth of the joists

Economy of Cantilevering

Cantilevering the joists, which may be done under L.C.C. and other by-laws, can effect considerable economy by often reducing the number of sleeper walls required, and also frequently allows better construction in air brick

FLOORING FOUNDATIONS

rick walls up to damp-course level, and surface concrete laid under main rooms to a pair of semi-detached garage-type houses. In the background on right are seen further stages of construction, with door and window frames either in position or ready for placing.

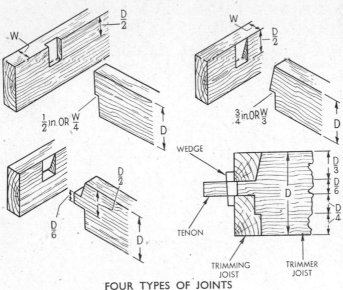

W

$\frac{D}{2}$

W

$\frac{D}{2}$

$\frac{1}{2}$ in. OR $\frac{W}{4}$

D

$\frac{3}{4}$ in. OR $\frac{W}{3}$

D

WEDGE

$\frac{D}{2}$

$\frac{D}{6}$

D

$\frac{D}{3}$

$\frac{D}{6}$

$\frac{D}{4}$

D

TENON

TRIMMING JOIST

TRIMMER JOIST

FOUR TYPES OF JOINTS

Fig. 19 (top left). Half-depth housed joint.
Fig. 20 (top right). Half-depth bevelled housed joint.
Fig. 21 (bottom left). Bevelled haunched mortised and tenoned joint.
Fig. 22 (bottom right). Tusk-tenoned joint.

work. A sleeper wall situated close to an external wall as Fig. 23 may cause the wall plate partly to foul the air brick.

The old offset method which is even nowadays shown by some drawings, is to be deplored because it prevents

damp-courses being used at different levels in main and sleeper walls; and also causes increased sizes of concrete bases to conform with the by-laws.

Sleeper walls, as Fig. 24, should not be higher than necessary to suit the respective levels of floor, surface concrete and the general ground; the floor should not be higher above ground level than is required for convenience and damp-coursing and the top of surface concrete should be as near general ground level as practicable to prevent unnecessarily deep surface excavation and to avoid the surface concrete collecting ground water.

Sleeper piers, as Fig. 25, represent good and economical construction, ensure

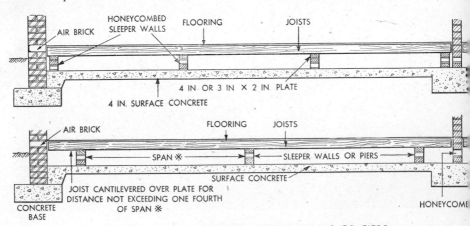

HONEYCOMBED SLEEPER WALLS

AIR BRICK

FLOORING

JOISTS

4 IN. OR 3 IN × 2 IN. PLATE

4 IN. SURFACE CONCRETE

AIR BRICK

FLOORING

JOISTS

SPAN ✳

SLEEPER WALLS OR PIERS

SURFACE CONCRETE

JOIST CANTILEVERED OVER PLATE FOR DISTANCE NOT EXCEEDING ONE FOURTH OF SPAN ✳

CONCRETE BASE

HONEYCOMB

GROUND-FLOOR JOISTS ON SLEEPER WALLS OR PIERS

Fig. 23. In the top diagram the joists are not cantilevered over sleepers. In the lower diagram the joists are cantilevered over end sleepers, which saves one run of sleeper walls, etc.

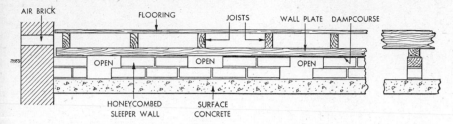

SLEEPER WALL

ig. 24. Sleeper walls should not be higher than is necessary to suit ground and floor levels; the top of the surface concrete should be as near ground level as practicable.

fficient ventilation to the floor, reduce he quantity of any damp-course materals, and, if the clear distance between he piers does not exceed about ten imes the depth of wall plate, the latter vill be of ample strength as beams to arry even heavy-duty floors.

Fender walls to hearths are clearly indiated by Fig. 2, and it will be noted that alf-brick fender walls, without footings, re all that are necessary. Note the imple construction of the timber work o act as the form-work for the concrete earth.

Ventilation of ground floors is of vital nportance to ensure the floor being ept dry and to avoid timber being ffected with rot. Air bricks should be so rranged in all external walls as to inuce through currents of air under all arts of the floor; there should be no arge pockets of stagnant air. Partition valls should have well-honeycombed ases, and "The number and size of air

bricks should not be stinted; 9 in. × 6 in. (and not 9 in. × 3 in.) should be the rule, and there should be not less than $1\frac{1}{2}$ sq. in. open area in air bricks per foot run of wall." This is a recommendation of the Building Research Station; but the writer prefers much more.

The by-laws for London and districts outside London are justly exacting as to timbers adjacent to fireplaces and flues, and are best explained in tabular form as shown in Table VII on the next page.

Unsuspended Floors

Plain Concrete Unsuspended Floors. Figs. 26 and 27 are popular, simple and economical to construct; they permit the application of any of the many classes of floor finishings or floorings which may be laid on concrete. They require care in designing and constructing to ensure that no grounddampness percolates through the concrete; or, if it does, means should be

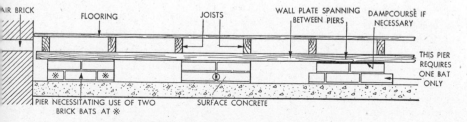

SLEEPER PIERS OF THREE DIFFERENT DESIGNS

g. 25. Although the central pier has a straight joint as shown, it is quite sound construction for a light load, ensuring efficient ventilation and economy in labour and materials.

Particulars of work	By-laws for London	By-laws for outside London
Projection of side of hearth on each side of fireplace opening (naked brickwork, etc.)	6 in.	6 in.
Projection of hearth in front of fireplace opening (measured from naked brickwork, etc.)	18 in.	16 in.
Thickness of hearth of incombustible materials	6 in.	6 in.
Level of hearth	With floor	With or above floor
Woodwork (except wood plugs) in any wall or chimney or any part thereof	Not nearer than 12 in. to any flue or inside of fireplace opening (naked brickwork)	Not nearer than 9 in. to inside of any flue or chimney opening (naked brickwork)
Woodwork (except wood plugs) under fireplace opening (not under front hearth)	Not within 10 in. from upper surface of the hearth of such opening, except fillets supporting a hearth	Not within 10 in. from the upper surface of the hearth
Woodwork (except wood plugs) near outer face of chimney where the material of which is less than 8½ in. thick	Not within 2 in. from the outer face	Not within 2 in. from the outer face unless latter rendered properly
Wood plugs	Not nearer than 6 in. to flue or inside of fireplace opening	Not nearer than 6 in. to inside of flue or fireplace opening
Iron holdfasts or other iron fastenings	Not nearer than 2 in. to flue or inside of fireplace opening	Not nearer than 2 in. to inside of flue or fireplace opening
Chimneys passing through any floor or roof within 9 in. of any combustible material or behind or against any woodwork	Outside of chimney to be rendered properly or pargeted	Not within 2 in. from face of chimney unless latter is rendered properly

Table VII. A valuable Table giving the by-laws, both for London and for districts outside London for the placing of timber adjacent to fireplaces and flues, with due precautions against fire risks

taken to safeguard the floorings and to avoid unhygienic conditions. The concrete acts as the floor and also as the surface concrete required by by-laws.

Foundation or ground should be considered with care so that the floor is not laid on any weak ground which may cause settlements and cracking in the concrete; nor should the floor be subject to the effects of frozen water immediately adjacent to its underside, effects

which are easily avoided as explained later.

The level of the upper surface of the floor is governed chiefly by the purpose of the building; it may be required to be above or about the same level as the external ground or pavings. This level, of course, regulates the foundation or formation level of the ground on which the floor is laid, and brings up the essential matter of providing a firm foundation

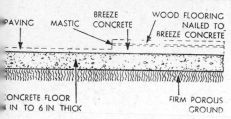

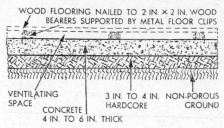

Fig. 26. Section of a plain concrete unsuspended floor constructed on porous ground.

Fig. 27. Plain concrete unsuspended floor constructed on non-porous ground.

Not many grounds are suitable for laying concrete floors directly on them. They require to be excavated at least a few inches deep to remove top soil, vegetable growth, etc. The following are good rules to practise:—

1) Excavate all soft, loose and vegetable earth down to a level to ensure the concrete being laid on firm ground.

(2) If such excavation causes more earth to be removed than is suitable for the necessary level of the concrete, then fill with hardcore and well consolidate it by ramming or rolling.

(3) If the ground has not a certain amount of porosity which will allow any water that may reach or drain under the concrete to

GROUND-FLOOR JOISTS IN POSITION

The sleeper walls, wall plates and ground-floor joists are supported on surface concrete. Note how the brickwork to the party wall, with its fireplace, breasts and external walls, is progressing

B.—E

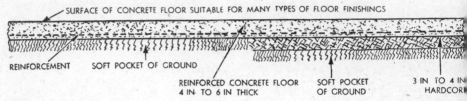

Fig. 28. Reinforced-concrete unsuspended floor, with the reinforcement placed near the underside

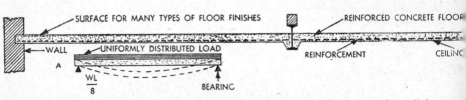

Fig. 29. Simple type of suspended reinforced-concrete floor—freely supported at all bearings

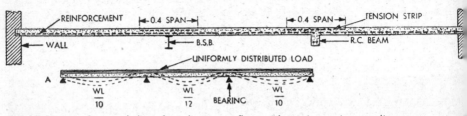

Fig. 30. Section of suspended reinforced-concrete floor with continuous intermediate over support

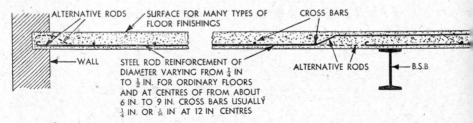

Fig. 31. Section of a typical reinforced-concrete floor with steel rod reinforcement.

soak away, then lay 3-in. or 4-in. thickness of hardcore. Suitable porous grounds are such as compact gravel, sandy gravel, and loamy soils with sand predominating. Clay is not porous, and if the concrete floor is laid directly on it, and any water does get between it and the concrete, the water, if it freezes, will probably cause trouble. The hardcore may be of broken brick of various sizes, ballast, broken stone, or hard vitrified clinkers.

Thickness of floors must not be less than specified in by-laws for surface concrete but otherwise make 4 in. thick for floors subject to superload not exceeding 80 lb. ft. super; 5 in. 100 lb. and 6 in. when over 100 lb. If there is dampness under the floor make the floor 6 in. thick.

Concrete composition is important to ensure proper strength and avoidance of dampness. Good proportions by volume are: For good-class work, and if laid direct on ground subject to dampness

1 part Portland cement and 6 parts of pit or river ballast with not more than 50 per cent of sand; or 1 part cement, 3 parts sand and 6 parts coarse aggregate not containing sand. For ordinary quality work laid on porous hard ground or hardcore the above proportions may be 1 : 8 or 1 : 4 : 8.

Breeze or clinker concrete should not be used for structural concrete, but only as a topping for fixing purposes. The thickness of such topping should be in addition to the ordinary concrete. The proportions may be 1 part cement to 6, 7 or 8 parts of the aggregate.

Pavings allowed in thickness of concrete. If the structural concrete is not less than 4 in. thick any cement and sand or granolithic paving may be considered as part of the thickness of the floor.

REINFORCED-CONCRETE UNSUSPENDED FLOORS are used when the foundation or ground is of low-bearing value, has pockets of soft or unreliable ground, and where it is advisable to ensure loads, and particularly heavy concentrated loads (such as from wheels of lorries, etc.) being distributed over a larger area of ground than would occur with plain concrete. The steel reinforcement increases the power of the concrete to withstand heavy and moving loads, and assists in avoiding cracking due to contraction in setting or temperature changes.

Fig. 28 shows typical construction, the reinforcement being placed near the underside of concrete with enough cover to protect the metal, the latter being usually of any of the well-known steel

FIRST-FLOOR JOISTS.

In the above illustration of the construction of flooring for a typical modern villa the first-floor joists are shown in position and most of the brickwork is built up to the first floor.

fabrics, such as mentioned below, the manufactuers of which should be consulted as to the correct material to use for particular conditions of ground, loading and concrete.

B.R.C. Fabric. For best quality work it is usually recommended to use No. 9 type with 5 and 10 S.W.G. longitudinal and transverse wires respectively or No. 65 type with all wires 5 S.W.G. If the floors are light and laid on good foundations then use No. 14 with 10 and 12 S.W.G. wires, or No. 610 with 10 S.W.G. wires.

EXPAMET. For best quality work use No. 11, 3-in. mesh with $\frac{3}{16}$-in. $\times$ $\frac{3}{16}$-in. strands; for light floors on good foundations employ No. 15, 3-in. mesh with $\frac{1}{8}$-in. $\times$ $\frac{1}{8}$-in. strands.

Foundations and Concrete. The same care must be exercised as for the foundations of plain concrete floors. As regards the concrete it is necessary to make it denser than plain concrete, not only for the sake of obtaining the maximum strength in combination with the steel, but to safeguard the latter against percolation of moisture.

Suspended Concrete Floors

SUSPENDED REINFORCED-CONCRETE FLOORS will, it is predicted, become very popular during the next decade, and, in addition to their present extensive use in flats, factories, business premises, etc., they will probably be adopted in some housing work.

Practical Considerations. The designing of reinforced concrete is the work of specialists, who have prepared considerable tabular information on this matter for use by architects, builders and their craftsmen in connection with most of the simpler classes of floors. Any work outside the range of simple structures should be designed by a competent engineer, as the subject requires specialized knowledge. Apart from this there is a con-

siderable bulk of reinforced-concrete floors which can be designed with the aid of the following information.

The fundamental principles of reinforced-concrete floors are: Plain concrete, which, compared with steel, is cheap, has a high compression value but has only a small permissible tensile strength. Steel has a very high tensile value, and within certain limits of ratio of slenderness has an equal value in compression. Therefore, we have a cheap bulk material in concrete which is capable of resisting compression stresses, and an expensive material in steel used sparingly capable of resisting tensile stresses which the concrete cannot resist.

Uniform Load Distribution

Now study Fig. 29 depicting the most simple type of reinforced-concrete floor freely supported at both bearings. At A is a diagram showing a uniformly distributed load which tends to deflect the floor as shown exaggeratedly by dotted lines, which is a condition that governs one of the simplest laws of the mechanics of structures, viz., loads producing bending stresses in beams and slabs. The upper part of the floor slab is compressed, and the lower part is elongated and is therefore in tension.

The concrete can take care of all the compression stresses, and steel is employed in the lower part to resist tension. These simple conditions call for the provision of enough concrete and steel, and the best disposition of the materials (and especially the steel) to meet the stresses.

Next consider Fig. 30 which shows a floor having bearings which are continuous over the supports, a quite usual method of construction. At A is shown how the floor tends to act under load and it will be noted that the majority of the floor between the supports bends similarly to A (Fig. 29); then there are points of contraflexure, from which the

CEILING JOISTS IN POSITION

irst-floor joists in position; brickwork up to roof-plate level; and ceiling joists in position. The floor at the right-hand bottom corner is a concrete-pugged floor over the garage.

loor reverses the shape, causing the upper part to be in tension and the lower in compression.

It is essential to consider carefully the respective economical advantages to be obtained by designing floors with free and continuous supports, that is, of course, if the general design of a building allows for continuity. The respective pending moment formulæ are given against the diagrams in Figs. 29 and 30, and it will be noticed that the comparative values are 8 for beams or slabs freely upported at both ends, 12 for continuity over supports and 10 where an end is freely supported and other continuous.

The simple meaning of these figures is that a floor with freely supported ends needs more material to resist the stresses than a floor with continuity over supports; and, other things being equal, less thickness of concrete and less steel are required in a concrete floor with continuous ends than with free ends. But it should not be overlooked that making slabs, etc., continuous over beams may cause increased height to a structure if it is necessary to have a specified height

Construction of a fireplace opening at ground-floor level and temporary brickwork supporting the brick arch over the opening.

below the bottom of beams; slabs with free ends may be supported on or near the bottom of beams, thereby saving height.

It is of great importance to ensure all steel reinforcement being in true position; it must be at the specified distance from the surfaces of concrete so as to make it resist properly the stresses and to provide adequate concrete cover. The

composition of the concrete is of great importance, and, although generally it should follow the above specification for reinforced-concrete unsuspended floors, it is advisable to follow most strictly the instructions given by the makers of the fabric type of reinforcement which is used, and also the building by-laws (especially those of the L.C.C.) to obtain the best results.

When steel rods are used instead of fabric, the designers will specify the concrete. Fig. 31 depicts a typical reinforced-concrete floor with rod reinforcement.

PROPRIETARY SUSPENDED FLOORS are fairly numerous, some of them being as follows:—

Precast Truscon floor (Fig. 32) consists of precast reinforced concrete units of length to suit small and large spans supported on main walls, or any usual type of beam without intermediate supports. Joints between units have steel continuity bars set in concrete. The structure may have many types of floor finishes, such as pavings, wood-block flooring, or boarded floorings, as shown by the illustration. The ceiling may be covered with building boards, or be plastered on lathing.

Precast Truscon suspended tread-type floor (Fig. 33) has precast reinforced concrete units of varying lengths, to suit

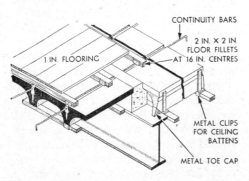

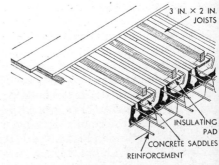

Fig. 32 (left). Precast Truscon floor.   Fig. 33 (right). Precast Truscon suspended tread-type floor.

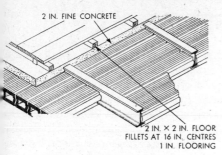

Fig. 34. King centreless floor.

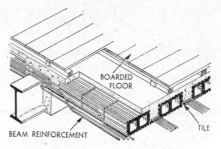

Fig. 35. Kleine hollow-brick floor.

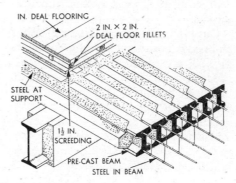

Fig. 36. Rapid floor with I section beams.

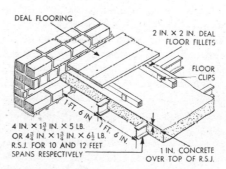

Fig. 37. Steel filler joists and concrete floor

mall or large spans, supported on main bearings of walls, or any usual type of beam without intermediate supports. Joints between units may be formed as reinforced concrete ribs. Concrete saddles with insulated pads form bearings for wood joists to support floor boards. The ceiling may be plastered, or battened and covered with building board.

The King centreless floor (Fig. 34) has self-centring floor tubes of clay tile material up to 3 ft. long and from 4 in. to 8 in. depth to suit various loads, supported by light filler steel joists which form intermediate supports between main walls and beams. Many kinds of flooring finishes may be laid on this type of floor.

Kleine hollow-brick floor (Fig. 35) has reinforced-concrete cast-in-situ ribs and hollow bricks, the concrete being filled between and over the hollow bricks. A continuous soffit which may be plastered is formed by tiles between the bricks. The flooring may be of many kinds, such as wood flooring or bearers, pavings, and other materials.

Rapid floor (Fig. 36) consists of pre-cast reinforced-concrete beams of I section, of sizes to suit small and large spans, supported on main walls and beams without intermediate supports. The level top surface and soffit allows for the application of many kinds of floor finishes and ceiling coverings.

Steel filler joists and concrete floors, as typified by Fig. 37, consist of light section steel joists, which span between main bearings, spaced at rather close centres to permit the use of plain or un-reinforced concrete. As concrete has but little and usually no allowable resistance to tension stresses it is only practicable to allow it to span up to 18 in. for ordinary floor thicknesses

FLOOR FINISHINGS

THERE are a great number of floor finishings suitable for the different types of structural floors already described. Some are solely for utilitarian purposes, and are subject to economical considerations; others are used both for utilitarian and artistic purposes, the latter often avoiding the necessity for floor coverings, such as linoleum and carpets.

ORDINARY FLOORING BOARDS, either plain edged or tongued and grooved, as Fig. 38, are the most commonly used. Modern research in timber used in building construction has forced a different view to that which formerly prevailed, when it was usual to use timber joists and bearers at about 16-in. centres with $\frac{7}{8}$ in. or 1 in. thick flooring boards, nailed rather indiscriminately.

Maximum Value from Joists

Now, and in the future, it will be found that: (*a*) joists and bearers will be at carefully calculated centres to cause the maximum value to be obtained from the joists, etc., and may be at centres much in excess of, say, 16 in.; (*b*) the joists, etc., will be spaced to suit the thickness of floorings and ceiling coverings; (*c*) floorings will be subject to nailing correctly with nails of proper length; and (*d*) by-laws and recommendations of certain authorities will have to be followed as to loading on flooring boards.

L.C.C. by-laws require flooring boards to be capable of carrying a superload of 200 lb. ft. super, or if it is not desired to calculate the thickness then the clear span of the flooring boards shall not exceed twenty-four times the actual (not nominal) thickness. Therefore, 1 in. thick nominal flooring which finishes $\frac{7}{8}$ in. thick may have a *clear* span between joists or bearers of 24 in. $\times \frac{7}{8}$ in. $=21$ in. The boards must not be less than $\frac{5}{8}$ in. finished thickness.

B.S.S. Recommendation

British Standard Specification 1018, Part I of 1942, Timber in Building Construction, is excellent in its recommendations which are: 200 lb. F.S. for plain-edged floor boards; if boards are tongued and grooved the superload to be not less than twice the specified imposed loading on the general floor construction, i.e., 40 lb. for domestic buildings; therefore, this means 80 lb. for the floor boards; and the boarding to be not less than $\frac{5}{8}$ in. thick.

As to nailing, the British Standard Specification states:—

a. (*i*) Floor boards, other than grooved and tongued, up to and including 7 in. wide shall be fastened with two nails or screws at each intersection with a joist not less than $\frac{1}{2}$ in. nor more than $\frac{3}{4}$ in. from the edges.

(*ii*) Floor boards, other than grooved and tongued, over 7 in. wide, shall be fastened with three nails or screws at each intersection with a joist, the outer nails being not less than $\frac{1}{2}$ in. nor more than $\frac{3}{4}$ in. from the edges.

(*iii*) Tongued and grooved floor boards shall be fastened with two nails or screws at each intersection with a joist.

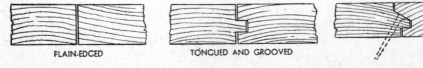

PLAIN-EDGED   TONGUED AND GROOVED

Fig. 38. The diagrams on the left and in the centre show two common joints for flooring boards. On the right is a joint, splay-rebated, tongued and grooved, and prepared for secret nailing.

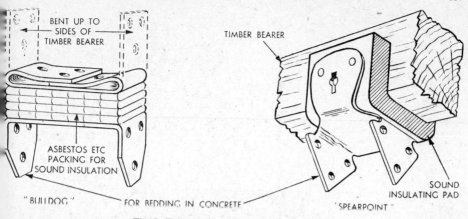

BENT UP TO SIDES OF TIMBER BEARER

TIMBER BEARER

ASBESTOS ETC PACKING FOR SOUND INSULATION

" BULLDOG "   FOR BEDDING IN CONCRETE

SOUND INSULATING PAD

" SPEARPOINT "

TWO TYPES OF METAL FLOOR CLIPS

Fig. 39. These special clips are largely used for supporting the fixing fillets on concrete floors.

(*iv*) Tongued and grooved flooring of not greater width than 4 in. on face may be fastened by one nail or screw at each intersection with a joist; the nails or screws shall have a length not less than twice the thickness of the flooring.

. Nails shall have a length not less than $2\frac{1}{2}$ times the thickness of the boards (*see a, (iv)*)
. Where screws are used their size shall be not less than that known as No. 8 and of a length not less than twice the thickness of the floor boards.

Ends of floor boards may cantilever over the side of a joist or bearer for a distance not exceeding three times the thickness of board.

STRIP FLOORINGS are usually splay-rebated, tongued and grooved and prepared for secret nailing as Fig. 38, and are prepared from many kinds of wood, often of the hardwood variety. They are in narrow widths ranging from $2\frac{1}{4}$-in. to about $3\frac{1}{4}$-in. faces and prepared from boards 3 in. to 4 in. wide, and up to about 1-in. nominal thickness. They are secret nailed as shown, and it is advisable to use two nails at each crossing over joists, etc.; the length of nails need not be more than twice the thickness of flooring owing to the nail heads being well below surface.

As to maximum spans between joists, etc., the general rules for ordinary deal

floors may be followed. Owing to the beauty of the wood used, these floorings are seldom covered, except with small rugs, and it is therefore necessary to lay them carefully.

SUPPORTS FOR ORDINARY AND STRIP FLOORINGS may be of any of the following:—

Timber joists as described under "Floors."

Small timber bearers or fillets as depicted in the illustration of various proprietary floors, to which they may be connected with metal floor clips as in Fig. 39. The bearers should be at centres to suit thickness of flooring; they should be kept free from concrete surface (which makes them beams spanning between the clips); and the distance apart of the clips, centre to centre, should accord with the following rule:—

C $d-a$ when C=24 for superload of 40 lb. F.S. on floor, 20 for 80 lb.; 19 for 100 lb.; and 17 for over 100 lb. d=depth of bearer in inches, and a=centres of bearers in inches.

A domestic floor with 40 lb. F.S. superload with 2-in. deep bearers at 18-in. centres should have the floor clips at centres of 24×2−18=30 in.

It is usual to make the bearers not less

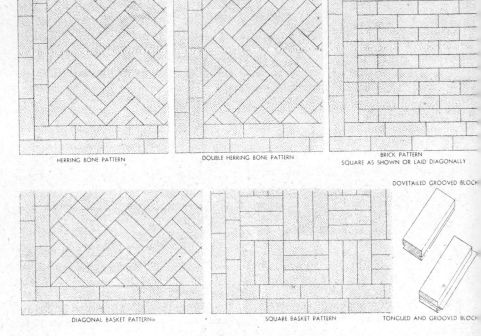

HERRING BONE PATTERN

DOUBLE HERRING BONE PATTERN

BRICK PATTERN
SQUARE AS SHOWN OR LAID DIAGONALLY

DOVETAILED GROOVED BLOCK

DIAGONAL BASKET PATTERN

SQUARE BASKET PATTERN

TONGUED AND GROOVED BLOCK

WOOD-BLOCK FLOORINGS

Fig. 40. Illustrating a few of the various patterns in which wood blocks are laid. On the right (below are shown two types of the blocks which are used for wood-block flooring.

than 2 in. deep, and their width should not be less than $1\frac{3}{4}$ in.

CEMENT AND SAND PAVINGS, laid on concrete, are usually $\frac{3}{4}$ in. or 1 in. thick laid in one coat, consisting of 1 part of Portland cement to $2\frac{1}{2}$ or 3 parts clean sharp sand, and their surfaces may be finished in either of the three following ways, the first being the cheapest and the last the most expensive. (1) Levelled with screeding rule and left with a fairly rough surface; (2) levelled with screeding rule and afterwards finished with a wood float to a sand-faced surface; (3) levelled with a screeding rule and afterwards finished with a steel float to a smooth surface.

GRANOLITHIC PAVINGS laid on concrete are of thicknesses varying from 1 in. to 2 in., and are generally heavy-duty pavings. They may be finished in either of the three ways stated above for cement and sand pavings, and, in addition, they may have carborundum to prevent slipping. They are composed of 1 part Portland cement to $2\frac{1}{2}$ or 3 parts of fine granite chippings usually $\frac{3}{8}$-in. gauge with a little granite dust or sand; they are usually laid in one coat.

WOOD-BLOCK FLOORINGS are also laid on concrete to various patterns as Fig. 40, which also shows two types of blocks which are 1 in. or $1\frac{1}{4}$ in. thick and 9 in. ×3 in. or 12 in.×3 in. The concrete floor must be made perfectly level with cement and sand screeding $\frac{1}{2}$ in. to $\frac{3}{4}$ in. thick on which the blocks are embedded in hot mastic, cleaned off and, if desired, the surface is beeswax polished or stained and polished.

QUARRY TILE PAVINGS are laid on a cement and sand screed on concrete or equal, and consist of quarries of such sizes as 6 in. × 6 in. × $\frac{5}{8}$ in. or $\frac{7}{8}$ in. thick, 9 in. × 9 in. × 1$\frac{1}{4}$ in. and 12 in. × 12 in. × 2 in. (Fig. 41). They are made in various colours as reds, browns, buffs and blues. It is advisable to lay the tiles as follows to prevent arching or detachment from the bedding material and a resulting sounding of hollowness:—

Lay the screeding on concrete while the latter is "green," i.e., fairly hard, but still damp; if this is impracticable and screeding must be laid on dry concrete, the latter should be brushed free of dust, roughened if necessary and well wetted before the screeding is laid. Adopt the same principle with the bedding material for the tiles. Where the concrete has a good surface, only the bedding layer is required.

The quarry tiles are usually laid by first soaking them for a period depending on their porosity and then bedding them in cement and sand 1 to 2 or 1 to 2$\frac{1}{2}$. It is a good practice after soaking them to brush a cement grout of cream consistency on the underside of the tiles twenty-four hours before bedding them. The joints should be wider than usual, not less than $\frac{3}{16}$ in. and in no circumstances should the joints be filled with cement grout or scum worked up from the bedding material. The concrete floor on which the paving is laid should be divided into expansion areas, as explained later.

TESSELLATED TILE PAVINGS (Fig. 42) are usually 4 in. × 4 in., 6 in. × 3 in. and 6 in. × 6 in., by $\frac{1}{2}$ in. thick, in red, buff, brown and black colours, and they are laid similarly to quarry tiles but usually with thinner joints—too thin being inadvisable. This type of paving is often laid to various patterns with different coloured tiles, including the use of white vitreous tiles.

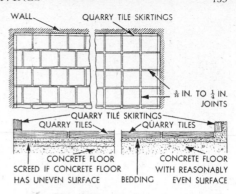

Fig. 41. Quarry tile paving.

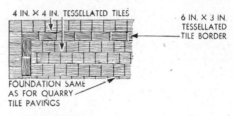

Fig. 42. Tessellated tile pavings.

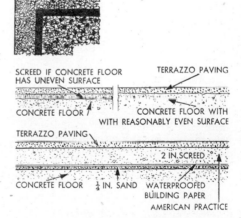

Fig. 43. Terrazzo pavings.

TERRAZZO PAVINGS (Fig. 43). The laid-in-situ variety consists of granulated marble or other similar material mixed with grey, white or coloured Portland cement, laid $\frac{5}{8}$ in. to $\frac{3}{4}$ in. thick on a cement and sand screed on concrete and afterwards rubbed down with

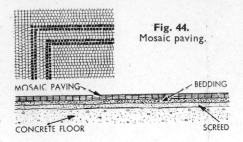

Fig. 44.
Mosaic paving.

carborundum blocks and polished. This type of paving is liable to cracking unless particular care is taken with its preparation, laying, foundation, and the provision of expansion strips. The aggregate must be graded carefully and an excess of cement avoided. The paving should be divided into small expansion areas as explained later.

MOSAIC PAVING (Fig. 44) consists of small regular-shaped marble or ceramic cubes from $\frac{1}{4}$ in. to 1 in. square or hexagonal on plan, and from $\frac{1}{4}$ in. to $\frac{1}{2}$ in. thick bedded in mortar on a level cement screed, the latter being proportioned 1 to 3. The mosaic cubes, etc., are generally glued to paper, on which the pattern is drawn, and then reversed for fixing, and set in mortar consisting of 1 part Portland cement, 2 parts sand, and sufficient hydrated lime to make the mortar plastic for embedding the mosaic. The paving is finally rubbed off with stone or carborundum rubbers either by hand or machine.

Methods of Avoiding Cracking

Cracking in paving is due to the expansion and contraction of concrete, screeding, bedding materials and the pavings, and also because the various materials often have varying co-efficients of expansion which are apt to set up different movements in the work.

To avoid cracking in pavings it is necessary to divide all or some of the various materials into panels with expansion strips between them so that each material may move without cracking the others. Where expansion strips are necessary in pavings it is seldom sufficient to allow them in the pavings only, but they must also be carried through the screeding and, if practicable, through the concrete floor or whatever other base is in use.

Unsuspended concrete floors of large areas should have expansion joints not more than 30 ft. apart either way, a good principle being to make bays 30 ft. long and 9 ft. wide. The joints may be formed by inserting bitumen strips which are left in, or alternatively $\frac{3}{8}$-in. wood strips may be used, which are eventually withdrawn and the space filled with bitumen or sand and tar.

Dividing the Screeding

The screeding should be divided by expansion strips to accord with the following rules for the different types of pavings. For quarry, tessellated and mosaic pavings—which are not laid with expansion strips—the screedings should have expansion strips similar to those in the concrete.

For terrazzo, which is very prone to cracking, special precautions are necessary; the expansion strips in the terrazzo should be continued downwards through the screeding to the concrete, but not through it. American practice is to separate a thick screeding and the terrazzo from the structural work as shown by the diagram.

Expansion strips in the pavings are not considered essential for quarry, tessellated, and mosaic pavings, but very necessary for terrazzo, which should be divided into panels, preferably about 3 ft. × 3 ft., but with a maximum of 16 sup. ft. with expansion strips of 20 S.W.G. brass, $\frac{1}{4}$ in. thick lead, $\frac{1}{4}$ in. thick vulcanite, or zinc, or some other similar kind of comparatively soft material.

PARQUET FLOORINGS (Fig. 45) consist
of $\frac{1}{4}$ in. thick wood of various lengths,
widths, and shapes to provide many
designs, the edges being square. Austrian oak, when obtainable, is the best
wood to use, as it is hard wearing and
economical. Walnut, mahogany, jarrah,
padauk, and other woods are used for
ornamental as well as for wearing
purposes.

Parquet flooring is laid on a dry wood
sub-floor which must be free from any
uneven surfaces. The parquet strips are
fixed by glueing and nailing from the
surface with 1-in. panel pins, which are
driven in and the small holes filled.

These floors are reasonable in cost, of
good appearance, wear well, are fairly
soft to walk upon and are usually
cleaned by polishing with beeswax, and
occasionally, say every eighteen months,
or more often if floors get very dirty,
with equal parts of petrol and turpentine substitute applied sparingly with a
cloth and when the fires are out.

COMPOSITION FLOORINGS (Fig. 46) are
usually $\frac{1}{2}$ in. to $\frac{3}{4}$ in. thick, $\frac{3}{4}$ in. being
laid in two coats, of red, brown or other
standard colours at basic costs, and blue-
green or black colours and mottled surfaces at an increased cost. They may be
laid on a perfectly dry wood sub-floor
or on dry concrete floors. When laid on
a wood floor the boards should be sound,
free from rot, and firm.

Reinforcing Methods

Reinforcement should be used such as
by laths nailed to the boards to which is
fixed galvanized wire netting; alternatively, expanded metal lathing may be
nailed direct to the boards. A concrete
floor should be of good quality concrete
without breeze or ashes in the aggregate,
and be level and left with a spade finish.

If the concrete has not a reasonably
level surface a $\frac{3}{4}$-in. cement and sand
screeding should be laid. The surface of

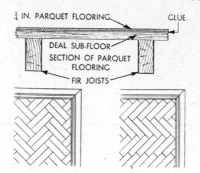

Fig. 45. Parquet flooring.

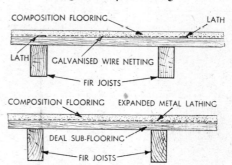

Fig. 46. Composition floorings on wood sub-
flooring. They are also laid on concrete floors.

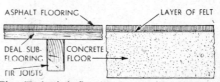

Fig. 47. Asphalt flooring on wood or concrete

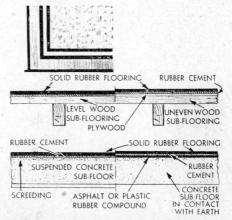

Fig. 48. Rubber flooring in sheets or tiles.

concrete or screeding should not be smooth, but if it is it should be hacked at about 6-in. centres.

ASPHALT FLOORINGS (Fig. 47) are of asphalt in which is incorporated colouring matter to provide red, grey and green colours of a permanent character. Black may also be obtained. The asphalt may have mixed with it black, white, or multi-coloured marble chippings, the surface being afterwards machine-ground in order to produce a terrazzo appearance.

Choice of Colours

The colour of the chippings is a matter of taste and is usually governed by the base colour. The floorings can be laid on wood or concrete, any dampness (while being inadvisable, particularly in wood), not affecting the flooring. It is usually laid about $\frac{5}{8}$ in. thick.

A felt underlay is recommended for wood and concrete, so that any movement in the wood or any cracking of the concrete will not affect the flooring.

Wood sub-flooring should be sound and firm, and free of any conditions that may induce dry or other rot. Concrete floors should be level and reasonably smooth.

SOLID RUBBER FLOORINGS (Fig. 48) are obtainable in sheet material, tiles, and units with vulcanized joints built on a sheet backing; the thicknesses are $\frac{1}{8}$ in., $\frac{3}{16}$ in., and $\frac{1}{4}$ in. Sheet material is made in plain and mottled colours, with or without borders, in long lengths and 3 ft. and 4 ft. wide.

Tiles are in sizes of 3 in. to 48 in. square, rectangular and other shapes and in many colours and designs. The units are of tiles, with designs not including curved lines, and are built up with any number of colours, or any combination of colours, in long lengths and 3 ft. to 4 ft. wide. Units built up on a sheet backing are similar to the units

last described, but usually consist of $\frac{3}{16}$-in. tiles fixed to $\frac{1}{8}$ in. thick rubber sheets.

A less expensive type consists of rubber on a foundation of durable sound-deadening fibre.

Rubber floorings are suitable for practically any type of building, but are not suitable when sub-floors or floorings are damp, or when oils or fats are liable to drop on them. They are very durable, hygienic, fire resisting, non-slippery, of good appearance, easily cleaned by simple washing, and are noiseless.

Foundation and Laying. The flooring may be laid on a wood sub-flooring or on a concrete sub-floor, both of which must be perfectly dry so that no dampness will get to the underside of the flooring. Wood sub-floorings must be level and smooth, and if they cannot be made so or there is any chance of warping a layer of 4 mm. plywood should be laid as a foundation for the rubber.

A concrete sub-floor laid direct on earth must be waterproofed with asphalt or a plastic rubber compound. The floorings are bedded with a rubber cement. Specialists usually supply and lay this type of flooring.

POILITE RUBBER ON ASBESTOS-CEMENT TILE FLOORINGS (Fig. 49) are of tiles with an asbestos-cement core and a rubber tread, and are made in sizes of 3 in. × 3 in., 6 in. × 2 in., 6 in. × 3 in., 6 in. × 6 in., 9 in. × 4$\frac{1}{2}$ in. and 9 in., and 12 in. × 12 in., all being $\frac{3}{8}$ in. thick. Diagonal halves are made of 3-in., 6-in., 9-in. and 12-in. square tiles. The tiles are made in a considerable variety of plain and mottled colours.

Foundation and Laying. Wood sub-flooring must be level and firm and painted with red lead priming; slight hollows or irregularities may be made up by applying a filler coat of the mastic used for fixing the tiles, a little dry sand being mixed with the mastic when deep

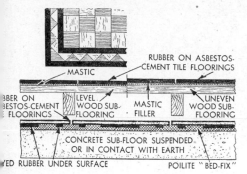

Fig. 49. Rubber on asbestos-cement tile floorings.

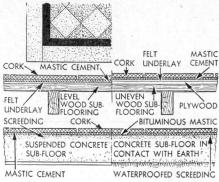

Fig. 50. Cork tile makes attractive flooring.

depressions have to be filled. This method of treatment avoids the use of plywood as specified for solid rubber floorings. The tiles, which have plain backs, are fixed by spreading a mastic, supplied by the makers of the tiles, along the underside of all four edges and a daub in the centre of the tile. The joints between the tiles should be a trowel thickness or $\frac{1}{16}$ in. Grouting may be with the mastic, Portland or white cement, but not with Keene's or plaster of Paris.

Laying on concrete is done in a different way from wood sub-flooring work, and the tiles used for concrete have a keyed rubber under-surface. Concrete floors should be dry and reasonably level. A screeding is only necessary when concrete is very uneven, as the Poilite bed-fix which is used for fixing the tiles is laid about $\frac{3}{8}$ in. thick and takes up any normal irregularities in the concrete floor. The bed-fix is first mixed dry and then 5 parts of it is mixed with not more than 1 part of water. It is then laid about $\frac{3}{8}$ in. thick on the concrete, which should first be well wetted and kept wet for at least an hour before application of the bed-fix. The tiles are slurried or buttered on the back with the fix, a brush being used for this purpose, and are then laid on the bed-fix and tapped to ensure proper bedding.

CORK TILE FLOORINGS (Fig. 50) are of cork tiles $\frac{1}{4}$ in., $\frac{3}{8}$ in. and $\frac{9}{16}$ in. thick, and in sizes of 4 in., 6 in., 8 in., 9 in. and 12 in. square, and 12 in. × 4 in., 12 in. × 6 in., 18 in. × 3 in., 18 in. × 12 in., and 36 in. × 12 in., and suitable widths for borders. They are made in light, medium, and dark shades of brown. Cork floorings are of good appearance, very durable, non-slippery, non-absorbent, resilient, dustless, hygienic, are usually kept polished, and when dirty may be washed with non-caustic soap and water.

Laying the Floorings

Foundation and Laying. The flooring may be laid on wood sub-flooring or concrete sub-floor. The former should be dry, firm, and perfectly level, and if new, should be of tongued-and-grooved flooring. An uneven or worn sub-flooring should be covered with plywood. Concrete sub-floors should be screeded with cement and sand not less than $\frac{1}{2}$ in. thick, trowelled to a smooth even surface. Concrete sub-floors laid on earth must be made waterproof. In such cases the tiles are fixed with a special bituminous mastic. On wood sub-floorings a felt-paper underlay is used. The tiles are bedded with a mastic cement to the felt underlay or screeding, and in the case of wood sub-flooring headless nails are driven in below the surface of the cork.

CHAPTER 4

ROOFS AND ROOF COVERINGS

Descriptive terms. Pitch. Materials. Classification. Roof trusses. Dormers. Verges. Gutters. Flat roofs. Drips and rolls. Zinc, copper, and asphalt roofing. Tiling. Pantiles. Roman, Italian and Spanish tiles. Slates and slating. Asbestos and concrete tiles. Asbestos, cement, and galvanized steel sheets.

THERE are several types of roofs used in building construction and they are designated according to their outline or form of construction, which are governed by: (a) the plan of the building; (b) distance apart of the supporting walls; (c) the character of the roof covering; and (d) the architectural features of the structure.

In selecting the roof covering care should be taken to find the most suitable and the least costly, at the same time bearing in mind whether the structure will be of a temporary or permanent character.

The designer has today a good choice of covering materials, which include: slates, clay, cement and asbestos tiles, steel and asbestos corrugated sheets, asphalt, lead, copper, zinc, shingles, etc. Insulation in recent years has played a very considerable part in all kinds of roof construction.

Preserving Temperature

Poor conductors such as slates and tiles make better coverings than those which conduct heat, such as corrugated steel, as they tend to preserve a more equable temperature in the interior of the building. However, where the latter material is adopted some form of insulating material can be used.

PITCH. The term pitch is applied to the amount of slope given to the sides of the roof, and may be stated either in terms of the number of degrees which the roof makes with the horizontal or by the ratio of the rise to the span; thus for a span of 20 ft. if the rise is 5 ft. the pitch is $\frac{5}{20}=\frac{1}{4}$; if the rise is 10 ft. the rise is a half.

Minimum Pitch

With lead, zinc, asphalt, the roof surface may be laid nearly horizontal, but slates, tiles and other material require a sloping roof, the inclination of which varies from about $\frac{1}{6}$ pitch upwards. The minimum pitch it is desirable to use for the materials in use for coverings is given below, and also in Fig. 1.

Materials	Angle with the horizon in degrees	Pitch
Lead . . .	$\frac{3}{4}°$	$\frac{1}{60}$
Copper . . .	$\frac{3}{4}°$	$\frac{1}{60}$
Zinc . . .	$\frac{3}{4}°$	$\frac{1}{60}$
Asphalt . . .	$\frac{3}{4}°$	$\frac{1}{60}$
Corrugated steel .	14°	$\frac{1}{8}$
Corrugated asbestos .	14°	$\frac{1}{8}$
Slates (large) . .	21° 48′	$\frac{1}{5}$
Slates (ordinary) .	26° 34′	$\frac{1}{4}$
Slates (small) . .	33°	$\frac{1}{3}$
Plain tiles . .	45°	$\frac{1}{2}$
Tiles (single lap) .	35°	$\frac{7}{20}$
Ruberoid . .	14°	$\frac{1}{8}$

Table I. The minimum pitch necessary for roof coverings of various materials.

ROOF PITCHES

Fig. I. The sloping lines give the roof pitches suitable for roofing materials. The pitches mostly used are quarter and one-third, though usually the steeper the pitch the better the appearance; but the expense is greater. Lead and asphalt roofs, though they have a slight pitch, are known as flat roofs. *See also* Table I.

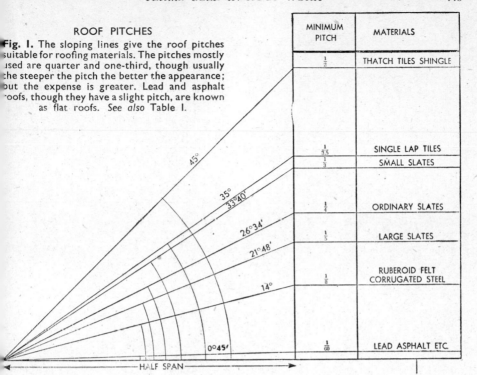

	MINIMUM PITCH	MATERIALS
45°	$\frac{1}{2}$	THATCH TILES SHINGLE
35° 33°40'	$\frac{1}{3.5}$	SINGLE LAP TILES
	$\frac{1}{3}$	SMALL SLATES
26°34'	$\frac{1}{4}$	ORDINARY SLATES
21°48'	$\frac{1}{5}$	LARGE SLATES
14°	$\frac{1}{8}$	RUBEROID FELT CORRUGATED STEEL
0°45'	$\frac{1}{60}$	LEAD ASPHALT ETC.

HALF SPAN

In exposed positions a slight increase in pitch or lap should be allowed.

PARTS OF A ROOF (Fig. 2). The *ridge* is the point or line of a roof where the two opposite slopes meet; the horizontal piece of timber forming the ridge is called the *ridge board*. The lower edges or parts of the sloping surface of the roof where the gutter is usually supported are called the *eaves*. The timbers that support the roofing material are termed *rafters*. They are usually supported at their ends by wall plates, ridges, hips, etc., and at intermediate points by purlins or other members if their length exceeds about 8 ft. The spacing varies from 15 in. up to 24 in. over the entire surface.

Wall plates to which the rafters are birds-mouthed and nailed should be bedded on the wall and preferably placed along the inside. A *gable* is the part of the roof formed by continuing the roof straight to the end of the wall, which is then built up to the slopes of the roof and ridge plate. The *verge* is that part of the roof covering which terminates at the gable end.

When the eaves are carried across the end of the building, thus forming a triangular sloping surface, this surface is called a *hipped end*. The two sides of this triangular surface meeting the two main slopes of the roof form the *hips*.

The rafter forming the hip is termed the *hip rafter*. The *valley* is the intersection of two roof planes containing an external angle less than 180 degrees. The rafter lying along the valley is termed the *valley rafter*. These rafters carry the short common rafters called *jack rafters*; where these rafters butt against a valley rafter and have no foot resting on a wall plate they are called *cripple rafters*.

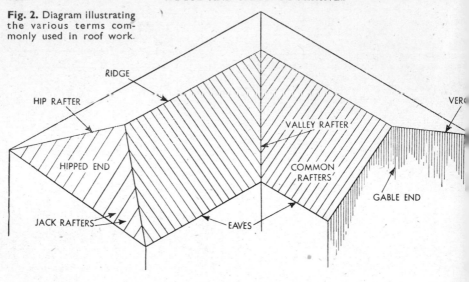

Fig. 2. Diagram illustrating the various terms commonly used in roof work.

CLASSIFICATION OF ROOFS. Roofs may be classified as follows: (*a*) single, (*b*) trussed, (*c*) composite (timber and steel).

Single Roofs consist of rafters secured at the ridge and wall plates. The various forms of this type are: lean-to, couple, couple-close, and collar-tie roofs.

The *lean-to* is the simplest form of pitch roof (Fig. 3). It slopes in one direction only; the upper edge butts against a wall where the rafters are fixed to a wall plate which is supported by a brick or wrought-iron corbel (Fig. 4).

A cheaper method sometimes adopted consists of nailing the upper ends of the rafters to a 3-in. × 2-in. wall plate plugged to the wall. Fig. 4 shows a lean-to roof suitable for spans up to 8 ft. Where the span exceeds 8 ft. *purlins* are introduced to support the rafters at an intermediate point. This purlin is supported at intervals by struts which take their support from the wall (Fig. 5).

The rafters are shown birds-mouthed to the wall plate to counteract the tendency for them to slide downwards. This

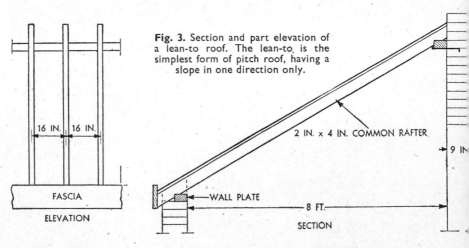

Fig. 3. Section and part elevation of a lean-to roof. The lean-to is the simplest form of pitch roof, having a slope in one direction only.

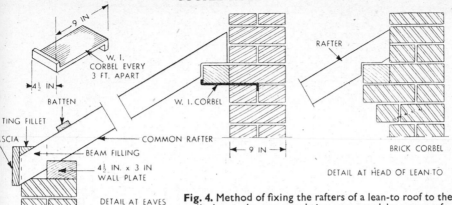

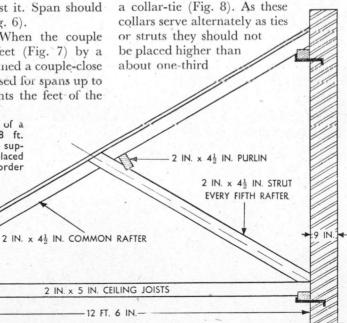

Fig. 4. Method of fixing the rafters of a lean-to roof to the wall plates, the top one being supported by means of a brick or wrought-iron corbel.

irds-mouth joint, or notch, should not xceed half the depth of the rafter.

Couple or Span Roof. As their name implies, couple roofs consist of pairs of rafters pitching against each other at the idge and fixed at their feet to a wall late. This is not a satisfactory type of oof, as it has a tendency to spread at the :et, due to the outward thrust of the rafters, except where the walls are suffiiently strong to resist it. Span should ot exceed 10 ft. (Fig. 6).

Couple-close Roof. When the couple oof is tied at the feet (Fig. 7) by a orizontal tie it is termed a couple-close oof, which may be used for spans up to 2 ft. The tie prevents the feet of the

rafters from spreading, and consequently avoids the danger of the walls overturning. These ties serve as ceiling joists where a ceiling is required, and are then termed *ceiling joists*; they are securely nailed to the rafter and wall plate. The depth of ceiling joists is made $\frac{1}{2}$ in. for every foot of span.

Collar-tie. When the tie is placed some distance above the wall plate it is called a collar-tie (Fig. 8). As these collars serve alternately as ties or struts they should not be placed higher than about one-third

Fig. 5. When the span of a lean-to roof exceeds 8 ft. purlins are introduced to support the rafters. Struts placed at intervals are added in order to give support.

2 IN. x 4½ IN. PURLIN

2 IN. x 4½ IN. STRUT EVERY FIFTH RAFTER

9 IN.

2 IN. x 4½ IN. COMMON RAFTER

2 IN. x 5 IN. CEILING JOISTS

12 FT. 6 IN.—

Fig. 6. Elevation and plan of a couple or span roof. The span should not exceed 10 ft. in this type of roof.

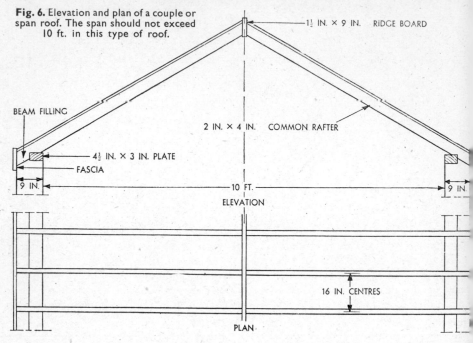

BEAM FILLING

1½ IN. × 9 IN.   RIDGE BOARD

2 IN. × 4 IN.   COMMON RAFTER

4½ IN. × 3 IN. PLATE

FASCIA

9 IN.

10 FT.

9 IN.

ELEVATION

16 IN. CENTRES

PLAN

the vertical height from the wall to the ridge. If placed higher than this the tie would lose its effectiveness in preventing the overturning thrust of the walls.

In view of the fact that the collar may change from tension to compression, or vice versa, it is desirable that every fourth or fifth collar should be halved to the rafter to form a shoulder. Care should be taken not to weaken the rafter at this point by cutting into it, to form the joint. A ½-in. sinking taken out c the rafter and a corresponding amoun taken out of the collar would suffice.

The remaining portion of the thick ness of the collar along its upper edge i dovetailed. This is termed a *dovetaile halving joint* (Fig. 9). The joint is furthe secured by spiking or bolting. A halvec and cogged joint may be used. Some times the rafters are doubled at thi point and the collar fixed between them

Fig. 7. A couple-close roof is a couple roof tied at the feet by a horizontal tie. The span should not exceed about 12 ft.

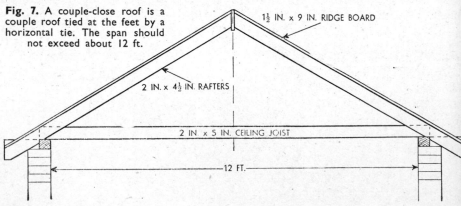

1½ IN. x 9 IN. RIDGE BOARD

2 IN. x 4½ IN. RAFTERS

2 IN. x 5 IN. CEILING JOIST

12 FT.

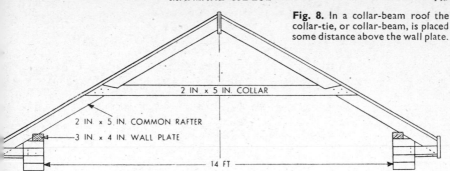

Fig. 8. In a collar-beam roof the collar-tie, or collar-beam, is placed some distance above the wall plate.

2 IN x 5 IN. COLLAR

2 IN x 5 IN. COMMON RAFTER

3 IN x 4 IN. WALL PLATE

14 FT

Collar-and-tie Roofs. In domestic work where roof trusses are not desired larger spans can be satisfactorily constructed by the use of ties, struts, and purlins; advantage being taken of any partition wall as an intermediate support. These are termed collar-and-tie roofs. The purlins are supported at their ends by a wall or hip rafter and at intermediate points along their length on the collars and struts (Fig. 10).

Preventing Sagging and Cracking

It is advisable to stiffen the ceiling joists to prevent their sagging and cracking the ceilings. This is done by nailing on the top of the joists a piece of timber 1 in. × 3 in. in section termed a *stringer* and supporting it from the rafters or purlins at intervals of about 4 ft. × 1 in. 1¼ in. × 3 in. vertical hangers.

The rule given to find the depth of ceiling joists is: half the span in feet equals the depth of joists in inches. Where hangers are used the depth of the joists may be reduced to a half.

Mansard Roof. There has been an increase in the use of these roofs recently for domestic work, their outline being modified to meet existing conditions.

The method at one time used for setting out these roofs was to draw a semi-circle and divide it into a number of parts, the main points of the roof outline passing through these parts. This has now been altered to an outline which is determined by the amount of head room required, the minimum height being 8 ft.

These roofs usually have two pitches and are sometimes referred to as *curb roofs* owing to the curb being used to support the rafters at the intersection of the two slopes. The lower slope should not exceed 75 degrees to the horizontal, while the upper slope is generally made half pitch, third pitch or quarter pitch according to the covering adopted. This type of roof allows a room to be formed entirely within the roof, light and air being obtained through a dormer window. Fig. 11 shows typical outline.

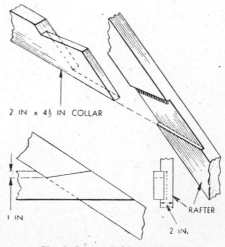

2 IN x 4½ IN COLLAR

RAFTER

1 IN

2 IN.

Fig. 9. Dovetailed halving joint.

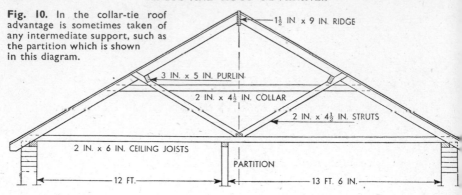

Fig. 10. In the collar-tie roof advantage is sometimes taken of any intermediate support, such as the partition which is shown in this diagram.

WALL PLATES. The size of wall plates varies from 4 in. × 2 in. to 4½ in. × 3 in. The joint at the angle of the plate and for lengthening it, if necessary, is the halving joint. The joint used in lengthening the plate should be two-and-a-half times to three times the thickness of the plate. The plate is usually placed along the inside of the wall.

ANGLE TIES. To help to resist the outward thrust of the hip rafter an angle tie is fixed to the plates across the angle, and the rafter is notched on to the tie in addition to the wall plate. The older method of using an angle tie with dragon beam is little used.

Plain ties from 2 in. × 3 in. to 4 in. × 4 in. housed ½ in. into the plates and dovetailed are used as shown in Fig. 12. These ties are set in a distance of from 15 in. to 18 in. from the outer angle of the wall plate depending in the pitch of the roof.

Another method is to board over the corners diagonally with 1-in. or 1¼-in. boarding about 12 in. wide. This forms a good seating for the hip, and is efficient and simple in setting out. The outer angle of the wall plates should be sawn off diagonally to a width equal to the thickness of the hip rafter and the hip reduced in depth to that of the common rafters, usually 4½ in.

Various methods are used for the junction of the hips and the ridge. Fig.

13 shows a simple and practical arrangement with the last common rafter a short distance from the end, and the hip splayed, one cut only being necessary. Fig. 14 is similar, but the hips are birds-mouthed.

Fig. 15 shows the end pair of common rafters tied together by nailing short lengths of 1¼-in. boarding across them and then mitreing the hips together against them. These joints are preferable to that shown in Fig. 16, where the centre rafter of the end, sometimes called the end common rafter, coming up against the ridge rather complicates the construction.

Roof rafters are usually made 2 in. thick. Long lengths should be avoided as they are expensive and difficult to obtain. The standard stock size for common rafters is 2 in. × 4 in. at 16-in. centres with supports every 8 ft., but reference should be made to Table II.

MINIMUM SIZE OF RAFTERS SPACED AT 16-IN. CENTRES	
Bearing not exceeding	*Dimensions*
ft. in.	in. in.
6 0	2 × 3
7 0	2 × 3½
8 0	2 × 4
9 0	2 × 4½
10 0	2 × 5

Table II. Minimum size of rafters spaced 16-in. centres.

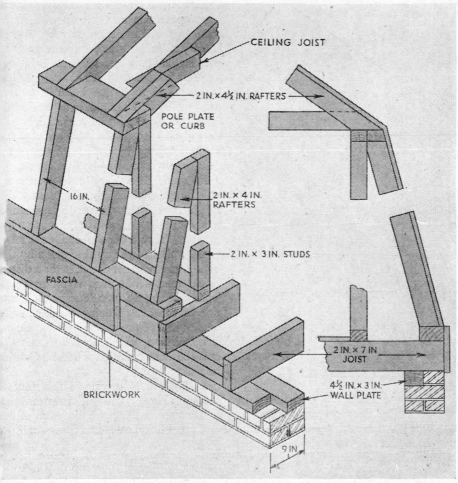

CEILING JOIST

2 IN. x 4½ IN. RAFTERS

POLE PLATE
OR CURB

16 IN.

2 IN. x 4 IN.
RAFTERS

2 IN. × 3 IN. STUDS

FASCIA

2 IN. × 7 IN
JOIST

4½ IN.× 3 IN.
WALL PLATE

BRICKWORK

9 IN.

MANSARD OR CURB ROOF

Fig. 11. Mansard roofs have two pitches and are sometimes referred to as curb roofs, owing to the curb being used to support the rafters at the intersection of the two slopes. The lower slope should not exceed 75 degrees to the horizontal, while the upper slope is generally made half pitch, third pitch or quarter pitch according to the covering adopted. The studding is shown fixed to the curb. This type of roof allows clear headroom for a room to be formed entirely within the roof, a dormer window being provided. Such a room is particularly suitable for a workroom or studio.

Fig. 17 is a roof plan showing various rafters and purlins.

Timber purlins vary in size according to span and loading, and form the intermediate support or supports for the common rafters between the ridge piece and the wall plate. The minimum sizes for various distances apart are given in Table III in the next column.

Span in feet	Distance apart not exceeding		
	6 ft.	7 ft. 6 in.	9 ft.
	in. in.	in. in.	in. in.
6	3 × 5	3 × 5½	3 × 6
8	3 × 6	3 × 7	4 × 7
10	4 × 7	4 × 8	5 × 8
12	4 × 9	4½ × 9	5 × 9
14	5 × 9	4½ × 10	4½ × 11

Table III. Minimum sizes for timber purlins.

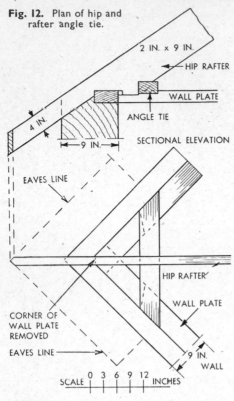

Fig. 12. Plan of hip and rafter angle tie.

2 IN. × 9 IN.

HIP RAFTER

WALL PLATE

ANGLE TIE

4 IN.

9 IN.

SECTIONAL ELEVATION

EAVES LINE

HIP RAFTER

WALL PLATE

CORNER OF WALL PLATE REMOVED

EAVES LINE

9 IN.

WALL

SCALE   0   3   6   9   12   INCHES

TRUSSED PURLINS. Where the span of the purlins becomes inconveniently large the latter are not economical and a trussed purlin might be adopted. It will be found suitable where there is not sufficient room for a principal and the space inside the roof can be utilized. The purlins should extend from wall to wall and rest on stone templets built into the wall. They should be kept clear of the ceiling joists.

The top and bottom members are usually 4 in. × 4 in. or 4 in. × 3 in. and the struts 4 in. × 3 in. or 4 in. × 2½ in. with ⅜-in. or ½-in. diameter bolts. All bolts must have washers top and bottom. The truss usually forms the ashlaring along the sides of the room and may be filled in with studding to receive the plaster or to be covered with fibre board (Fig. 18).

Light roof trusses for comparatively large spans can be built up with small scantlings of various lengths and placed side by side. In these types it is usual to place a pair of rafters a few inches apart to allow for another member being fitted between them. These latter members are formed with shoulders at their ends which bear on the double members and extend into the adjacent members in the form of a tenon for fixing or as support for the purlins at their upper ends.

BELFAST ROOF TRUSSES. The best-known type of this construction is the Belfast roof truss, sometimes termed *lattice* or *bowstring*, with the upper edge curved. This curve should take the form of a parabola—the outline given by the bending movement diagram for a distributed load—though it is often struck from a centre and made segmental, the rise in the centre being usually made one-eighth of the span. They are constructed for spans up to 100 ft. and are covered with corrugated steel or felt or boarding.

A single-line diagram of this roof is shown in Fig. 19, which gives alternative methods of finding the direction of the lattices. The curve is first drawn and the

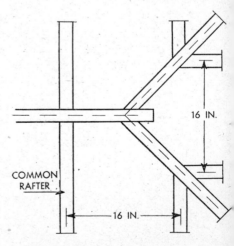

16 IN.

COMMON RAFTER

16 IN.

Fig. 13. Hip rafters splayed to the ridge.

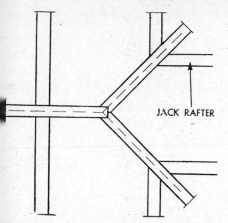

Fig. 14. Hip rafter mitred and splayed to ridge.

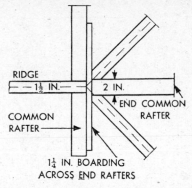

Fig. 15. Pair of common rafters tied together by means of short lengths of boarding.

position of the purlins marked on at about 3-ft. centres. From these points, as shown on the left-hand side of the drawing, the centre lines of the braces are obtained by drawing lines making angles of 45 degrees with the lines radiating from the centre from which the curve is struck.

On the right-hand side of the centre, lines of the lattices are drawn to points below the springing at each end equal to a distance of half the span.

The radius may be obtained by the formula:—

$$\text{Radius} = \frac{(\frac{1}{2}\,\text{span})^2 + \text{rise}^2}{2\,\text{rise}}$$

For a 40-ft. span a rise of $\frac{1}{8}$ span the radius will be:—

$$\text{Radius} = \frac{(\frac{1}{2} \times 40)^2 + 5^2}{2 \times 5} = 42\cdot5\ \text{ft.}$$

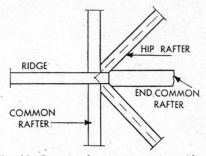

Fig. 16. Centre rafter jutting against ridge—not such a good joint as in Fig. 15.

Each truss consists of two strings and two bows with the braces fixed between them. The strings are given a camber of $\frac{1}{2}$ in. in 10 ft.

The sizes of the members adopted are given below in Table IV.

A tongued piece about 5 ft. long, 1 in. deeper than the sole piece and equal in thickness to two lattice boards, should be fixed between the ends of the sole pieces.

Span	20 ft.	30 ft.	40 ft.	50 ft.	60 ft.	70 ft.	80 ft.
Sole piece (double) .	$\frac{3}{4}'' \times 4\frac{1}{2}''$	$1'' \times 7''$	$1\frac{1}{8}'' \times 8''$	$1\frac{1}{4}'' \times 9''$	$1\frac{3}{8}'' \times 10''$	$1\frac{5}{8}'' \times 11''$	$1\frac{5}{8}'' \times 12''$
Bows (double) .	$\frac{3}{4}'' \times 1\frac{1}{2}''$	$1'' \times 2''$	$1\frac{1}{8}'' \times 2\frac{1}{4}''$	$1\frac{1}{4}'' \times 2\frac{1}{4}''$	$1\frac{3}{8}'' \times 2\frac{3}{4}''$	$\frac{1}{12}'' \times 3''$	$1\frac{5}{8}'' \times 3\frac{1}{4}''$
Lattices .	$\frac{3}{4}'' \times 3''$	$\frac{3}{4}'' \times 3''$	$\frac{7}{8}'' \times 3''$	$\frac{7}{8}'' \times 3\frac{1}{2}''$	$\frac{7}{8}'' \times 3\frac{1}{2}''$	$\frac{7}{8}'' \times 3\frac{1}{2}''$	$1'' \times 4''$

Table IV. The sizes of the members of the Belfast roof trusses are given in convenient tabular form.

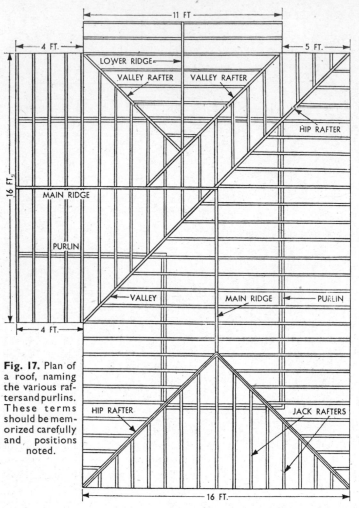

Fig. 17. Plan of a roof, naming the various rafters and purlins. These terms should be memorized carefully and positions noted.

space between the nearest convenient common rafters, by timbers or plates of stouter section than the common rafters and spiked thereto; or in high-class construction the trimming rafter would be of heavier dimensions and the trimmers properly tusk-tenoned between them. The other rafters are then fitted between the ridge and the upper edge of the trimmer.

Provision must be made by fitting boarding of suitable width on bearers between the outer line of the roof rafters and the vertical face of the chimney stack to form a gutter, subsequently to support a zinc or lead gutter with its appropriate flashings (Fig. 21).

The same arrangement of trimmed rafters is necessary around a skylight or other roof opening, except that in this case the trimmers are usually fixed with the inner faces at right angles to the outer face of the rafters and subsequently lined. Unless every care is taken in fixing skylights they are a source of trouble through leakages.

Provision should be made around the

The trusses should not be more than 8 ft. or 9 ft. apart. The purlins are 2 in. × 3½ in. placed 2 ft. apart. Cross bracing ¾ in. × 4½ in. is placed between the trusses as shown. A sketch showing the construction is given in Fig. 20. These trusses will be found to be the most economical form of construction that can be employed.

TRIMMING. Where a chimney stack emerges from an angle of the roof, the rafters have to be trimmed. In these cases all that is necessary is to span the

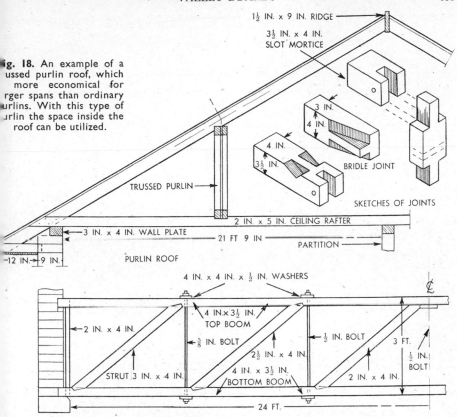

1½ IN. x 9 IN. RIDGE

3½ IN. x 4 IN. SLOT MORTICE

Fig. 18. An example of a trussed purlin roof, which is more economical for larger spans than ordinary purlins. With this type of purlin the space inside the roof can be utilized.

3 IN.

4 IN.

TRUSSED PURLIN

4 IN.

3½ IN.

BRIDLE JOINT

SKETCHES OF JOINTS

2 IN. x 5 IN. CEILING RAFTER

3 IN. x 4 IN. WALL PLATE

21 FT 9 IN

PARTITION

12 IN. 9 IN.

PURLIN ROOF

4 IN. x 4 IN. x ½ IN. WASHERS

℄

2 IN. x 4 IN.

4 IN. x 3½ IN. TOP BOOM

⅝ IN. BOLT

½ IN. BOLT

3 FT.

½ IN. BOLT

STRUT 3 IN. x 4 IN.

2½ IN. x 4 IN.

4 IN. x 3½ IN. BOTTOM BOOM

2 IN. x 4 IN.

24 FT.

dges of the skylight for an outwardly rojecting lining, about 4 in. above the oof surface, to support the flashing and o prevent the gutter on the top side overflowing during heavy rain. Where he lining is at right angles to the roof lope, chamfered fillets are used, but his method makes a less satisfactory ob (Fig. 22).

Small intersecting roofs to bay windows or dormers are constructed to intersect the main roof. There are one or two ways of forming the roof over a bay. The main roof rafters may be framed in valley rafters, or the main roof rafters carried down to the wall plate, which would be made continuous. Pieces of boards termed *valley boards* are fixed along the top edge of the rafters to form

a bearing and fixing for the feet of the jack rafters of the projecting roof (Fig. 23).

DORMERS are fitted into the trimmed opening prepared in the roof. The framework consists of 2-in. × 4-in. studs and 3-in. × 4-in. or 4-in. × 4-in. posts to form the checks and to support the roof of the dormer. The studs are tenoned into a head or plate and nailed at their lower ends to the rafters.

The checks and ceiling would be lathed and plastered on the inside and the checks and roof (where flat) boarded on the outside to receive the covering.

Where the roof over the dormer is pitched, ceiling rafters are fixed by nailing to the feet of the roof rafters to form a small couple roof which is

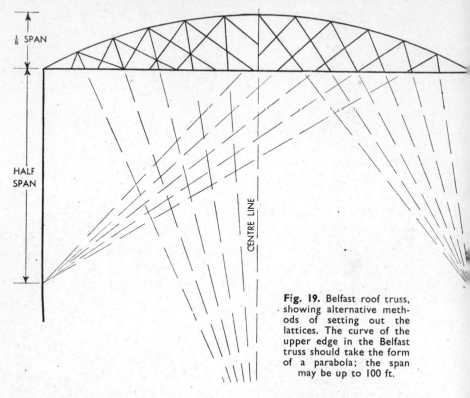

CENTRE LINE

Fig. 19. Belfast roof truss, showing alternative methods of setting out the lattices. The curve of the upper edge in the Belfast truss should take the form of a parabola; the span may be up to 100 ft.

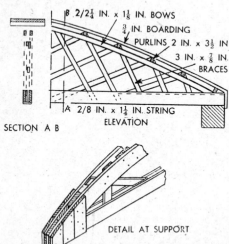

SECTION A B

Fig. 20. Sketches showing the construction of a Belfast roof truss. Cross bracing ¾ in. x 4½ in. is placed between the trusses. These trusses are a very economical form of construction.

covered with slates or tiles fixed t battens on boarding (Fig. 24).

The checks are finished with eithe slate or tile hanging, or covered wit lead.

Where the dormers are shallow th studding becomes unnecessary and th checks in these cases need only to b enclosed in 1-in. boarding fixed diagon ally.

VERGES. There are many methods c terminating the roof at the verge o gable end, much of the appearance c the building depending upon the way i which this is done. In one commonl used plan the tiles or slates terminat almost flush with the outer face of th wall, only projecting a very smal amount, the ends of the tiles being pointed or filled in with mortar (Fig. 25) Barge boards were at one time muc

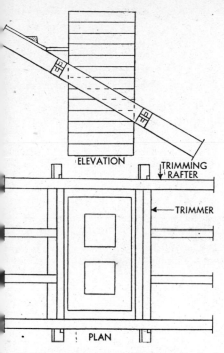

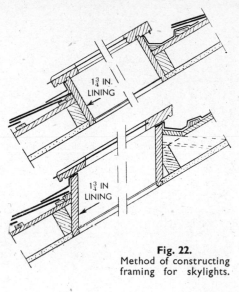

Fig. 22.
Method of constructing framing for skylights.

g. 21. Elevation and plan showing method of trimming roof rafters for a chimney stack.

nployed as a finish to a verge but they e little employed in modern design. The soffit is the visible underside ortion of the roof between the outer lge and the face of the wall (Fig. 26),

and is in general practice filled in by boarding or by lathing and plastering. The soffit may also be finished with plain tiles.

The fascia board is subsequently used to support the guttering rainwater fittings, etc. It should also project above the plane of the roof, usually 1 in. or so, to give the requisite tilt to the under-eaves slate or tile so that they will be close along the outer edge.

ROOF TRUSSES

‾OR spans over 20 ft. a truss becomes necessary. As a rough guide it may e taken that the tie-beam requires a upport every 15 ft. at least and the prin-pal rafters a support every 8 ft. These usses are placed at intervals of from ft. to 12 ft. and simply act to carry the oof proper.

According to the above rule, for spans p to 30 ft. the tie-beam should have an itermediate support. This is done by eans of a vertical member called a

king-post and the truss is known as a king-post roof truss (Fig. 27).

The members are: (1) The tie-beam; (2) king-post; (3) two principal rafters; (4) two struts.

The tie-beams should have a bearing of 9 in. at each end and rest on stone templets. The distance from centre to centre of the bearings is known as the *effective span*.

The various members are framed to-gether with mortise and tenon joints and

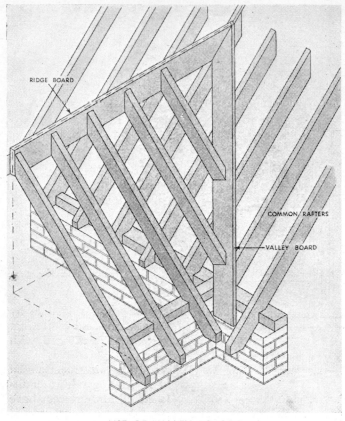

RIDGE BOARD

COMMON RAFTERS

VALLEY BOARD

USE OF VALLEY BOARDS

Fig. 23. Method of constructing a roof over a bay, showing how the feet of the jack rafters are supported by valley boards.

are further secured with straps and bolts. The roofing (common rafters, boarding felt, battens and slates) between the trusses is supported by means of purlins carried by the truss.

The truss should be set out so that the centre line of the principal rafter and tie-beam coincides with the centre bearing on the wall.

The thickness of the members is next added, and the joints between the members completed.

The principal rafters are in compression and the weight is carried down to the tie-beam, which prevents the feet of the rafter spreading outwards. . This

causes tension in the tie-beam.

The king-post supports the tie beam at the centre and is also in tension. The tie-beam should be given camber of about in. in 10 ft.

The struts from the base of the king post support the principal rafters at their centre, and are in compression. The intersection of the centre lines of the struts and the king post is usually made equal to the depth of the tie-beam above centre of tie-beam.

King-post trusses are connected by transverse members called purlins. At the apex they are connected by the ridge board, which is let into the top of the king-posts.

The king-post, owing to its shape, is formed from a piece of timber about twice the width at the centre. The exact size at the ends is found by marking the bevels of the rafter and strut joints keeping them as near as possible at right angles to the inclination of those members. The arrangement of the king-post joints is shown in Fig. 28.

Three-way straps are usually bolted across the joints to hold the members together, and the stirrup which supports the tie-beam is generally supported by cotter pins through the post.

Heel straps or a bolt are used to hold principal rafters to tie-beam (Fig. 29)

PARAPET GUTTERS

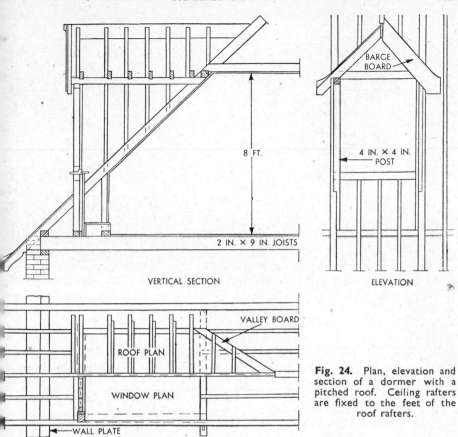

8 FT.

2 IN. × 9 IN. JOISTS

VERTICAL SECTION

BARGE
BOARD

4 IN. × 4 IN.
POST

ELEVATION

VALLEY BOARD

ROOF PLAN

WINDOW PLAN

WALL PLATE

13½ IN.

Fig. 24. Plan, elevation and section of a dormer with a pitched roof. Ceiling rafters are fixed to the feet of the roof rafters.

The purlins, which support the common rafters at their centres, are generally put immediately over the tops of the struts so as to prevent bending in the principal rafters. The common rafters are fitted and nailed to the ridge board and at the bottom they are birdsmouthed to a wall plate or pole plate. They are notched 1 in. to the purlins. The purlins are cogged to the back of the principal rafters and nailed on, and a cleat is fixed on their lower side to prevent them from slipping or turning over under the downward pressure (Fig. 30).

This figure also shows a parapet gutter. The gutter boarding is supported by 3-in. × 1½-in. bearers and is covered with sheet lead. The lead is turned up against the wall 5 in. or 6 in. and on the slope 9 in.

Types of Gutters

GUTTERS. In addition to the ordinary cast-iron gutter at the eaves of a roof, other gutters termed tapering or parallel or box gutters are used to carry off the water from sloping roofs.

Tapering gutters occur behind parapet walls and these taper on one side only. They are usually called *parapet gutters*, and are formed on the top of the common rafters, on an arrangement of gutter bearers which are fixed at varying heights owing to the fact that the gutter

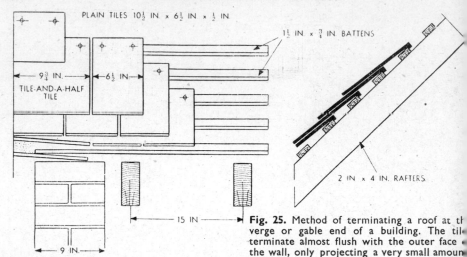

Fig. 25. Method of terminating a roof at the verge or gable end of a building. The tiles terminate almost flush with the outer face of the wall, only projecting a very small amount

must have a minimum fall of 1 in. in 10 ft. A gutter should run in lengths of not more than 9 ft., and the joint across the gutter formed with a drip not less than 2 in. in depth. In long gutters it is necessary to introduce two or more cesspools, or outlets, to prevent the width of the gutter becoming excessive.

Lead Joints

When two adjacent gutters fall in opposite directions the joint between the lead sheets is formed with a wooden roll over which the lead is dressed. The joints across the gutter are formed with a drip not less than 2 in. in depth. Along the top edge of the drip a rebate 1 in. wide is formed into which the edge of the undercloak is finished and is fixed with copper nails. The overcloak is carried over the drip and taken down to finish usually 1 in. on the lower gutter.

The sides of the sheet extend 2 in. or 3 in. forward on the wall and roof side to lessen the risk of water passing between the sheets where they overlap. The overcloak is sometimes stopped $\frac{1}{2}$ in. from the sole of the lower gutter to prevent capillary attraction, and in some cases a capillary groove is cut in the face of the

drip for the same purpose. The gutter at its narrowest part should not be less than 9 in.

The lead forming the gutter is turned up 5 in. or 6 in. against the wall and its upper edge covered with a hanging flashing. The edge of the lead on the roof side is taken up and dressed over tilting fillet which is placed 3 in. above the sole of the gutter and parallel to it. The sheet is dressed over the tilting fillet to a height of 9 in., or to a vertical height corresponding to the lead on the wall side. Fig. 31 shows a tapering gutter between the two roof slopes, and in Fig. 32 the section is shown.

Gutters and Cesspools

Figs. 33 and 33A give details of the setting out width of the gutters, gutter drips, and cesspool.

The cesspools to the gutters have a minimum depth of 6 in. and are 9 in. square on plan. They are lined with 6-lb. or 7-lb. lead bossed out of a single sheet or cut and soldered at the angles, the latter being the more usual way. From the cesspool the water is conveyed through a 3-in. or larger pipe to a rainwater head on the outside of the wall this pipe is soldered to the lining of the cesspool.

Parallel or box gutters have their sides parallel and are formed by placing two pole plates at the required distance apart, usually not less than 12 in. To the sides of the pole plates are fixed small bearers at intervals of about 16 in. to 18 in. and at heights to suit the fall, to support the gutter boarding and lining. A section is shown in Fig. 33A and a plan in Fig. 33. Where the gutter is shallow the lead may be in one width, but if the gutter is deep then the upper edges should be finished with a flashing.

Where a shoot is adopted for the outlet to the rainwater head the lead is dressed over the opening in the wall and its edges are turned up and they are finished with a flashing.

Flat Roofs. The simplest form of roof is a flat roof consisting of joists in the form of bearers, spaced as for floor joists and covered with boarding and sometimes felt (Fig. 34).

Forming the Slope

Flats differ from floors in that they are given a slight fall on the top surface to throw off the water. The amount of slope is usually specified as 1½ in. in 10 ft. but 2 in. would be preferable. The slope is formed by cutting the joists or bearers to the rake for small spans, but for larger

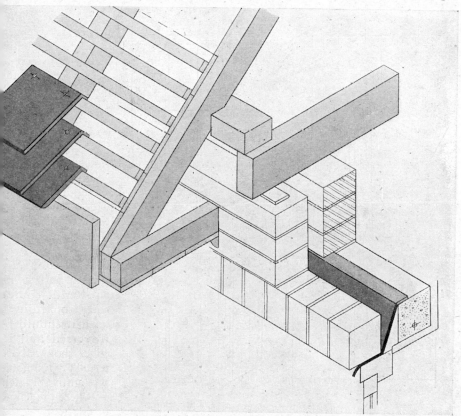

CONSTRUCTION OF THE FINISH TO EAVES

g. 26. The soffit is the visible underside portion of the roof between the outer edge and the face of the wall. The soffit is filled in either by boarding, lathing and plastering, or tiles.

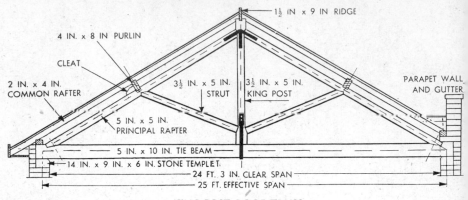

KING-POST ROOF TRUSS

Fig. 27. For spans up to 30 ft. the tie-beam should have an intermediate support. This vertic
member is known as a king-post and the truss is called a king-post roof truss.

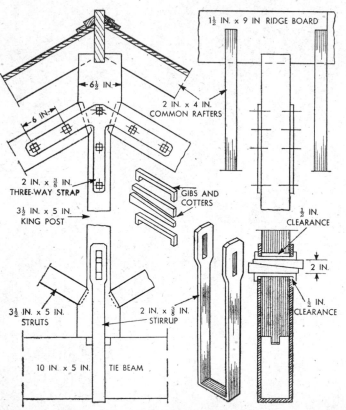

KING-POST JOINTS

Fig. 28. Arrangement of various joints used with a king-post. The lower
joint is known as a gib and cotter joint; note particularly the clearances
to allow for tightening up the joint.

spans the slope i
obtained by *firring*
up the joists. The
firring is arranged
so as to allow the
boarding to run in
the direction of the
flow because if laid
at right angles the
boards may warp
and interfere with
the free flow of the
water.

The boarding
should be in narrow
widths and $1\frac{1}{4}$ in.
thick, though 1 in.
is more usual, and
the roof covered
with felt to give a
smooth surface for
the lead. When
rough boarding is
used it should be
traversed and its
edges shot. All ex
ternal angles should
be slightly rounded
Where the length
of the slope exceeds
9 ft. for lead, 7 ft.
4 in. for zinc and

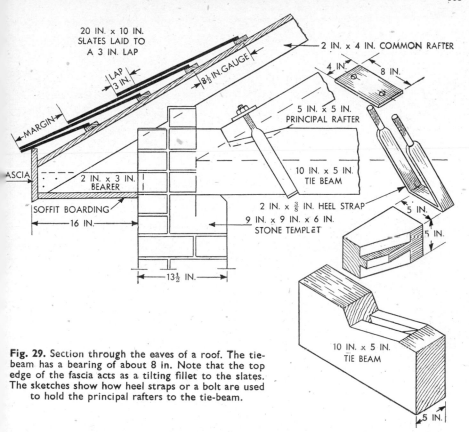

Fig. 29. Section through the eaves of a roof. The tie-beam has a bearing of about 8 in. Note that the top edge of the fascia acts as a tilting fillet to the slates. The sketches show how heel straps or a bolt are used to hold the principal rafters to the tie-beam.

ft. 8 in. for copper a drip becomes necessary, and in the width a joint becomes necessary for lead at 2 ft. 8 in., 2 ft. 9 in. or zinc and 2 ft. 4 in. for copper. These sizes are a maximum and should therefore not be exceeded.

LEAD FLATS. Owing to the expansion and contraction in lead the maximum size of sheet that can be used satisfactorily is 10 ft. × 3 ft. 6 in., which can be cut without waste from a roll measuring 30 ft. × 7 ft.

DRIPS. The joint across the end of the sheet is formed by a step or drip which should not be less than 2 in. deep, though 2½ in. is preferable to ensure a sound and waterproof job. These drips are similar to those described for gutters.

The face of the drip is usually vertical but sometimes an angle fillet is used.

ROLLS. The joint along the side of the sheet is formed by turning the edge of sheet over a wooden roll, or turning the edges over a hollow roll or seam roll formed of the material itself. The latter is not altogether suitable on flat work, as it is liable to damage from traffic across the roof, its use being confined to pitched roofs.

Wood rolls vary in size from 1¼ in. to 2 in., according to size of flat. They are rounded or splayed in section and are nailed to the boarding (Fig. 35).

The joint is formed by dressing the undercloak around the rolls about two-thirds and fixing the edge by copper

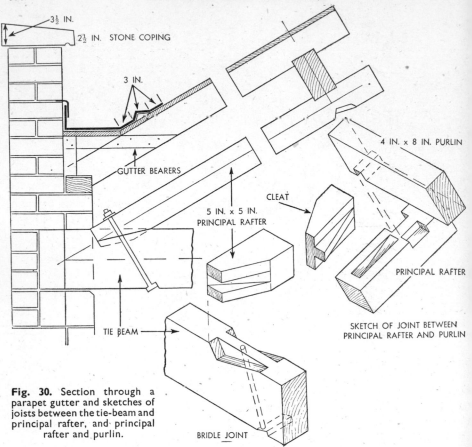

$3\frac{1}{2}$ IN.

$2\frac{1}{2}$ IN. STONE COPING

3 IN.

4 IN. x 8 IN. PURLIN

GUTTER BEARERS

CLEAT

5 IN. x 5 IN.
PRINCIPAL RAFTER

PRINCIPAL RAFTER

SKETCH OF JOINT BETWEEN
PRINCIPAL RAFTER AND PURLIN

TIE BEAM

BRIDLE JOINT

Fig. 30. Section through a parapet gutter and sketches of joists between the tie-beam and principal rafter, and· principal rafter and purlin.

nailing; the overcloak is next carried over the top of the roll and dressed down to lie 1 in. to $1\frac{1}{4}$ in. on the flat.

Sometimes the overcloak is made to finish $\frac{1}{2}$ in. from the flat. The amount of material allowed for forming the roll is 9 in., and this amount deducted from the width of the sheet gives the maximum width of bay as 2 ft. 9 in. or 2 ft. 10 in. from centre to centre of roll.

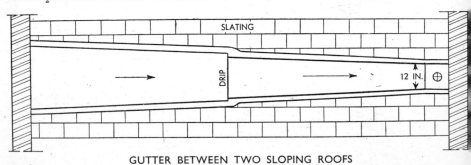

SLATING

DRIP

12 IN.

GUTTER BETWEEN TWO SLOPING ROOFS

Fig. 31. The arrows show the direction of the flow of rain water. Note how the gutter tapers between the two roofs, owing to its fall between the roof slopes.

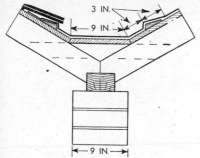

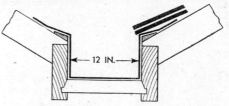

Fig. 33a. Section of the parallel or box gutter, of which the plan is given in Fig. 33.

Fig. 32. Section through the tapering gutter, of which the plan is given in Fig. 31.

For the length of the bays those at the top end require an upstand of 6 in. and for a 3-in. drip another 4 in., making the maximum length of bay as 9 ft. 2 in. The centre bays (if any) would be 9 ft. 4 in., and the bays at the bottom adjacent to the guttering about 9 ft. 5 in. It is most important to note that all lead work should be fixed along one edge only, the other edge left free to allow for the expansion and contraction.

Where pitched roofs are covered with lead a *lapped* or a *welted joint* is used across the end of the sheet. The lapped joint is formed by lapping the sheets 6 in. and fixing the upper edge of the lower sheet with copper nails.

The welting joint is formed by fixing lead or copper tacks to the roof about 2 ft. 6 in. apart, and folding them together.

FLASHINGS. The sheet of the bay adjacent to the wall has its upper edge, termed the upstand, protected by a piece of lead 5 in. or 6 in. wide termed a flashing. Its upper edge is turned into a joint of the brickwork wedged with oak or lead wedges, and the joint afterwards pointed. They are up to 7 ft. in length, and are lapped at their ends 4 in. to 6 in., being called *passings*. Further to secure the flashing small strips of lead 2 in. wide called *tacks* or *tingles* are placed at intervals of 3 ft. 6 in., so arranged to occur at the passings (Fig. 36).

ZINC ROOFING. Good zinc is uniform in colour, and on exposure to the atmosphere forms its own protective coating, which is basic carbonate.

The life of a zinc roof, properly laid with a suitable gauge of metal (No. 14 zinc gauge or thicker), and laid to adequate falls, is upwards of forty years.

The expansion and contraction of zinc being greater than that of lead, it must therefore be free to move, and it should not be placed in contact with copper, iron, or oak which set up galvanic action, the effect of which will soon destroy it.

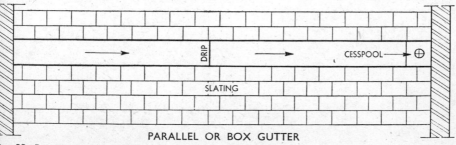

PARALLEL OR BOX GUTTER

Fig. 33. Box gutters have their main sides parallel, and are formed by placing two pole plates about 12 in. apart, as shown in section in Fig. 33a.

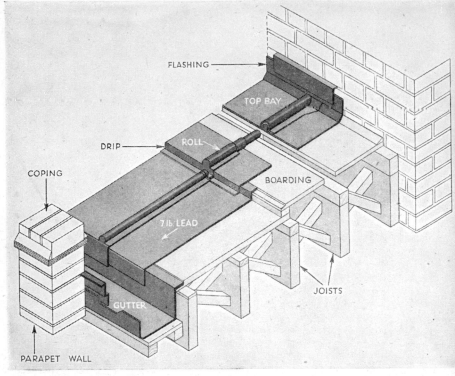

LEAD FLAT ROOF

Fig. 34. Flat roofs consist of joists in the form of bearers spaced as floor joists and covered with boarding or felt. The fall to the flat is given by firring strips of different thicknesses which are nailed to the upper edges of the joists as shown in the illustration.

Zinc is one of the lightest permanent roof coverings obtainable. Its specific gravity is 7·2, and therefore a cubic foot weighs 450 lb. and the thickness of a square foot weighing 1 lb. is $\frac{12}{450} = \frac{1}{37·5}$ in. or 0·0266 in.

The gauges usually employed on roofs are Nos. 14, 15 and 16, weighing $18\frac{2}{3}$ oz., $21\frac{2}{3}$ oz., $24\frac{2}{3}$ oz. per sup. ft. respectively. For good-class work nothing lighter than No. 16 gauge should be employed.

Sheets are manufactured in lengths of from 7 ft. up to 10 ft., and 3 ft. wide, but the sizes of sheets used for roofing purposes are 3 ft. wide and 7 ft. and 8 ft. long.

The weight of a square (100 ft. sup.) of zinc roofing for No. 14 gauge is 144 lb.; No. 15 gauge, 169 lb.; and No. 1 gauge, 192 lb. respectively.

The nails for fixing should be made of zinc or heavily galvanized.

The preparation of the roof for the zinc covering for a flat roof is carried out in the same manner as that used for lead. The rolls, however, differ from those used for lead, and the standard is $1\frac{3}{4}$-in. high, $1\frac{1}{2}$ in. at the base and splayed to $1\frac{1}{4}$ in. across the top. The size varies in practice but the minimum height is 1 in. (Fig. 37).

Zinc cannot be readily dressed round the rolls in the same way as lead, so the edges of the sheet are simply turned up $1\frac{1}{2}$ in. against the side of the roll, slight clearance for expansion being left

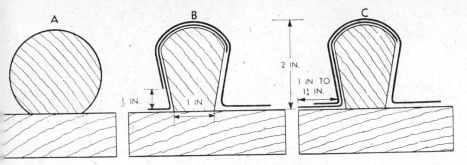

WOOD ROLLS FOR LEAD ROOFS

Fig. 35. Wood rolls for lead roofs vary in size from $1\frac{1}{4}$ in. to 2 in. A is a rounded roll; B, undercloak two-thirds round roll, with overcloak stopped $\frac{1}{2}$ in. from flat; C, overcloak carried over roll to lie on flat 1 in. to $1\frac{1}{4}$ in. The rolls are nailed to the boarding.

between the bottom of the turn-up and roll. Using a 3-ft. sheet this gives a maximum spacing of 2 ft. 5 in. between the rolls or say 2 ft. $10\frac{1}{2}$ in. centre to centre of the rolls (Fig. 38).

Clips 9 in. $\times 1\frac{1}{2}$ in. are placed at least 3 ft. 6 in. apart fixed under the rolls and are bent up to grip the turn-up side edges of the sheets. Each side edge is held by at least two clips as shown in Fig. 37.

The bay adjacent to the wall will be narrower to allow for the extra few inches required for the upstand against the wall. This adjustment will also be necessary to the top bay for the same reasons as given above.

Method of Capping

Capping is made by drawing or bending, and covers the rolls and edges of the sheets; capping is fixed by means of holding-down clips. These are bent up as shown and are $4\frac{1}{2}$ in. long with a $1\frac{1}{2}$ in. turn back across the lower end. A clip is nailed over the top end of the lower length of capping and the upper length is fitted into the turn back. This gives a watertight joint and allows for expansion (Fig. 39).

DRIPS. Flat roofs should be constructed with falls of not less than $\frac{1}{2}$ in. in 8 ft. to allow for drainage.

If the roof has a fall of less than 1 in. in 8 ft., drips must be provided to form the joint along the end of the sheets. These are made at depths of $2\frac{1}{2}$ in. and are spaced at 7 ft. 6 in. as a maximum

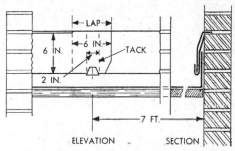

Fig. 36. Elevation and section of roof flashing.

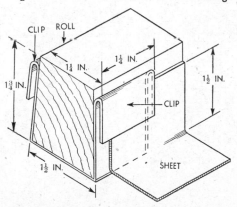

Fig. 37. Wood roll, as used for flat zinc roofs, showing clips in position.

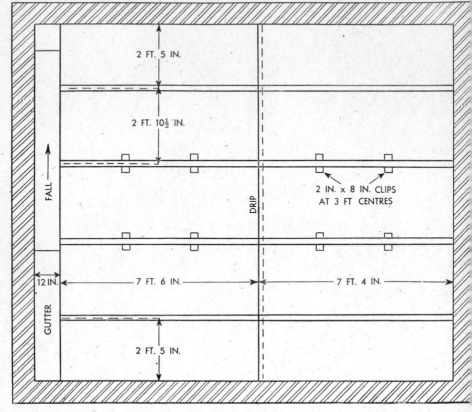

PLAN OF ZINC FLAT

Fig. 38. Zinc cannot be dressed round rolls as readily as lead. The edges are simply turned up 1½ in. against the side of the roll, leaving a slight clearance for expansion.

for an 8-ft. sheet, which allows 6 in. for forming the joint. The edge of the drip may be either beaded or welted, and these are termed beaded drips or welted drips. Welted drips can be 2 in. deep instead of 2½ in. required for beaded drips.

Forming the Bead

Where the sheets are joined at drips by means of a bead the upper edge of the sheet below the drip is turned up 3½ in. and is then turned out 1 in. in line with the top of the boarding. Next a ¾-in. bead is formed on the lower edge of the sheet above the drip, by means of a

beading rod over which it is dressed to shape.

The beaded sheet is then fitted over the turned-out end of the lower sheet and fixed (Fig. 40).

Welted Drips. To form a welted drip the edge of the sheet is stiffened by bending it back ½ in., and then further bending this formed edge back 1 in. This is then fitted over the upper end of the sheet below in the same manner as with beaded drips. The method is shown in Fig. 41.

On pitched roofs drips are not necessary and a welted joint can be used instead. The welt is formed by bending ack 1¼ in. of the top end of the sheet. The sheet is then secured to the roof boarding by clips 3 in. × 4 in. bent to shape (Fig. 42). The bottom end of the sheet above is then turned back and fitted into the fold on the lower sheet and the upper sheet pushed into position and the welt dressed down tight. It is the usual practice to allow two clips to the width of a sheet.

COPPER ROOFING

SHEET copper provides an excellent material for roof coverings. It is highly durable, being entirely unaffected by the atmosphere. After a few years' exposure to moist air it becomes covered with a film of insoluble basic sulphate and basic carbonate, commonly called *verdigris*, which forms the well-known green patina of copper and permanently protects the metal from any further action.

In addition to its durability it is extremely light, and copper of No. 24 gauge may be considered as equivalent to about 6 lb. lead for use in a similar position which gives a large saving of dead load in the roof.

Standard Copper Gauges

Its specific gravity is 8·9, therefore a cubic foot weighs 558 lb. and the thickness of a square foot weighing 16 oz. = $\frac{12}{558}$ = ·022 in.

The thickness of the sheets is specified by the Birmingham Wire Gauge and the Standard Method of Measurement states that the Imperial Standard Wire Gauge (I.S.W.G.) shall be given. There is, however, little or no difference between B.W.G. and S.W.G. within these particular number limits.

For covering flat roofs, lining gutters, and roof work in general, No. 23 or 24 gauge is mostly used but No. 22 is sometimes employed.

For hips, ridges, and dormer cleats No. 22 to No. 24 gauge would be used, and for step or covering flashings a lighter gauge, say No. 25 to 27.

The approximate thickness in inches and the weight per super foot is given in Table V below.

B.W.G. or S.W.G. gauge	Thickness of B.W.G.	Weight per super foot in ounces
22	·028	22
23	·025	19
24	·022	16
25	·020	14
26	·018	13
27	·016	11½
28	·0142	10

Table V. Copper-wire gauges, giving thickness in inches and weight per square foot.

The size of sheets used for roofing purposes are 5 ft. 3 in. × 2 ft. 8 in. and 4 ft. × 3 ft. 6 in., both having the same area of 14 sq. ft.

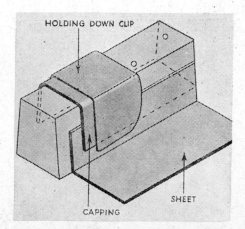

HOLDING DOWN CLIP

CAPPING

SHEET

Fig. 39. Method of capping and using holding-down clip on a flat zinc roof. This gives a watertight joint and allows for expansion.

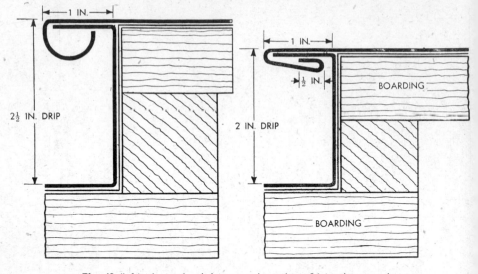

Fig. 40 (left). A zinc bead drip must be at least 2½ in. deep, as shown.
Fig. 41 (right). The minimum depth of a welted drip should be 2 in.

The *basic price* is the cost per pound for sheets not exceeding this area. Sheets larger than the basic area (about 8 ft. ×3 ft. of 16-oz. copper) will be found more economical, as they require less jointing and fewer cleats, and also less labour.

The preparation of the roof for copper is similar to that used for zinc or lead. The addition of a layer of paper, felt, or Ruberoid on the boarding is useful in preventing unevenness in the boarding, prevents condensation forming on the

Fig. 42. A welted joint can be used on a pitched zinc roof instead of a drip.

underside of the metal, and provides a certain amount of thermal and sound insulation.

Where the structural roof is formed with concrete the surface should be finished with a cement screed to give an even surface for the material.

The sheets are fixed to the concrete surface by means of dovetail wooden battens preferably placed across the slope. These battens should be spaced at distances of from 12 in. to 15 in. of the fixing cleats, where a standing seam joint is adopted; and at from 18 in. to 24 in. where wood rolls are used.

The minimum falls for flats should not be less than 2 in. in 10 ft. or 1 ft. in 60 ft. (Fig. 43).

ROLLS. The jointing of the edges of the sheets is made over wood rolls measuring 1¼ in. ×1¼ in., but conical-shaped roll 1¾ in. at the base and 1⅝ in. in height are found to be superior, and are now in general use. The allowance for rolls is 5 in., that is, 2 in. for the undercloak and 3 in. for the overcloak (Fig. 44).

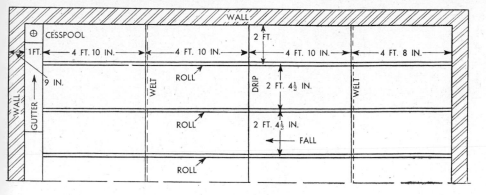

PLAN OF A COPPER FLAT

Fig. 43. The minimum fall for a flat roof should be not less than 2 in. in 10 ft. or 1 ft. in 60 ft.

If 5 ft. 3 in. ×2 ft. 8 in., the rolls will be spaced at 2 ft. 3 in. apart or 2 ft. 5 in. centre to centre. The bays adjacent to the wall will be about 3 in. less in width, the extra material being required to form the upstand. This adjustment will also be required for the top bay.

Clips 6 in. ×2 in. placed under the roll at 2-ft. 6-in. centres are folded in between the undercloak and overcloak, which is finished by a welted joint along one side of the roll. The ends of the rolls at the drips are finished with a saddle piece, which has its upper edges welted

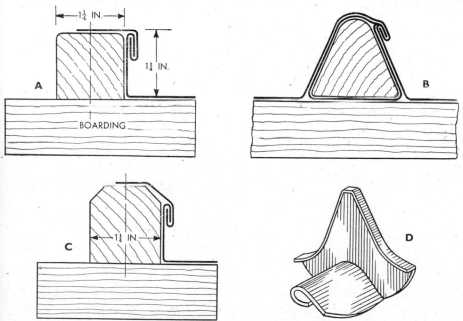

TYPES OF ROLLS

Fig. 44. A, square roll; B, Ewart's conical roll, showing concealed clip; C, chamfered roll; D, patent saddle piece. The allowance for rolls is 5 in. (2 in. for undercloak and 3 in. for overcloak).

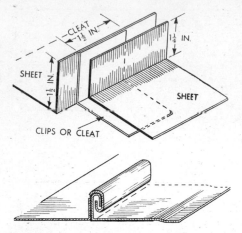

Fig. 45 (above). Preparation for forming a standing seam. **Fig. 46** (below). Completed standing seam. The standing seam is suitable for pitched roofs, where there is no traffic to cause damage.

to the edges of the overcloak of the upper flat.

The *standing seam* is generally used on pitched roofs only, because of its liability to damage where there is traffic across flat roofs, and the consequent injury to the joint would spoil its usefulness as an expansion joint (Figs. 45 and 46).

Drips are not generally necessary in copper roofing as in lead roofs, because copper, unlike lead, cannot creep, particularly where the fall allowed is a liberal one. But where the area covered is a large one it is an advantage to employ them at about 10 ft. apart as in Fig. 47. A welted gutter drip is shown in Fig. 49.

Where the pitch is not less than 8 degrees drips may be dispensed with, and the joints between the sheets both vertically and horizontally, formed by double welts which should be turned in the direction of the flow of water. *Double welts* (Fig. 48) or *double-cross welts* are preferable to *single welts* or *single lock seams*. To prevent the danger of water lying along the top of the drip owing to its thickness, a groove should be cut in the boarding the width and thickness of the welt, thus giving a level surface.

FLASHINGS. Cover flashings are made 6 in. wide, and are lapped 3 in. in every 3 ft. The lower edge is formed with a single welt turned backwards in order to stiffen it, as owing to its thinness it is apt to curl outwards. The clips to secure the bottom edge of the flashing are bent and then doubled twice in order to stiffen them (Fig. 50).

CONCRETE FLATS. Timber roofs covered with sheet metal have now been largely replaced by flat roofs formed of concrete and covered with materials that can be laid directly upon the concrete.

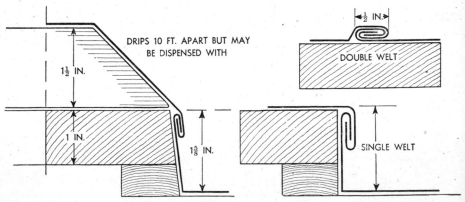

Fig. 47. Drips into a gutter; where the area covered is a large one, it is an advantage to place the drips about 10 ft. apart. **Fig. 48** (top right) is an example of a double welt.

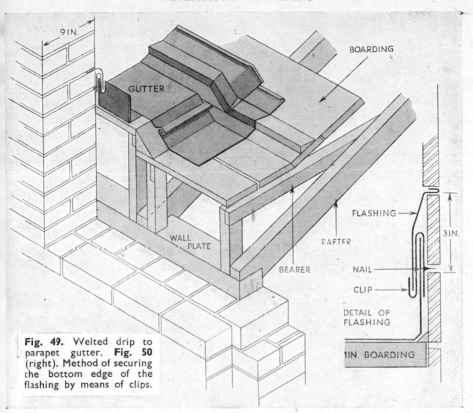

9 IN.

GUTTER

BOARDING

WALL PLATE

BEARER

RAFTER

FLASHING

3 IN.

NAIL

CLIP

DETAIL OF FLASHING

1 IN. BOARDING

Fig. 49. Welted drip to parapet gutter. **Fig. 50** (right). Method of securing the bottom edge of the flashing by means of clips.

The structural part of the roof can be constructed in reinforced concrete, steel and concrete, or a combination of hollow tiles and reinforced concrete. The proportions of the concrete should not be weaker than 4 : 2 : 1. The thickness of the concrete and the amount of reinforcement will depend upon the span of the roof, the calculations being similar to those used in reinforced concrete floor slabs.

Where the roof area is large it is usual to divide it up into a number of bays by the introduction of beams to lessen the span of the slab. These beams are either of steel or reinforced concrete.

Careful construction is required to render the roof watertight and the surface should be finished with an impervious material. When the concrete is in position it should be kept damp for several days so as to prevent cracking from exposure to the heat of the sun; and in order to counteract expansion compressible linings should be inserted around the walls.

Fall for Flat Roofs

Flat roofs differ from floors in that they are given a fall not less than 2 in. in 10 ft. to throw off any water, which further assists in making the roof more watertight. The fall is obtained by covering the structural floor with coke breeze, pumice or foamed slag to an even surface, and finishing the surface with a cement and sand screed, which can be rendered waterproof with waterproofing compounds, "composite" built-up roofings, or mastic asphalt.

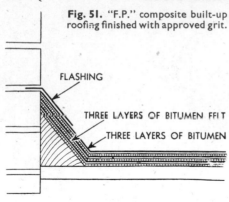

Fig. 51. "F.P." composite built-up roofing finished with approved grit.

FLASHING

THREE LAYERS OF BITUMEN FELT

THREE LAYERS OF BITUMEN

COMPOSITE FLEXIBLE BUILT-UP ROOF-ING. This forms the most reliable and durable roofing or waterproof covering to any kind of building or structure.

Where not required to take heavy or constant traffic it forms the finished roofing, or if so required it forms an imperishable waterproof base to other roof pavings. It is laid in separate layers, i.e., 1-ply one layer, 2-ply two layers, etc., of bitumen roofing felt. Each layer is separately laid, the first layer, if on boarding, being nailed down through the laps; if on concrete it is bedded down with hot bitumen mastic, and the following layers separately laid, each breaking joint and bedded down to the underneath layer with hot bitumen mastic.

The surface is coated with hot bitumen mastic and, if it is to form the finishing roofing, fine, dry, clean

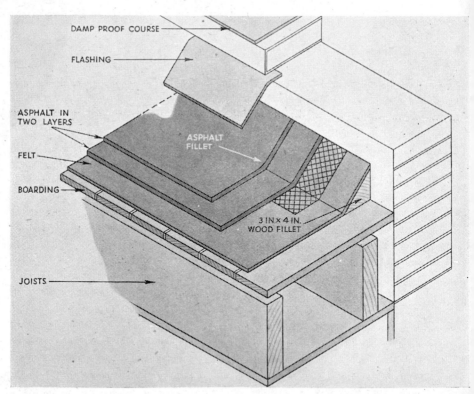

DAMP PROOF COURSE

FLASHING

ASPHALT IN TWO LAYERS

ASPHALT FILLET

FELT

BOARDING

3 IN. × 4 IN. WOOD FILLET

JOISTS

FINISH OF ASPHALT TO WALLS

Fig. 52. In asphalt roofing the falls must be provided for in the base before the asphalt is applied. An underlayer of waterproof building paper or asphaltic felt prevents dampness from coming through.

Bridport or other approved grit embedded into the face; or the surface double coated with hot bitumen mastic and $\frac{3}{8}$-in. gauge dry, clean, pebble shingle embedded into the bitumen coating whilst hot. This gives $\frac{1}{2}$-in. protective layer over the bituminous roofing layers.

An excellent form of roofing of this description is known as "F.P." composite built-up roofing (1-, 2- or 3-ply), with finished Bridport or other approved grit embedded; also "F.P." (1-, 2- or 3-ply) pebbled flexible roofing.

The roof illustrated in Fig. 51 is composed of three distinct and separate layers of bitumen roofing felt, each laid breaking joint and thoroughly bedded down to under layer with boiling bitumen of best quality.

At the junction between the wall and the roof a $4\frac{1}{2}$-in. × 3-in. angle fillet is fixed, and the roofing layers turned up and the top edge finished with a flashing of lead, copper or zinc. A damp-proof course should be inserted three courses above the flat in all parapet walls or the bituminous roofing can be carried over the angle fillet and continued through the wall to form damp-proof course.

ASPHALT ROOFING. No naturally impregnated rock has sufficient bitumen content to produce a mastic asphalt for roof work, and further bitumen has to be added when cooking down the rock to make it mastic. It is of the utmost importance that this added bitumen should also be a natural material, and refined Trinidad Lake bitumen is generally used, having proved the most satisfactory over a number of years.

Providing the Falls

The falls required for an asphalt roof must be provided for in the base, whether of wood or concrete, because it is practically impossible to correct a defective fall when applying the asphalt. All concrete should be screeded over

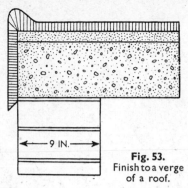

Fig. 53.
Finish to a verge of a roof.

LEAD APRON

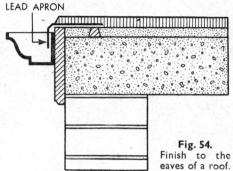

Fig. 54.
Finish to the eaves of a roof.

with cement and sand, and finished with a smooth surface to receive the covering.

The asphalt should be laid in a thickness of not less than $\frac{3}{4}$ in.; and in two layers breaking joint. An underlayer of waterproof building paper or asphaltic felt prevents dampness in the concrete coming through. Felt or waterproof paper must be placed between the wood and asphalt where a wood base is provided (Fig. 52).

Fig. 53 shows the finish to a verge, and Fig. 54 the finish to the eaves of a roof.

At the junction of the wall and roof, on a timber constructed roof, the proper finish is to provide a 4-in. × 3-in. wood fillet fixed in the angle, and the asphalt carried over the fillet together with the felt. A narrow strip of expanded metal is placed across the angle to form a key and prevent the asphalt from sagging. A lead or copper flashing is fixed to a brick joint and covers the upper edge of the

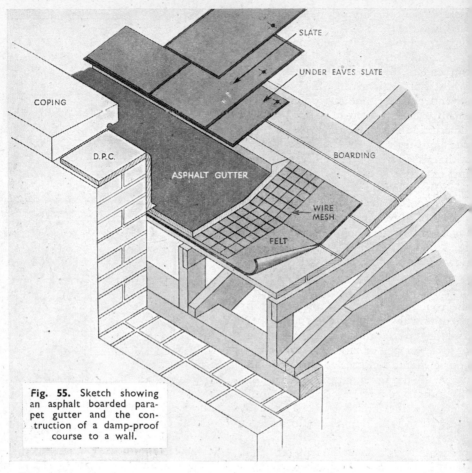

Fig. 55. Sketch showing an asphalt boarded parapet gutter and the contruction of a damp-proof course to a wall.

skirting. This allows free movement and the subsequent shrinkage in the timber. A separate damp-proof course should be built in the wall three courses above the flat as in Fig. 52. Fig. 55 shows an asphalt boarded parapet gutter.

Asphalt to all pitched roofs over 10 degrees should have wire netting or light expanded metal to form a key for the asphalt.

These roofs can be insulated by placing insulated boards on a layer of bitumen felt. The boarding is then covered with a layer of inodorous or asphaltic felt and the asphalt subsequently laid over in order to complete the roof.

TILES. Roofing tiles are made from clay or concrete. Clay tiles because of their thinness require careful selection of the material and great skill in their manufacture.

Hand-made tiles are preferable to machine-made tiles because they are more uniform and less liable to lamination, and when properly selected will be found to give long service. Many tiled roofs fail owing to the corrosion of the nails or the decay in the battens.

The bedding of tiles is to be avoided, as the mortar holds the water and the tiles are rarely dry, and among other risks they are liable to be broken during frost. The pitch at the eaves must not be made too flat where sprockets are introduced, because of the great amount of water which causes moisture on the surface, giving trouble at a later period. Lap and gauge are also very important.

The maximum gauge between nails should be 4 in., giving a lap of $2\frac{1}{2}$ in. with $10\frac{1}{2}$-in. tiles. Sometimes $3\frac{3}{4}$-in. or even $3\frac{1}{2}$-in. gauges are used, which are better, giving more protection against driving rain and snow. A good rule is "the flatter the pitch the greater the lap."

A good camber to the tiles is desirable. Approximately $\frac{1}{4}$-in. camber or housing in the length of the tile is required.

PREPARATION OF TILING. Tiles may be fixed to battens only; battens and paper or felt, counter battens and battens.

Close-boarding

The best method of preparing the roof is to close-board it and lay over it a good non-conducting felt; the nibs are knocked off the tiles, which are then nailed on the top of the felt. This method is usually adopted where a very cold and damp climate obtains. Tiles without nibs are also obtainable.

For good-class jobs the roof is close-boarded and sarked as before; vertical battens or counter-battens, size 2 in. $\times$ 1 in., or 2 in. $\times \frac{3}{4}$ in., are nailed through the felt and boards over the centre line of rafters. The tile battens are fixed across these and the tiles hung by their nibs on the laths. This gives a warm roof in the winter and a cool roof in summer, owing to the insulation given between the tiles and boarding.

PLAIN TILES. Plain tiles measure $10\frac{1}{2}$ in. $\times 6\frac{1}{2}$ in. $\times \frac{1}{2}$ in. thick and 11 in. $\times 7$ in. $\times \frac{3}{8}$ in., $\frac{1}{2}$ in. or $\frac{5}{8}$ in., the former size being the one in general use. Two nibs are formed on the underside at the top for hanging to the battens. Two nail holes are provided in each tile.

DEFINITIONS. The terms employed in tiling are as follows: The underside of the tile when laid is called the *bed*, and the upper side the *back*. The lower edge is called the *tail* and the upper edges the *head* (Fig. 56).

The *margin* is the name given to the area of the tile exposed to view when laid on the roof. The gauge is the distance from nail hole to nail hole, which is the same length as the margin, and is obtained by deducting the lap from the length of the tile and dividing by two. This rule may be stated thus:—

$$\text{Gauge} = \frac{\text{length of tile } minus \text{ lap}}{2}$$

The gauge generally adopted is 4 in. The lap is the amount by which one tile covers the next but one below it.

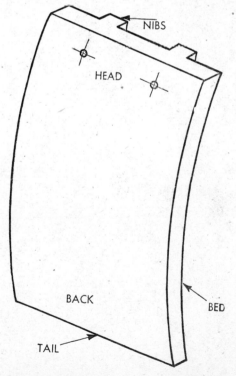

Fig. 56. Sketch of tile, showing terms employed. Tiles are slightly curved (shown exaggerated) so that they will bed to a close joint.

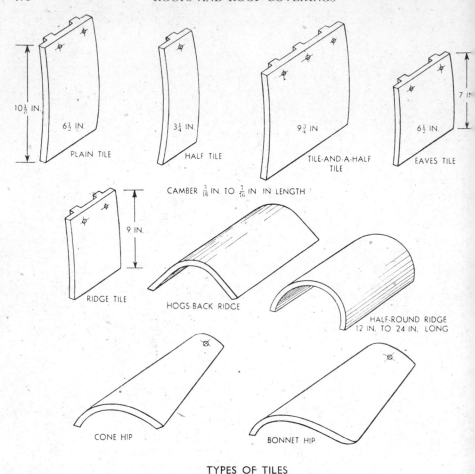

PLAIN TILE

HALF TILE

TILE-AND-A-HALF TILE

EAVES TILE

CAMBER $\frac{3}{16}$ IN. TO $\frac{7}{16}$ IN IN LENGTH

RIDGE TILE

HOGS-BACK RIDGE

HALF-ROUND RIDGE 12 IN. TO 24 IN. LONG

CONE HIP

BONNET HIP

TYPES OF TILES

Fig. 57. The diagram gives examples of plain tiles, hip tiles and ridge tiles, which are made i sizes to suit various purposes. Ridge tiles vary in length from 12 in. to 24 in.

EAVES AND RIDGE TILES. To avoid cutting ordinary tiles special tiles are made for the under-eaves and under-ridge. The under-eaves tile is made 7 in. long (Figs. 57 and 63) and the under-ridge tile 9 in. long, the width being the same as ordinary tiles.

To obtain bond in the course, a *half-tile*, i.e., $3\frac{1}{4}$ in. wide, or a *tile-and-a-half tile* measuring $9\frac{3}{4}$ in. wide, is introduced at the verge or the start of each alternate course. The tile-and-a-half tile is preferable because a better fixing is obtained.

RIDGES. Various types of tiles are used for particular purposes. Of these th ridge tiles are those which span the ridg and are known as half-round, hog's back, and angular, sufficiently wide to give the necessary lap to the tiles on each slope. They are supplied in varying lengths from 12 in. to 24 in. (Fig. 57)

Where the ridge of an adjacent roo intersects the main roof at a point below the ridge of the main roof, the junction should be formed with a lead saddle piece dressed over the ridge of the

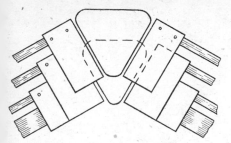

Fig. 58. Valley formed with valley tiles.

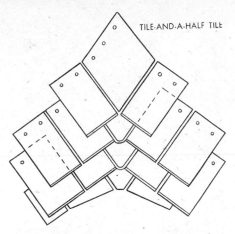

TILE-AND-A-HALF TILE

Fig. 60. Laced valley, in which the tiles when laid have a pronounced upward sweep.

djacent roof and to the slope of the main roof. Special three-way tiles are made to fit the ridge intersections when they are at the same level.

HIP AND VALLEY TILES are made a special shape to fit the hips or valleys of a tiled roof. Their purpose is to complete the tiling at the hips and valleys respectively. Every care should be taken that the pitch of the valley does not become too flat. A roof pitch of, say, 40 degrees gives a valley pitch of 31 degrees. The valley tile (Fig. 58) is perhaps the most serviceable form for use with plain tiling. It is made angular or rounded and should be used in preference to open or secret gutters.

The mitred valley is not so much used in modern work and the open valley only occasionally (Fig. 59). The mitred valley is made watertight by the use of soakers which are placed across the angle and lapped.

Secret gutters are not advisable as they are liable to become choked with dirt, and are difficult to clean.

Laced and swept valleys are more difficult to make watertight and are more costly in labour and material, as a number of tiles must be cut. They have a good appearance when laid.

In a laced valley a tile-and-a-half tile is placed across the valley with its point lower than the tiles in the same course. A wide board is laid along the valley in order to flatten the angle and the battens finished against it. These tiles when laid have a pronounced upward sweep, as shown in Fig. 60.

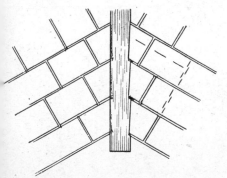

Fig. 59. Open valley gutter with metal sole.

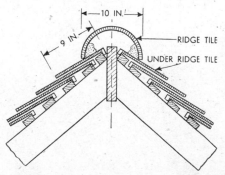

10 IN.

9 IN.

RIDGE TILE

UNDER RIDGE TILE

Fig. 61. Section showing under-ridge tiles.

PANTILE ROOFING

A charming effect is produced by the use of pantiles in suitable surroundings. In the above pictur the effect is heightened by the curve of the wall, the gateway on the right and the use of harmonizin ridge and hip tiles. Pantile roofing is becoming increasingly popular in modern houses.

HIP TILES. Hips may be covered with *half-round, cone, angular* or *bonnet* tiles as in Fig. 57.

Half-round ridge may be used with either hand-made or machine-made tiles, but is out of scale on the hips of small roofs. Each tile must be nailed at the head and it is advisable to point up the joints after placing, in addition to bedding along their lower edges (Fig. 61). The bonnet hip tiles are usually found in good-class hand-made tile work, and make a pleasing finish.

Construction of Verges

VERGES. Verges are generally given a projection over the wall of about 2 in. One or two courses of tiles are bedded on the wall as an undercloak to form a tilt along the edge, which helps to prevent water from dripping over the edge of the verge. Where vertical tiling occurs under a verge the undercloak gives a neat finish between the wall and the roof tiling. In order to obtain a fixing for the end tile a piece is cut off the side of the last two tiles. This leaves a nail hole in each tile

and provides a neat finish to the verge When the vertical tiling is finished i this way it is generally known as th Winchester cut.

NAILS AND NAILING. The various kind of nails used for slating and tiling are o zinc composition and copper.

Galvanized nails are only used whe low cost is the prime consideration. Zin nails are popular for ordinary work, bu are liable to perish in sea air.

Copper nails are employed in im portant buildings, but composition nail made from an alloy of copper, zinc an tin are harder and more readily driven

Copper, composition, and zinc nail should be avoided in gas, chemical, an other such works as they deteriorat rapidly, and chrome-iron nails or lea pegs should be used to fasten the slate to which can, be bent the steel angles

The heads should be kept as thin a possible, so that they do not projec above the surface of the slate as to inter fere with the bedding of the slate above

The size and weight of nails is gov erned by the size and thickness of th ates. The length may be obtained by king twice the thickness of the slate and dding 1 in. Nails a little longer than is are necessary for the first and second urses at the eaves.

NUMBER OF TILES. Adopting a 4-in. auge the number required to cover a uare, i.e., 100 sup. ft., is:—

$$\frac{\text{area of square}}{\text{width of tile or slate} \times \text{gauge}}$$

aking a $10\frac{1}{2}$ in. $\times 6\frac{1}{2}$ in. tile laid to a -in. lap the number required will be $\frac{) \times 144}{5 \times 4} = \frac{14400}{26} = 554$ tiles. The usual lowance for waste is 5 per cent, which ves 582 as the total number of tiles quired.

The number of slates per square is und in a similar manner.

Another class of tile is larger in dimen-

sions, much thicker and generally of some curve, or curves, in section.

Among these are the pantile, Roman (double and single), Italian and Spanish These tiles are laid on the roof in such a way that only their edges overlap and a single layer only is necessary to cover the roof; they are therefore generally known as *single-lap tiles* (Fig. 62).

Sizes of Pantiles

PANTILES are one of the oldest of roof tiles, and measure about $13\frac{1}{2}$ in. or 14 in. long and 9 in. to 11 in. wide, and curved in section to a flat ogee curve. One special type is known as the "Pinion" pantile measuring 15 in. $\times$ 11 in., moulded with two lugs on the under side, which makes them more water-tight. Waterproof paper or under

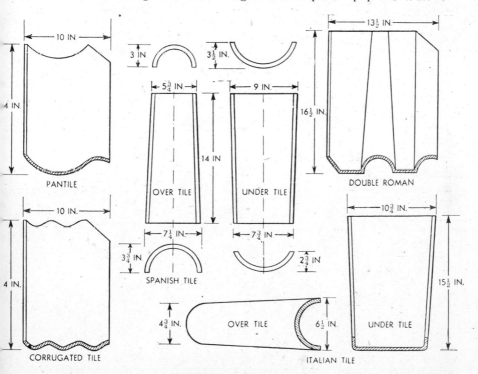

SINGLE-LAP TILES

g. 62. Single-lap tiles are longer and thicker than the ordinary tile, and are usually curved in section. They include pantiles, and Roman, Italian and Spanish tiles.

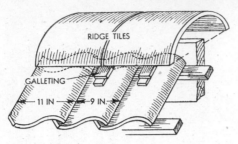

Fig. 63. Pantiles finishing against a ridge. A more level bedding is given by filling in with pieces of waste tiles cut to fit.

felting is advisable to ensure against the elements. To allow proper bedding the opposite corners diagonally are splayed.

It is usual to bed one course of plain tiles at the eaves below the first course of pantiles as a precaution against wind pressure. The hollows in the tiles at the ridge are often filled in with pieces of waste tiles cut to fit. This gives a more level bedding for the ridge tiles (Fig. 63).

Pantiles are best suited to simple roofs with gables, but valleys can be formed without much difficulty. A double-roll pantile is provided to finish the left-hand edge. Verges in single-lap tiling have a course of plain tiles as an undercloak.

SINGLE AND DOUBLE ROMAN TILES measure 15 in. × 10 in. and $16\frac{1}{2}$ in. × $13\frac{1}{2}$ in. respectively, and differ in that one has a single and the other a double roll. The modern type is an interlocking tile with a broken joint, but arranged in such a way that the joint appears straigh The Reynardo is a double Roman ti with a larger roll made in colours (Fi 62). These tiles can be fixed by th secure system for extra security. Th pitch for these tiles is 35 degrees. For less pitch the roof should be boarde and felted.

ITALIAN TILES have a flat under-ti tapered on plan with the edge turne up. It measures $9\frac{1}{4}$ in. at the narrow er and $10\frac{1}{4}$ in. at the wide end, and is 1 in. long. The over-tile is half-round ar tapers from $4\frac{3}{4}$ in. to $6\frac{1}{2}$ in., allowing t tile in the next course to fit closely wi a lap of 3 in. The roof preparatic requires vertical battens 1 in. × 2 i placed between the under-tiles to whi the over-tiles are fixed with one n (Fig. 62).

SPANISH TILES are somewhat simil to the last named, but in this case t lower tiles are half-round in sectio instead of being flat. They are ve effective, but require an additio amount of ground work which mak them more costly (Figs. 62 and 64).

Technical information in connectic with tiles is given below in Table V

Slates and Slating

Slates come from North Wales, Wes morland, Cumberland, Lancashire ar South Wales. The Welsh slates are blu purple or greenish grey, and dressed regular sizes and as thin as possible. T

Type of tile	Size in inches	Size of horizontal battens in inches	Size of vertical battens	Covering capacity per square	Weight per square cwt.
				No.	
Pantile.	$13\frac{1}{2} \times 9\frac{1}{4}$	$1\frac{1}{2} \times \frac{3}{4}$	—	165	$6\frac{1}{4}$
Double Roman . . .	$16\frac{1}{2} \times 13\frac{1}{2}$	$1\frac{1}{2} \times \frac{3}{4}$	—	85	6
Double "Reynardo" . .	$16\frac{1}{2} \times 13\frac{1}{2}$	2×2	—	85	6
Italian	$15\frac{1}{2}$ long	1×2	$\frac{7}{8} \times 3$	100	8
Spanish	14 long	boarding	2×4	500	—
Spanish "Lido" . . .	—	—	—	200	—

Table VI. Sizes and various particulars of pantiles and other single-lap tiles.

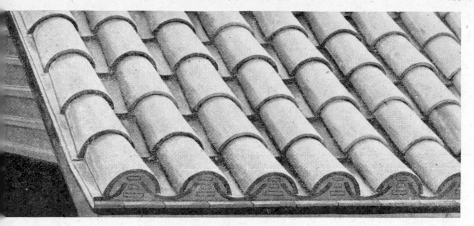

SPANISH TILES

Fig. 64. Spanish tiles are somewhat similar to Italian tiles, but the lower tiles are half-round in section instead of flat. The additional ground work required makes Spanish tiles somewhat more costly than Italian tiles. The method used for the end fillings should be noted.

lates from Westmorland have a granular cleavage, and are generally dressed to random sizes, thicker and stouter than Welsh slates, in sea green or dark blue.

Slates from Cumberland and South Wales are intermediate in thickness and texture between Welsh slates and Westmorland slates, dressed to random sizes and in colour grey, grey-green and rustic red. Sized slates are produced, but randoms and rustics are obtainable. Rustics are slates that have taken on a stained appearance. Random sizes range from 24 in. × 14 in. down to 13 in. × 9 in.

Welsh slates are classified as best, seconds, thirds or strongs, extra strongs, and their thickness varies from $\frac{1}{6}$ in. to $\frac{2}{3}$ in. Randoms vary from $\frac{1}{4}$ in. to $\frac{1}{2}$ in.

Sizes of Slates

The sizes range from 26 in. × 16 in. down to 10 in. × 6 in.; the most common sizes in use range from 24 in. down to 16 in. The system of naming slates is now little used and as a rule sizes only are given.

The terms best, seconds, and thirds simply denote a difference in the thickness of the slate and have nothing at all to do with the durability of the slates.

TESTS. A good slate is generally one which, besides being hard and tough, emits a sharp metallic ring when struck with the knuckles. A good slate should also be easily holed, should not split under the slater's zax, and should not absorb more than 2 per cent of its weight in water.

Head-nailed and Centre-nailed

Slates can either be *head-nailed* or *centre-nailed*; the latter method is usually adopted as being a better protection against strong winds.

The holes are punched or drilled at a distance from the tail to allow the nail to clear the top of the slate in the course below. This distance will be, measured from the tail, equal to the gauge plus the lap plus $\frac{1}{4}$ in. For 24-in. slates laid to a 4-in. lap this will be: 10 in. + 4 in. + $\frac{1}{4}$ in. = $14\frac{1}{4}$ in.

Holes are placed $1\frac{1}{4}$ in. or $1\frac{1}{2}$ in. from the long side of the slate.

Machine holing is recommended as this gives a much cleaner result and also forms a standard size hole from the edge of the slate. Peggies (as small randoms are generally called) may be fixed by means of single nails at the head.

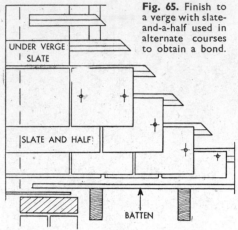

Fig. 65. Finish to a verge with slate-and-a-half used in alternate courses to obtain a bond.

UNDER VERGE SLATE

SLATE AND HALF

BATTEN

The rules given for slating are:—

The steeper the pitch the smaller the slate; as the pitch increases more weight is thrown on the nails, therefore by using a smaller slate the weight is reduced.

Larger slates of good width should be used on roofs of flat pitch. Roofs of less pitch than 30 degrees should have slates not less than 12 in. wide, and this gives less risk of spreading water. Watertightness does not depend on the length of the slate, but on the proportion of the width to the length and on the lap given.

Lap depends on the construction of the building and pitch of the roof, the site of the building, and the custom of the district. In most parts of the country a 3-in. lap is common; but the lap should be varied to suit the pitch. The minimum values are given in the following Table as a guide for different roof pitches.

Pitch of roof at eaves	Normal site
21° 50′ ($\frac{1}{6}$)	4$\frac{1}{2}$-in. lap
26° 34′ ($\frac{1}{4}$)	4-in. lap
30°	3$\frac{1}{2}$-in. lap
37$\frac{1}{2}$°	3-in. lap
45° ($\frac{1}{2}$)	2$\frac{3}{4}$-in. lap
60°	2$\frac{1}{4}$-in. lap

Table VII. Minimum roof pitches for slates

DOUBLE EAVES COURSE. The eaves require a doubling course, the lower slate of which is termed the *under-eaves slate*. This course is laid with the smooth side up, and in the case of centre-nailed slates is head-nailed.

A similar double course is laid at the ridge and is termed the *double-ridge course*. A tilting fillet is required in both these cases in order that the slates at these points may lie closer.

VERGES should have a slate undercloak bedded solidly on the wall in cement mortar and the outer edge pointed. Slate-and-a-half slate should be used in alternate courses to obtain bond, and a slight tilt given to the edge to prevent water running over the face of the gable wall (Fig. 65). A definite tilt should be arranged against all vertical surfaces.

HIPS. There are various methods of dealing with these. They may be finished with a hip tile, close mitred with secret gutter, or close mitred with soakers underneath placed across the angle. Close-mitred hips are suitable where Westmorland slates are used and have a good appearance (Fig. 66). There is no difficulty in this form of hip where the pitch is 45 degrees or more.

But if the pitch is less than 45 degrees or slates over 8 in. wide are used, there is sometimes difficulty in obtaining slates wide enough to cut the mitre slates, since stock sizes run to 12 in. wide only. Secret gutters under the hip are not desirable as they become sooner or later a source of trouble. The weight of lead used in this position is 4 lb. per sq. ft.

RIDGES are somewhat similar in construction to hips. The forms of tiles used are *half-round* and a *hog's-back*. These tiles are bedded at the joints only and pointed in cement. Ridges for slates are obtainable formed with two wings and a roll. Lead is also used for ridge coverings. A wooden roll is first placed in position

nd the lead dressed over it and carried
down each slope about 6 in. The lead is
fixed in lengths of 7 ft. and lapped
jointed at the ends. Pieces of lead 2 in.
wide and 20 in. girth called *tacks* are
placed at 3 ft. 6 in. centres arranged so
that one comes under each lap (Fig. 67).

VALLEYS may be formed as open or
close-mitred in a similar manner to hips.

Open valleys should be at least 8 in.
wide and slightly wider towards the
eaves. The lead covering the valley is
turned over a tilting fillet to a height of
2 in. under the slates on each side.

RANDOM SLATING, as the term denotes,
is slating carried out with slates of
random sizes varying from 26 in. down
to 9 in. and in proportionate widths.

They are laid in graduated courses,
commencing at the eaves with the
largest and the thickest, and working
upwards on the roof with the shorter
lengths and thinner slates to the ridges,
where the smallest sizes are used.

OPEN SLATING. For sheds and other
outbuildings where strict economy is
desired *open* or *spaced* slating is employed.

The slates are laid from 2 in. to
4 in. apart. This method effects a saving
in slates, increases ventilation, and
although rainproof it does not resist
driving snow.

To prevent rain and snow entering
between vertical surfaces and the roof,
various methods are used in order to
render the junction weatherproof. The

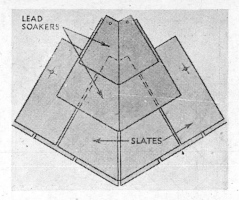

Fig. 66. Close-mitred hips, with soakers underneath placed across the angle, are suitable for
use with Westmorland slates, where the pitch
of the roof is 45 degrees or more

best method is to insert pieces of lead
termed *soakers* between the courses of
slates and to turn them up against the
wall. The length of these soakers will
vary according to the length of the slate
used and will be equal to the gauge plus
the lap plus 1 in. The edge is turned up
$2\frac{1}{4}$ in. and is covered with a flashing,
the upper edge of which is turned into
the joints of the brickwork.

Steel roofs usually have timber ground
work to which the slates are fixed. Steel
angles may, however, be used alone and
spaced to suit the gauge of the slates. In
this case large slates will be found more
economical. They are fixed with two
copper pegs which pass through two
slates and then bend round the angle.

Where roofs are built over gas or

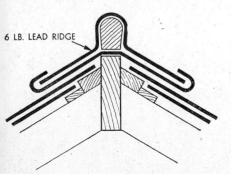

6 LB. LEAD RIDGE

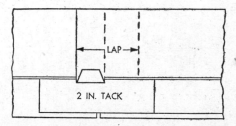

LAP

2 IN. TACK

Fig. 67. A ridge finished with a lead roll, showing
how the lead tacks are placed

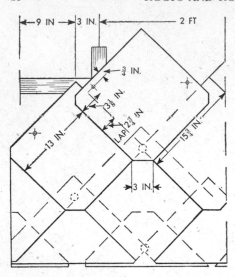

Fig. 68. Honeycomb-pattern asbestos cement slates, showing method of fixing.

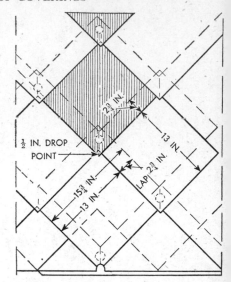

Fig. 69. Method of arranging diagonal-pattern asbestos cement slates.

chemical works, chrome-iron nails or lead pegs are used to fasten the slates.

ASBESTOS CEMENT SLATES OR TILES are made in various patterns, which are termed honeycomb, diagonal, and straight. The latter are similar to ordinary slates and laid in the same way, but with a disk rivet at the tail.

The standard size for the honeycomb and diagonal patterns are $15\frac{3}{4}$ in. $\times 15\frac{3}{4}$ in. $\times \frac{3}{16}$ in. thick (Figs. 68 and 69).

In the honeycomb method the tiles are cut at their lower part to a 3-in. edge where they meet the slates in the centre below. The diagonal method is considered to give a more watertight roof. The minimum lap for the various pitches is given below:—

Pitch of roof	Minimum lap
25°	4-in. lap
30°	$3\frac{1}{2}$-in. lap
35°	3-in. lap
40°	$2\frac{3}{4}$-in. lap

Table VIII. Minimum lap for various pitches for honeycomb tiles.

CONCRETE TILES are now extensively used for roof coverings. The material used in making the tiles requires careful selection owing to their thinness and liability to warp.

ASBESTOS CEMENT SHEETS are obtainable in various types, in lengths from 3 ft to 10 ft. rising in 6-in. increments and in the widths given in Table IX.

The side lap varies according to the type of sheet used, but the end lap should not be less than 6 in. with a slight increase allowed for low-pitched roofs (Fig. 70).

The sheets can be fixed to timber or steel purlins spaced at a distance up to 4 ft. 6 in. The fixing to wooden purlins is by means of 3 in. or $4\frac{1}{2}$ in. $\times \frac{1}{4}$ in. or $\frac{5}{16}$ in. galvanized screws, with cupped washers, and to steel purlins by means of hook bolts with cupped washers or clips. One screw or bolt should be provided at each side lap where crossing the purlin, the holes being carefully drilled. The diameter of the hole should be $\frac{1}{8}$ in. bigger than the diameter of the bolt. This allows for any movement due to

Type	Width		Width when laid		Thickness	Sidelap	Corrugations	Pitch	Depth
	ft.	in.	ft.	in.	ins.	ins.	No.		
1	3	8	3	4	$\frac{1}{4}$	4	4	$13\frac{1}{2}$	2
2	3	$5\frac{1}{2}$	3	$3\frac{1}{2}$	$\frac{1}{4}$ to $\frac{9}{32}$	2	$7\frac{1}{2}$	$5\frac{3}{4}$	$2\frac{1}{8}$
3	4	$5\frac{1}{4}$	4	0	$\frac{1}{4}$	$5\frac{1}{4}$	4	16	$4\frac{1}{2}$
4	2	6	2	0	$\frac{1}{4}$	4	10	$2\frac{7}{8}$	$2\frac{7}{8}$

Table IX. Widths and other particulars of various types of asbestos cement sheets.

xpansion or contraction in the steel members or timber purlins. Special tiles are made for the ridges and hips.

Asbestos cement sheets form an economical and satisfactory covering for roofs of cinemas and factories, and have largely taken the place of corrugated steel sheets.

GALVANIZED-STEEL SHEETS are manufactured in sizes varying from 5 ft. up to 2 ft. rising by increments of 1 ft.

The gauges used for roofing range from No. 16 to No. 24 B.W.G. according to the class of work.

The corrugations vary in width from in. to 5 in., but sheets having eight -in. corrugations are most commonly used.

The fixing is similar to that employed for asbestos corrugated sheets. Additional fixing is obtained by the use of -in. diameter rivets or bolts, so that the sheets are fastened at every third or fourth corrugation horizontally, and from about 2 ft. along the side of the sheet.

These fixings are made with washers through the top of the corrugations. The washers used with the bolts are diamond or limpet type. Galvanized clips take the place of hook bolts and are made from 1 in. $\times$ $\frac{3}{16}$ in. The purlins are spaced at intervals of from 3 ft. up to 6 ft. according to the gauge of the sheets.

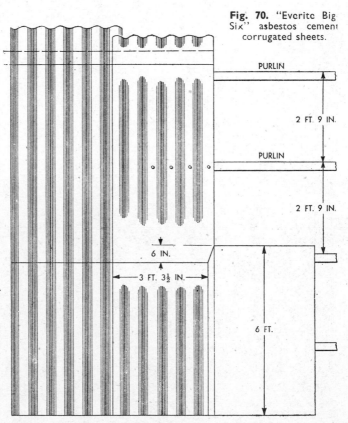

Fig. 70. "Everite Big Six" asbestos cement corrugated sheets.

PURLIN

2 FT. 9 IN.

PURLIN

2 FT. 9 IN.

6 IN.

3 FT. 3½ IN.

6 FT.

FIRST STAGE IN THE CONSTRUCTION OF GROUND FLOORS

Wall plates are seen placed in position on the walls ready for the floor joists. The materials for the next stages of construction are assembled in the background ready for use.

CONSTRUCTION OF GROUND FLOORS: SECOND STAGE

The floor joists are now in position. Note the honeycombing in the sleeper walls to allow for air circulation. The above two illustrations are typical examples of the combination of joinery and brickwork in building construction.

CHAPTER 5

JOINERY

arious types of doors. Setting out. Joints. Mouldings. Jamb lining. Panelling. lywood for panels. Window frames and sashes. Casement windows. Pivoted shes. Steel frames. Skirtings and architraves. Fixing joinery. Stairs and balusters. Geometrical stairs. Handrails.

THE simplest type of door is the *ledged and braced* type, illustrated in Fig. 1. Vertical boards, or *ttens*, ¾-in. to 1-in. thickness, are ngued and grooved together and iiled to horizontal *ledges* as shown. The iils should be clinched, and screws are etter em-
oyed at the ids of the dges. Weath-
ing in the rm of a bevel chamfer is pplied to the pper edges of e ledges.
A similar iamfer is orked on one lge of the races, and the short ioulder be-
veen ledge id brace bi-
cts the angle etween these embers, a itisfactory nish is ob-
iined. The races must have their lower ends near ie hanging side, thus preventing the por dropping and assuming the outline hich is shown dotted in the diagram.

This type of door is employed mainly for outbuildings and in positions where appearance is of little consequence.

FRAMED, LEDGED AND BRACED DOOR. A door very superior to that just des-
cribed is given in Fig. 2. A frame of stiles and top rail, $4\frac{1}{4}$ in. $\times 1\frac{7}{8}$ in., and middle and bottom rails $8\frac{3}{4}$ in. $\times$ 1 in. is formed. Stiles and top rail are grooved so as to take the tongue on the match-
boarding.

A section through the stile and matchboard-
ing is given in Fig. 3, and Fig. 4 is an isometric view of the upper end of a stile. The tenons on the middle and bottom rails are bare-
faced, as seen in Fig. 5. This also shows the arrangement at the lower end of a brace, with the shoulder forming a mitre between the two chamfers.
If the door is to be hung in an exposed

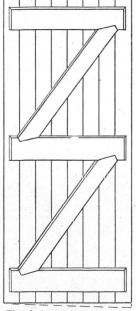

Fig. I. Ledged and braced, the simplest type of door, as used for outbuildings.

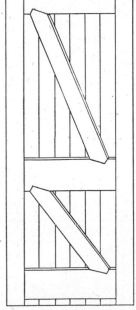

Fig. 2. Framed, ledged and braced door; superior to that shown in Fig. I.

position, the sur-
faces of tenons and
mortises should be
painted and not
glued. All tongues
and grooves, and
the backs of the
middle and bottom
rails should also be
painted prior to
assembly.

It is also import-
ant to fit the match-
boarding so that room for expansion is
provided. If fitted tightly between the
stiles, any swelling may cause the boarding to buckle away from the lower rails
to which it is nailed.

FOUR-PANELLED DOOR. Fig. 6 is an
elevation of the very familiar four-
panelled type. The standard size is
6 ft. 6 in. × 2 ft. 6 in., and generally if the
width is in-
creased by an
amount the
height is add-
ed to by the
same dimen-
sion. Thick-
ness varies up
to $1\frac{7}{8}$ in., but
the widths of
the members
are usually:
stiles, top rail
and muntins,
$4\frac{1}{4}$ in.; bottom
and middle
rails, $8\frac{3}{4}$ in.

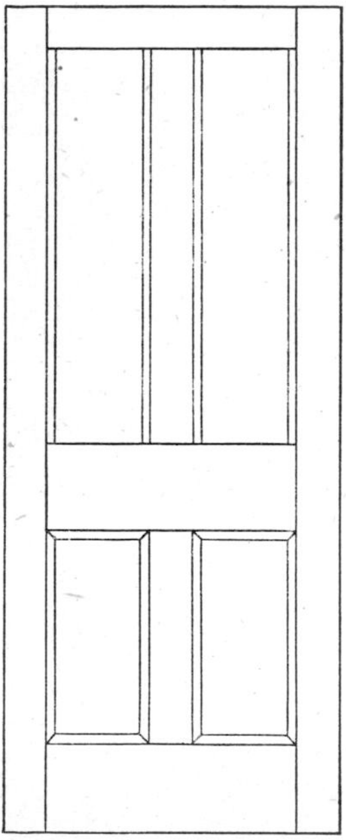

The height
of the top edge
of the middle
rail is about 3
ft. 2 in., which
provides a
comfortable
height for lock
and handle.

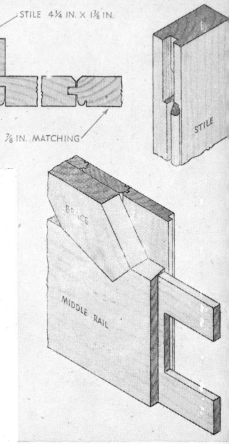

Fig. 3 (top left). Section through the stile and
matchboarding of the door shown in Fig. 2.
Fig. 4 (top right). Isometric view of the upper
end of the stile in Fig. 2.
Fig. 5 (below). Arrangement on the lower end
of a brace, with the shoulder forming a mitre
between the two chamfers.

The arrangement of the tenons
indicated in Fig. 7. On each rail the
width of the tenons equals that of the
hauncheons, the short tenons filling the
plough groove. The thickness of the
tenons should approximate to, but not
exceed one-third the door thickness.

The panels shown finish flush on one
side. The top panels are described a
bead butt, the lower as bead flush. The
method of returning the bead across the

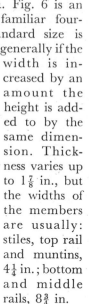

Fig. 6. Four-panelled door
—a very familiar type; the
standard size is 6 ft. 6 in.
by 2 ft. 6 in.

d of a bead flush panel illustrated in Fig. 8. A bate is worked across e panel end and stop-d against the vertical ads worked on the nel.

These solid beads are itred to receive the ose end beads, which e glued and bradded to position. Sometimes e rebate is worked mpletely round the nel, and all the beads e applied.

HALF-GLASS DOOR. A or, the upper part of nich is glazed, is shown Fig. 9. The stiles in ch work are often re-iced in width above e middle rail, and are en known as *diminished.* nis diminish is effected bevelling the shoul-rs on the middle rail, d the method of form-g the joint is illustrated the sketch, Fig. 10.

The double tenons own are seldom em-oyed on work 2 in. ick and less, other than iere a mortise lock is be fitted.

The sections of the les above and below e middle rails are own in Fig. 11. The iss in the glazed por-n is usually placed in e centre of the thick-ss, and secured with izing fillets. These fil-s are generally fixed th panel pins, but iewal of the glass is

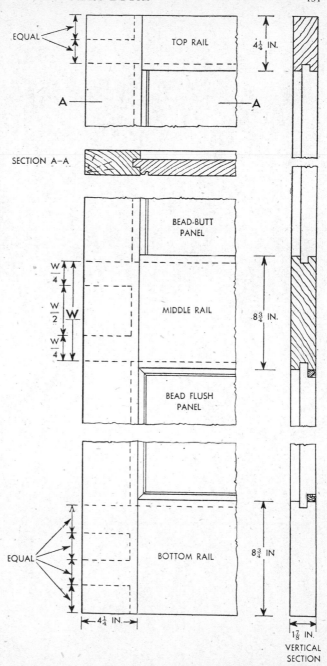

Fig. 7. Arrangement of the tenons in the four-panelled door shown in Fig. 6. On top and bottom rails the width of the tenons equals that of the haucheons; the thickness of the tenons is approximately one-third the thickness of the door.

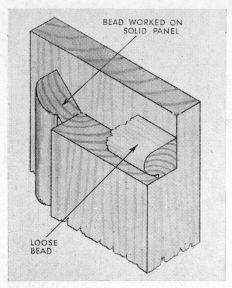

Fig. 8. Method of returning the bead across the end of a bead-flush panel in a four-panelled door.

considerably simplified if small screws and cups are used.

The section of the glazing bar warrants attention. The thickness of the web shown is $\frac{5}{16}$ in. If less than this they are very frail and easily damaged. The square on a bar of this section determines the thickness of the tenons, and consequently cannot well be below $\frac{5}{16}$ in.

The panels are finished on one side with a simple sunk moulding $1\frac{1}{4}$ in. wide. These mouldings are bradded to the framing and not to the panels. Wide, thin mouldings are unsuitable, as they tend to curl away from the face of the panel.

PAIR OF DOORS. The elevation, Fig. 12, shows a pair of swing doors possessing fire-resisting qualities. This type is much employed in public and office buildings. Regulations govern the construction of such doors. Generally they must be at least $1\frac{1}{4}$ in. thick throughout, of oak, teak, or other approved hardwood, and the doors must be so hung that they return automatically to closed position.

The glass must be $\frac{1}{4}$ in. thick in sm pieces set in copper glazing, and t panes thus formed are restricted in are Reinforced glass is now available.

The details of Fig. 13 give sections the stiles above and below the midd rail. Glazing the upper half is obvious necessary where a door swings in bo directions. Bars must be at least $1\frac{3}{4}$ i wide, and not reduced in section I mouldings. Panels are flush both side and a slight rebate or chamfer serves break the joint against the stiles.

Each door swings on vertical pivots one fixed to the head of the door fram the other being connected to powerf springs. These springs, which bring t door to the closed position, are hous in a metal box let into the floor.

A metal shoe fits over the lower piv and receives the bottom hangi corner of the door. The top pivot is engaged by a plate let into the upper end of the door stile.

The procedure of hanging is as follows. The doors are brought to size and the edges rounded. The round on the hanging stiles is sufficient to prevent the passage of light through the joint against the frame. The closing

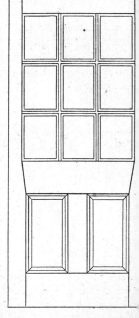

Fig. 9. Half-glass door, w the upper part glazed. T stiles are reduced in wid above the middle rail, and a known as *diminished*.

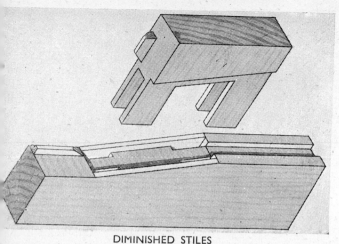

Fig. 10. Method of effecting the diminish by bevelling the shoulders on the middle rail as referred to in Fig. 9, and forming the joint.

These mouldings are rebated over the edges of the stiles and rails, and are glued and screwed at the mitres as shown in Fig. 16. The frames thus formed are screwed to the panels through slots, which allow the panel to shrink slightly without splitting.

Finally the panel mouldings on the back face of the door are pinned to the framing, covering the screws fixing the bolection moulding.

Two alternative arrangements at the edges of the panels are given in Fig. 17. At A the framing is glued up without the panels and the door cleaned off. Fillets are then fixed into the plough grooves, and the bolection moulding screwed to these. The panels are then inserted and secured by the panel mouldings.

At B the mouldings, back and face, are worked on the same piece of material

les are rounded on an arc having the vot point as a centre. The shoes are ted and the stile end plates fixed. The upper pivot, by the turning of an jacent screw, recedes until it is con-ned by the head of the door frame. hen the pivot is in this position the or is slipped into the shoe, turned into open position and the top pivot ewed down. Slight adjustments for gnment are made by means of screws crating at the lower pivot.

ENTRANCE DOORS.

pair of entrance ors suitable for bank or similar ilding is given in vation in Fig. 14, d section in Fig. . The doors are in. thick, and in nsequence double ions should be ed throughout. e panels on the e side are raised, nk and fielded. e moulding is cribed as *bolection* lding.

.—G

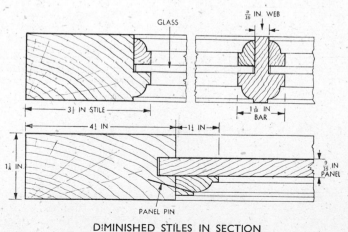

Fig. 11. Sections of the stiles of the half-glass door which is illustrated in Fig. 9, shown above and below the middle rail.

Fig. 12. Pair of swing doors, with fire-resisting qualities, as used in public and office buildings. Doors are made of hardwood such as oak or teak, at least 1¾ in. thick.

mitred around the panel, and screwe at the mitre. The framing is put togethe dry (without glue), and any face abov which the moulding projects cleaned o:

The panel and mouldings are the fitted and the door glued up. Th method is little employed, due main to the cost. Both methods are equal applicable where doors have bolectio mouldings on both sides.

The elevation at the end of the frie rail is seen in Fig. 16. The mouldin above the rail are removed to show t: arrangement of the shoulder line to c incide with the outside edge of t| bolection moulding. This refinement not often adopted.

Entrance doors of this type rema open during business hours, and wh opened they frequently form part of t: vestibule panelling. A method of han ing to provide for this is indicated Fig. 15.

FLUSH DOORS. These doors are main the product of specialist firms employi modern expensive machinery ar presses. With this equipment sheets

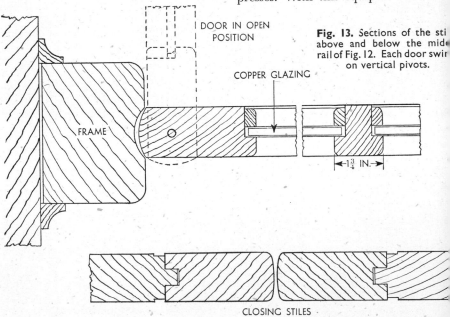

DOOR IN OPEN POSITION

COPPER GLAZING

FRAME

←1¾ IN.→

Fig. 13. Sections of the sti above and below the midd rail of Fig. 12. Each door swin on vertical pivots.

CLOSING STILES

ywood are cemented to the faces of amed or solid cores.

A few of the numerous ways of aming cores are indicated in Fig. 18. he wider members are usually stub-noned together, and the narrow inter-ediate members, if any, are halved. 'here narrow stiles occur they are idened at the centre to provide fixing r a lock.

Solid cores are built up of many strips 'material. The thickness of these strips uries, but in most cases the timber is ln-dried western red cedar.

Edging pieces cover the edges of the ywood facings, and conceal the soft-ood core. Frequently the whole of each ce is covered with an expensive veneer. me methods of jointing the edging eces to the core and facings are shown the sections in Fig. 18.

MANUFACTURE OF DOORS. A large oportion of the cheaper varieties of ors is now mass-produced, and made standard sizes and thicknesses. The ortise and tenon joint is employed and wel pins are frequently used.

The production of such doors involves achinery which is not useful to the erage builder or joinery manufac-rer, and which can only be employed ofitably when thousands of an identi-l item are required.

While machinery of a highly special-ed type is not employed in normal anufacture, the amount of hand labour

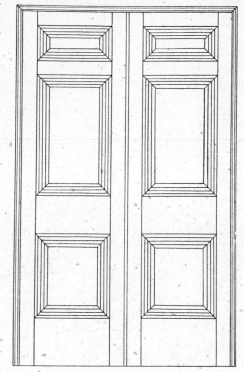

Fig. 14. Pair of entrance doors, suitable for such buildings as banks. Doors are 2¼ in. thick, with double tenons. See sectional drawing, Fig. 15.

is not great, and in most instances con-sists of finishing the mouldings, fitting the joints, glueing up the work, and in some cases, cleaning off and finishing the faces. The mode of procedure now described refers to this class of work.

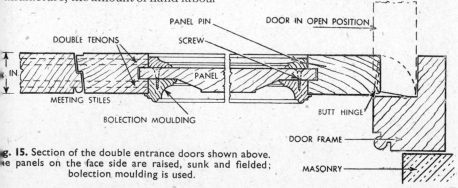

g. 15. Section of the double entrance doors shown above. ie panels on the face side are raised, sunk and fielded; bolection moulding is used.

The first operation is to draw full-size vertical and horizontal sections of the door. From this *rod*, the term by which the drawings are known, the dimensions of the material required are taken off. Fig. 19 shows the rod and material sheet for the doors of Fig. 14. The material is cut and planed to these dimensions.

To mark out the timber for the machinists requires a sound knowledge of construction and an equally thorough understanding of machine processes. The following are the principal points:

All mortises have to be marked, both on the face and back edges of the stiles.

Several similar stiles are fixed together in light cramps and the lines drawn across in one operation.

Mortises that occur between shoulders as for the vertical bars of Fig. 9, are best set out after the shoulders are cut.

Shoulder lines need be placed on one only of a number of similar rails.

The sections of the various members are drawn on the pattern pieces, but where mouldings occur the machinist should be provided with a tracing of the architect's full-size detail.

The amount of work remaining after the machinists have finished, depend upon the type and quality of the door. A simple four-panelled softwood doc should be ready for assembly. Wher stiles diminish, or mitres occur, fittin is necessary.

The rail first fitted is the middle, an other rails are sighted through and mad to correspond. Any tendency to twist c wind is easily corrected by easing th appropriate shoulder, and, if necessar the mortise face also.

Plain panels may be completely fir ished in the mill, and are frequently c plywood or manufactured board. Raise panels require careful finishing. Th mitre line formed by the bevelled su faces must be an exact continuation c the mitre made by the panel moulding

The truth of these mitres is checke by placing the panels in the framing an marking along the edge of a piece of th moulding to be used. The mitres on th panel should pass through the poin where the pencil marks intersect. Ob viously all sunk panels must be finishe before final assembly.

The glueing up of the work is of grea importance, and many failing joints i

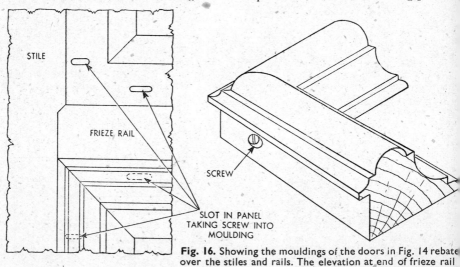

STILE

FRIEZE RAIL

SCREW

SLOT IN PANEL
TAKING SCREW INTO
MOULDING

Fig. 16. Showing the mouldings of the doors in Fig. 14 rebate over the stiles and rails. The elevation at end of frieze rail also shown.

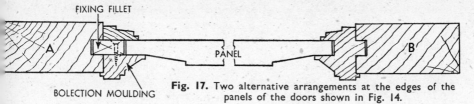

FIXING FILLET

A   PANEL   B

BOLECTION MOULDING

Fig. 17. Two alternative arrangements at the edges of the panels of the doors shown in Fig. 14.

oors and sashes are due entirely to the amping of this operation.

If a cramping machine is not avail-ole, blocks about 4 in. × 3 in., and oout 9 in. longer than the width of the oor are fixed across the bench, with ieir upper surfaces out of winding. otches in these blocks seat a long amp which serves to pull up the joints etween rails and muntins, or rails and azing bars. Cramps, placed over the oor, pull up the joints along the stiles. lue should be applied thinly, but on l surfaces which are fixed together.

No glue must be allowed to run into the plough groove and fix a panel liable to shrink. When using hot glue the work-shop should be well warmed and the surplus glue squeezed out before chilling takes place.

To glue and wedge up a door is a two-man operation. The wedges fixing the wider rails are driven first, and judicious driving will position the rails relative to the mitres, muntins, or sight lines. The wedges should compress the tenons more closely at the root (near the shoulder) than at the ends.

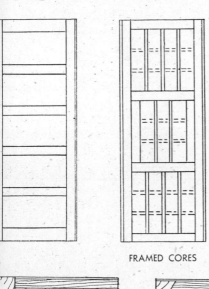

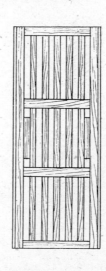

Fig. 18. Some of the numerous ways of framing cores are shown in top portion of the illustration. The wider members are usually stub-tenoned together, and the narrow in-termediate members are halved. The sec-tions shown below indicate some of the methods of jointing the edging pieces to the core and facings.

FRAMED CORES

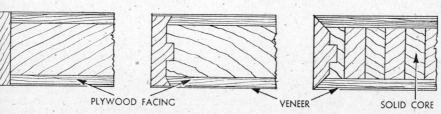

PLYWOOD FACING   VENEER   SOLID CORE

NAME OF JOB *Entrance Doors, 51 High Street*

JOB NUMBER *B 1385*

FINISH *Polished*

Fig. 19. From this *rod*, whi is a thin board on which fu size vertical sections are draw the dimensions of the materia are taken off.

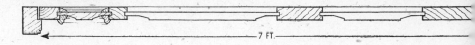

←————————— 7 FT. —————————→

←———— 4 FT 3 IN. ————→

The Table below gives t detailed sizes for cutting a planing the doors in Fig.

No.	Description	Length	Section	Material
4	Stiles	7 ft. 3 in.	4 in. × 2¼ in.	
2	Bottom rails . . .	2 ft. 4 in.	11 in. × 2¼ in.	
2	Middle rails . . .	2 ft. 4 in.	9 in. × 2¼ in.	
2	Frieze rails . . .	2 ft. 4 in.	3½ in. × 2¼ in.	
2	Top rails . . .	2 ft. 4 in.	4 in. × 2¼ in.	
2 } 2	Panels	{ 1 ft. 9 in. } { 2 ft. 6 in. }	1 ft. 7½ in. × 1¼ in.	
2	Lay panels . . .	1 ft. 8 in.	11 in. × 1¼ in.	Mahogany
2 } 2 } 2	Bolection moulding , . .	{ 6 ft. 9 in. } { 8 ft. 3 in. } { 5 ft. 3 in. }	2 in. × 1¼ in.	
2 } 2 } 2	Panel moulding . .	{ 6 ft. 9 in. } { 8 ft. 3 in. } { 5 ft. 3 in. }	1¼ in. × ¾ in.	
2	Jambs	7 ft. 9 in.	5¼ in. × 4¼ in.	
1	Head	5 ft. 6 in.	5¼ in. × 4¼ in.	

The cleaning off of the faces should not be attempted until the glue has set, otherwise the shoulders may need to be again rubbed down flush. The majority of doors are cleaned off by machinery, but if done by hand each face must be brought to a plane surface.

A straight edge must be applied frequently along the rails and muntins and across the shoulders. Work to be French polished must have the surfaces damped with warm clean water and rubbed down with fine glasspaper. With some timbers this must be repeated several times. All sunk panels, moulded bars and edges must be polished prior to assembly. Panel mouldings are polished prior to mitreing.

DOOR FRAMES AND LININGS. Doors are hung to either *frames* or *linings*. Broadly speaking frames are used for openin in the outer walls and linings for interi doorways.

The size of the material from whi frames are worked varies, but few a lighter than 3 in. × 2½ in., or heavi than 6 in. × 4 in. A simple section shown in Fig. 20, which also illustra the method of making the joint betwe the head and the jamb.

A method of making a satisfacto joint where the material is wide, a without employing double tenons given in Fig. 21. The shoulders are ke narrow, and the webs formed on t head running through the correspon ing slots in the jambs keep the faces of t joint flush, and give increased gluei surface.

Whenever the width of the mater

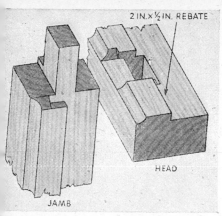

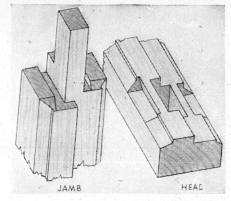

Fig. 20. Showing method of making the joint between the head and the jamb of a door frame.

Fig. 21. How to make a satisfactory joint between the head and the jamb without employing double tenons, where material used is wide.

permits double tenons should be used. A sketch of a joint employed in the frame shown in section Fig. 13 is given in Fig. 22. Double tenons are used, each being kept its own thickness from the face of the frame.

In the sketches, a hauncheon is shown in each case. This is the method applied when the head is cut off flush with the outside of the jambs. Frequently door frames are built in, and in such cases the head may run by the jambs, and the tenons can be of full width.

For further strengthening of the joints dowel pins are often inserted. These dowels are made to act as draw-bore pins by staggering the holes through the cheeks of the mortise with that through the tenon. The method of doing this is indicated in Fig. 23, which is a vertical section through the centre of the borings. Note that the dowel is kept as near to the shoulder as possible.

The fitting and glueing up of heavy frames is made easier if the tenons project about 3 in. beyond the head, and permit the use of draw-bore pins. Extra

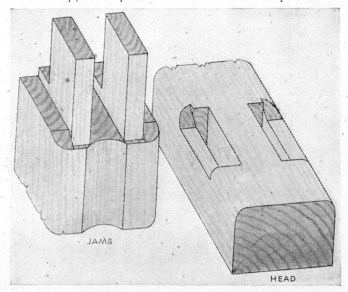

SWING-DOOR FRAME JOINTS

Fig. 22. Sketches of a joint employed in the frame, the section of which is shown in Fig. 13. Double tenons are used, each being kept its own thickness from the face of the frame. A hauncheon is shown in both sketches.

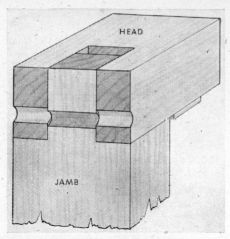

Fig. 23. Method of strengthening joints by the use of dowels. Note that the dowel is kept as near the shoulder as possible.

timber across the ends of the jambs and pulling against this.

Before glueing, the jambs are fixed the correct distance apart by means of a temporary stretcher; in painted work this stretcher is nailed into the rebate about 1 ft. above the floor line, but for polished frames blocks are screwed to the backs of the jambs, and the stretcher fixed to these.

Squaring the Frames

Frames are squared by testing the lengths of diagonals with a light lath. When the diagonals are equal the frame is square and is maintained so by means of a temporary brace fixed across from head to jamb. The stretcher and brace are shown in the elevation of the frame in Fig. 24.

A type of frame much employed is shown in elevation in Fig. 24 and in section in Fig. 25. These frames are used

material is required, but this expense is offset by the economy in labour costs. If pins cannot be employed, the joints may be cramped up by placing a heavy

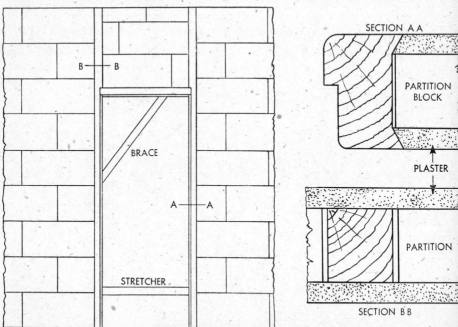

PARTITION DOORWAY FRAME

Fig. 24 (left). Elevation of a door frame of a type in common use for light slab partitions. The temporary brace and stretcher are shown. **Fig. 25** (right) shows sections of this door frame

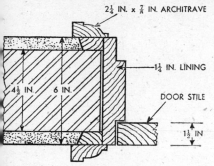

2¼ IN. × ⅞ IN. ARCHITRAVE

1¼ IN. LINING

DOOR STILE

4½ IN. 6 IN.

1½ IN

g. 26. Horizontal section through a simple rm of jamb lining. When double rebated the door can be hung at either edge.

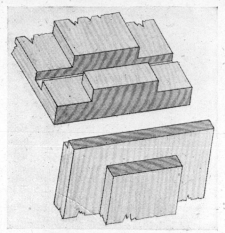

Fig. 28. Simplified version of the joint between the head and jamb shown in Fig. 27.

light slab partitions, which are built ;ainst the frames after they are fixed. he jambs run from floor to ceiling and .e posts are reduced above the head to low the plaster to cover the woodwork. JAMB LINING. Jamb linings serve a ual purpose. They provide a hanging r the door, and line or cover the brick-ork revealed by the opening.

The simplest form is that shown in .g. 26, which is a horizontal section .rough a jamb. The lining is a double :bated piece of 6 in. × 1¼ in. material. he joint between the head and jamb is .own in Fig. 27, while a simplified

version of the same joint is shown in Fig. 28.

When the thickness of the wall exceeds 9 in. it becomes necessary to frame up the linings and they become narrow pieces of panelling (Fig. 29).

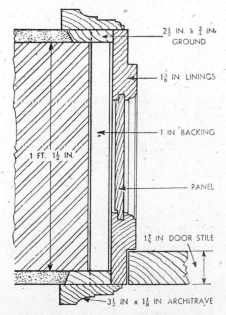

2½ IN. × ¾ IN. GROUND

1⅜ IN LININGS

1 IN BACKING

1 FT. 1½ IN.

PANEL

1⅞ IN DOOR STILE

3½ IN × 1⅛ IN ARCHITRAVE

Fig. 29. If the wall is more than 9 in. thick, it is advisable to frame up the linings in the form of narrow pieces of panelling, as shown.

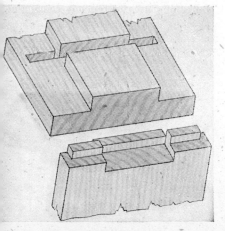

g. 27. Joint between the head and jamb of e jamb lining illustrated in Fig. 26 above.

B —G*

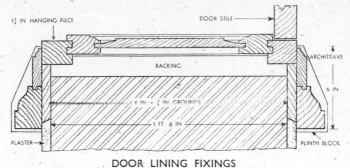

DOOR LINING FIXINGS

Fig. 30. Section through door lining of a more elaborate type. Thick hanging pieces are tongued and grooved round the edges of the centre panelling, and are set back to form a rebate.

The stiles are rebated and the rails are kept at the same height and conform to those of the door. The joint between jamb and head is the same as that given in Fig. 27. This requires the end rails of the head lining to be wide enough to reach to the back of the vertical lining.

With the types given in Figs. 26 and 29 the thickness of the jambs is reduced by $\frac{1}{2}$ in. at the edges where the hinges are fixed. This gives little material to take the screws fixing the butts. The difficulty may be solved by fixing blocks to the back of the lining immediately behind the hinges.

A better solution, however, is shown in Fig. 30, which is the section through a more elaborate type of lining than those already mentioned. Around the edges of the centre panelling thick hanging pieces are tongued and grooved and set back to form the rebate.

Wood Panelling

PANELLING is a term in general use for the lining of interior wall surfaces with some form of wood finishing. Before the introduction of the many kinds of manufactured boards now available, the work was built up of stiles, rails and muntins filled with panels. Nowadays, however, much of the work is of plywood or other board.

When the pan ling terminates sh of the ceiling, it m be referred to as *d panelling*, and Fig. is an elevation o simple example. T framing is $1\frac{1}{4}$ thick and consists top and bottom r and intermedia muntins. An ov moulding is work on the face edg

To increase the boldness of the effe the panels are kept as far from the fa of the work as possible. This is done rebating the edges of the panels. Cappi moulding finishes the framing at t upper edge and the skirting at the ba

The stiles of the panelling should r down to the floor to provide a fixing the skirting. Intermediate fixing may obtained either by means of verti grounds or by making the bottom rail the panelling wider.

In painted work the capping is nail to the grounds and framing, but polished work it is usually screwed a pelleted.

Figs. 32 and 33 give a method finishing the panelling against a d opening. Fig. 32 is the horizontal secti A-A of Fig. 31, and shows the architr covering the joint between the stile a

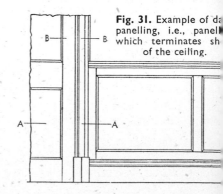

Fig. 31. Example of d panelling, i.e., panel which terminates sh of the ceiling.

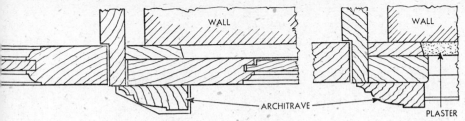

WALL

WALL

—ARCHITRAVE—

PLASTER

DOOR PANEL FINISHING

Fig. 32 (left) and **Fig. 33** (right) show a method of finishing the panelling against a door opening.
Fig. 32 is a horizontal section of A–A in Fig. 31, and Fig. 33 is a horizontal section of B–B.

the jamb lining. Above the capping the architrave stands away from the plaster face by an amount equal to the thickness of the panelling, and a backing piece is employed as shown in Fig. 33, which is the horizontal section B-B of Fig. 31.

Interior angles in plan between pieces of panelling are formed by a tongue and groove joint as at A, Fig. 34. It is convenient if the groove is worked on the framing to be fixed first, and when setting out the work consideration must be given as to which of the adjoining pieces of panelling this will be.

A tongued and grooved joint applied to an exterior angle is given at B, Fig. 34. The ovolo moulding is applied to dispense with the sharp arris otherwise formed, but the moulding must be stopped below the capping and above the skirting. Fig. 35 is a sketch of such a stop, which may be formed on the solid or consist of a piece glued on the edge of the stile.

A more elaborate piece of panelling than that of Fig. 31

is given in elevation (Fig. 36). Such work is often applied to bank interiors, to board-rooms, and similar positions where an imposing appearance is of importance, and this panelling is usually executed in expensive hardwood.

Where large areas have to be panelled the framing must be made in sections. These sections are connected by *pilasters*,

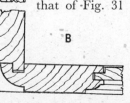

A

Fig. 34. Plan showing method of forming interior angles between pieces of panelling by a tongue and groove joint as at A; an exterior angle is formed as shown at B.

B

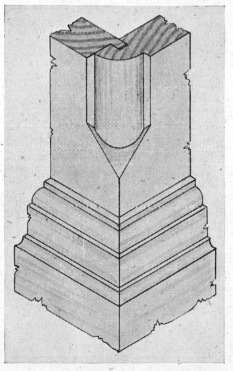

Fig. 35. Method of stopping the moulding below the capping and above the skirting.

1 FT. 9 IN.

6 FT. 9 IN.

2 FT. 9 IN.

$1\frac{1}{4}$ IN.

$1\frac{1}{2}$ IN.

A

TYPICAL EXAMPLE OF BOARD-ROOM PANELLING

Fig. 36 (top left). Panelling made of expensive hardwood and typical of the work used for board-rooms, banks and similar offices. Note the pilaster which connects up the sections. **Fig. 37** (below) is the enlarged horizontal section and **Fig. 38** (top right) the enlarged vertical section of the pilaster

which may project from, or stand behind the face of the framing.

The pilaster illustrated is a simple solid rectangular projection, but frequently the pilasters are framed up about a long, narrow panel. Where beams are formed in the plaster work of the ceiling, the pilasters may quite suitably take the form of half-column

Fig. 37 is the horizontal section and Fig. 38 the vertical section of the given pilaster. The edges are grooved to take the tongues on the stiles of the panelling, and the pilaster projects an amount sufficient to stop the dado moulding. The plinth and capping are mitred around and should be sunk into the pilaster as shown in the enlarged section in Fig. 38.

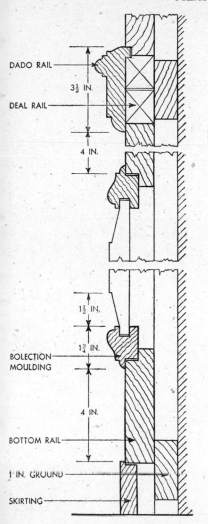

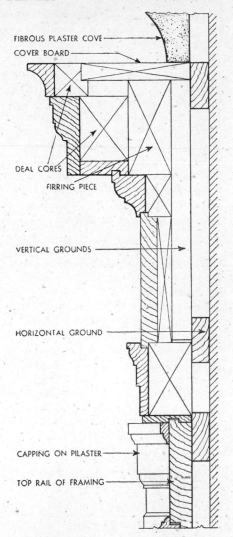

Fig. 39. Method of tongueing the dado rail into the framing. The rail behind the dado is made of deal for the sake of economy.

Fig. 40. How the cornice is built up, showing also the position of the grounds and the firring piece to which the cornice is attached.

The three-reed mouldings on the face are shown worked on the solid, but they may well consist of separate pieces glued into grooves as indicated at A in Fig. 37. This latter arrangement would provide a secret fixing, with the screws being driven through the groove, and subsequently covered by the loose bead.

For convenience of handling and transport the framing is made in two horizontal sections with the dado rail covering the joint. This rail is tongued into the framing as shown in Fig. 39, which is the lower part of a vertical section through the panelling. The rail behind the dado mould is usually deal.

The panels are raised and the bolection moulding is so arranged that the fielded surface of the panel stands in front of the face of the framing. The moulding is mitred around the panels and screwed at the mitres.

When the moulding is a heavy one, a better job is obtained by employing light handrail bolts and cross tongues at the mitres. The framing is glued up, finished and polished before the panels and bolection mouldings are inserted. The panels and mouldings are fixed by screwing from the back of the framing into the bolection moulding.

Building up the Cornice

The method of building up the cornice is indicated in Fig. 40. Economy of hardwood is achieved by providing cores of deal behind the moulded facing. The core and facing are glued together before the mouldings are worked.

By tonguing together the sections of the cornice the correct margins are ensured, and by arranging rectangular members the cutting and fitting of the mitres is rendered more simple than would be the case if the back of the moulding is inclined to the vertical.

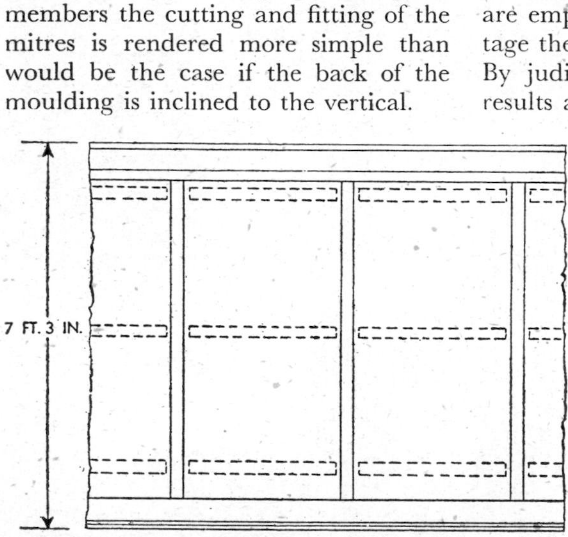

PLYWOOD FIXINGS

Fig. 41. Fixing plywood to the grounds of panelling. Rebated bearers are fixed to the back of the panels. The positions of the bearers are indicated by dotted lines.

The positions of the grounds and fi ring pieces to which the cornice is fixe are given in Fig. 40. Each piece of th cornice would be screwed to the grounds from the top; by this method r fixing need be driven through the fac

The execution of a complete piece panelling of which Fig. 36 can be r garded as but a part elevation, enta considerable skill. When setting out th rods all the details of construction mu be carefully considered, especially points such as fire-places, door ar window openings.

The method of erection and fixing h also to be decided at this stage. Th actual fixing is not the least importa part of the work, and if a first-class fini is required ample equipment and cor fortable conditions must be provided.

Plywood Applied to Panelling

The use of plywood and manufacture board as a wall panelling material mak possible a mode of design in keeping wi modern tendencies. Large plain surfac are employed which display to adva tage the veneers covering the plywoo By judicial selection of these venee results are possible which could not k obtained by the mouldings the more traditional style Heavy projections and re cesses are not necessary, an the effect of shadow may k obtained by introducing band of veneer, darker tha that of the adjacent surface

The simplest method covering a wall surface wit plywood is to fix the shee directly to the grounds wit panel pins. The edges of th sheets are usually bevelled t form a V joint.

With this method of featur ing joints endless designs ar possible, but the disadvantag driving pins through the face of he work is a serious one; for no matter ow well the holes are stopped they ventually become obvious.

A better but more expensive method f fixing boards directly to the grounds is pplied to the example in Fig. 41. Re-ated bearers are fixed to the backs of he panels and engage a corresponding ebate on the grounds. In the example ven the bearers are screwed to the anels, but where thinner boards are sed they would be glued.

A section of the bearers and grounds given in the vertical section of the aming in Fig. 42. The positions of the earers are indicated by dotted lines in he elevation (Fig. 41).

Fixing the Panelling

The skirting is in two sections. The ower member is screwed to the floor and rovides a seating for the tongue on the ower edge of the upper portion. This ection is fixed to the ground along the op edge. The panelling drops down on o the skirting, the joint being made ith a tongue of thin plywood.

The object of forming the cornice of wo members is to provide a means of xing other than through the face. The ower edge would be glued to the panels nd the top edge nailed or screwed to he grounds. The uppermost member ould be fixed from the top which is well bove eye level. These details are shown n Fig. 42.

Fig. 43 is a horizontal section through muntin. These members would prob-bly be faced with a different veneer om that on the panels. The slight set-ack provides interest and permits a over for the joint. The muntin would e fixed vertical to the ground by screws hrough the rebate.

The work would be fixed in the follow-ng manner. The skirting would be fixed rst. The muntins would then be

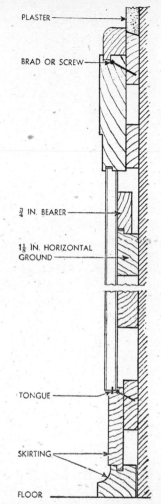

PLASTER

BRAD OR SCREW

¾ IN. BEARER

1⅛ IN. HORIZONTAL GROUND

TONGUE

SKIRTING

FLOOR

Fig. 42. Enlarged vertical section of bearers and grounds of the framing shown in Fig. 41, in which the positions of the bearers are shown by means of dotted lines.

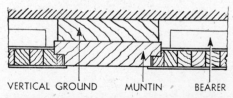

VERTICAL GROUND   MUNTIN   BEARER

Fig. 43. Horizontal section through a muntin. It is usual to face the muntins with a different veneer from that used on the panels. The muntin would be fixed vertical to the ground by screws through the rebate.

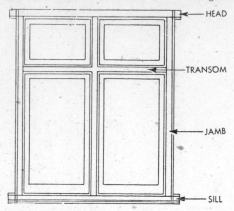

HEAD

TRANSOM

JAMB

SILL

Fig. 44. A typical casement frame window with opening-out sashes. Casements are a most popular type of window in modern houses.

screwed into position. Panels could then be dropped into place and secured by fixing the cornice. Carried out in this manner no fixing need disfigure the face of the work.

WINDOW FRAMES AND SASHES. The principal types of windows constructed of wood are the *casement* variety, and the *cased* window. In the former the frame is of solid sections with the sashes hung on butt hinges, while the frame of the latter type is built of several members arranged so that the sashes, counterbalanced by weights, slide vertically.

CASEMENT WINDOWS. At the present time this window is undoubtedly the most popular. The two main reasons are that: it lends itself to cheap methods of mass production; it allows of a full opening; and for domestic work it is easy to treat architecturally. Compared with the cased variety, however, it has some disadvantages.

It is less easy to render weather and draught resisting, and ventilation is usually accompanied by a current of air directly into the room. In favour it is claimed that the cased frame is more expensive to make, and that the sash cords need periodic renewal.

A typical example of a casement

frame with outward opening sashes is shown in elevation in Fig. 44 and in section in Fig. 45. The jambs, head, and mullions are worked from 4 in. × 3 in material, the transom from 4½ in. × 3 in., while the sill requires a piece of 6 in. × 3 in., which should be of oak or teak. The framing, except the sill and transom, is ovolo moulded on both faces.

A small hollow moulding, called a throating, is worked along the internal angle formed by the faces of the rebate This throating is a measure to prevent water being forced by air pressure completely through the joint between sash and frame.

The sill, seen in section in Fig. 45, is designed for a position in which a stone tile, or other form of sub-sill is not included. This requires the wood sill to

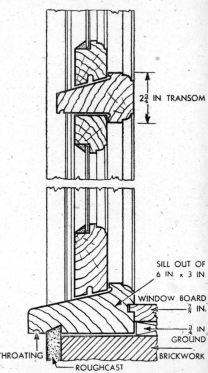

2¾ IN TRANSOM

SILL OUT OF
6 IN × 3 IN.

WINDOW BOARD
⅞ IN.

¾ IN
GROUND

THROATING

BRICKWORK

ROUGHCAST

Fig. 45. Enlarged section of the casement sill shown in Fig. 44, giving details of sizes and showing clearly the method of construction

overhang the outer face of the wall, which, in the case illustrated, is assumed to be covered with a rendering.

The sloping upper surfaces of the sill and transom are called weathered surfaces or weatherings. To prevent rain driving under the bottom edges of the sashes, the angle of slope of these weatherings cannot well be less than that shown.

Bringing the frame near the outer face of the wall means that the window gains little protection from the adjacent brickwork. Consequently a projection in the brickwork or rendering should be formed immediately above the head of the frame, and a drip made to cause the water running down the wall to fall clear of the woodwork.

Although this is not a joinery detail, its omission frequently results in a well-designed window failing to give satisfaction. At the transom the problem is solved by allowing that member to project well beyond the face of the sash, and by providing a throating on the under side. The projection is carried across the jambs and is housed into them to a depth of about $\frac{1}{4}$ in.

The sashes shown are $1\frac{7}{8}$ in. thick, which provides for a bold moulding on the face and a wide rebate to take the glass and putty fillet. The thickness of the tenon, as already mentioned, is the same as the width of the square on the edge of the sash.

Rail and Stile Joints

Two methods of making the joints between the rails and the stiles are given in Figs. 46 and 47.

The method illustrated in Fig. 46 is the one used when the joint is made by hand, with the scribe carried but a short way across the end grain of the shoulder. In the machine-made joint which is illustrated in Fig. 47, the scribe is worked completely across the shoulder.

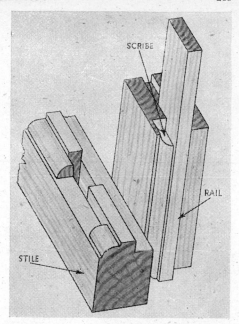

Fig. 46. Joint made by hand between rails and stiles, with the scribe carried only a short way across the end grain of the shoulder.

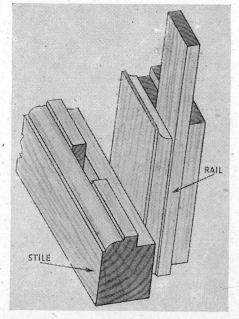

Fig. 47. A machine-made joint with the scribe worked completely across the shoulder.

The line of intersection between the mitred surface and the surface of the moulding is also the line of intersection between the moulding and the scribed surface.

The hauncheon in sash construction is formed by leaving the projection on the stile, and by providing a corresponding socket on the end of the rail. This method is adopted to provide a greater length for the wedge on the outside of the tenon than would be possible with the normal hauncheon.

CASEMENT FRAMES WITH INWARD-OPENING SASHES. Casement sashes are seldom hung to open inwards. This does not apply where two thicknesses of sashes occur in the same opening, but as such construction is little used in Britain it does not warrant consideration.

If difficulties occur in rendering weather-proof outward opening sashes, it is obvious that when the sashes open into the room the difficulties become still greater. The first of these troubles is that wind pressure tends to force open the sashes.

This weakness is, of course, most marked along the joint between the frame and the closing stile, and the normal method of fixing the sash by engaging a sash fastener at about the mid-point of the stile is adequate only on very short sashes.

Espagnolette Bolt

To stiffen the closing stile a relatively expensive fitting called an espagnolette bolt is sometimes used. This bolt runs the whole length of the stile, is in two separate lengths, and so coupled that a turn of the handle causes the extremes to engage sockets in the frame at the head and sill. Various types of this bolt are manufactured.

It is at the sill, however, that the chief difficulty is met. In Figs. 48 and 49 vertical sections indicate methods of

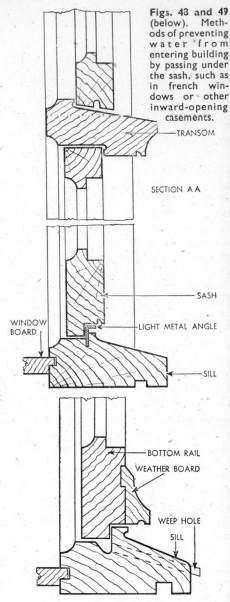

Figs. 48 and 49 (below). Methods of preventing water from entering building by passing under the sash, such as in french windows or other inward-opening casements.

—TRANSOM

SECTION A A

WINDOW BOARD

—SASH

—LIGHT METAL ANGLE

—SILL

—BOTTOM RAIL

WEATHER BOARD

WEEP HOLE

SILL

preventing water from working its way under the bottom of the sash.

The principal check to this action in the design shown in Fig. 48 is a piece of light metal angle. This angle, which should be of some non-ferrous metal, is let into the sill and is cut tightly between the jambs. The function of the angle is to prevent the water from being forced over the top of the sill and into the joint.

The weakness of the joint as given is that, apart from the drip on the under edge, there is nothing to prevent the water that runs down the outside of the sash being driven through the joint and on to the window board.

In the design of Fig. 49 a weather-board is incorporated. Although somewhat cumbersome in appearance, a bold weather-board is an effective method of throwing water clear of the joint. When the sash is narrow, however, the amount of splay on the end of the board, necessary to allow the sash to open, presents a difficulty.

This disadvantage does not arise when the sashes are hung in pairs. Another point worthy of note (Fig. 49) is the provision made to dispose of water that may enter the joint. The sill carries a sinking along the upper edge which collects the water, and from this channel weep holes of copper tubing conduct it to the outside. Similar measures are used in situations where excessive condensation is likely.

Hanging Sashes

PIVOT OR CENTRE HUNG SASHES. This method of hanging sashes is more complicated than the normal way, but if it is remembered that the sash is slipped into position from the inside of the frame and over the top of the pivot, little confusion need occur.

The frame surrounding the sash is not rebated, but a rebated joint is formed by beads around both sides of the sash. Part of these beads is fixed to the sash and the remainder to the frame. The beads used should be worked with a good thickness of quirk, so that the joint between frame and sash may be contained within this thickness.

The example shown in Fig. 50 is a

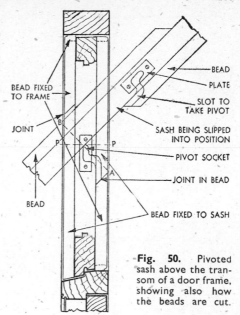

Fig. 50. Pivoted sash above the transom of a door frame, showing also how the beads are cut.

sash above the transom of a door frame, and to appreciate the drawing it is necessary to imagine that the nearer jamb of the frame has been removed.

Thus we see the outside edge of the sash stile. The pivot is not seen, as this is fixed to the jamb, but the slotted plate forming a socket for the pivot is indicated. To cause the sash to close by virtue of its own weight, the pivots are fixed a little above the mid-point of the stiles.

This renders the part below the pivot heavier than that above, and the sash is hung so that the lower portion swings outward.

The way in which the beads are cut is shown in the diagram. For convenience the cuts across the beads are at 45 degrees, and to permit the sash to open these cuts cannot be nearer the centre of rotation than the points marked A and B. These points are found by drawing a line through the centre at 90 degrees to the cuts.

Point B, however, is too low to permit

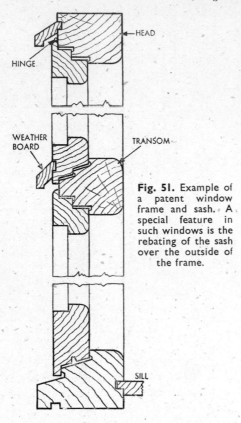

HEAD

HINGE

WEATHER
BOARD

TRANSOM

Fig. 51. Example of a patent window frame and sash. A special feature in such windows is the rebating of the sash over the outside of the frame.

SILL

the top of the pivot. This line is marked PP on Fig. 50.

The pivot plates are then removed and the sash already shot to size, is placed in the frame. By transferring the line PP on to the edge of the sash, the precise position of the socket plate is obtained. Once the sash is hanging correctly it is a simple matter to fix the beads. The sash is then taken out and the backs of the beads planed down flush with the edges of the sash to form the joint.

Patent Window Frames and Sashes

Several firms are now manufacturing frames and sashes, the designs of which are protected. The drawing in Fig. 51 is not of any particular example, but shows the type of section employed.

The first important departure from normal design is the rebating of the sash over the outside of the frame. This requires the use of purpose-made hinges and the inclusion of some form of weather-board immediately over the top edge of the sash.

The advantage gained is a real one for there is no open joint into which the wind can force both itself and rain. It is of interest to note that this idea, though somewhat new to ourselves, is common on the Continent, and has long been employed for internal doors as well as for sashes.

Another feature of most designs is the wide joint allowed around the edges of the sashes, many of which are double rebated as shown. The cover afforded by the lip on the sash makes the wide joint possible. This joint permits the material to swell in damp weather without binding the sash.

FRAMES FOR STEEL FRAMES AND SASHES. Steel frames and sashes are frequently set in wooden frames, which are built in or otherwise fixed into the wall openings. The production of steel

the sash being slid into place, and the joint is moved upwards to the position shown. The slots in the back of the upper inside beads are not as deep as the beads are thick, and are not visible when the sash is hung.

These slots guide the sash over the pivots and into position. Those beads fixed to the sash are the lower outside and the top inside beads. This is perhaps more clear in the part of Fig. 50 in which the sash is shown being slid into position. The remaining beads are fixed to the frame.

To hang a sash on centres is not difficult if the following method is adopted. First, the plates carrying the pivots are let into the jambs and a line squared across the edges of the jambs level with

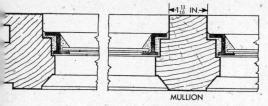

Fig. 52. Horizontal section of a wooden window frame of a size to fit the standard steel frame.

windows is now standardized, and in consequence the majority of the wooden frames are also made to conform to a standard. Figs. 52 and 53 are sections of such a frame.

The jambs and head are worked from material $3\frac{3}{4}$ in. $\times 2\frac{1}{2}$ in., transom and mullions from $3\frac{3}{4}$ in. $\times 3$ in., and the sill from a 6 in. $\times 3$ in. section. The method of double rebating the edges of the frame to receive the metal section is clearly shown in the drawing.

To keep the water clear of the joint between wood and metal, drips are worked on the under edge of the head and transom. The junction between wood and metal is made waterproof by means of a special mastic capable of withstanding the movement of the metal frame due to temperature changes. The actual fixing is by screws driven through holes in the metal section.

The metal frames shown are fixed, but whether the metal sash is fixed or hung the wooden frame remains the same.

Manufacturing Methods

MANUFACTURE OF CASEMENT FRAMES AND SASHES. The bulk of the casement frames and sashes used in the construction of house property is manufactured by mass-production methods. By employing machines such as double-ended tenoners and gang mortise machines the amount of hand work required is very small. Such methods, however, are not generally applicable, and the general mode of procedure is briefly as follows:—

A rod is set out giving the full-size vertical and horizontal sections of the frames and sashes, and from the rod a material sheet is prepared. The sections of the various members are as given in the architect's full-size details. Reference to Figs. 20, 21 and 22 should make this point clear.

Owing to the difficulty of under-cutting a shoulder on a tenon machine and the difficulty of working the sill with precision, the shoulders that abut on to the weathered top of the sill are left about $\frac{1}{2}$ in. long of the finished length.

These shoulders are then cut to the correct length by the joiner in the following manner. The tenon on the

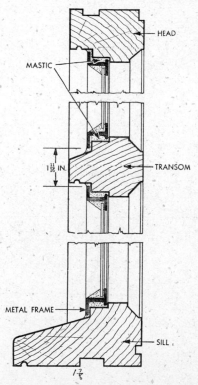

Fig. 53. Vertical section of the wooden window frame which is shown in Fig. 52.

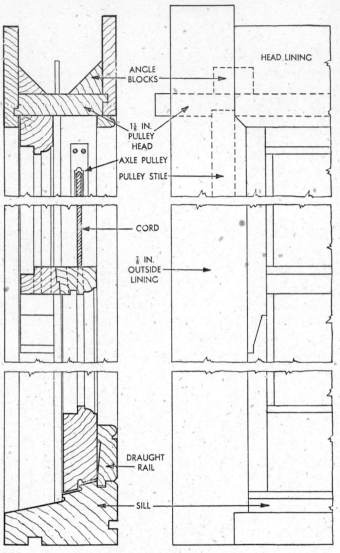

dividers are moved across the weathering, the other point will scribe a parallel on the face of the rebate. The shoulder is cut to this parallel.

The glueing up and cleaning off are again very similar to the corresponding operations applied to door frames. Drawbore pinning is a great help, but being complete frames, cramps are easily employed. The frames are checked for square by a rod applied diagonally.

CASED FRAMES AND SASHES. This type of frame, if well made and designed, is most efficient. It is draught and weather resisting, and with the sashes sliding vertically no difficulties occur with blinds and hangings. Ventilation is easily obtained and may be better regulated than with the casement type of frame.

By lowering the upper sash an opening is made at the top through which stale air may escape from the room, while at the same time fresh air may enter at the meeting rails. In addition, a wide draught rail at the sill permits the raising of the bottom sash to provide ventilation at the meeting rails, without the discomfort of a direct current of air passing into the room.

HEAD LINING
ANGLE BLOCKS
1⅛ IN. PULLEY HEAD
AXLE PULLEY
PULLEY STILE
CORD
⅞ IN. OUTSIDE LINING
DRAUGHT RAIL
SILL

CASED FRAME WINDOW DETAILS

Fig. 54 (left). Vertical section of a cased frame window and **Fig. 55** (right), part outside elevation of the same.

lower end of the jamb is placed in its mortise and the jamb lined up.

Because of the long back shoulder the face shoulder is open or off. A pair of dividers is set to the width of this open joint and with one point resting on the weathered surface of the sill, while the

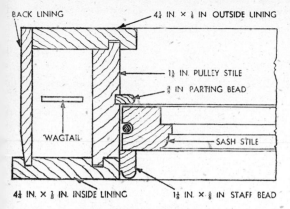

BACK LINING   4¼ IN × ¼ IN OUTSIDE LINING

1⅛ IN. PULLEY STILE

⅜ IN PARTING BEAD

WAGTAIL

SASH STILE

4¼ IN. × ⅞ IN. INSIDE LINING   1⅛ IN. × ⅝ IN STAFF BEAD

Fig. 56. Horizontal section through a jamb of a cased frame of good quality.

The frame consists of a *sill*, two *pulley stiles*, a *pulley head*, and *inside and outside linings*. In addition $\frac{5}{8}$-in. $\times 1\frac{1}{8}$-in. *staff beads*, and $\frac{3}{8}$-in. $\times \frac{7}{8}$-in. *parting beads*, form guides against which the sashes run. The *back linings*, closing the box containing the counterbalancing weights, are usually unplaned offcuts, and of similar material are the slight division pieces called *wagtails* suspended from a mortise in the pulley head. At the lower ends these wagtails finish 2 in. or 3 in. clear of the sill, and their function is to prevent the weights from coming into contact with each other.

Fig. 54 is a vertical section, Fig. 55 a part outside elevation, and Fig. 56 a horizontal section through the jambs of a cased frame of good quality. The $1\frac{1}{8}$ in. thick pulley stiles are housed into both the sill and the pulley head. At the sill they are secured by folding wedges and nails as illustrated in the sketch of Fig. 57, which shows the stile and wedges raised above their correct position. The joint between the pulley stiles and pulley head is a plain housing secured by nails, as suggested by the dotted lines in Fig. 55.

The inside and outside linings are tongued and grooved to the pulley stiles and head, housed across the edges of

the sill, and fixed with oval brads. The method of cutting the ends of the sill to take the linings is shown in Fig. 57, and the elevation of the joint between sill and outside lining is seen in Fig. 55.

This method of making the joint is, of course, inapplicable when the sill projects beyond the outer face of the frame. Then the outside linings finish on the weathered top of the

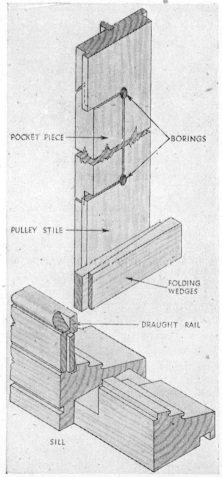

POCKET PIECE   BORINGS

PULLEY STILE

FOLDING WEDGES

DRAUGHT RAIL

SILL

Fig. 57. Showing method of cutting the ends of the sill in order to take the linings.

sill. Some authorities suggest that these linings should always finish thus whether the sill projects or not, and they argue that to substitute a deal member for part of a hardwood sill which is in a position exposed to the effects of the weather is quite unreasonable.

To stiffen the head linings and to fix them in the plane of the frame face, angle blocks are fixed at intervals of 9 in. to 12 in. as shown in Figs. 54 and 55. Note that a block should always occur behind the joints between the vertical and horizontal linings.

The section of the sill as given is quite a common one and would be described as double-weathered, throated and sunk. The groove on the face is for the tongue on the window board, and that on the underside is to receive a metal water bar sealing the joint between the wood and stone sills.

The function of the wide draught rail has been mentioned already, and the method of tonguing this rail into the sill and the edges of the linings is shown in Figs. 54 and 57. When fixing the inside linings the draught rail is first placed between the linings and the three members tapped down until the rail is in position.

Fixing the Sash Lines

To fix the sash lines, it is necessary to have access to the weights contained in the boxes formed by the linings and the pulley stiles. In most cases this is provided by a pocket piece arranged as shown in Fig. 57. The length of this opening varies with the size and weight of the sash, and its determination is largely a matter of experience. Usually, however, it is possible to arrange the upper joint to be always covered by the lower sash when hung.

Needless to say, it is better to provide a liberal opening than one not giving easy access to the top of the weights when

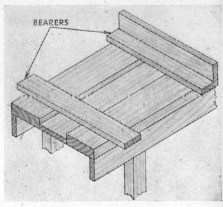

Fig. 58. Method of fixing bearers across the bench when assembling cased frames, after the pulley head has been nailed on to the stiles.

these are resting upon the sill. The manner of cutting the pockets is as follows:—

First, holes are bored in the backs of the stiles opposite the cuts and directly behind the groove for the parting bead. One of these holes penetrates to the bottom of the groove, the other need go but halfway through the thickness of the stile. Through the former boring a pad saw is used to begin the cut down the groove.

The cut is finished with a hand saw. The cuts across the stiles are made with the toe of a fine dovetail saw, the holes on the back and the groove on the face giving sufficient clearance to allow a saw to be used.

A wide thin chisel is made for the purpose of making these cuts, but it is not a popular tool. The short vertical cuts in the centre of the thickness are made by knocking the pocket pieces free by a blow from the back, but this is not done until immediately before the back linings are fixed.

The assembly of the frame is done in the following order. The working of the various members is nowadays a matter for the machine shop, but the parts are equally simple to work by hand. The

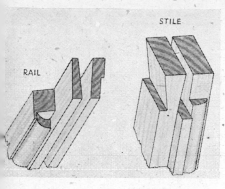
RAIL
STILE

ig. 59. Fixing the rail and stile on the bottom ish of a cased frame. The pins of the dovetail are worked on the rail ends.

xle pulleys are housed in individually nd the pocket pieces are cut as escribed.

When these operations are completed he pulley stiles are wedged and nailed) the sill. The edges of the stiles should e parallel to the face of the sill, and, ore important, they must not wind ith each other. The pulley head is now ailed on to the stiles. Bearers are then xed across the bench, out of winding, nd as indicated in Fig. 58.

One bearer is a plain board about in. × 1 in., but the second consists of a imilar board fixed to a heavier timber, sually about 4 in. × 3 in.

The frame is secured to the bench y screwing the sill to the heavy earer and by lightly bradding the ead to the plain bearer.

The frame is squared by testing the ngths of the diagonals before these rads are driven. It is economical to ave the sashes completed before assem ling the frame. They may then be fitted hen the frame is on the bench, for if the itside linings are fixed first, the sashes e brought to size when the frame is versed for the purpose of fixing the side linings.

The finish of the outside linings at the ead is shown in Fig. 55. The inside

lining requires practically no fitting other than at the end of the draught rail as already mentioned.

The removal of the tongues on the pocket pieces must not be overlooked and no nails should be driven through the lining. The back linings are scribed over the sill and cut to fit under the head. The beads are fitted and lightly fixed, as they must be removed when the sashes are hung. This cannot be done until after they are glazed and their weights determined.

The sashes are seen in the vertical section of Fig. 54 and the joint between the upper and lower meeting rails is clearly shown. The faces of the joint are bevelled to ensure a tight fit when the sashes are closed. The joint between the meeting rail and the stile is a simple one where the stile projects and forms a moulded horn.

A normal mortise and tenon is used, with the projecting part of the rail housed into the stile to a depth of about $\frac{1}{8}$ in. On the bottom sash, however, it is not customary to allow the stile to run above the meeting rail, and the best solution of the joint is that shown in Fig. 59. The pins of the dovetail are worked on the rail ends and arranged as in the diagram.

Machine Shop Methods

A common method in machine shops is to form a joint similar to that used on the upper sash, and to screw through the tenon from the back side. The horn is afterwards cut off flush with the top of the rail. The result is a slot mortise and tenon, which is secured with glue and a screw.

Provision for fixing the cord must not be omitted. Usually this consists of a groove in the back edge of the stile, terminating in a shallow hole about 1 in. in diameter. A knot in the end of the cord is nailed into this sinking, and

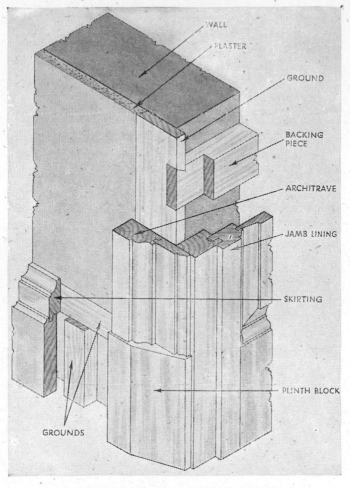

WALL

PLASTER

GROUND

BACKING PIECE

ARCHITRAVE

JAMB LINING

SKIRTING

PLINTH BLOCK

GROUNDS

FIXING SKIRTINGS AND JAMB LININGS

Fig. 60. Skirting here consists of two members tongued and grooved together. By this method of construction narrow boards can be used.

In its simplest form a wooden skirting consists of a plain board scribed to the floor. Such, however, is apt to appear heavy and the upper edge is usually eased back to the wall surface by means of a simple moulding. Often the skirtings are more elaborate and have sections such as those in Figs. 32 and 60. In the latter example the skirting consists of two members tongued and grooved.

By this means of construction narrower boards can be used, material is saved and the fixing of the skirting is simplified.

Skirtings should be fixed to grounds which in turn are fixed to wooden plugs driven either into the joints of the brickwork, or else to special fixing bricks built in at intervals. One horizontal ground having its upper edge about $\frac{1}{2}$ in. below the top of the skirting is required. The remaining grounds are usually vertical as shown in Fig. 60.

The joint between the skirting and the floor is usually plain. Very rarely the skirting carries a tongue on its lower edge which fits a groove worked in the flooring. This method is expensive, but eliminates the unsightly joint caused by

further clout nails are driven along the length of the cord, but enough line must be left free at the top of the stile to allow it to pass over the pulley.

SKIRTINGS AND ARCHITRAVES. The chief function of skirting boards and architrave mouldings is to cover the joint between a plaster surface and the adjacent woodwork. Being primarily finishing members they are often highly moulded and frequently form quite an important part of the decoration.

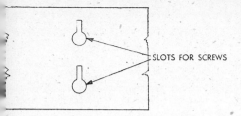

SLOTS FOR SCREWS

Fig. 61. Part of the back of a skirting showing the vertical position of the slots for screws.

both the floor joists and the skirting shrinking away from each other.

When fixing skirting it is usual first to fix a board having internal angles at both ends. This board is cut in tightly between the return surfaces, and the adjacent boards have their ends scribed to it. In good work the plain parts of the boards are tongued and grooved together. The groove is worked in the first board fixed, and the tongue on the board abutting against it. External angles are mitred.

Where the work is painted a plain mitre is made and the joint fixed with brads, but in work of consequence a secret dovetail joint should be used.

Fixing Skirtings

Skirtings are generally nailed to the grounds, and when they are to be painted this method is satisfactory. With polished work, however, they should be fixed with slot screws or by means of screws and pellets. In the former method, holes large enough to take a No. 12 or 14 screw and about $\frac{3}{8}$ in. or $\frac{1}{2}$ in. deep are bored in the backs of the skirting opposite the points of fixing.

Slots are then formed vertically as indicated in Fig. 61, which shows part of the back of a skirting to be fixed by slot screws.

A screw similar to those to be used is driven into a hardwood block, and the head left standing the $\frac{3}{8}$ in. or $\frac{1}{2}$ in. This screw head is then placed in the hole and, by tapping the block,

driven along the slot. Screws are then fixed in the grounds directly opposite the slots in the skirting, which is then driven down into position.

If the fixing screws project from the grounds slightly less than did the one from the block above mentioned, the

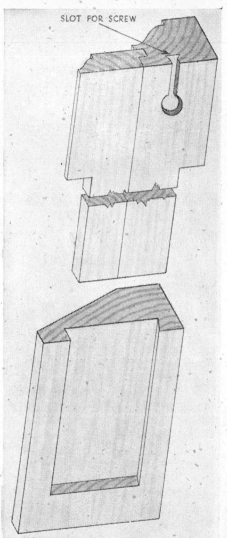

SLOT FOR SCREW

Fig. 62. Architrave built up of two members and terminating in a plinth block, which is fixed to the architrave. A dovetailed sinking is worked in the block and a corresponding projection formed on the architrave.

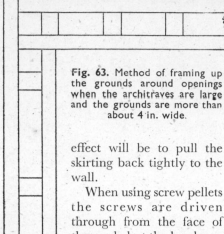

Fig. 63. Method of framing up the grounds around openings when the architraves are large and the grounds are more than about 4 in. wide.

effect will be to pull the skirting back tightly to the wall.

When using screw pellets the screws are driven through from the face of the work, but the heads are sunk into borings about $\frac{1}{2}$ in. deep. These holes are then filled with plugs slightly conical in shape, and so worked that the grain runs across and not parallel to the axis of the plug. If these pellets are carefully made from the same material as that which is being fixed, this method of plugging can be both efficient and practically secret.

ARCHITRAVES. In joinery an architrave is a member framing an opening and covering the joint between the door frame, window frame, or lining, and the plaster work. It may be simple in section, or highly carved and elaborated.

Three typical sections are given in Figs. 26, 29 and 30. The latter moulding is again shown in the sketch of Fig. 60 which illustrates the construction at the base of the jamb lining shown in section in Fig. 30. In this example the architrave is built up of two members and terminates in a plinth block, which is best fixed to the architrave as in Fig. 62.

A dovetailed sinking is worked in the block and a corresponding projection formed on the architrave. The fixing is done by means of glue and screws.

The mitres made in architraves are usually left plain when the section is small, but when the work is important some means of keeping the intersections of the mouldings correct should be employed. The simplest method is to form a groove in both mitred surfaces and to insert a cross-grained tongue, but by far the most effective way is to use this tongue in conjunction with a light handrail bolt.

Fixing Architraves

Architraves are fixed back to the grounds in much the same way as skirtings. With expensive work the sets of architrave are often put together in the workshop, and stretchers and braces screwed across the back. These sets are then fixed by slot screwing, or by screws and pellets.

If the edge of the architrave is thin it is often necessary to use fine panel pins to prevent the edge curling up, but where the work is polished the main fixing should not consist of nails.

The grounds around openings are frequently framed, that is, they are mortised and tenoned and glued up in the workshop. If the architraves are large and require grounds wider than about 4 in., the width is obtained by framing up narrow material and short rails, as shown in Fig. 63, which is an elevation of part of a ground 8 in. wide.

The jambs and head would be glued up and cleaned off before the whole ground was assembled. The joint between head and jamb is designed to permit a cramp to be applied across the frame.

FIXING JOINERY. The various operations involved in fitting and fixing grounds, architraves and skirtings, and the securing of door and window frames, linings and the like are included under the general heading of fixing.

Door and window frames may either

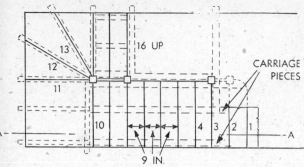

ig. 64. Plan of a close newel, or dog-leg stair. Newel stairs are divided into close newel and open newel forms.

to provide a fixing for joinery.

This ground is made by first driving plugs into the joints of the walling and cutting them off so that the ends are contained by a plane. The wooden grounds are then fixed.

Stairs

A most interesting branch of joinery is the construction of stairs. Great variety of design occurs and each requires individual consideration.

Stairs constructed of wood are of two types: the *newel* stair and the *geometrical* stair. In the former type newel posts occur at the points where the stair changes direction, and receive the ends of the stringer boards, or *strings*, as they are commonly called. A geometrical stair is one in which the string continues unbroken around a turn in plan. The

e built in, or they may be placed into osition after the brickwork is comleted. In the first case the frames are xed by hoop iron, expanded metal, or imilar material, nailed to the back of he frame and bedded into the joints of he walling.

Screws sunk below the surface of the ebate, with the holes pelleted, make he best fixing. Folding wedges immedately over each jamb, driven between he head and the lintel, ive additional rigidity. he frames must be fixed lumb and must be out f winding.

Jamb linings are fixed o grounds and backng pieces, as shown in he sketch of Fig. 60. he fixing of skirtings nd architraves has een already menioned.

Examples of wall anelling and their xings have been reerred to earlier. The rounds to which such vork is fixed should e very carefully preared. Unfinished vall surfaces are not ufficiently accurate

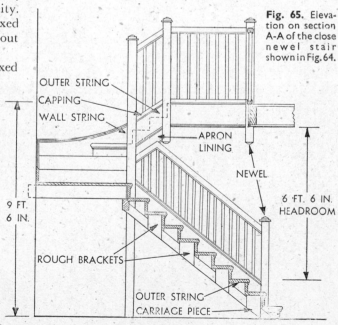

Fig. 65. Elevation on section A-A of the close newel stair shown in Fig. 64.

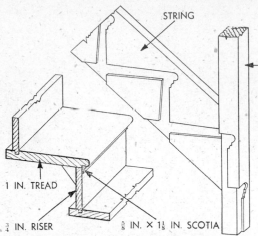

Fig. 66. Housing on the lower newel at the end of a long flight of stairs.

1 IN. TREAD

¾ IN. RISER

⅜ IN. × 1⅛ IN. SCOTIA

STRING

NEWEL

down to the floor. The function of the other newels is mainly to provide support for the handrail.

Sketches of the newels at the ends of the long flight are given in Figs. 66 and 67. Fig. 66 shows the housing on the lower newel, and Fig. 67 is a sketch of the upper newel prepared to take the ends of the winders. In the latter sketch the end of the upper string is drawn illustrating the tenons which fix the string to the newel. These tenons are secured by dowel pins as already described.

The common method of jointing together treads and risers to form the steps

newel variety is by far the most important of the two and will be considered first.

Newel stairs are again divided in the close newel and open newel forms. An example of a close newel, or dog-leg stair, is given in plan in Fig. 64 and in elevation in Fig. 65. In this type the outer strings of the separate flights have the same plan.

The total *rise* of the example given is 9 ft. 6 in. and with sixteen risers each step has a rise of just over 7 in. The width, or *going*, of each step has been obtained by applying the rule: twice the rise plus the tread equals 23 in. Thus 2×7 in. $+9$ in. $=23$ in., which gives a 9-in. tread width or going.

The half-turn in plan is obtained by means of a quarter-space landing followed by three *winders*, or tapered steps. The placing of the winders above the landing is a necessary precaution. Narrow-ended winders are a frequent cause of accident, and should not occur at the top of a flight.

The principal newel is that about which the winders turn. It supports the stair and is shown running

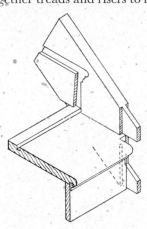

Fig. 67. The upper newel prepared to take the end of the winders. The end of the upper string shows the tenons, secured by dowel pins, which fix the string to the newel.

is seen in Fig. 66. The tread overhangs the riser face and is grooved to take a slip called a *scotia*.

By glueing the scotia into the groove a rebate is formed, and into this rebate the riser is fixed by means of glue and angle blocks.

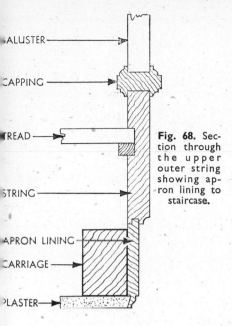

BALUSTER

CAPPING

TREAD

Fig. 68. Section through the upper outer string showing apron lining to staircase.

STRING

APRON LINING

CARRIAGE

PLASTER

The lower edges of the risers are shown tongued into the treads, but this construction is not always adopted. Instead, screws are driven up into the risers from the underside of the tread.

The steps are carried by the strings into which they house to a depth of about ⅜ in. The housings in the strings are tapered to accommodate the wedges which, when glued and driven behind the treads and risers, fix the steps to the string.

Thickness of Strings

The thickness of strings varies, but it is customary to make the wall string thinner than the outer string, which cannot well be less than 1⅜ in. thick unless supported by a *spandril* wall or framing. The spandril is the triangular space formed by the floor, the newel, and the under edge of the outer string. This variation of thickness does not occur where fire-resisting qualities are required. Then all treads, risers, and strings must be of approved hardwood,

and worked from material 2 in. thick.

When the top edge of a string is parallel to the pitch or inclination of the stair it is called a *close string*, and generally carries a capping mould along its upper edge, as seen in the diagram. This capping improves the appearance and provides a seating for the *balusters*. The winders are constructed in the same way as the *fliers*, as the parallel steps are called, except that the lower edges of the risers are seldom tongued into the treads.

Setting Out Winders

Winders are set out full size, usually on a piece of plywood, and from this plan the lengths of the housings on the wall string and on the newel faces are obtained.

When there are three winders, as in the given example, it is satisfactory to divide the plan angle of 90 degrees into three equal parts. The method of setting out the position of the riser faces by means of a walking line will be explained later.

Additional support for the winders is obtained by short joists running from the newel to the wall.

The landing is treated as a small floor carried by joists, which are shown in the

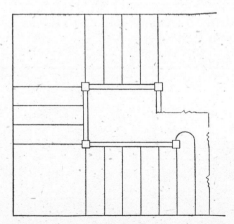

Fig. 69. Round-ended step at the foot of a stair. It is usual to form the first step of a staircase in rounded form to ensure easy approach.

Fig. 70. Vertical section of a bullnose step, showing how the solid scotia is screwed first to the riser and then to the tread.

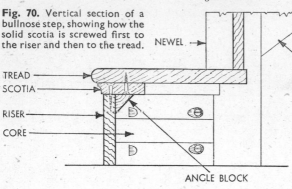

NEWEL →

STRING

TREAD ——
SCOTIA ——
RISER ——
CORE ——

ANGLE BLOCK

the lower edge of th
outer string.

This board is calle
an *apron lining*. I
covers the rough cai
riage-piece and provides
finish between the soffit an
the string. A section throug
the upper outer string is give
in Fig. 68.

Handrails are tenoned int
the newels and the whole sec
tion should be housed to
depth of $\frac{1}{2}$ in. The joints are fixed b
dowels through the tenons.

An exception to this is where the rail
run under the return string. The finis
here is as shown in Fig. 65 where th
short piece of handrail rebates over th
apron lining. The height of the handra
over the stair is 2 ft. 9 in. measured in th
plane of a riser face. Over a landing
height of 3 ft. is regarded as a minimum

When planning stairs an importan
point to consider is that of head room
which is the distance from a tread sur
face to any obstruction situated abov
the stair.

Sometimes this distance is measure
at 90 degrees to the pitch of the stair
but as the dimension should vary wit
the pitch, it is safer to measure vertically
The 6 ft. 6 in. given in Fig. 65 is
reasonable minimum, for althoug
few people would be inconvenience

elevation and indicated by dotted lines in the plan. On top of the landing a skirting connects the upper and lower wall strings.

Three *carriage pieces* are suggested by dotted lines in the plan (Fig. 64). These members add stiffness to the stair and form a fixing for a lath and plaster or other soffit covering. Where the stair is narrow and there is no plaster under, a centre carriage only is common.

To this carriage are fixed short pieces of board called *rough brackets*. These brackets fit tightly under the treads and transmit loads on to the carriage. Where no spandril filling occurs, and under upper strings, a cover board is tongued into

LAMINATED CORE ——→

SCREWS

FOLDING WEDGE

RISE

Fig. 71. Method of forming the rounded end to the riser by means of a core which is built up and cut to shape. A pair of folding wedges, which draw the veneer tightly around the core, is also shown.

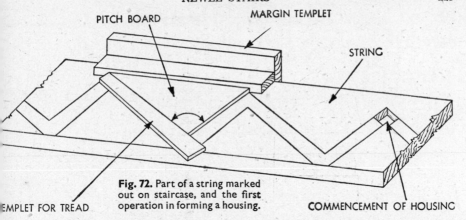

PITCH BOARD

MARGIN TEMPLET

STRING

EMPLET FOR TREAD

Fig. 72. Part of a string marked out on staircase, and the first operation in forming a housing.

COMMENCEMENT OF HOUSING

the head room were 6 ft., it must be remembered that the upper floors of a house have to be furnished.

To permit the stair to be easily approached it is customary to form a rounded end to at least the first step. When this step is planned like that shown in Fig. 65 it is called a *bullnose step,* and the plan in Fig. 69 is described as a *round-ended step.*

Construction of Steps

The method of constructing these steps is illustrated in Figs. 70 and 71. Fig. 70 is a vertical section of the bullnose step and illustrates the manner in which the solid scotia is screwed first to the riser, and then to the tread. This scotia board is widened at the end to carry round and into the newel. The method of forming the rounded end to the riser is indicated in Fig. 71.

A core is built up and cut to the shape shown. The riser is reduced to the thickness of a veneer for a distance equal to the length of the curved surface of the core, plus ½ in. This ½ in. accommodates a slight pair of folding wedges, also seen in Fig. 71. When core and riser are prepared, they are glued and screwed in the position of the sketch. The remainder of the core and veneer are then glued and the core gently rolled round into posi-

tion. The wedges, easily driven, draw the veneer tightly around the core, which is finally fixed by screwing to the riser.

OPEN NEWEL STAIRS. These stairs are an improved variety of the type just discussed. A wider space is required to accommodate such a stair, but if treated generously the resulting effect can amply repay the expenditure. Fig. 69 is the plan of an open newel stair with a total rise of 9 ft. 6 in., and with 9-in. treads, as in the previous example. No winders are introduced, for if these were used in place of either quarter space landing, a dangerous stair might very easily result.

The method of constructing and supporting the stair does not vary in essentials from that already described, and elevations and sections may be worked up in the manner illustrated in Fig. 65.

SETTING OUT NEWEL STAIRS. The setting out of stairs and handrails is now regarded as the work of a specialist. Few joiners, however, should find difficulty in marking out newel stairs. Although the design is not the province of the man making the stair he should, by inspecting the site and by checking dimensions, verify that the drawings are correct and that they include no impossible factors.

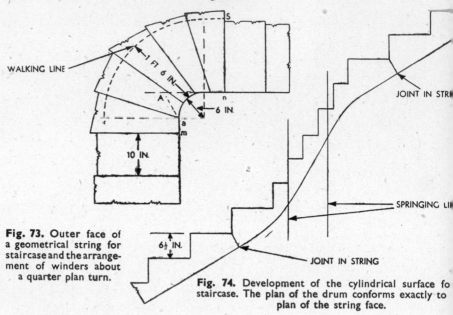

WALKING LINE

1 FT 6 IN.

A

6 IN.

n

s

10 IN.

a

m

6½ IN.

JOINT IN STRI

SPRINGING LI

JOINT IN STRING

Fig. 73. Outer face of a geometrical string for staircase and the arrangement of winders about a quarter plan turn.

Fig. 74. Development of the cylindrical surface fo staircase. The plan of the drum conforms exactly to plan of the string face.

If obvious improvement of design is possible, suggestions should be submitted to the architect. When measuring, the amount of the total rise is noted. This dimension is marked along a lath called the *storey rod*, and is divided into as many equal parts as there are risers in the flight. A division is the width of all risers.

Unless winders occur, all lines may be put directly on to the material, the sizes of which can be obtained from scale drawing in conjunction with the full-size details. Winders are set out full size. To mark out the string a *pitch board* and a *margin templet* are prepared. These are shown in Fig. 72 which illustrates the method of applying them.

To mark the back edges of the housings two other templets are made, one for both tread and riser. Fig. 72 shows part of a string marked out and the first operation in forming a housing. A sinking is formed at the angle and in this a tenon saw is worked in order to make the cuts which bound the housings.

The length of the string is fixed marking out the necessary number steps. Shoulder lines on the strings fixed by measuring back the distar seen in plan from the riser face to edge of the newel. Strings must be out as pairs.

The marking out of the newels simple if the plan, showing the manr in which string and riser faces inters the newel face, is frequently referred

GEOMETRICAL STAIRS AND HANDRA ING. The scientific approach to t branch of the subject cannot be ma without a fairly sound knowledge descriptive geometry.

The example taken is that given plan in Fig. 73 which shows the ou face of a geometrical string and arrangement of winders about a quar plan turn. The positions of the riser fa of the first and last fliers are assumed be fixed by circumstance, and althou a better-looking string and rail could obtained by altering these positions su an arrangement is not always possit

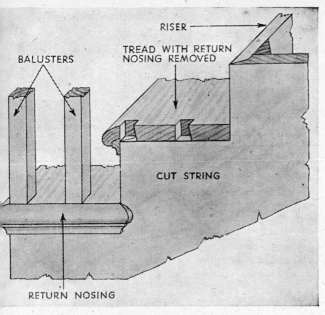

BALUSTERS

TREAD WITH RETURN
NOSING REMOVED

CUT STRING

RETURN NOSING

STAIRCASE CONSTRUCTION

Fig. 75. Method of constructing the cut string in a staircase and showing fixing of balusters and return nosings.

sary, to give the development of tread and riser.

The wreath is worked from a shape cut from the plank. The outline is obtained by marking about the face mould. The ends are planed true and square to the face of the material, and through the centre point of each the appropriate twist bevel is applied.

Fig. 76 is a sketch of the material with the bevels applied, and with lines square to the ends marked across the face from the points where the bevel intersects it. Similar lines are placed on the under surface of the material. About the bevel lines as a centre line the rectangular section of the rail is drawn on the joint surfaces, and from these sections it is apparent how the face moulds must be applied to the faces of the material.

When in position, the tangent lines on the face moulds must coincide with the lines marked AB and BC in the sketch.

The shape of the string is found by developing the cylindrical surface of which it is part. Such development is given in Fig. 74. The string is constructed by reducing to a veneer the curved portion falling between the developed springing lines, thus allowing the string be bent around a drum.

Staves are fitted and glued to the back of the veneer after the string has been bent around the drum in the correct position. These form and maintain the required curve, and restore the string to original thickness.

The method of constructing the cut string is shown in Fig. 75.

The method employed in setting out the handrail is that known as the square cut and tangent system. The plans of the straight rail continued are regarded as the horizontal traces of vertical tangent planes. These planes, and the points where the riser faces intersect them, are turned about, where neces-

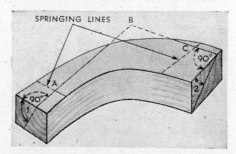

SPRINGING LINES B

Fig. 76. The wreath for a staircase handrail, showing shape cut from a plank. The outline is obtained by marking round the face mould.

CHAPTER 6

SERVICES

Drainage systems. Sewers and drains. Gully traps. Inspection chambers. Testi
drains. Ventilation. Water supply systems. Cisterns. Hot water systems. Puri
of water. Methods of testing. Gas and gas fittings. Reading the meter. Electric
terms. Lights and bells. Heating and ventilation. Panel heating.

THE planning of the drainage system of a building is a most essential matter, and one to which the most careful consideration has to be given. It is no overstatement to say that the installation of an efficient system is vital to public health.

In the Public Health Act, 1936, and the previous Act of 1875 it was laid down that local authorities are to be responsible for the provision and maintenance of proper sewers and sewage disposal works, or other effective means of dealing with and disposing of waste matter.

The Industrial Revolution brought with it a great influx of the population into the towns, where the workers gathered in great sprawling, unorganized communities around the new factories. Matters were thereby brought to a head, and sewerage and sanitation became of urgent and imperative importance.

Safeguarding Public Health

The various nineteenth-century enactments took the preliminary steps to safeguard the public health and to prevent a recurrence of plague and epidemic conditions, which in a modern community would constitute nothing less than a national disaster.

Realizing the importance of sanitation in relation to the health of the community, it is obvious that the greatest care and attention is required in a matters connected with drainage, pa ticularly as the majority of the work underground and not readily open inspection and immediate rectificatic of defects.

Modern Drainage Systems

The sewerage and drainage system a modern community falls into tw main classifications:—

(1) Public sewers, which are constructe and maintained by the local authorit

(2) Individual house drainage provide by private enterprise and capital, i cluding the proper connection of suc drainage to the public system.

In order to ensure that drainage wo carried out by private persons is eff ciently done, it is incumbent on the loc authority to approve the lay-out of ne systems and supervise their constructio

The first point to be cleared should be the position and size of the existir sewer and its construction, i.e., earther ware pipes, masonry culvert, etc., to gether with all particulars relating to i depth and direction of flow.

It should also be ascertained whethe any existing system is separate c whether it is combined or partiall combined with adjoining systems. I may be found that it is possible to cor nect two or more houses to a commo drain, and, if this is so, particulars c

228

xisting agreements and conditions will
▸e required.

The type of connection to be used in
▸onnecting the house drains to the sewer
▸ill be decided by the shape of the latter.
'he actual connection is usually made
y the local authority, who recharge the
▸ost involved to the owner. This pro-
▸edure ensures that the work is properly
▸arried out, and that nothing is done to
▸terfere with the efficiency of the main
ystem, or any foreseeable future develop-
▸ents. It is very essential that no con-
▸ection should be made at right angles
▸ the main flow, as a chokage at the
▸nction may be caused thereby. Con-
▸ections are, therefore, made slanting
▸to the main pipe, towards the direction
f flow.

Drainage Pipe Standards

The standard internal diameter of
▸rainage pipe used for domestic build-
▸gs, where no considerable flow is anti-
▸pated, is 4 in. Where several houses are
▸rained by a common pipe, or in the
▸ase of a large building or institution,
▸here a considerable flow is expected, a
-in. pipe will be required. All drains
▸nd sewers must be laid so that they have
▸ self-cleansing velocity, and an appro-
▸riate fall is obtained by allowing 1 in.
▸ fall for a horizontal length equivalent
▸ ten times the diameter of the pipe
▸mployed. Hence, from this rule the
▸llowing minimum permissible falls
▸ay be evolved (Table I).

Careful attention should be given to

Diameter of pipe in inches	Vertical falls in inches	Horizontal distance in inches
4	1	40
6	1	60
9	1	90
12	1	120

able I. A useful table giving the minimum permissible falls for drains and sewers.

securing a proper fall, as excessive
gradients will prove damaging, and
obviously flat pipes will be inefficient
because they will not be self-cleansing.

All sewerage systems fall into one of
three classes, viz.: (1) separate; (2)
partially separate; (3) combined.

In the separate system there are two
sewers, one being for surface and storm
water, the other solely for soil and foul
water. The combined system consists of
only one pipe, through which is conveyed both surface and foul water.

The design of house drains will be
governed by what type of public sewer
exists in the locality. If the latter is
separate all house drains will have to
consist of two pipes, one for foul and one
for surface water; if the main system is
combined then only one pipe will, of
course, be required for house drains.

Figs. 1 and 2 are typical examples of
the separate and combined systems.
In the case of a partially separate
system, the roof water and surface
water from the rear of the building are
taken into the foul-water drains for
ensuring additional flushing and cleansing, while that from the front is dis-
posed of independently.

Lay-out of Sewers

Provided that all drains have a good
fall, separate systems are the most desirable and the modern practice is to adopt
them wherever possible; since it follows
that the flow to be dealt with at the
sewage disposal works will remain
practically constant throughout the
year, and there will be no waste of time,
money and plant in dealing with comparatively unpolluted surface and storm
water. The latter would be discharged
into convenient streams and watercourses.

The lay-out of all sewers, of whatever
type, is the responsibility of the local
authority, and naturally attention will

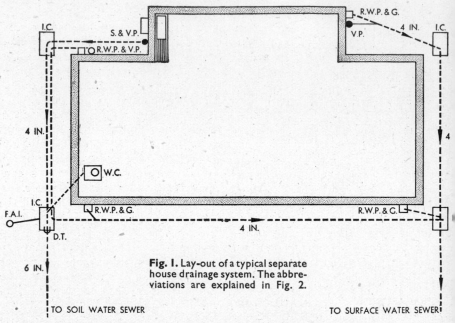

Fig. I. Lay-out of a typical separate house drainage system. The abbreviations are explained in Fig. 2.

TO SOIL WATER SEWER   TO SURFACE WATER SEWER

be paid to the most economic methods to be used having regard to local conditions such as the availability of watercourses and streams, and the nature of strata. By providing a separate system the size and cost of the foul-water sewer can be reduced, and convenient watercourses greatly assist towards a saving in the length and cost of piping.

So far as house drains are concerned, the separate system almost doubles the drainage cost as compared with the combined method. There are cases where it has an advantage, in the fact that there is less likelihood of flooding during times of heavy rainfall.

Planning Sanitation

The arrangement of the sanitary fittings should be so planned that the scheme may fulfil its purpose in the most economical manner. Good grouping of the fittings will often avoid undue expense on long, surplus lengths of pipes, and other unnecessary work; a bad lay-out will waste a good deal of money and will probably provide an unsight arrangement of pipes and fittings arou the building. For instance, it can oft be arranged for rain-water down pipes discharge over the sink and bath wast thus saving the cost of two separa drains, and this method is also adva tageous in ensuring that the water se in the gullies does not evaporate if t sanitary fittings are not used for sor time.

The object to be aimed at in disposi of all foul water or sewage should be remove it from the building as quick as possible. In normal dwelling-hous this can be effected by grouping t w.c.s, lavatory basins and other sanita fittings, in one part of the building, b in larger buildings such as hospitals ar hotels, the fittings can usually arranged to come one above the oth on the various storeys.

Carrying the drains too deep must avoided, as this only increases the cc of excavation and will make subseque maintenance very expensive. The upp

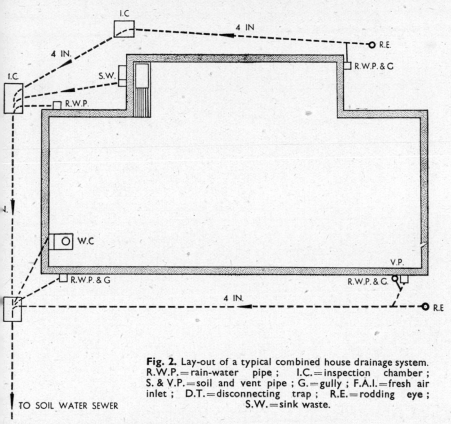

Fig. 2. Lay-out of a typical combined house drainage system.
R.W.P. = rain-water pipe ; I.C. = inspection chamber ;
S. & V.P. = soil and vent pipe ; G. = gully ; F.A.I. = fresh air
inlet ; D.T. = disconnecting trap ; R.E. = rodding eye ;
S.W. = sink waste.

d of the system should be kept as high possible and the fall so arranged that is the minimum required to give a f-cleansing velocity.

The first inspection chamber need ly be about 2 ft. in depth with the propriate fall from this chamber to sequent chambers, and finally to the ercepting chamber; but below the ercepting chamber the fall will, of urse, have to vary with the depth of e main sewer.

Careful levels over the site and the eparation of working sections showing e depth and position of the existing ver and other features will greatly ist the proper planning and econom l lay-out of the house drains.

A copy of the drainage plans of every building should be in the hands of the owner, together with the usual property papers and deeds; this plan would prove particularly useful in case of defects and would help the owner to carry out his own inspections from time to time to satisfy himself that the system is working efficiently, and would also serve as a permanent record available in the case of alterations or additions.

Glazed stoneware or heavy cast iron are usually employed for drainage work, although other suitable materials are on the market.

The usual size of pipe for domestic purposes is 4-in. internal diameter and this is regarded as the minimum size which is adequate for all drains carrying sewage and foul water.

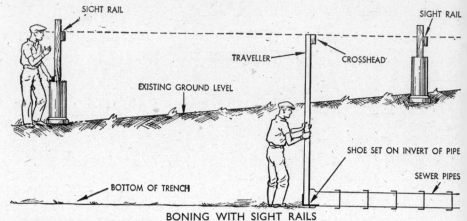

BONING WITH SIGHT RAILS

Fig. 3. Use of boning rods and sight rails for laying drain-pipes to the proper fall.

Pipes are laid to proper falls with the aid of boning rods and sight rails (Fig. 3). A tapered board cut to the appropriate fall is always useful, although not so accurate over a long length of drain. This board is used together with a spirit-level for grading the trench bottom to a proper fall (Fig. 4). All drains must be laid on a good solid bottom to prevent subsidence and consequent fracture, and the best practice is to put down a 6-in. layer of concrete under all pipes, whatever the condition of the trench bottom may be.

If at all possible, drains should not be laid under buildings, but if this is quite unavoidable the pipes should be completely surrounded by 6 in. of concrete or, alternatively, cast-iron pipes should be used (Fig. 5). An access must, of course, be provided outside the buildin in a convenient position for rodding.

Drains should always be kept we clear of external walls, 4 ft. being th minimum permissible distance. Wher this cannot be obtained concrete mus be rammed in well underneath the wa footings (Fig. 6).

In the case of drains passing throug a wall the weight of the latter must b carried by a lintel, or suitable relievin arch (Fig. 7).

If it is necessary, owing to levels, t construct drains above ground, cast iron pipes should always be used, bu they must be properly supported b piers at each joint.

In estate development the commo

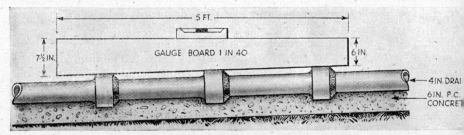

DRAIN LAID TO A FALL BY GAUGE BOARD

Fig. 4. Tapered gauge board, used in conjunction with a spirit level, for grading the trench bottom to a proper fall. This method is not accurate over a long length of drain.

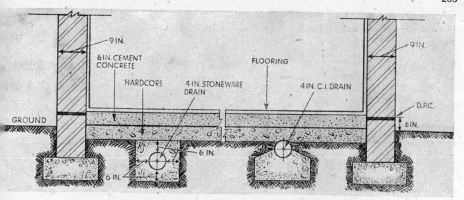

TREATMENT OF DRAINS UNDER BUILDINGS

g. 5. The pipes should be entirely surrounded by 6 in. of concrete, or cast-iron pipes should be
ed. Drains under buildings should be avoided if possible. An access for rodding is essential.

pe system is often employed. This pipe connected to the main sewer and the arious houses are connected into it. his saves a great number of individual ppings of the main sewer and will ove quite efficient provided not more an six houses are connected to the mmon pipe. The size of such a pipe ould be 6 in. after the first two houses, d all connections to the sewer should 6 in. in diameter from the last house spection chamber to the sewer.

The pipes are laid at such a fall that ey possess a self-cleansing velocity; if sufficient fall is provided solids will be posited in the pipe and eventually oke the drainage; on the other hand o much fall will cause the effluent to n off quickly, leaving the solid matter hind, where it will gradually accumu-te and decompose.

Glazed stoneware drain pipes are ually jointed with cement mortar con-sting of 1 part of Portland cement and parts of sand. In order to prevent inting material getting inside the pipe is a good plan to insert a few strands tarred gasket or hemp before cement-g the joint, and in all cases special tention should be paid to cleaning out operly the interior of the pipes as

—H*

the work proceeds with a half-moon scraper or swab. Cast-iron pipes are jointed with gasket and metallic lead.

Gully traps are used to collect waste water from scullery and kitchen sinks, lavatory basins, baths and rain-water pipes. They are also used for the removal of surface drainage from paved areas and yards. They are made in various sizes and types, the main features of a good gully being: (a) simplicity of con-struction and freedom from flaws in the stoneware or any other defects; (b) to be completely self-cleansing; (c) to have a thoroughly adequate water seal of approximately $2\frac{1}{2}$ in.

Gully Traps

A gully consists of a pipe bent into such a shape that it forms a trap which provides a water seal and prevents the escape of gases and ventilation from the drain or sewer. The gully is usually square at the inlet and provided with a light metal grating to arrest solids liable to cause obstruction. A back inlet is provided in some gullies which takes this water into the gully below the grating, but above the water seal. This type is very suitable for receiving roof water, and is less likely to become obstructed,

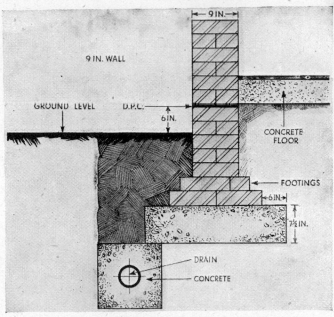

TREATMENT OF DRAIN ADJOINING MAIN WALL

Fig. 6. Where a drain cannot be kept well clear of external walls concrete must be rammed in underneath the wall footings as shown.

grating. If this channel is too long it will tend to become offensive owing to the deposit of foul matter and it should not, therefore, be more than about 18 in.

At any abrupt change in the direction of a drain or the junction of three or more pipes it necessary to provide an inspection chamber. These chambers allow easy access the drain for examination and the removal of any chokage by rodding or other means. In planning a drainage system attention should be paid to combining the drains in such a manner that the number of inspection chambers is reduced to a minimum, otherwise considerable expense will be incurred. Depth and number of branches are governing factors in determining the size required for a chamber. A width of 2 ft. by a length of 2 ft. 6 in. adequate for shallow chambers, and

inasmuch as an ordinary gully often becomes choked on the grating with leaves and other material; a side or back inlet consequently obviates this trouble.

In buildings where large quantities of grease and similar matter is expected in the waste water, a special form of gully is used, known as a grease trap.

Regular cleaning out should be given to all gullies, otherwise it will be found that an accumulation of grease and other matter contained in the waste water may give rise to fouling of the gully. Common washing soda and hot water will perform this cleansing quite satisfactorily. Gullies should be fixed perfectly level and bedded with Portland cement concrete and connected to the drain. The trap of a gully is usually brought up level with the surrounding paving and it may be finished off with a small fender wall around a channel leading to the trapped gully

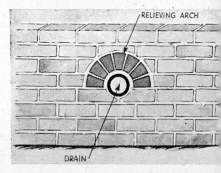

Fig. 7. Where a drain passes through a wall the weight of the latter must be carried by a lintel or relieving arch as shown above.

e length should be increased by a rther 9 in. for every additional con-ction over the number of one.

Chambers are usually built in 9-in. ickwork carried up from the level of e drain invert to such a height that the st-iron cover, when fixed, will be flush ith the surrounding ground level. The terior of the chamber must be rendered ith Portland cement and clean, sharp nd, or alternatively, faced with glazed icks. The walls must stand on a con-ete base 6 in. thick, carried right over e bottom of the chamber (Fig. 8).

Coated cast-iron covers must be ed to all chambers, either light or heavy pattern, according to the weight of traffic to be carried, and the clear opening should be at least 24 in. × 18 in.

Chambers of 3 ft. or more in depth must be provided with suitable cast-iron coated step irons, built into the brick-work at 18-in. intervals.

Step irons consist of a shaped project-ing tread and two ends which are let into the jointing of the chamber. They form a ladder for use by workmen. In the case of deep chambers care should be taken to avoid connecting any drain through the walling and dis-charging the contents at such a level to make the steps inconvenient for use.

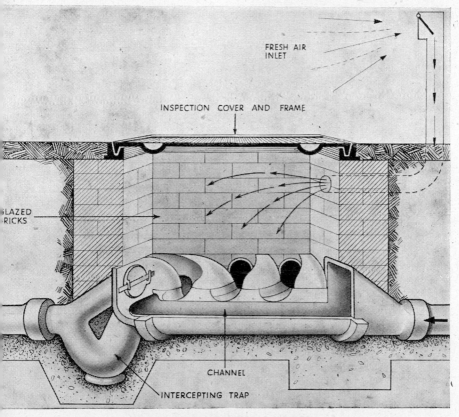

FRESH AIR INLET

INSPECTION COVER AND FRAME

LAZED RICKS

CHANNEL

INTERCEPTING TRAP

DRAINAGE INSPECTION CHAMBER

g. 8. Where the direction of a drain changes abruptly, or at the junction of three or more es, an inspection chamber is necessary. It allows of easy access to the drains for testing and aning. An intercepting trap is provided in the chamber which is nearest to the sewer.

Half-round, glazed, earthenware channels must be used in the bottom of chambers, and special channels of appropriate shape are obtainable for this purpose. Channels can also be constructed in cement concrete, finished in cement and sand to a smooth face and curved properly according to the direction of flow. The bottom of the chamber must be properly benched up in concrete around the channels and finished off with a smooth rendering.

Chambers must, in every case, be constructed in a watertight manner to prevent flooding and chokage of the drain.

Intercepting Chambers

The lowest chamber in the system before the drain connects up with the main sewer should be a disconnecting, or intercepting chamber. These chambers are constructed in precisely the same manner as described above, but are provided with an intercepting trap at their lower end. The function of this trap is to prevent gas and fumes from the sewer finding their way back into the drains and possibly into the building. These traps are provided with a cleaning eye and stopper, bedded in clay.

Attention should occasionally be given to this stopper, as it sometimes happens that it gets removed and lodged in the pipes, causing an obstruction. The intercepting chamber serves to ventilate the house drain by means of its fresh-air inlet. It prevents the escape of gases from sewers or cesspits and it is useful for inspection or cleansing purposes.

Both the house drains and the connection to the sewer may be rodded, if necessary, from this chamber. The covers of all chambers should be airtight, and this is usually effected by providing a seal of grease or plastic compound in the frame.

It is not infrequent to find chambers constructed of concrete, rendered over internally. This is quite a satisfactor procedure, provided the chamber i watertight and the walls are non absorbent.

Under the building by-laws all nev drains are thoroughly tested as cor struction proceeds. This duty is pel formed by the building inspector c surveyor to the local authority.

Upon arriving on the site he wi probably first of all carry out an inspec tion of the exterior of the drains, satisfy ing himself that they are not laid irregu larly, the joints having a satisfactor appearance and that all pipes ar properly supported and protected.

He will also satisfy himself that onl best-quality pipes have been used, a second-quality pipes are not permissibl for soil drains. Second-quality pipes ar marked by a black ring painted aroun them. A check will also be made o whether all jointing material has bee removed from the bore of the pip either by a scraper or swab, and he ma even roll a ball through the pipes t assure himself that they are not in an way obstructed.

Water Test of Drains

The drains will next be subjected to water test under pressure. This metho of testing is severe, but is quite fai having regard to the fact that condition are being artificially set up which woul in fact, take place in the event of blockage. Before commencing the te one should, of course, be satisfied tha all joints are quite hard and properly se as a green joint will obviously blow o under pressure.

It is best to adopt a logical sequenc in making a test, and it is a good plan t test all branches first. The upper length of the system should also be taken firs so that the water released from ther may be subsequently utilized for th lower portions of the drain.

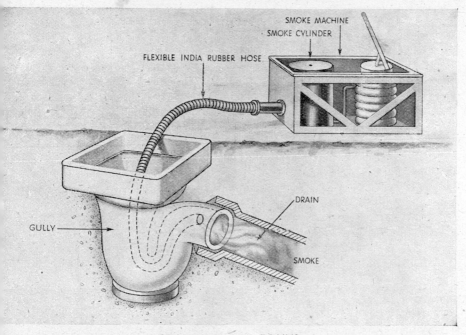

SMOKE MACHINE
SMOKE CYLINDER

FLEXIBLE INDIA RUBBER HOSE

DRAIN

GULLY

SMOKE

SMOKE TEST FOR DRAINS

Fig. 9. Smoke-testing machines consist of a container for burning treated material, and a fan for forcing the resulting smoke through a length of rubber piping into the drain.

A rubber plug or bag is used to stopper the drains, and these are inserted in the pipes, where they enter an inspection chamber. The length of drain is then completely filled with water until about 3 ft. of head is obtained. It will probably be necessary to plug up the gullies before this head is achieved. Care should also be taken to see that no air remains trapped in the pipes. The danger of this is obviated by pushing a length of rubber tubing into the gully over the trap, and blowing into it; after the blowing any trapped air will be forced back through the tube.

Having filled the drains properly, the level of the standing water is carefully observed, and it is a good idea to place a piece of paper or a matchstick on the surface. The drains should then be left for about an hour. If at the end of this period any fall in the water level has

occurred or any movement of the marker has taken place, a leak in the drain would be indicated. Each joint should again be examined from the exterior for evidence of leakages and the undersides felt with the hands for traces of moisture. Any defective joint found is marked with a chalk cross, and must be chiselled out and rectified.

Practical experience will show that a little absorption takes place, due to the very slight natural porosity of the materials, and atmospheric conditions may give rise to what is known to the building man as weeping, or slight moisture around the joints. The practical man will soon know how to allow for these points.

When all defects have been remedied the drains will be once more tested and if found watertight, the trenches may be filled in. Filling in must be carefully

TWO IMPORTANT PROCESSES IN BUILDING CONSTRUCTION

(Above). Method of construction of fender wall and chimney breasts. Note the damp-pr
course under the ground-floor joists. The strips on top of joists are temporary distance pie

(Below). Ashlar stones in course of erection. All stones are set upright and tested with a plumb-r

arried out with a layer of fine earth
rst placed around the pipes; large
ones may cause damage. When the
uilding is completed a final water test
10uld be carried out to make sure that
o damage has been caused to the
rains during the course of the building
perations.

Smoke Test

Drains may also be tested by means
f smoke. There are various types of
ood smoke machines on the market for
1e purpose. In principle these machines
onsist of a container for burning
eated material and a fan for forcing
1e resulting smoke through a length of
1bber piping into the drain (Fig. 9).
ormerly smoke tests were carried out
y firing a smoke rocket into the pipes,
ut this method is now obsolete, as quite
bviously it does not secure good diffu-
on of the smoke pressure inside the
rain.

The smoke test is, of course, not as
:vere as the water test, but may be used
ith a good effect on surface-water
rains and is used for existing soil
rains. Any leakage of smoke through
1e joints will indicate a defect, and one
dvantage of this method is that defects
1 covered drains can be traced, as the
noke will force its way up through the
oil.

The importance of proper testing can-
ot be over-emphasized. Once drains
re filled in, they tend to be forgotten,
nd undetected defects may soon give
se to undesirable and dangerous con-
itions.

Testing the length of pipe between the
terceptor and the sewer is a difficult
roblem, as there will be no means of
ugging the pipes. This length, should,
owever, be the subject of special care,
oth in construction and examination
All sewers must be properly venti-
ted, but the method adopted may vary

in the districts of different local authorities. This affects the builder and house-
holder in that his local authority may
or may not call for the provision of an
intercepting trap.

As previously explained, the intercepting trap is built in the lowest
chamber on the system, usually near the
boundary of the property and the point
where the private drain enters the
public sewer. A fresh-air inlet is usually
provided in an intercepting chamber
and, together with a ventilating shaft at
the higher end of the system, serves to
ventilate the drain. This is easily understood if we bear in mind the fact that air
in a drain is nearly always warmer than
the external air. Thus the heavy cold
air forces its way down the fresh-air
inlet, displacing the warmer air in
the drain, which is gradually pushed
out through the ventilating shaft.

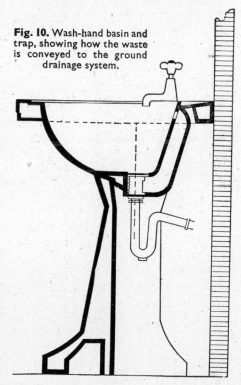

Fig. 10. Wash-hand basin and
trap, showing how the waste
is conveyed to the ground
drainage system.

A fresh-air inlet should be carefully fixed in a suitable position, where it is not liable to damage or likely to become choked by weeds or vegetation. It should be carried up about 3 ft. clear of the ground and fixed so that its inlet faces the prevailing wind.

The principle of omitting the intercepting trap, and ventilating a main sewer through private house drains, is not so objectionable as it sounds. It can be argued that an inter-cepting trap impedes the proper flow in the drain, and is bound to cause a deposition of offensive matter, owing to the fact that the intercepting trap can never be properly flushed. In this case gases given off from this decomposing matter can be quite as bad as the sewer gas itself.

In practice the method has not been found to have any harmful effects upon public health. It will be appreciated that where sewers are constructed with a proper self-cleansing velocity no deposition of offensive matter will occur and gases in the pipes should not, therefore, be any more dangerous than those in a house drain. Having regard to this fact the omission of the intercepting trap should not necessarily be harmful.

Cast-iron pipes give an excellent job and are to be preferred if a really high-class or especially efficient system is required. Cast iron pipes are advantageous in that they are more quickly laid, require less jointing, and, if properly constructed give an airtight drainage system for many years.

Every necessary type of fitting in the way of gullies, bends and traps is manufactured in cast iron, and a suitable type of fitting to fit in with any scheme can usually be found. Square

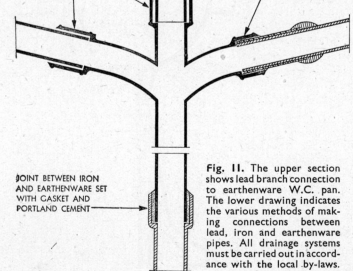

SOCKETED BRASS INTERNAL THIMBLE SET WITH GASKET AND PORTLAND CEMENT

LEAD

JOINTS BETWEEN IRON AND IRON SET WITH GASKET RUN WITH LEAD

JOINTS BETWEEN LEAD AND IRON SHOWING BRASS SLEEVE AND WIPED JOINT

JOINT BETWEEN IRON AND EARTHENWARE SET WITH GASKET AND PORTLAND CEMENT

Fig. 11. The upper section shows lead branch connection to earthenware W.C. pan. The lower drawing indicates the various methods of making connections between lead, iron and earthenware pipes. All drainage systems must be carried out in accordance with the local by-laws.

gullies are best used if they can be placed at right angles to the building; a trap and circular gully top in two separate pieces will fit any position. Special deep-seal gullies are made for yards and garages, and are provided with a movable lifting bucket.

The wastes from the roofs, closets, baths, lavatories and other points are conveyed to the ground drainage system by pipes of materials and sizes to comply with the local by-laws (Figs. 10 and 11).

Generally speaking the two-pipe system of plumbing is adopted, but lately there has been a tendency to adopt the one-pipe system in which one down stack is used for both roof water and soil drainage as shown in Fig. 12. This system has the advantage of reducing the number of pipes and connections.

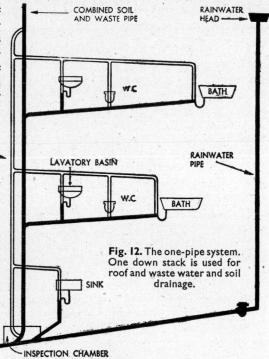

Fig. 12. The one-pipe system. One down stack is used for roof and waste water and soil drainage.

Flushing Cisterns

The following sketches indicate the principles underlying the construction of flushing cisterns. In Fig. 13 the handle when pulled lifts water into the bend, setting up siphonic action. The cylinder c is closed at the top and open at the bottom. It is the disk D which lifts the water. Fig. 14 is of a similar type in which the cylinder c can be raised by pulling the handle and lifting a body of water on the disk D.

There are very many types of flushing cisterns for water-closets and other similar purposes, which work on the principle of siphonic action.

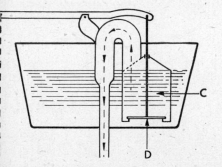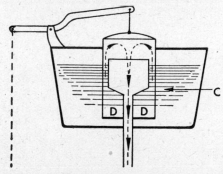

Fig. 13 (left) and Fig. 14 (right). Illustrating the principles of flushing cistern construction. The pulling of the handle sets up siphonic action, as fully described in the text.

COLD AND HOT WATER SUPPLIES

WATER can be obtained for drinking purposes from many different sources, viz.: (1) rain-water; (2) distilled sea-water; (3) river, stream or lake water; (4) spring and well water.

In this country we are, however, only likely to be concerned with the last two. Water is conveyed from its gathering grounds and sources by underground pipes and conduits, either by gravitation or boost pumps, or a combination of both, to great artificial lakes and reservoirs, where it is stored and, if necessary, suitably treated, before distribution to the consumers.

Distributing Mains

In modern towns and communities this is carried out by means of a system of underground water-pipes known as distributing mains, which usually vest in the local authority or come under the control of a public utility company.

These mains consist of cast or spun iron pipes of 4-in. internal diameter or upwards and laid at a minimum depth of 3 ft. 6 in. to guard against damage by traffic and frost action. The joints are usually lead caulked or flanged and washered, although a more recent method of jointing employing flexible connections can now be used, and is advantageous where a small amount of relative movement between the pipes is required, thereby saving the use of specials.

Asbestos cement pipes are now widely used for water mains and give an excellent job, being considerably lighter than the iron types, and thus effecting a reduction in haulage and laying costs.

Contained in the main system are sluice valves and fire hydrants. Sluice valves should be fixed at every point where branch mains occur and at other necessary places, their purpose being to enable a section of main to be isolated in the event of damage or necessity for repair. Their positions should be carefully chosen so that, when they are turned off, the minimum of inconvenience is caused to consumers.

Sluice valves are enclosed in small surface boxes constructed in 9-in. brickwork on a foundation of 6 in. of cement concrete. The two bottom courses of brickwork should be built dry to allow leakage water to drain away. The dimensions of surfaces boxes will vary according to the size of the valve, but should allow ample room for the insertion of a key for the purpose of opening and closing down the valve.

Fire hydrants are provided for fire-fighting purposes and also for filling water carts. They should be spaced at approximately 300-yd. intervals and be of the screw-down type.

Constant and Intermittent Systems

Water may be supplied by either constant or intermittent systems.

A constant system, as its name suggests, is one in which the supply of water is unvarying and the pipes are always under pressure. By this method fresh drinking water is always obtainable straight from the main and there is always an ample supply of water for fire-fighting purposes.

In districts where there is a shortage of water an intermittent system may be adopted, in which the water is only supplied through the mains during certain hours of the day in order to conserve supplies.

With intermittent systems it is necessary to instal large storage cisterns. Drinking water becomes, therefore, more liable to contamination due to

REAR ELEVATION OF SMALL BRICK HOUSE

The house walls are in modified Flemish bond, one header to three stretchers in each course. The stone terrace is carried out in random rubble. Note the french doors and modern horizontal arrangement of glazing bars, which give better vision from inside.

standing and also because of contact with the material of the cistern; and over a period of time this will cause water to become flat and unpalatable.

Pipes connecting individual buildings to the water mains are known as service pipes. These pipes may be of lead, wrought iron, steel, copper, galvanized iron or other approved material. Lead pipes should only be used where the source is in a limestone stratum of sandy country, as water containing calcium carbonate or silica will deposit a protective lining on the interior of the pipes, thus preventing actual contact between the water and the lead. Soft water, such as rain-water and salt-water, will dissolve lead, and consequently there will be considerable risk of lead poisoning in these cases. But public supplies of soft water are treated before distribution through the pipes, to reduce danger. Chemical action with the lead is most

likely in very pure and very impure water; as little as one-twentieth of a grain of lead dissolved in a gallon of water is dangerous. If it is possible to use lead pipes, however, they will be found the most serviceable.

Use of Copper Pipes

Copper pipes may be used inside buildings provided the gauge adopted meets the requirements of the water company; their advantages are easy fixing and good appearance.

Some authorities allow the use of galvanized wrought-iron pipes, others do not. There is a definite risk of contamination by zinc due to chemical action, but as in the case of lead pipes, this does not occur with hard waters.

Galvanized pipes are also liable to corrosion around the joints and at other places where the galvanizing has been interfered with, and should only be used where a cheap supply for non-drinking purposes is required.

All service pipes must conform to the relevant British Standard Specification as regards weights in relation to pressure. These specifications may be obtained from the British Standard Institution, 28 Victoria Street, London, S.W.1.

Iron pipes fall into three categories, viz., gas, water, and steam according to strength. Steam quality should always be specified for water supplies.

Service pipes, like mains, must be laid at a sufficient depth to protect them from frost, the minimum permissible being about 2 ft. 6 in. All parts of the service exposed to the weather should be adequately protected.

Actual tappings into the mains for service connections are made by the water company, to whom application should be made, when the trench has been opened. Mains are tapped under pressure by means of a special machine, which drills a hole and then by revolving its cover allows a ferrule to be inserted. In this manner connections can be made without turning off the water. The consumer will have to pay the water company for time and materials expended in carrying out the connection.

Service Pipe Protection

Service pipes should never be laid through drains or inspection chambers, owing to the risk of contamination. In new buildings it is quite common to find the same trench being used for drains and water services. This practice, however, should not be encouraged. In cases where it is unavoidable to lay a water pipe in proximity to or through foul soil, the company should be advised, and the service properly protected by a cast-iron covering pipe or other suitable means.

It is desirable that two stopcocks should be provided on every service, one being within the curtailage of the

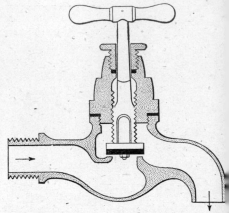

Fig. 15. Sectional drawing showing the principle on which the ordinary water tap works. The flow of water is indicated by arrows

building, and the other on the public footpath or grass verge; the latter is for use of the water company. By repeated use a stopcock may become worn and defective. The second stopcock is then a great advantage whilst repairs are being carried out. Another stop-valve should, if possible, also be placed just inside the building itself.

From the point at which the service pipe enters the building it rises direct to the storage cistern. It should be noted here that the pipes should be so installed that they have a fall to a stop-tap at the lowest point on the system, so that all the pipes may be drained for repairs or during severe frosts.

Cisterns may be constructed of galvanized iron, lead, zinc, iron, stone asbestos or slate.

Galvanized-iron cisterns are most often employed, and the danger of poisoning by slight traces of dissolved zinc is negligible.

Iron cisterns are objectionable as they will obviously rust in course of time

Stone cisterns give ideal storage, but are impractical on account of their weight, except in underground positions. Slate cisterns are quite good, but watertight jointing without the use of red lead is a very great difficulty.

Cisterns should be placed in such a position that they are readily accessible for cleaning and repair purposes, and where the least amount of damage will occur to the house in the event of defects and leakages. They should be provided with a suitable cover to prevent fouling of the water, by dust and dirt.

The following figures are useful in calculating the size of cisterns.

(1) **Amount** of water required per day **per person**—16 to 20 gallons, i.e., 10 **to 12 gallons** for drinking, washing, cooking and household purposes; 5 to 8 gallons for flushing drains, filling baths, etc.

(2) One gallon of water weighs 10 lb.

(3) One cubic foot of water weighs 62·4lb.

(4) One cubic foot of water contains approximately $6\frac{1}{4}$ gallons.

From the cistern, pipes are taken off to the various points to be supplied. The size of the main service pipe and the branch pipes will be governed by the number of fittings required and the working pressure of the supply. Service pipes to houses are 1-in. internal diameter with $\frac{1}{2}$-in. branch pipes supplying water-closets, lavatory basins, sinks, and other fittings. Hot water boilers, baths and other large fittings require a $\frac{3}{4}$-in. supply.

Every water company is empowered to make by-laws concerning the construction, workmanship and materials of all water and sanitary fittings.

The form of such by-laws has been codified by the Ministry of Health in *Model By-laws*, Series XXI, and all such fittings as taps, cisterns, ball-valves, stopcocks and water-closet flushes should conform to the standard laid down therein. Fig. 15 shows the working principle of the common tap.

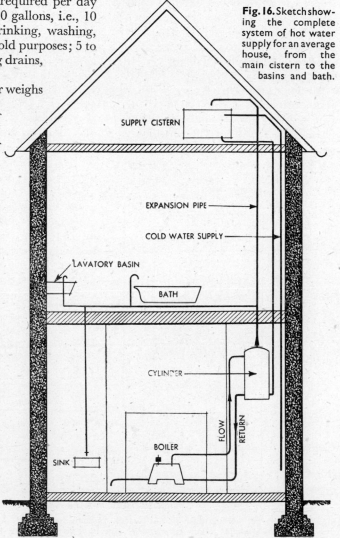

Fig. 16. Sketch showing the complete system of hot water supply for an average house, from the main cistern to the basins and bath.

SUPPLY CISTERN

EXPANSION PIPE

COLD WATER SUPPLY

LAVATORY BASIN

BATH

CYLINDER

SINK

FLOW

RETURN

BOILER

For hot water supplies to baths and washbasins, either the tank or cylinder system may be adopted or a combination of both, but the cylinder system is to be preferred. This method gives a liberal supply of hot water at all points, and is quite safe owing to the fact that it is impossible to empty the cylinder by means of the draw-off points, as the cylinder is low down and close to the boiler.

The size of the boiler, tank or cistern can be calculated from the number of points to be supplied and the likely demand on them having regard to the number of persons resident in the building.

All hot water systems operate by the simple principles of convection. Heated water increases in volume and therefore decreases in density; it will consequently rise and be displaced by colder water.

The boiler is thus placed at the bottom of the system and the cold water supply tank at the top. The hot water storage cistern is placed in an intermediate position. Water, after being heated in the boiler, rises through the primary flow pipes connected near the top of the boiler and run into the top of the hot water cistern. Return pipes are taken from the bottom of this cistern to the bottom of the boiler; constant circulation of hot water is, therefore, obtained.

Supply pipes to the various hot water points are taken off from the top of the storage cistern. A boiler should always be provided with a safety valve and there should be a tap by means of which the whole system can be drained if necessary. All the pipes in the system should be laid to a fall for draining purposes. Fig. 16 shows a typical arrangement of this system.

In large installations secondary flow and return pipes are provided with branches taken off, where necessary, to supply the hot water points (Fig. 17).

A secondary system may either be on the up-feed or down-feed principle. In the former type, flow and return mains are run horizontally from the storage cistern to feed vertical flow and return risers, returning up through the

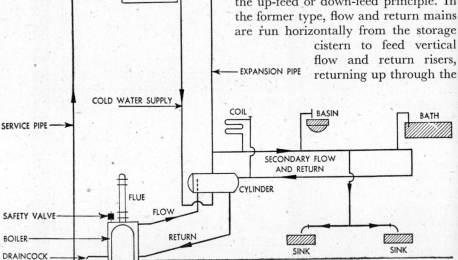

CYLINDER HOT WATER SYSTEM

Fig. 17. In large installations of hot water systems secondary flow and return pipes are provided, with branches taken off, where necessary, to supply the various hot water points.

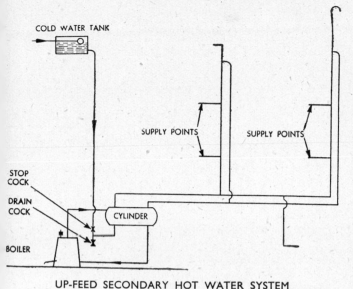

COLD WATER TANK

SUPPLY POINTS

SUPPLY POINTS

STOP
COCK

DRAIN
COCK

CYLINDER

BOILER

UP-FEED SECONDARY HOT WATER SYSTEM

Fig. 18. Secondary system of hot water supply on the up-feed principle. Flow and return mains are run horizontally from the storage cistern or cylinder to feed vertical flow and return risers.

In low-pressure systems an escape or vent pipe for air and steam is fixed at the highest point. The water in the pipes is therefore at atmospheric pressure and cannot reach a temperature higher than 212 degrees F. or 100 degrees C. (the boiling point of water). The vapour pressure in the pipes will consequently always be below atmospheric pressure. The water in low-pressure systems is usually kept at temperatures ranging between 150 to 200 degrees F. Pipe sizes for gravity systems range from $1\frac{1}{4}$ in. to 3 in. in diameter for average work.

High-pressure systems have no air vent and so the temperature of the water can be raised above boiling point. The heating pipes are wrought iron of $\frac{3}{4}$-in. to $\frac{7}{8}$-in. internal diameter and always run full. They are constructed in the boiler in a helical coil, and run from the top of the coil around the building and return to the bottom. In this type of heating system the temperature of the water is maintained at 250 to 350 degrees F.

The purity of a water supply depends upon three main points:—

(1) The source of the supply.

(2) The method of conveying the supply from the source to the reservoir, and conditions whilst in the latter.

(3) The method of distribution, including the nature of individual storage tanks and supply fittings.

Water is usually quite pure if obtained from deep wells, artesian wells and

building (Fig. 18). In the down-feed system the heated water is taken direct from the storage cistern to the top of the building, and then injected into the various down pipes in order to serve the hot water points (Fig. 19).

The secondary return main should be connected as closely as possible to the top of the cistern to make sure that the hottest water is obtained.

A vent or expansion pipe should be fitted to all storage cylinders or tanks, and this pipe may discharge either through the roof into the open air or be turned over and allowed to run into the cold water storage tank.

Hot water systems are widely used as a means of heating the atmosphere of buildings. Heating houses by hot water pipes may be done either on the low-pressure or high-pressure system.

Both these systems consist of a boiler with flow and return pipes running through the various rooms of the house which are to be heated.

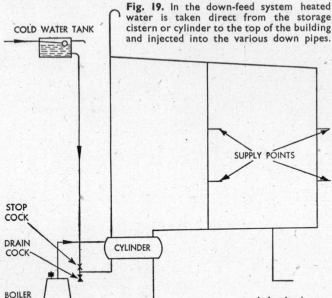

COLD WATER TANK

Fig. 19. In the down-feed system heated water is taken direct from the storage cistern or cylinder to the top of the building and injected into the various down pipes.

SUPPLY POINTS

STOP COCK

DRAIN COCK

CYLINDER

BOILER

impurity in the way of dissolved lime salts and should be well aerated.

The presence of various types of bacteria must always be guarded against. Most dangerous in this respect are the germs of cholera and typhoid fever and the eggs of various types of parasitic worms, which breed in the human body.

The following method provides a good and easy test for organic and bacteriological contamination.

Take equal quantities of the water under consideration and pure water (distilled or otherwise sterilized).

Add enough Condy's fluid to each liquid in separate vessels until a bright pink colour is obtained. Allow a contact period of three to four hours. If at the end of this time the suspected sample appears to have lost some of its colour it can be reasonably assumed that the water is contaminated.

Water Purification Methods

Water is made suitable for drinking purposes by either or all of the following methods, according to the degree and type of contamination: (1) filtration, (2) aeration; (3) sterilization.

The purpose of filtration is to remove suspended impurities and secure oxidization of organic matter.

The sand filter is most widely used and gives excellent results. After a settling period in which a good deal of the larger suspended solids are precipitated, the water is passed into the filter beds. These beds consist of layers of sand and gravel

springs or collected from the surface of upland country. These sources are either below, or otherwise beyond the reach of, possible contamination.

Water collected from agricultural and cultivated lands, and rivers and streams passing through populated districts must be regarded as dangerous, as it is likely to be contaminated by sewer discharges, trade wastes, and animal excrements.

It is necessary at this point to differentiate between chemically pure and bacteriologically pure water. Water suitable for drinking purposes need not be perfectly pure from the chemist's point of view, but should show no evidence of bacteriological contamination.

To be physically and chemically pure, water must contain no suspended solids or dissolved substances. Distilled water and cleanly caught rain-water fulfil these conditions, but such water is flat and insipid and rather unpalatable. To be palatable water must, therefore, contain a certain amount of chemical

rranged according to size. First of all comes a layer of fine sand 2 ft. to 3 ft. in thickness. This rests on another 2 ft. of graded gravel, the fine material being on top, and the coarser grades at the bottom. The whole bed is laid on two layers of bricks; after passing through these, the water is collected in pipes and run off into the storage reservoir.

The same filter beds should not be in continuous use, but must be exposed to a free passage of air at regular intervals. The top 3 in. or 4 in. of the layer of fine and will become choked with impurities after a while and this layer must be changed at intervals. The filter bed should be completely renewed about every two years.

Besides the mechanical part of filtration which secures the removal of suspended solids, there is also what is known as the vital action. This is brought about by the formation of a layer of gelatinous matter containing various micro-organisms and can be seen on the top of the filter bed after it has been in use for two or three days.

As the water passes through this gelatinous layer the micro-organisms exercise an oxidizing effect upon any organic impurities that may be present and tend to remove harmful microbes.

The aeration of water may be a natural process or can be performed by artificial means and merely mean the absorption of oxygen by the water and organic matter it may contain.

Natural aeration in rivers and streams takes place to a surprising degree, and the results of samples show that a river contaminated by a town sewer outfall in its upper reaches is quite often reasonably pure a few miles lower down. The natural corrective and recuperative effects of air and sunlight on water are certainly great enough to demand serious consideration.

Water is artificially aerated in specially constructed fountains known as aerators, by passage over weirs, and by the infusion of compressed air in some types of filtration plant.

Water containing serious bacteria contamination will have to be sterilized by chemical means. This is effected by using one or other of the various available methods of dosing the water with chlorine.

Several good types of chlorinators are produced; the main principle involved is the infusion of chlorine gas into the water at a controlled rate. The average

REINFORCED-CONCRETE CONSTRUCTION
An interesting example of timber form-work for a hollow-tile floor and for a flight of reinforced-concrete stairs leading off it.

rate of dosage for normal drinking supplies varies between 0·1 and 0·5 parts of chlorine per million gallons.

For ease of transport and storage the chlorine is usually contained under pressure in liquid form in special cylinders. It is converted into gaseous form by removal of the pressure controlled by means of a simple wheel valve.

Most large cities and towns and all county councils have on their staffs qualified public analysts, to whom samples of the public water supply are regularly submitted for analysis.

These samples are usually taken by the water engineer or sanitary inspector and are sent to the analyst's laboratory in specially sterilized sample bottles and containers sent out for the purpose.

The following precautions should always be carefully observed by the person taking the sample. First wash the hands thoroughly, preferably in an antiseptic solution. Always leave the sample bottle in its container until it is actually required. Do not take it out and lay it down in the grass or elsewhere, where it is likely to pick up contamination. Keep the fingers away from the neck of the bottle and be sure never to touch the part of the stopper which fits into the bottle.

If the sample is to be collected from a draw tap, the latter should be first sterilized by flaming with a spirit lamp. This can easily be done with a piece of cotton wool soaked in methylated spirit and fixed on the end of a piece of wire. After flaming, allow the water to

FORM No. 1	WATER SAMPLE FOR BACTERIOLOGICAL ANALYSIS LABORATORY REF. No....................
1. Source of water, i.e., reservoir, spring, stream, etc.	....
2. Time and date sample taken . . .	....
3. Position and description of supply . .	....
4. No. of persons supplied	....
5. Method of sampling	....
6. Where sample collected. Giving particulars of type of passage if not collected direct from source	....
7. Particulars of any infiltration . . .	....
8. Type of country and nature of strata from which collected	....
9. Position and nature of possible sources of contamination	....
10. Ref. No. and date of any previous analysis	....

Inspector's signature..

Date..

Fig. 20. Water analysis form for use with samples of water from reservoirs, springs and rivers.

FORM No. 2	WATER SAMPLE FOR BACTERIOLOGICAL ANALYSIS LABORATORY REF. No.....................

1. Name and position of well . . . .

2. Time and date of sampling . . . .

3. Draw well or pump and type of cover . ...

4. Approximate depth . . . .

5. Description of well and type of lining, etc.. ....

6. Details of possible sources of contamination ....

 Approx. distance from:—

 (a) Houses . . . .

 (b) w.c., earth closet or privy (state which) ....

 (c) Cow-stalls and stables . . . .

7. Particulars of surrounding ground, i.e., whether cultivated, etc. . . . .

8. Nature of strata . . . .

9. Amount of rainfall during last few days . ...

10. Ref. No. and date of any previous analysis. ....

Inspector's signature...

Date...

Fig. 21. Water analysis form for use when the sample of water is taken from a well or borehole.

run through the tap for a few minutes before proceeding to take the sample. Never allow the bottle to touch the tap in case of possible contamination.

When collecting the sample from a reservoir, spring, stream or river, remove the bottle from its container, and, leaving in the stopper, immerse it completely under the surface. Then remove the stopper holding it only by the flattened end; allow the bottle to fill and replace the stopper before removing from the water.

The bottle or container must be labelled with the following information: (a) place from which sample taken; (b) date and time of sampling;

(c) signature of person collecting sample.

All samples should be in the hands of the analyst as soon after being taken as possible; if there is likely to be any delay or the samples have to be transported for some considerable distance they should be packed in ice.

The fullest possible information should be supplied with each sample, for the assistance of the analyst in making his test and report. The following forms are specimens of the types required: Form No. 1 (Fig. 20) is for use with samples from reservoirs, springs and rivers; Form No. 2 (Fig. 21) should be employed if the sample has been taken from a well or borehole.

GAS SUPPLY FROM MAINS TO BURNER

THE sections of a gas installation may be described under the following headings: (1) The service pipe from the main to the building; (2) the meter; (3) carcass pipes serving the appliance points.

The service pipe supply may be distributed by the low-pressure or high-pressure system. In the former method the service pipe is carried direct from the street main to the main cock of the meter. The pipe is laid with a slight fall to the main for the removal of condensation, and where this is not practicable it is usual to provide a siphon at the lowest point. Usually the street main is low enough for the fall to be made in the right direction. With the high-pressure system the service pipe is about half the diameter of that required for the low-pressure system, but it is necessary to connect it into a high-to-low-pressure service governor before carrying the pipe to the meter.

Laying the Service Pipe

The service pipe is usually laid in a straight line at a convenient depth so that it enters the building below the ground level. The builder makes provision for the pipe by means of a suitable sleeve in the main wall in a position giving direct access to the meter. Most gas companies will bring the service pipe up to the meter, and even go so far as to run the pipes through to the required points.

The gas meter is a very accurate instrument for measuring the consumption of gas, consequently careful consideration should be given to its position in the building. Trouble and inconvenience can be avoided if the meter is planned to occupy a position which is easy of access, well lighted and ventilated. Meters are of two types, wet and dry. The type known as the dry meter consists of suitable mechanism tested to measure gas within the limits of 3 per cent slow against the gas undertaking and 2 per cent fast against the consumer. The dry meter is the most popular type and needs very little attention. Slot meters are of this type.

Iron and Compo Pipes

Wrought-iron or compo pipes are mostly used on all internal fitting work. Compo is easily worked round bends but it is inclined to sag.

With iron pipes the jointing is made with red lead, and screwed in much the same way as for water services. No supply pipe should be less than $\frac{1}{4}$ in bore and should be laid with a fall towards the service pipe from the meter. Wall hooks or clips not more than 10 ft apart are used to secure the pipes.

The size of pipes will depend upon the number of appliances and in theory the installation will be designed to pass the gas required for simultaneous use at all such appliance points.

The carcassing should be put in hand before the internal work of the building has been completed. Supplies will run in the same direction as the floor joist where possible so as to avoid cutting. In some cases it will be necessary to do certain amount of cutting, but this must only be sufficient to lay the pipes in with a minimum of cover. A certain amount of chasing in the fabric is also necessary to provide adequate cover over the pipes. All supplies are carried as near as possible to the gas appliances, so as to enable the connections to be made later without spoiling the finished work. It is usual to test the installation upon completion of the carcassing. A gas fir

Fig. 22. Gas fire fitted in fireplace, showing connections and jets for heating the radiants or elements. There are many types of gas fires, designed specially to suit their surroundings.

and a gas geyser are shown in Figs. 22 and 23.

Gas in many districts is priced per therm, which is a unit of heat used as a basis for the sale of gas. A therm is equal to 100,000 British thermal units, and a British thermal unit is the amount of heat required to raise the temperature of 1 lb. of water through 1 degree F.

The Gas Regulation Act, 1920 requires all companies to declare the calorific value of the gas, and this is tested at regular intervals to check the standard so declared. For example, if the declared calorific value of gas is 500 British thermal units per cubic foot, then on the assumption of the following meter readings the therms chargeable at (say) 1s. 3d. would be as follows:—

METER READINGS

cubic feet
4,200 present quarter
5,700 last quarter

$$\frac{8,500 \times 500 \text{ British thermal units}}{100,000} = 42 \cdot 5 \text{ therms}$$

and 42·5 therms at 1s. 3d. would equal a charge to the consumer of £2 13s. 2d.

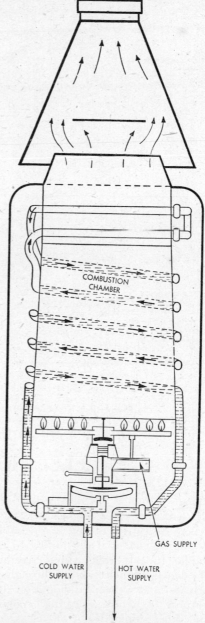

Fig. 23. Section through a gas geyser. Cold water enters the combustion chamber by means of a pipe, which is coiled and heated by gas burners. As the hot water is drawn off it is replaced by a further supply of cold water. Gas geysers are usually fitted with thermostatic control, which automatically reduces gas pressure when the water reaches a certain temperature

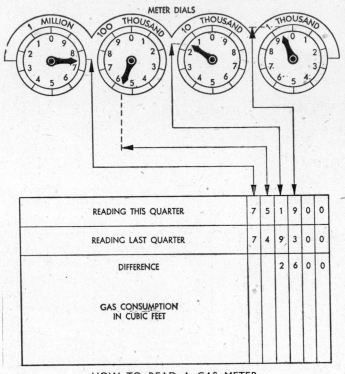

HOW TO READ A GAS METER

Fig. 24. Write down the figures shown by the pointers in the dials, reading the dials from left to right. If the pointer is between two figures always take the lower; if it is between 9 and 0 always write down 9 and add two ciphers at the end. The above reading is 751,900 cub. ft.

It is very important that the consumer should know how much gas is being used, and he should be able to read the meter for the purpose of checking the account. This is done as follows (Fig. 24). Take the dials from left to right and write down the figures shown by the pointers.

If the pointer is between two figures, write down the lower number, and if the pointer is between 9 and 0 write down 9 and add two ciphers at the end. The meter index in the diagram reads 751,900 cub. ft. 2,600 represents the gas used for the last quarter in cub. ft.

ELECTRICAL WORK

THIS section is not intended to deal with the type of plant necessary to generate electric current, or the cables through which it is distributed to the public. It deals briefly with the method of conveying electricity throughout private and other buildings, for the purpose of lighting, heating, cooking and other similar uses.

In some establishments it is claimed that a private plant is more economical than obtaining electricity from the public supply companies. The latter system of supply, however, is the most usual and is now becoming standardized under the grid system.

Before proceeding further it will be found useful to understand the more general electrical terms employed.

VOLT. This is the name given to the unit of electro-motive force from a company or a private plant. It may be given at 230 volts, in which case the use of lamps and other appliances must be suitable for that voltage.

AMPERE. The unit of strength of an electric current.

OHM. The unit of electrical resistance.

WATT. The unit of electrical power, obtained by multiplying the volts by the amperes.

CABLE. Insulated material used to convey electrical power to the points of consumption.

SWITCH. A device for making or breaking an electrical circuit.

FUSE. A wire on a porcelain insulator that will easily melt when the electric current is overloaded. It is placed on each circuit.

CIRCUIT. A run of cable (or flex) from a source of supply and back to it, providing electrical service on the way.

Wiring Systems

Current is distributed within the consumer's premises by means of a wiring system which must be in accordance with the requirements of the local supply authority. These should be a main switch, fuse, and meter, fixed in a convenient position just inside the building. From the meter the electricity is distributed by a series of circuits which run from a main fuse and distributing switchboard. Electricity is thus conveyed to different parts of the house for lighting, heating and cooking.

The wires are of copper, insulated by two layers of india-rubber or other similar material, and may be drawn through metal conduits, or sheathed in lead, lead alloy, tinned copper or specially treated tough rubber covering.

If the wiring system is carried out in metal conduits, provision is made in the walls and floors of the building for the conduits and draw-in boxes. This system is to be recommended because of the permanent nature of the work. The conduit can be incorporated in the constructional work of the building and if the system should fail the cables can be readily withdrawn and replaced where necessary. To make this installation safe the conduits must be earthed and tested

Lead-sheathed wiring is a system that is very suitable for installations in existing buildings. It is neat in appearance and easily fixed. Tough rubber sheathing has also the advantage of flexibility and cheapness. These last two methods, however, have not the advantages of the metal conduit system, where reliability and high-class work are the main essentials.

Lighting Problems

A very high degree of efficiency has been reached in illumination. In all buildings it is necessary to take into consideration the intensity of light required, and whether the light is to be concentrated over certain spots or uniformly distributed. The wattage necessary to give the desired effect is obtained and the number and size of lamps can be selected to satisfy the conditions.

The position and type of the lighting units will depend upon the requirements of the completed scheme. They must be selected and arranged to suit the style of decoration adopted. It is also necessary to have in mind the cost of maintenance. Suitable facilities must be provided for the renewal and cleaning of lamps. If there is no means of access for such purposes the efficiency of the whole scheme is impaired owing to the difficulty of reaching high lights for cleaning.

Electric Bells

A simple bell board and circuit is shown in Fig. 25. A small bell board (A) holds the electro-magnet (B), the contact pillar (E), spring and armature (F), a bell of good tone (G), and connections to complete the circuit. When the bell rings, the current passes from batteries or the main supplies to the contact pillar (E) and along the armature spring (F) to one end of the electro magnet coil and from there it passes round again to the contact pillar.

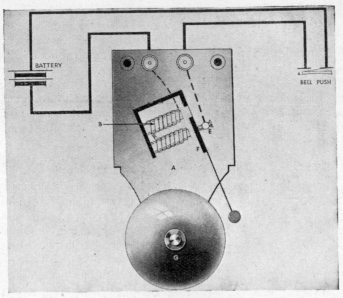

ELECTRIC BELL CIRCUIT

Fig. 25. The bell board A holds the electro-magnet B, the contact pillar E, the spring and armature F, the bell G and the connections which complete the circuit. The working of the circuit is described in the text.

The bell wire should be of the best quality 1/·03 tinned copper covered with a layer of india-rubber and two layers of cotton Such wires must be kept separate from the lighting wire and may be concealed in a conduit embedded in the walls.

In large installations it will be necessary to provide and fix an indicator to show which bell is ringing. A suitable type is known as the drop-front mechanical replacement indicator

The electro-magnet now attracts the armature which in turn causes the striker to sound the bell. The moment this occurs the circuit is broken and the striker leaves the bell to remake the circuit and so cause a repetition of such movements while the push is depressed.

with the names and numbers of the various rooms clearly printed in block letters or figures.

Electric current for bells may be obtained from dry or wet batteries, or from the mains supply, reduced in voltage by a transformer.

HEATING AND VENTILATION

HEAT may be conveyed in three different ways, viz., radiant, convected, and conducted.

RADIANT HEAT is transmitted directly from one body to another through the atmosphere and its intensity decreases as the square of the distance. Open fires, gas fires and oil stoves are good examples of radiant heat.

CONVECTED HEAT is that which is conveyed in liquids when warmed from below. Upward currents from the source of heat are created while the cooler

liquid from the sides forces and feeds the upward currents. This process is constantly repeated until all the liquid is heated. Good examples of convected heat are modern hot water system radiators, and electric heaters.

CONDUCTED HEAT is heat imparted from one portion of a medium to another as in open and closed ranges or stoves

Local heating systems suitable for the intermittent heating of rooms have the advantage of avoiding unnecessary heat losses. The usual methods are by means of coal fires, gas fires, electric fires, and stoves.

Open coal fires are the most popular. The most effective and economical is the well type of grate. The sides and back are formed of one piece of firebrick shaped so as to throw the heat forward into the room. Firebrick is used because it will not disintegrate under great heat. Ordinary bricks made of clay do not possess such fire-resisting qualities.

Modern gas and electric fires have many advantages. They are hygienic, clean and neat in appearance, and supply immediate heat at any time. An electric fire is readily moved to any suitable position for plugging in, but in some districts the cost of current may make it a somewhat expensive method of warming rooms.

Slow-combustion stoves are also useful in many ways, and are frequently used in small halls where space is limited. They are generally made of wrought iron and lined with firebrick. Mica panels are often put in the front fire door to give a warm and cheerful appearance. Stoves of this type are very economical and burn on anthracite, coke, or patent fuel.

HOT WATER AND STEAM INSTALLATIONS. By far the most common method of central heating is the low-pressure hot-water installation. This form of heating can be effected from one boiler and has the advantages of low running costs, the scientific distribution of heat, low fire risks and cleanliness. The apparatus may be designed with gravity circulation or with a mechanical device known as an accelerator for assisting the circulation.

The apparatus consists of an independent boiler situated in a boiler house on the lowest floor. Flow and return pipes are connected to the boiler for the circulation of the heated water. The size and type of boiler and pipes will depend upon the heating surface, but it is usual to allow a generous margin over the heat required for economical working and the possibility of extensions. Radiators through which water circulates are connected to the pipes for heating the various rooms and corridors. The inlet of the radiator is attached to the flow pipe, and the outlet of the radiator is connected to the pipe which returns the cooled water to the boiler. The heated water rises, owing to reduced density and the cold water falls to the lower level, that of the boiler, where heat is applied. The temperature increases and the newly heated water rises. The process continues and forms a current circulating through the circuit or system.

The methods of arranging the pipes vary according to circumstances. For small installations the one pipe system is suitable and economical

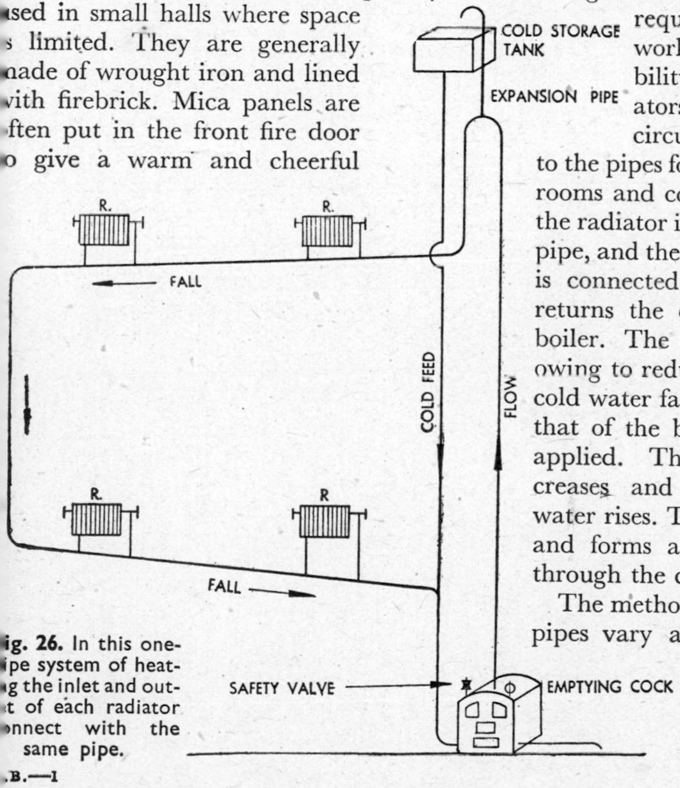

Fig. 26. In this one-pipe system of heating the inlet and outlet of each radiator connect with the same pipe.

B.—I

(Fig. 26). The inlet and outlet of each radiator is connected to the same pipe. For larger and more important jobs the two-pipe system is preferred because all radiators are fed with heated water at much the same temperature (Fig. 27). All the cooled water is collected by the return pipe, whereas in the one-pipe system the water from a radiator goes forward to feed the next radiator on the system, with the result that the radiators farthest from the boiler house cannot be expected to radiate the same heat as those that are more fortunately placed.

A third method of arranging pipes in a low-pressure hot water installation is known as the drop system. This is a very convenient arrangement for a high building. The drop system is clearly indicated in Fig. 28.

STEAM INSTALLATION. Steam-heating systems may be of two types, either low or high pressure, according to the pressure at which the apparatus works.

With a low-pressure steam apparatus the arrangement of the system consists of strong wrought-iron pipes, circulating steam to radiators from a boiler usually situated in a basement. The pressure at which the apparatus works is about 5 lb. per sq. in., and as the steam rapidly condenses into water in contact with the internal pipe surfaces it follows that the pipes must be laid to a fall so that the condensation water can drain back to the boiler.

The arrangement of the work is some-what similar to the low-pressure he water installations, and the one-pip two-pipe, or drop system is adopte according to the requirements be suited for the job.

High-pressure steam installatio have working pressures greater tha 5 lb. per sq. in. They require a Corni boiler or a similar type to provide stea through the pipes for the radiators coils. This system is suitable when hig pressure steam is required in a buildir for a number of purposes.

The advantages of heating a buildir by low or high-pressure steam install tions are as follows :—

(1) Effective utilization of waste stear
(2) The circulation will cover a wi area without difficulty.
(3) Radiators are quickly raised their full temperature.

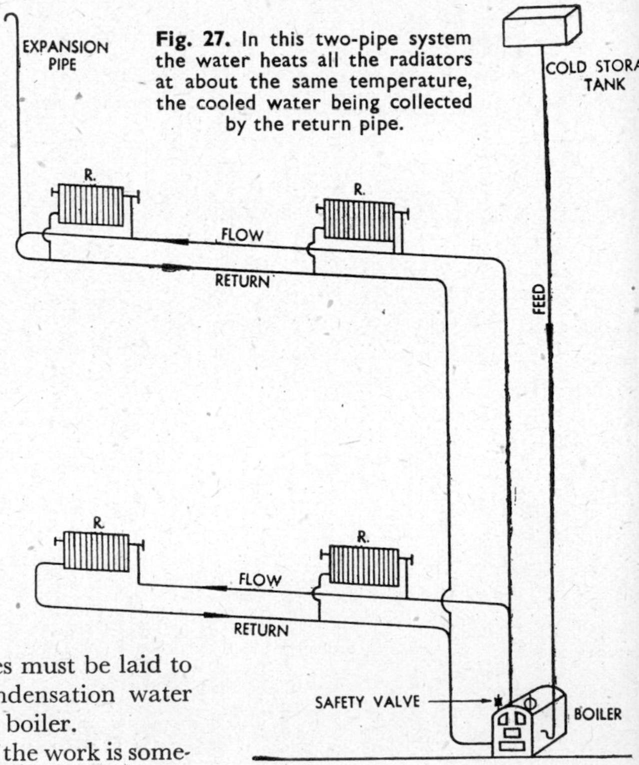

Fig. 27. In this two-pipe system the water heats all the radiators at about the same temperature, the cooled water being collected by the return pipe.

EXPANSION PIPE

COLD STOR TANK

R.

FLOW

RETURN

FEED

R.

R.

FLOW

RETURN

SAFETY VALVE

BOILER

4) Radiators or coils are not as large as those required for hot water installations owing to the high temperature of the steam.

Steam heating, however, presents a few difficulties. Radiators cool quickly, and sudden changes of temperature occur with all steam heating when heat is withdrawn. Skill is required in designing a satisfactory system to eliminate water hammer. This latter item is perhaps the most objectionable feature of steam heating and is caused by insufficient falls on the pipes and lack of relief valves for removing the condensed water.

PANEL HEATING. Pipe coils or surface plates are used for the system of panel heating and the arrangement is particularly suitable for large public buildings, in which special consideration must be given to the architectural and decorative features. The invisible form of heating offered by pipe coils is a great help in this direction. The panels consist of coils of mild-steel jointless tubing made up to a pattern as shown in Fig. 29. They are welded, tested and embedded against walls, ceilings or floors.

The surface over the panels is finished in the usual way, leaving no visible evidence of central heating. The resulting radiant heat is pleasant, and can be controlled to any required temperature throughout the building.

Where the type of embedded panel has a certain amount of resistance to the flow of hot water through the pipe coils, it will be found necessary to provide a

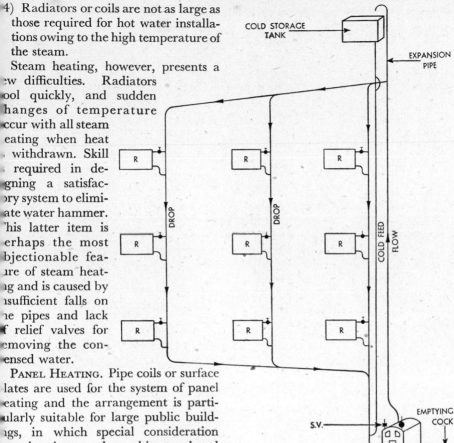

Fig. 28. Showing arrangement of pipes in the drop system of low-pressure central heating, which is particularly suitable for high buildings.

pump for forcing the circulation. On the other hand the forced circulation system can be avoided by designing a grid type of embedded panel which reduces the resistance to the flow of water. In this case the circulation would be by gravity.

Plate panels have water ways at the back, heating the whole area of the panels which are built up in sections according to the heating surface required. They are usually insulated at the back so as to increase the heating value.

PLENUM SYSTEM. This system of

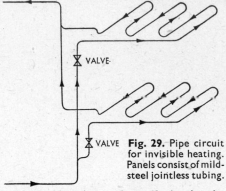

VALVE **Fig. 29.** Pipe circuit for invisible heating. Panels consist of mild-steel jointless tubing.

combined heating and ventilating is suitable in buildings with wide rooms and floor areas such as theatres. The air is drawn in by means of a fan at the fresh-air intake, and discharged through the distributing ducts to any desired position. The plant usually consists of (a) an air-washer; (b) a centrifugal fan, (c) air-heater; and (d) distributing duct-

work. Thus the plenum system can provide clean air at the correct temperature and humidity.

By humidity is meant the water-vapour content of the air, which must be controlled if comfortable conditions are to be expected. In hot weather the air is generally cooled to extract excess moisture and reheated to the required temperature. Likewise in cold weather the moisture content of the air is raised a little to avoid parchness.

A typical arrangement of plenum heating suitable for a large building is shown in Fig. 30. The system is rather complicated and needs skilled attention. In order to guard against the serious consequences of a breakdown it is advisable to duplicate the centrifugal fans. It will be appreciated that the conditioning of air required for large crowded buildings is very necessary.

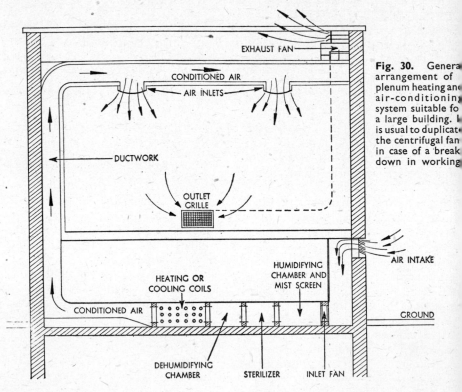

Fig. 30. General arrangement of plenum heating and air-conditioning system suitable for a large building. It is usual to duplicate the centrifugal fan in case of a break down in working

CHAPTER 7

MECHANICS

Force and stress. Principle of moments. Beam reactions. Vectors. Tension and compression. Roof trusses. Beams and their loads. Steel joists. Resisting moments. Columns and Struts. Moment of Inertia. Radius of Gyration. Lifting loads.

MECHANICS is the science which deals with forces and their action upon bodies. The section of mechanics which deals with bodies at rest is called statics. Dynamics is that section concerned with bodies in motion. This chapter is devoted almost entirely to the subject of statics, as most of the mechanics problems which have to be solved by the builder deal with bodies at rest.

A force may be defined as any cause which produces, or tends to produce, motion in a body. When the resistance to motion is greater than the force applied the body remains at rest, but its shape is altered.

Should the force applied be a pull, the body will be lengthened, and is said to be in *tension*.

When the force is applied as a push, the body is shortened, and is said to be in *compression*.

STRESS is the force exerted on unit area of a body. Thus the value of the stress is obtained by dividing the force applied by the area resisting that force. The result may be expressed in pounds per square inch, tons per square inch, tons per square foot and so on.

EXAMPLE 1

The tie rod in a steel roof truss is $1\frac{1}{2}$ in. diameter, and is pulled with a force of 9 tons. The cross-sectional area of the tie rod is 1·77 sq. in. (Fig. 1).

Tensile stress in the rod = load ÷ cross-sectional area

= 9 ÷ 1·77

= 5·08 tons per sq. in.

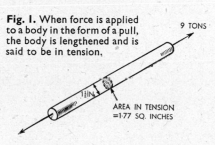

Fig. 1. When force is applied to a body in the form of a pull, the body is lengthened and is said to be in tension.

9 TONS

$1\frac{1}{2}$ IN.

AREA IN TENSION
=1·77 SQ. INCHES

EXAMPLE 2

A short concrete pier is 3 ft. long × 2 ft. wide, so that the area of the top face is 6 sq. ft. This supports a load of 90 tons (Fig. 2).

Compressive stress in the pier = load ÷ area

= 90 ÷ 6

= 15 tons per sq. ft.

EXAMPLE 3

A long flat plate tie forming part of a large roof truss is made in two lengths. These are joined together by twelve rivets each $\frac{3}{4}$ in. diameter. The pull in the tie is 30 tons, so that the force tending to shear off each rivet is 30 ÷ 12, which is 2·5 tons (Fig. 3). Now the area which is resisting this force of $2\frac{1}{2}$ tons is the cross-sectional area of one rivet, that is, the area of a circle $\frac{3}{4}$ in. diameter. This is ·442 sq. in.

Shear stress in rivet = load ÷ area

= 2·5 ÷ ·442

= 5·66 tons per sq. in.

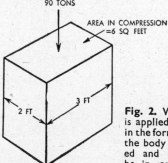

90 TONS

AREA IN COMPRESSION
=6 SQ FEET

2 FT

3 FT

Fig. 2. When force is applied to a body in the form of a push, the body is shortened and is said to be in compression.

261

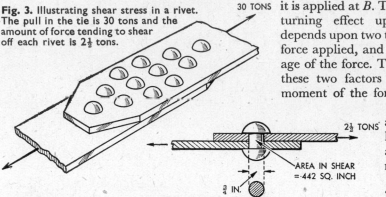

Fig. 3. Illustrating shear stress in a rivet. The pull in the tie is 30 tons and the amount of force tending to shear off each rivet is 2½ tons.

30 TONS

2½ TONS

AREA IN SHEAR
=·442 SQ. INCH

⅞ IN.

it is applied at *B*. The twisting o turning effect upon the nu depends upon two things: (1) th force applied, and (2) the lever age of the force. The product c these two factors is called th moment of the force.

Thus whe a force of 3 lb. is applie at *A*, the mo ment is 30 × 12 which i 360 lb. in.

When the same force is applied at *E* the moment is only 30 × 6 which is 18 lb. in. Leverage is measured at righ angles to the line of action of the force

Thus the inclined force *P* acting at *.* has an effective leverage of only 7 in the 7 in. being measured at right angle to the line of action of the force *P*.

When a body is at rest, all the force acting upon it must balance on another. Such a body is said to be i equilibrium. If the forces did nc balance one another, then the bod would move in one direction or an other, and would no longer be at res

Fig. 5 shows a horizontal rod whos weight we shall neglect. This rod i first balanced upon the fulcrum *F* whic is at the top of a compression balance A weight of 3 lb. is hung at the left-han end of the rod, 12 in. from the fulcrun and a weight of 4 lb. is adjusted on th right-hand side of the fulcrum until balance is obtained and the rod is i

Each part of a structure should be designed in such a way that the stress in it when loaded shall not exceed a certain value. This value will depend upon the material used, and is called the *safe stress* or *safe working stress*. The following are typical values for the safe working stresses in various materials.

Material	Safe working stress	Tons per sq. in.
Mild steel . .	In tension . .	8
Mild steel . .	In compression .	12
Mild steel . .	In shear . .	6
Cast iron . .	In tension . .	2
Cast iron . .	In compression .	10
Timber, hardwood .	In tension (abt) .	1
Timber, softwood .	In tension (abt) .	¾
Brickwork in 3 : 1		*Tons per sq. ft.*
lime mortar	In compression .	6
Brickwork in 4 : 1		
cement mortar .	In compression .	12
Concrete, 4 : 2 : 1 mix	In compression .	30

MOMENTS. A knowledge of the principle of moments is necessary to calculate the upward reactions of the supports of a loaded beam or roof truss, and to understand the theory underlying the design of beam sections.

In addition to these, there are many other instances of the application of the principle to building problems.

Experience tells us that we can screw up a nut more tightly when we apply a force at the *end* of a spanner, than when we apply the same force closer to the nut. Thus in Fig. 4, the force is more effective when applied at *A* than when

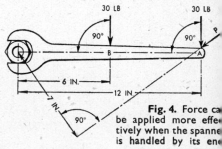

30 LB   30 LB
90°   90°
              P
B
A
6 IN.
12 IN.
7 IN.
90°

Fig. 4. Force ca be applied more effe tively when the spanne is handled by its en

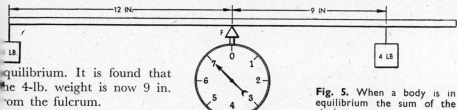

quilibrium. It is found that
he 4-lb. weight is now 9 in.
·om the fulcrum.

Measuring the leverage from
he fulcrum F in each case, we
ow have:—

Moment of the 3-lb. weight$=3 \times 12$
   $=36$ lb. in.

Moment of the 4-lb. weight$=4 \times 9$
   $=36$ lb. in.

Ve see that the two moments are equal.
)ne moment tends to turn the rod in
he same direction as the hands of a
lock, and the other in the opposite
irection. Hence one is said to be a
lockwise, and the other an anti-clock-
/ise moment.

Not only in this case, but in every
ase of a body in equilibrium, it can be
·hown that the sum of the clockwise
noments is always equal to the sum of
·e anti-clockwise moments.

Leaving the weights in the same posi-
·on on the rod, let us now think of the
·ft-hand end of the rod as the fulcrum.
·n other words the rod is now free to
·tate about its left-hand end in either
·clockwise or anti-clockwise direction
·ig. 6).

The total load on the rod is 4 lb.+3
).=7 lb. This is shown on the dial of

Fig. 5. When a body is in equilibrium the sum of the clockwise moments is always equal to the sum of the anti-clockwise moments.

the compression balance in Fig. 5.
Therefore the balance is pushing upwards with a force of 7 lb.

Measuring the leverages from the
new fulcrum at the left-hand end of the
rod, we now have:—

Clockwise moment$=4 \times 21 = 84$ lb. in.

Anti-clockwise moment$=7 \times 12 = 84$ lb. in.

Again we find that the opposing
moments are equal. It can be shown
that, for any body in equilibrium, the
sum of the clockwise moments is equal
to the sum of the anti-clockwise moments, no matter about what point the
moments are measured.

Notice that the 3-lb. weight had no
leverage about the left-hand end of the
rod, and therefore its moment was zero.

Again, the total downward force
on the rod is $4+3=7$ lb.

ig. 6. Another method of showing that the opposing moments are equal, irrespective of the oint about which the moments are measured.

Fig. 7. How to find the upward force, or reaction, at each support in the case of a beam resting on two supports 18 ft. apart, and carrying one load of 6 tons and one of 9 tons.

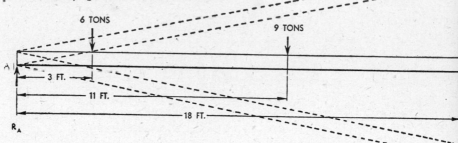

Total upward force on the rod is that exerted by the compression balance $=7$ lb. Thus we see that the total upward force is equal to the total downward force. This is always true when a body is in equilibrium.

Fig. 7 shows a beam resting upon supports 18 ft. apart, and carrying two loads, one of 6 tons, and one of 9 tons.

If we neglect the weight of the beam itself, it is clear that the supports must exert a total upward force equal to the total load, namely $9+6=15$ tons.

To find the upward force, or *reaction*, at each support we proceed as follows. Consider the beam to be pivoted at A and to be free to rotate clockwise or anticlockwise about that point as shown by the dotted lines and arrows. Taking moments about A we have:—

Total clockwise moment$=$Total anticlockwise moment

$$6\times3+9\times11=R_B\times18$$
$$18+99=R_B\times18$$
$$117=R_B\times18$$
$$117\div18=R_B$$
$$6\tfrac{1}{2}\text{ tons}=R_B$$

To find R_A we have:—

Total upward force$=$Total downward force

$$R_A+6\tfrac{1}{2}=9+6$$
$$R_A=15-6\tfrac{1}{2}$$
$$R_A=8\tfrac{1}{2}\text{ tons}$$

The supports A and B may now be

designed to take the loads of $8\tfrac{1}{2}$ tons and $6\tfrac{1}{2}$ tons respectively.

VECTORS are straight lines which are used to represent directed values such as displacements, velocities, forces, etc.

Fig. 8 shows a vector representing a force of 5 lb. acting in a direction northwest. It is drawn to a scale of $\tfrac{1}{4}$ in.$=1$ lb and is therefore $1\tfrac{1}{4}$ in. long.

When a number of forces act upon a body their sum is called the *resultant*, and this is found by adding the force vectors.

Vectors are added by placing them end to end, tail to arrowhead, their angles of inclination remaining unaltered. The resultant is the vector drawn from the tail of the first to the arrowhead of the last of the added forces

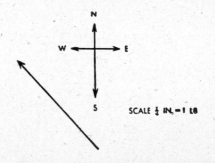

Fig. 8. Vector representing a force of 5 lb. acting in a north-westerly direction.

This is shown in Fig. 9. The *space diagram* shows three forces acting at a point. The *force diagram* shows these

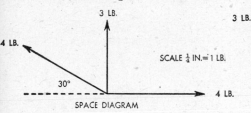

SCALE ¼ IN.=1 LB.

SPACE DIAGRAM

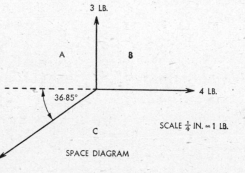

4 LB.

3 LB.

R=5·03 LB.

4 LB.

Fig. 9. The resultant is a vector drawn from the tail of the first force to the arrowhead of the last force.

FORCE DIAGRAM

forces added together as vectors. They are drawn to a scale of ¼ in.=1 lb.

The resultant, marked R, is 5·03 lb. Notice that this is much less than the arithmetical sum of the numbers 4, 4 and 8, which is 11.

If the three original forces applied be replaced by their resultant of 5·03 lb., this would have the same effect on any structure.

If a number of forces are added as shown above, and the arrowhead of the last force added coincides with the tail of the first, it is clear that no resultant can be drawn. In other words, the resultant is zero. Therefore the forces have a combined effect which is nothing, and this means that the point at which they act is in equilibrium.

Such a case is shown in Fig. 10. Forces of 3 lb., 4 lb. and 5 lb. act at a point. When added they form a triangle. No resultant can be drawn and so we know that the three forces produce equilibrium.

Notice the method of lettering used in the diagrams. In the space diagram the spaces are lettered with the capitals A, B, C, and the forces are called after the spaces they separate. Thus AB is 3 lb., BC is 4 lb., and CA is 5 lb. In the force diagram small letters a, b, c are placed at the ends of the forces. This method of lettering is known as Bow's Notation.

From the foregoing it will be seen that when a body is in equilibrium, the force diagram will close, with the arrowheads all pointing in the same rotary direction. This fact will now be made use of in finding the forces in the members of various structures.

Fig. 11 shows a wall bracket supporting a load of 1½ tons. Bow's Notation has been used to letter the space diagram, and it is required to find the forces in the two parts of the bracket, the members BC and CA.

Now it is clear that the point where the load is applied is in equilibrium under the action of the three forces AB,

Fig. 10. Showing an example where no resultant can be drawn, and the resultant is therefore zero, and the three forces produce an equilibrium.

3 LB.

A   B

36·85°

4 LB.

C

5 LB.

SPACE DIAGRAM

SCALE ¼ IN. = 1 LB.

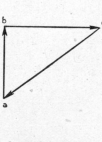

b   c

a

FORCE DIAGRAM

.B.—I*

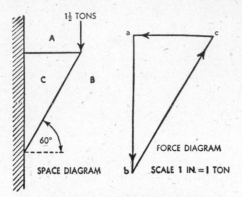

Fig. 11. Diagram of a wall bracket supporting a load of 1½ tons. The space diagram is lettered in accordance with Bow's Notation.

BC, and *CA*, and therefore these three forces must, when drawn to scale, form the sides of a triangle. We commence by drawing the known force *AB* to a scale of 1 in. = 1 ton.

The next force, taking the forces in a clockwise order, is *BC*, but as we do not yet know the position of *c*, we draw a long line parallel to *BC* through the point *b* in the force diagram. The third force, which must close the diagram, is *ca*, and this must end at the point *a*. Therefore we draw a line parallel to *CA* through the point *a* in the force diagram. The point of intersection of these two last lines must be the position of the point *c*.

We know the direction of the arrowhead in the force *AB* as it is a force acting vertically downwards, and so we are able to insert arrowheads for the other two forces, making all three point in the same rotary direction (in this case anti-clockwise.)

Measuring the two required forces to scale on the force diagram, we find that *BC* = 1·73 tons, and *CA* = ·866 ton.

When we place a coiled spring between the palms of our hands and then press them together, we can feel the spring pressing outwards to resist the pressure applied to it. In the same way,

when any part of a structure is in compression, that part will exert an outward push at each end. This is shown in Fig. 12. A stretched spring exerts an inward force at each end.

In the same way, a member in tension will be indicated by a line having two arrowheads pointing inwards. This appears to be just the opposite of what we expect, but we must remember that we are dealing with the forces *inside* and not the forces applied *outside*.

The fact that a member is in compression is usually indicated by the sign +, and tension by the sign —. Notice that it is impossible for *both* arrows point in the same direction. A member with two such arrows would not be in equilibrium. Knowing this, we can readily draw the second arrow on a member if the direction of the first arrow is known.

Fig. 13 shows a pin-jointed wall bracket having six members. It will be seen that there are three points away from the wall which are kept in equilibrium by the forces in the members. The force diagram for each of the points must be drawn.

We commence with the point where the known force (*AB* = 4 tons) acts. It is drawn first to a scale of ¼ in. = 1 ton and then lines parallel to *BC* and *CA* complete the triangle shown at (1).

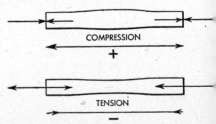

Fig. 12. Illustrating the outward push when part of a structure is in compression and inward pull when it is in tension. The plus sign is always used to denote compression and minus sign to denote tension.

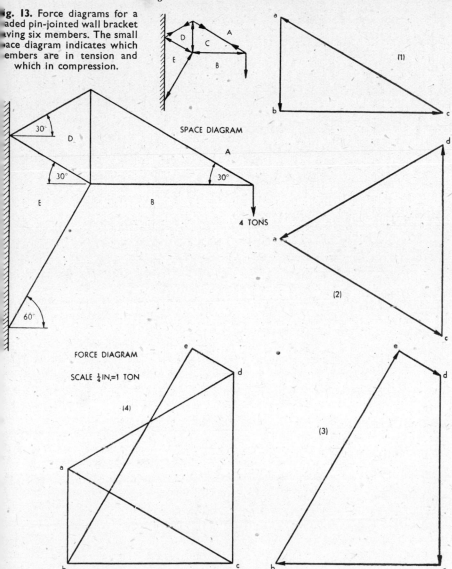

Fig. 13. Force diagrams for a loaded pin-jointed wall bracket having six members. The small space diagram indicates which members are in tension and which in compression.

SPACE DIAGRAM

4 TONS

FORCE DIAGRAM

SCALE ¼ IN.=1 TON

(1)

(2)

(3)

(4)

When the arrows are inserted we see that the member *BC* exerts a push to the right, while the member *CA* exerts a pull upwards to the left at an angle of 30 degrees. These arrows may now be transferred to the space diagram, and inserted *close up to the point we are considering*. At the opposite ends of the members

BC and *CA*, arrows having the opposite direction are inserted.

This has been done on the small space diagram. We now see that *BC* is in compression and *CA* is in tension.

We next draw the force diagram for the point at the top of the bracket. We cannot draw the force diagram for the

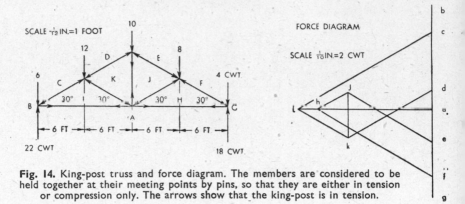

Fig. 14. King-post truss and force diagram. The members are considered to be held together at their meeting points by pins, so that they are either in tension or compression only. The arrows show that the king-post is in tension.

point below, where the forces *CB*, *BE*, *ED*, and *DC* act, because there are more than two unknown forces there.

To draw this second force diagram we copy the force *AC* to scale, but with the arrow reversed, as we are dealing with the other end of the member. Continuing around the point in a clockwise direction, we take the other two forces in order, drawing lines parallel to *CD* and *DA*. These complete the triangle as shown at (2).

The force diagram for the third point may now be drawn, copying *DC* from (2), *CB* from (1), and completing the diagram with lines parallel to *BE* and *ED*. This diagram is marked (3).

Combining Force Diagrams

It will be seen that a great deal of the work has been duplicated in the drawing of these three diagrams, and errors may have been made in transferring lines from one diagram to another. For these reasons it is usual to combine all the force diagrams as shown in (4). This combined diagram is drawn direct from the space diagram. The diagrams (1), (2), and (3) have been included here for instructional purposes only, because they will help to make clear the method of building up the combined diagram. Notice that no arrows are inserted in

the combined force diagram. This is because they would be pointing in opposite directions on each force, and this would lead to confusion.

The direction of one arrow being known, the directions of the others are noted mentally on the force diagram, and are then transferred to the space diagram where they are inserted *close up to the point where the forces act*. The forces in the members of the wall bracket, when scaled off the force diagram, are found to be as follows:—

AC—8 tons. *AD*—8 tons. *BC*+6·93 tons. *BE*+10·39 tons. *CD*+8 tons. *DE*+2 tons.

Before leaving this example we can find a suitable diameter for the tension members *AC* and *AD*. The load on each will be 8 tons. If of mild steel the safe working stress will be 8 tons per sq. in. Therefore the cross-sectional area must be load ÷ stress = 8 ÷ 8 which is 1 sq. in.

Now the area of a circle $1\frac{1}{8}$-in. diameter is ·994 sq. in., which is too small. The area of a circle $1\frac{1}{4}$-in. diameter is 1·226 sq. in., which is ample. Therefore both members, *AC* and *AD*, should be made from $1\frac{1}{4}$-in. diameter mild steel.

Although a wooden roof truss is rendered more rigid by the special design of its various joints, we can determine the forces in its members if we assume the truss to be a pin-jointed structure. This means that we assume the members to be held together at their meeting points by pins in such a way that they are in either tension or compression only, and cannot be bent by the loads they support.

Such an assumption has been made in dealing with the king-post truss shown in Fig. 14. Before starting the force diagram, it is necessary to calculate the upward reactions, GA and AB. This must be done because, at present, each junction point in the structure has more than two unknown forces. Taking moments about the left hand support, we have:—

Total clockwise moments=Total anti-clockwise moments.

$12 \times 6 + 10 \times 12 + 8 \times 18 + 4 \times 24 = GA \times 24.$

$72 + 120 + 144 + 96 = GA \times 24.$

$432 = GA \times 24$ from which we find that $GA = 18$ cwt.

The other reaction AB=Total load $-GA$; and this is 40 cwt. $- 18$ cwt. $= 22$ cwt.

In drawing the force diagram, it is a good plan to commence with all the external forces BC, CD, DE, EF, FG, GA, and AB, in that order. These will all be on a vertical line as shown. Next commence at the left-hand reaction with the known forces AB and BC, completing the diagram for this point with lines parallel to CL and LA. Next take the point where the strut joins the principal rafter. Draw the known forces LC and CD, and complete this diagram with lines parallel to DK and KL. Next take the point at the ridge, and then the other two points to the right of it.

A check on your diagram is afforded by now going around the point where the tie beam, struts, and king-post meet. The arrows have been inserted in the space diagram, and it will be noticed that they show the king-post to be in tension, which would be difficult to estimate without the force diagram.

From the force diagram the forces in the various members may now be scaled off and tabulated, the appropriate $+$ or $-$ sign being placed before each.

The roof truss shown in Fig. 15 is symmetrically loaded, and therefore each reaction is equal to half the total load, i.e., 2 tons. The external forces BC, CD, etc., are drawn first in the force diagram, and then we commence at the left-hand reaction as before. From the force diagram, the direction of the various arrows have been noted and then inserted in the space diagram.

Using the given scale, the forces in the members may be taken from the force diagram and tabulated, the signs $+$ or $-$ being inserted as before.

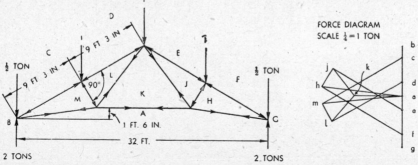

Fig. 15. Force diagram for a roof truss, which is symmetrically loaded. Each reaction is equal to half the total load, i.e., 2 tons. The direction of the arrows should be noted.

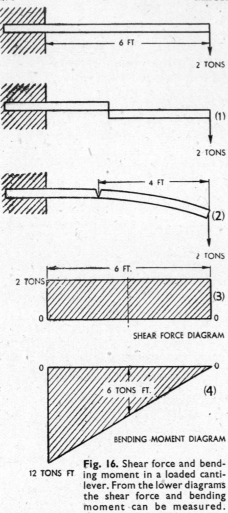

Fig. 16. Shear force and bending moment in a loaded cantilever. From the lower diagrams the shear force and bending moment can be measured.

break in either of two ways. The fibre may shear off in a vertical plane as shown at (1) due to a vertical shear force of 2 tons, or the cantilever may bend until it breaks as shown at (2) due to a bending moment of 2 tons × 4 ft =8 tons ft. If we neglect the weight of the beam, we see that the shear force or force tending to shear the beam in a vertical plane, will be 2 tons at every point along the beam.

This fact is shown diagrammatically at (3). The figure is like a graph, and as the depth of it is constant from end to end, it tells us that the shear force is always the same, namely, 2 tons throughout the exposed length of the cantilever. This is called the shear force diagram.

The bending moment, which was 8 tons ft. at the point we first considered, will become greater as we approach the wall, because the leverage of the 2 tons load will increase. The maximum bending moment will occur at the face of the wall, and will be 2 tons × 6 ft.=12 tons ft. At the other end of the beam, where the leverage will be nothing, the bending moment will be nothing. This is shown in the bending moment diagram at (4).

Shear Force and Bending Moment

Looking at the two diagrams, we see that the maximum bending moment is equal to the area of the shear force diagram. Also the bending moment halfway along the beam is equal to the area of half the shear force diagram. In all the cases with which we are about to deal, it is true to say that, starting from the end where the bending moment is zero, *the area of the shear force diagram up to any point is equal to the bending moment at that point.* This fact will be made use of later.

Fig. 17 shows a cantilever with several loads. The sum of these loads

The study of the forces acting in a loaded beam is complicated by the fact that tensile, compressive, and shear stresses are set up in the material.

It will be well to remember that, at any point in a loaded beam, the forces acting in one direction must be exactly equal to the forces acting in the opposite direction and that the clockwise moments about that point must be equal to the anti-clockwise moments.

Consider the loaded cantilever shown in Fig. 16. There is a tendency for it to

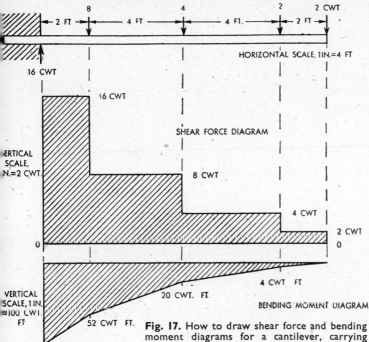

Fig. 17. How to draw shear force and bending moment diagrams for a cantilever, carrying several loads which total 16 cwt.

by 4 cwt. ×4 ft. = 16 cwt. ft. Therefore the bending moment at this point is 4 +16=20 cwt. ft. Adding up the areas in this way we arrive at the left-hand end where the maximum bending moment is equal to the total area of the shear force diagram, namely 84 cwt. ft.

Figure 18 shows the signs usually given to shear force and bending moment. The diagrams require no explanation, but the signs should be memorized.

6 cwt., and therefore there must be an pward thrust of 16 cwt. at the wall to ounteract this total load. To draw the near force diagram we start with a orizontal line, and at the left-hand end e go up 16 cwt. to scale.

Next proceeding horizontally until ne 8-cwt. load is reached we come own 8 cwt. Continuing to come down t each load in this way, we eventually rrive back on the horizontal line at ne right-hand end. This completes the near force diagram.

To draw the bending moment diaram we start again with a horizontal ne. Beginning at the right-hand end vhere the bending moment is zero, we ee that the area of the shear force iagram up to the second 2-cwt. load 2 cwt. ×2 ft. = 4 cwt. ft. This is the ending moment at this point.

From here to the 4-cwt. load the hear force diagram increases in area

As the load is central in the beam shown in Fig. 19, each reaction will be equal to half the load, namely 3 tons. The shear force in the left-hand portion of the beam will be positive, so we start the shear force diagram at the left-hand end. The line goes up 3 tons, then along to the middle of the beam at which point the line goes down 6 tons.

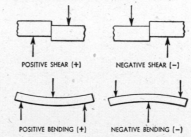

Fig. 18. The signs which are generally adopted for shear force and bending moment.

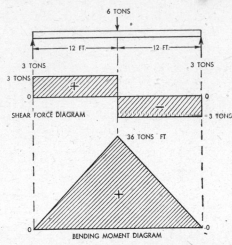

Fig. 19. Example of concentrated load on beam, with the load central. Each reaction is equal to half the load, namely 3 tons.

To the right of this point the bending moment becomes less because the area of the shear force diagram which is now added is negative. Upon reaching the right-hand end of the beam the bending moment is again zero, this being the sum of the upper and lower portions of the shear force diagram, 36 tons ft. added to minus 36 tons ft.

Beam with Several Loads

This is shown in Fig. 20. Taking moments about the left-hand support, the reactions are found to be 4 tons and 10 tons. Both the shear force and bending moment diagrams are started at the left-hand end. It will be seen that part of the bending moment diagram is below the base line.

This negative bending indicates that that part of the beam is convex on the

After moving to the right horizontally, the line comes up 3 tons at the right-hand reaction and so reaches the horizontal base line. That part of the diagram which is above the base line shows positive shear, the part below the base line shows negative shear.

As the beam is going to bend down in the middle, positive bending is indicated, and we start the bending moment diagram at the left-hand end.

The bending moment will be zero here, and will increase in proportion to the distance along the beam until the middle is reached. At this point the area of the shear force diagram is 3 tons × 12 ft. = 36 tons ft.

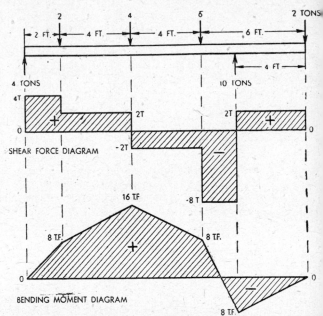

POINT OF CONTRAFLEXURE

Fig. 20. In this example both the shear force and the bending moment diagrams are started at the left-hand end. The part of the bending moment diagram shown below the line indicates that part of the beam which is convex on the upper face. The point where the bending moment changes from positive to negative is known as a point of contraflexure.

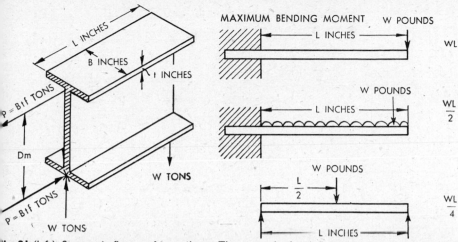

Fig. 21 (left). Stresses in flanges of a cantilever. The strength of each flange is its breadth multiplied by its thickness multiplied by the strength per square inch of the steel. (Right) Diagrams showing concentrated and distributed loads on cantilevers and central load on beam, with formulæ which indicate the maximum bending moments.

upper face. The point where the bending moment changes from positive to negative is called a point of contraflexure.

It is now possible to give a general definition of bending moment. *The bending moment at any point in a beam is the algebraic sum of all the moments acting on one side (either right or left) of that point.*

Consider a point above the 10 tons reaction in the last example. The only force acting to the right of this point is one of 2 tons at a leverage of 4 ft. Hence the bending moment at this point is 8 tons ft.

As this moment will make the beam bend *down* to the right (being a clockwise moment) the bending moment is negative. The forces acting to the right of a point under the 6 tons load are 2 tons, leverage 6 ft., giving a clockwise moment of 12 tons ft., and a reaction of 10 tons, leverage 2 ft, giving an anticlockwise moment of 20 tons ft. The algebraic sum of these two is an anticlockwise moment of 8 tons ft.

As this will bend the beam *up* to the right, it follows that the bending moment at this point is positive and is 8 tons ft. The bending moment at other points along the beam may be found in the same way.

Resisting Moment

When a bending moment is applied to a beam, the beam is deformed. Some of the fibres are stretched, and some are shortened. In this way tensile and compressive stresses are set up in the material. These stresses exert a moment which tends to straighten the beam by opposing the applied bending moment. This internal straightening moment is called the *resisting moment*.

It will be obvious that, for a beam in equilibrium, the resisting moment equals in magnitude the bending moment.

Fig. 21 shows an R.S.J. arranged as a cantilever with a load of W tons hung at the end. For simplicity we shall neglect the strength of the web. The area of each flange is Bt sq. in., and if the safe working stress is f tons per sq. in., then the safe pull in the top flange will be Btf tons. The push in the bottom flange must be the same for equilibrium.

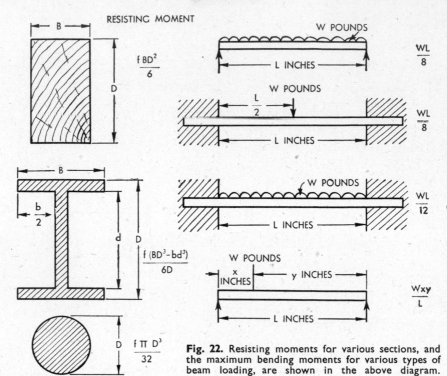

Fig. 22. Resisting moments for various sections, and the maximum bending moments for various types of beam loading, are shown in the above diagram.

These forces may be assumed to act at the centre of each flange, the vertical distance between them being the mean depth of the joist, D_m in.

Taking moments about the point X, the clockwise moments must equal the anti-clockwise. Therefore:—

$$W \times L = Btf \times D_m.$$

WL ton in. is the bending moment, and $BtfD_m$ ton in. the resisting moment.

EXAMPLE. An R.S.J. 6 in. wide, 10 in. deep, with flanges $\frac{1}{2}$ in. thick, projects 8 ft. horizontally from the face of a wall. Taking the safe working stress for steel as 8 tons per sq. in., find the greatest safe load which may be hung at the free end.

Bending moment = Resisting moment
$$WL = BtfD_m$$
$W \times 96$ in. $= 6$ in. $\times \frac{1}{2}$ in. $\times 8 \times 9\frac{1}{2}$ in.;
from which we find that $W = 2\frac{3}{8}$ tons.

If B is the breadth, D the depth, and f the safe working stress for a rectangular beam, it can be shown that the resisting moment is $\frac{fBD}{6}$.

EXAMPLE. What is the greatest safe load which may be hung at the end of a red pine beam 9 in. deep, 3 in. wide, projecting 6 ft. horizontally from the face of a wall? Take the safe working stress for red pine as 12 cwts. per sq. in.

Bending moment = Resisting moment
$$WL = \frac{fBD^2}{6}$$
$W \times 72$ in. $= \dfrac{12 \times 3 \text{ in.} \times 9 \text{ in.} \times 9 \text{ in.}}{6}$;
from which we find that $W = 6\frac{3}{4}$ cwt.

It will be seen that in all these cases we start by equating the bending moment to the resisting moment, being careful to see that we use the same units of length and force on each side of the equation.

Fig. 22 shows the resisting moments for various sections, and the maximum bending moments for various types of beam loading.

By pairing the appropriate bending and resisting moments from this collection, many practical problems in connection with beams may be solved.

EXAMPLE 1. A beam 10 in. deep, 4 in. wide, rests on two walls 14 ft. apart. What is the greatest safe load which can be carried by this beam at a point 5 ft. from one of the walls? The safe working stress f for the timber is 12 cwt. per sq. in.

Bending moment = Resisting moment

From Fig. 22 we have $\dfrac{Wxy}{L} = \dfrac{fBD^2}{6}$

Putting

L in inches $\dfrac{W \times 60 \text{ in.} \times 108 \text{ in.}}{168 \text{ ins.}} = \dfrac{12 \times 4 \times 10 \times 10}{6}$;

from which we find that $W = 20 \cdot 7$ cwt.

EXAMPLE 2. A floor is supported by 9 in. × 3 in. joists spaced 15 in. centre to centre, and resting on walls 16 ft. apart. Neglecting the weight of the floor itself, calculate the safe load per square foot for this floor.

Take f as 1,200 lb. per sq. in.

We first find the safe distributed load for one joist.

Bending moment = Resisting moment

From Fig. 22 we have $\dfrac{WL}{8} = \dfrac{fBD^2}{6}$

$\dfrac{W \times 192 \text{ in.}}{8} = \dfrac{1200 \times 3 \times 9 \times 9}{6}$;

from which we find that $W = 2,025$ lb.

Now this load is distributed over an area 16 ft. × 15 in., which is 20 sq. ft. Therefore the load per square foot = 2,025 lb. ÷ 20 sq. ft. = $101\frac{1}{4}$ lb. per sq. ft.

Columns and Struts

Columns, stanchions, pillars, struts, and props, are all members in compression. When such members are short and thick it is safe to assume that the compressive stress is uniform over the whole cross-section and equal to load ÷ area. When, however, these members are long and thin, they tend to buckle, or bend in the middle, the stress is no longer uniform over the whole cross-section, and the safe load is considerably reduced.

Formulæ for dealing with these long columns were obtained by Euler two hundred years ago, and Gordon, Rankine, Fidler, Johnson, and others have devised formulæ for use in the design of columns of medium length and thickness. More recently the problem was tackled by the British Standards Institution, and the result of their work is now incorporated in British Standard Specification No. 449. As the method there described is the one in general use, we shall explain it in this chapter.

The moment of inertia of a beam section or column section is a measure of its resistance to bending by a load applied at right angles to its length.

Moment of Inertia

The value of the moment of inertia of a section is found by splitting the section up into an infinite number of strips (Fig. 23). The area of each strip is then multiplied by the square of its distance from a given axis (usually the neutral axis) and the sum of all these products is I, the moment of inertia. In practice, of course, we cannot take an infinite number of strips, but the required result may be obtained mathematically, and this has been done for most of the more common sections. For example, the moment of inertia of a rectangular section D in. deep and B in. broad about a centre line at right angles to the depth, is $\frac{BD^3}{12}$. The moments of inertia for various steel sections such as broad flange beams, British Standard

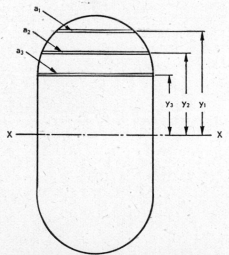

Fig. 23. The value of the moment of inertia of a section is found by splitting the section up into an infinite number of strips. The moment of inertia about the line X—X in the above diagram = $A_1 Y_1{}^2 + A_2 Y_2{}^2 + A_3 Y_3{}^2 +$, etc.

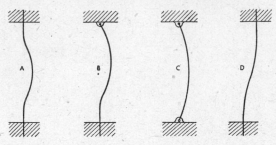

Fig. 24. The effective length of a column is taken as some fraction or multiple of the actual length. The fraction depends on the method of securing the ends.

joists, channels, angles, tees, etc., will be seen in the tables issued by the makers.

Radius of Gyration

In finding the moment of inertia, we multiplied the area of each strip by the square of its distance from an axis. If, instead, we multiplied the *whole area* by the square of *one distance* to obtain the same answer, then that distance would be the radius of gyration, k. If A is the total area of the section, it follows that $A \times k^2 = I$. Therefore, the radius of gyration $k = \sqrt{\frac{I}{A}}$. It may be defined as the radius at which the whole area may be assumed to be concentrated when calculating the moment of inertia.

It will be obvious that a column which is gripped firmly top and bottom will be capable of carrying a larger load than one which is merely pivoted at each end, because the latter, being unrestrained, is more liable to buckle. For this reason the effective length, l in., of a column is taken as some fraction or multiple of the actual length, L in., as shown in Fig. 24. It will be seen that the fraction depends upon the method of securing the ends of the column.

In A, both ends are held in position and both are restrained in direction.

In B, both ends are held in position, but only one restrained in direction.

In C, both ends are held in position,

but neither are restrained in direction.

In D, one end is held in position, and both ends are restrained in direction.

For case A, $l = \cdot 7L$; for case B $l = \cdot 85L$; for case C, $l = L$; and for case D, $l = $ from L to $1 \cdot 5L$ according to the degree of restraint. For columns these sizes are usually in inches.

The *slenderness ratio* takes account of the proportions of a column, i.e., whether it is short and thick, or long and thin. The effective length of the column, l in., is divided by the least radius of gyration of the cross-section, k in.

Thus slenderness ratio $= \frac{l}{k}$.

Having found the slenderness ratio the safe working stress for a column is obtained by referring to the following Table given in B.S.S. 449.

Ratio of effective column length to radius of least gyration $\frac{l}{k}$	Working stress in tons per square inch of gross section Fl Mild steel
20	7·17
30	6·92
40	6·64
50	6·30
60	5·89
70	5·41
80	4·88
90	4·33
100	3·81
110	3·34
120	2·93
130	2·58
140	2·28
150	2·02
160	1·81
170	1·62
180	1·46
190	1·33
200	1·21
210	1·10
220	1·01
230	0·93
240	0·86

When this safe working stress is multiplied by the cross-sectional are

f the column, the result is the safe
xial load which the column will be
ble to support.

Thus the safe axial load for column
$=F_1 \times A$ tons.

EXAMPLE. A rectangular steel column is 6 in.
× 4 in. and 15 ft. high. Both ends are fixed and
restrained in direction. Calculate the safe axial
load in tons.

The section is shown in Fig. 25. About the
axis xx the moment of inertia, $\frac{BD^3}{12} = \frac{1}{12}$
× 4 × 6 × 6 × 6 = 72. The radius of gyration is
therefore $\sqrt{\frac{I}{A}} = \sqrt{\frac{72}{24}} = 1.7321$. About the axis
yy the moment of inertia is $\frac{1}{12} \times 6 \times 4 \times 4 \times 4$
= 32, and the radius of gyration is $\sqrt{\frac{32}{24}}$
= 1.155.

Taking the least radius of gyration, the
slenderness ratio is $\frac{l}{k} = \frac{.7 \times 15 \times 12}{1.155}$ which comes
to 109·1. Notice that the ·7 is used because both
ends of the column are fixed and restrained in
direction as in case A (Fig 24). The 12 is
required to convert the length to inches.

Referring to table shown from B.S.S. 449,
we find that a slenderness ratio of 109·1 has a
corresponding safe stress of 3·3 tons per sq. in.
Hence the safe axial load for this column is
·3 × 24 = 79·2 tons.

EXAMPLE. From the manufacturer's catalogue
is found that a broad flange beam 6·3 in.
× 6·3 in. has a cross-sectional area of 9 sq. in.
The value of I_{xx} is 63·3, and the value of I_{yy} is
3·0. What will be the safe axial load for a
column 10 ft. high made from such a beam, if
the lower end is both held and restrained, and
the upper end merely held in position?

Taking the least moment of inertia, we have
$= \sqrt{\frac{23}{9}} = 1.599$. As this is an example of case
B (Fig. 24), the effective column length is
·85 × 10 × 12 = 102 in.

The slenderness ratio $\frac{l}{k} = \frac{102}{1.599} = 63.8$.

Referring to B.S.S. 449, we find the safe
stress $F_1 = 5.71$ tons per sq. in.

Safe axial load = safe stress × area = 5·71 × 9
= 51·4 tons.

It will be observed that the method
of calculating the safe axial load for a
column is divided into 5 parts, as
follows:—

1) Find least radius of gyration, k
$= \sqrt{\frac{I}{A}}$.

2) Find the effective length using the
appropriate fraction for cases A, B,
C and D (Fig 24).

3) Calculate the slenderness ratio $= \frac{l}{k}$.

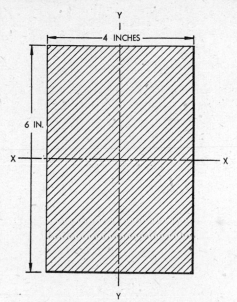

Fig. 25. Diagram showing how to calculate in
tons the safe axial load of a steel column.

(4) From B.S.S. 449 obtain the corresponding safe stress F_1.

(5) Calculate the safe axial load in tons
$= F_1 \times$ cross-sectional area.

Machines

The machines which are of interest
to the builder are those which make it
possible to lift a large load by the
application of a comparatively small
effort. Crowbars, wedges, pulley blocks,
screwjacks and winches are included.

With each of these machines the small
effort is exerted through a big distance
in order to lift the big load through a
small distance. The ratio, distance
through which effort acts ÷ distance
through which load is lifted, is called
the velocity ratio (V.R.) of the machine, and its value varies from, say 3,
for a simple set of rope blocks, to over
300 for a screwjack.

The type of machine to be used on
any particular job will depend upon the
size of the load to be lifted, and the

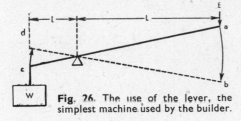

Fig. 26. The use of the lever, the simplest machine used by the builder.

power available for the effort. The height of the lift must also be considered.

The ratio, load ÷ effort, is called the force ratio, or mechanical advantage (M.A.), and its value is always less than that of the velocity ratio. When the frictional resistance in a machine is small, the difference between the M.A. and the V.R. is small, but when the frictional resistance is great, the difference between the M.A. and the V.R is great.

If frictional resistance could be eliminated altogether, the M.A. would be equal to the V.R. As these two are so intimately connected, we shall deal first with the velocity ratio, the value of which may be found without conducting an actual test upon the machine concerned.

Leverage

Fig. 26 shows a lever, the simplest machine used by the builder. When the effort, E, acts through the arc, ab, the load, W, is raised through the arc, ed. Now the arc ab is greater than the arc cd in the same ratio that the radius L is greater than the radius l. Hence the velocity ratio of the lever is ab/ed and this is equal to L/l.

Use of Wedge

Fig. 27 shows a wedge of length L and thickness T. To drive the wedge home, the effort, E, must act through a distance, L, and this will have the effect of raising the load through a distance of T.

Hence the velocity ratio of such a wedge will be L/T.

A set of rope blocks is shown in Fig. 28. The top block contains 3 pulleys, and the bottom block, 2 pulleys. In the sketch, the pulleys are shown with different diameters. This is done to make the action clearer, but in an actual set of blocks, the pulleys are all of the same diameter.

If we allow the effort, E, to act through a certain distance, say 10 ft., then 10 ft. of rope will be taken away from the five ropes connecting the upper and lower blocks. This means that each of the five ropes a, b, c, d, e, has been shortened by $10 \div 5 = 2$ ft. Hence the load has been raised 2 ft.

The velocity ratio is therefore $10 \div 2 = 5$. In general, the velocity ratio of a set of rope blocks is equal to the number of supporting ropes.

This is usually the same as the total number of pulleys, as in the case just considered. An exception is the case where the effort acts upwards. Here the effort rope becomes a supporting rope, and the velocity ratio is one more than the number of pulleys.

Chain Blocks

Weston's chain blocks, shown in Fig. 29, are an improvement on the old-fashioned Chinese windlass. The two top pulleys are cast in one piece, and so

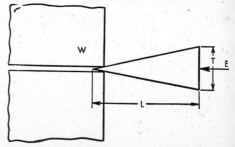

Fig. 27. Effect of driving a wedge in order to raise a load. When the wedge is driven fully home, the load will be lifted to the distance shown by the arrows at T.

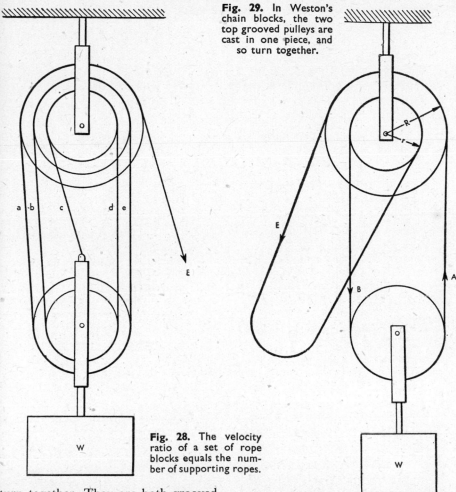

Fig. 29. In Weston's chain blocks, the two top grooved pulleys are cast in one piece, and so turn together.

Fig. 28. The velocity ratio of a set of rope blocks equals the number of supporting ropes.

turn together. They are both grooved, and in the grooves are small teeth which engage with the links of the chain to prevent the latter slipping. In order to turn the two top pulleys through one revolution, the effort, E, must act through a distance, $2\pi R$. The chain A, will move up a distance of $2\pi R$, and the chain B, will move down a distance of $2\pi r$.

This means that the net, or effective movement of chain A will be $2\pi R - 2\pi r$ $= 2\pi(R - r)$. The lower pulley and the load will be lifted only a half of this $= \pi(R - r)$. So the velocity ratio of this

machine is $2\pi R \div \pi(R - r) = 2R \div (R - r)$. As the teeth in both the upper grooved pulleys are spaced at the same distance apart, the number of teeth in each will be proportional to their circumferences, and therefore will be proportional to their radii. It follows that if N be the number of teeth in the larger pulley, and n the number of teeth in the smaller, then the velocity ratio will be $2N \div (N - n.)$

Fig. 30 (left) shows the side view of a crab winch. If the handle were connected at A, the velocity ratio would

Fig. 30 (left). Side view of a crab winch and (right) the lever velocity ratio of the winch.

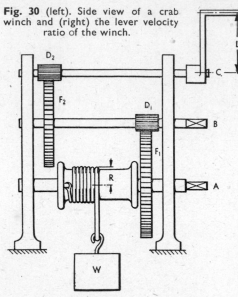

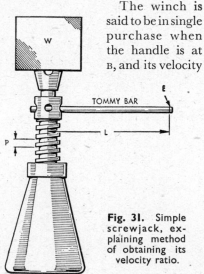

Fig. 31. Simple screwjack, explaining method of obtaining its velocity ratio.

be $L \div R$, as it would be equivalent to the simple case of a lever as shown in Fig. 30 (right).

When the handle is attached at B, the velocity ratio is increased in the ratio $F_1 \div D_1$ where F_1 is the number of teeth on the first cogwheel, and D_1 is the number of teeth on the first pinion.

The winch is said to be in single purchase when the handle is at B, and its velocity

ratio is $L \times F_1 \div R \times D_1$. When the handle is at C, the velocity ratio is increased to $L \times F_1 \times F_2 \div R \times D_1 \times D$ and the winch is said to be in double purchase.

Fig. 31 shows a simple screwjack. The effort is applied at a distance of L in from the centre of the jack. The pitch of the screw thread is p in. When the effort, acting at the end of the tommy bar, turns the screw through one revolution, the load is lifted through a distance equal to the pitch, p in. At the same time the effort acts through a distance equal to the circumference of a circle of radius, L in., and this is $2\pi L$ in. Therefore the velocity ratio of the screwjack is $2\pi L \div p$.

The efficiency of a machine, expressed as a fraction, is:—

Work got out $\div$ work put in.

Now the work got out is the product of the load and the distance the load is lifted. The work put in is the product of the effort and the distance through which the effort acts. It follows that the efficiency is $\frac{\text{Load} \times \text{distance load is lifted}}{\text{Effort} \times \text{distance effort acts}}$ and this is $\frac{\text{Mechanical advantage}}{\text{Velocity ratio}}$. Another way of expressing the efficiency is $\frac{\text{Load}}{\text{Effort} \times \text{Velocity ratio}}$

EXAMPLE. A screwjack has a pitch of $\frac{7}{16}$ in. and the effective length of the tommy bar is 21 in. To lift a load of 1 ton, an effort of 40 lb is required. What is the efficiency of the jack?

Velocity ratio $= \frac{2\pi L}{p} = \frac{2 \times 22 \times 21 \times 16}{7 \times 7} = 301 \cdot 7$

Efficiency $= \frac{\text{Load}}{\text{Effort} \times \text{Velocity ratio}} = \frac{2240}{40 \times 301 \cdot 7}$

$= \cdot 186$ or $18 \cdot 6$ per cent.

CHAPTER 8

PAINTING AND DECORATING

Drying oils. Synthetic resins. Oil colours. Preparation of surfaces. Plaster boards. Woodwork and ironwork. Ceilings and walls. Flat oil paints. Undercoats and finishes. Distempering. Principal stains. Varnishing. French polishing. Paper-hanging on walls and ceilings.

THIS important section of the building trade is primarily concerned with the preservation of those materials which, if unprotected, would rapidly decay. The painting of all wood and metalwork, both exterior and interior, constructional or otherwise, is included in this category and must be finished in oil paint, oil varnish or other equally durable coating to achieve that particular purpose.

On interior work, hygienic requirements must be adequately satisfied, and though these may appear to be of secondary importance, the treatment and materials employed should conform to the special needs of the room or building. In this connection, one should bear in mind that the walls of a hospital ward, for example, will require washing down as frequently as the woodwork; therefore a smooth enamel-like finish is necessary.

Scope for the Craftsman

Decoration may be regarded as all painting, supplementary and additional to the foregoing. Here is unlimited scope for the craftsman to express his ideas in terms of colour, pattern, texture and various media, while at the same time making full use of technique to produce a variety of stippled, shaded, scumbled or other broken-colour effects of high decorative value. A good sense of design and colour, some originality,

the ability to draw, and sound craftsmanship, are all qualities which can be acquired, but without which no decorator could produce a scheme capable of satisfying the æsthetic demands of his client.

Research on Materials

Intensive research on the part of paint and varnish manufacturers has resulted in the production of materials so widely different in composition, methods of application and subsequent behaviour as to call for particular attention. To simplify classification we must for the moment ignore the colouring matter or pigment and concentrate upon the various liquid mediums or binding agents which are directly responsible for that difference.

LINSEED AND OTHER DRYING OILS impart toughness, elasticity, weather-resisting qualities and gloss to oil paints. These oils dry by the absorption of oxygen from the air; a process which, when accelerated by the addition of certain metallic salts known as *driers*, is still slow enough to allow easy working under the brush and yet to become firm overnight.

Drying oils are treated in various ways with the object of improving the body or thickness and thereby increasing the gloss. Cooking for several hours, during which time resin is usually added, produces varnish of extreme durability for use either as a transparent coating or as a medium for enamel or enamel paint.

The more general use of artificial resin has made possible the production of many types of varnish and enamel paint of undoubted value to the decorator. An important point to ascertain when selecting such material is its precise effect upon undercoats of the linseed oil type. Some synthetics contain thinners which have a strong solvent action upon ordinary paints; therefore, an undercoating supplied by the manufacturer will in such cases be necessary. The chief advantages of the synthetic product are its drying speed (4 hr. and upwards) and its weather-resisting properties.

Considerations which govern surface preparation will vary according to the material to be painted, its chemical nature, position (interior or exterior), present condition, whether old or new and the type of finish to be used; nor must it be assumed that because less labour is involved new surfaces present fewer problems than older ones. A study of the facts will prove that the reverse is more often the case.

Painting in Oil Colour

To attain success in the use of oil paints, certain general principles must at all times be observed. All surfaces, whether new or previously painted, should be quite hard, clean, smooth and above all, bone dry. Good preparation should aim at producing these conditions with occasional exceptions in regard to smoothness, which, in the case of textured surfaces for instance, is intentional.

Among faults arising from the non-observance of these principles are blistering, cracking and peeling of the new paint. Imprisoned moisture will vaporize under slight heat, forming blisters; while dirt and grease prevent the proper adhesion and hardening of an undercoat, with the result that sooner or later unequal expansion will cause superimposed coats to crack. The principle of building up from hard undercoats to softer and more elastic finishes, and allowing sufficient time for each to harden, has long been regarded as sound procedure in the prevention of painting defects.

Ceilings and Walls

Ceilings and walls provide not only the larger areas but also a wide variety of materials upon which to work. Nowadays one must expect to find plaster board, asbestos sheets and perhaps composition wall-board, supplementing the lime plaster, hardwall plaster or Portland cement finishes. The three latter surfaces must be allowed ample time to become thoroughly dry and hard before oil paint is applied otherwise the strongly alkaline solution which exudes, will saponify (change into a tacky soap) the oil medium.

LIME PLASTER AND PLASTER BOARD Here, the comparatively simple preparation of making good any cracks or slight defects with Keene's or other hardwall plaster (Fig. 1); smoothing the whole surface by rubbing down with No. 2 glass-paper; and finally sweeping off and removing the accumulated dust will render the job fit for its first or priming coat of paint.

WALL-BOARD usually presents a good surface for paint, though, as might be expected, the joints, left slightly open to permit expansion, and any dents or other damage sustained when fixing will have to be made good after the priming coat is dry. Alabastine filler applied with a broad scraper (Fig. 2 or filling knife, is ideal for the purpose but should afterwards be smoothed down with glass-paper and excessive

Fig. I. "Making good" any defective plaster involves undercutting the edges to provide key for the new material as shown above.

absorption checked by touching-up with paint.

A suitable primer for the foregoing materials can be mixed from white lead plus 5 per cent red lead, reduced with 3 of oil to 1 of turpentine and made rather thin.

Where wall-board is intended to form a permanent finish, the practice of covering all joints with a wooden fillet or moulding effectively hides those fine cracks which sooner or later appear.

HARDWALL PLASTER. Owing to lack of key presented by such hard glossy surfaces, the usual procedure is to apply a thin, sharp (4 of turpentine to 1 of oil) priming coat prepared from white lead, immediately the plaster is sufficiently firm to withstand the pressure of the paint-brush. This means following up the plasterer within about two hours, and although it would appear contrary to the general principles already mentioned, it does not, if reasonable time lapses before the second coating, prevent the natural drying out of the plaster.

The alternative, employed when the plaster has properly hardened off, in-

volves glass-papering to score the surface lightly and so form key or grip for the paint by mechanical means.

Portland Cement

Portland cement often retains chemically active moisture for as long as twelve months, so one is well advised to use oil-bound distemper or other non-saponifiable paint (there are many reliable proprietary makes) when decorating for the first time.

ASBESTOS SHEETS. Because of their high Portland cement content, asbestos sheets, when fixed in damp situations, absorb moisture which becomes alkaline and reacts upon oil paint. Preventive measures must aim at waterproofing behind the sheets before fixing. Prior to painting, all joints are made good with Keene's cement (for obvious reasons Portland is always undesirable as a stopping), afterwards smoothed down and the whole surface coated with a good oil-bound distemper or a proprietary sealing solution.

The preparation described for woodwork will cover all processes up to and including priming. Needless repetition

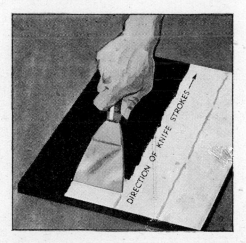

Fig. 2. Spreading a white paste filler. The broad scraper for applying the alabastine filler should be held at an angle of about 30 degrees.

will thus be avoided, as all this work is grouped under the heading "Previously Painted Surfaces."

Although for priming purposes, woodwork will be classified as soft or hard according to its degree of porosity, one can still generalize upon the more immediate requirements of dryness, smoothness and cleanliness. The first is best ensured by priming before work leaves the joiner's shop, which is by far the most thorough and economical procedure. Smoothness and cleanliness involve the use, where necessary, of No. 1½ glass-paper, but the chisel knife is more effective for the removal of any spots of glue or plaster.

Treatment of Woodwork

Sometimes oil, grease, creosote or tar are present and must be scraped and washed off with clean rag and turpentine. Finally, after dusting down, paint all knots, traces of tar, creosote and even copying-ink pencil marks, with genuine shellac knotting (an efficient sealing solution), which prevents these destructive substances from discolouring superimposed coats of paint.

Teak, Columbian pine and to a lesser extent, pitch pine, are well known as anti-drying materials requiring a special primer prepared by mixing equal parts of Japan gold-size and turpentine. Other woods are primed with paint made from white lead, plus 5 per cent red lead and 5 per cent paste driers, thinned with linseed oil and turpentine in proportions calculated to check porosity of surface and yet permit deep penetration into the pores of the timber. For softwoods, use 2 parts oil to 1 of turpentine, and for hardwoods, reverse these proportions, making the paint of rather thin consistency and sieving through fine muslin before use.

STOPPING or filling up nail holes, etc.,

may be proceeded with when t priming is dry. For best work, ha stopping (made from equal parts linse oil putty and dry white lead mixed wi gold-size) is employed; and for rough work, putty alone. By using the fl edge of the knife, stopping is press tightly home and left perfectly smoot after which the job is again ready i painting.

Primings for Ironwork

IRONWORK is usually primed with r lead or red oxide paint immediate after the casting or smoothing proc has been completed.

In our humid climate, corrosi should be prevented from the ve beginning, for once started, painti cannot effect a complete cure. Prepar tion would therefore aim at the remov by scraping thoroughly or chipping any rust which may be present, t washing off with turpentine substitt (never water) of any oil or grease; ar in the case of highly polished meta the formation (by rubbing with fi emery paper) of some key to assist t adhesion of paint. Such impervious st faces as metal and glass demand pai

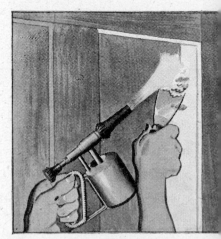

Fig. 3. Burning off old paint from a door means of the standard type of petrol blow lan

maximum tenacity, a quality obtained by the addition of a liberal amount of boiled oil or, better still, a good elastic varnish.

Previously Painted Surfaces.

Preparation can only be decided upon by ascertaining the condition of the various parts of the job in question. One frequently finds part of the work fairly sound and the remainder badly blistered or otherwise defective, but whatever the condition, good preparation must be designed to produce a surface conforming to the general rules previously laid down. Fig. 3 shows the method of burning off the old paint from a door by means of a blow lamp.

CEILINGS AND WALLS may be papered, distempered, coated with oil-bound distemper, or finished in oil paint. The first two should be removed by repeatedly soaking with hot water and then scraping off with a 2½-in. scraper in the case of wall-paper; or in the case of distemper, by washing off with the brush and sponge, changing the water very frequently until the bare plaster is left quite clean.

Removing Casein-bound Distemper

Fig. 4 shows a casein-bound distemper being removed by scraping and washing. Any trace of paper, paste, size, or distemper left on the surface will prevent the proper adhesion of later coatings and be directly responsible for the paint chipping or peeling off in places. For details of stopping and priming, see the paragraphs on lime plaster and wall-board on page 282.

OIL-BOUND DISTEMPER is insoluble in water and therefore cannot be removed by washing, but a combined washing and scraping process will, by displacing dirt and loose material, create a good firm surface which only requires stopping and glass-papering, before priming

Fig. 4. The removal of casein-bound distemper by a combined washing and scraping process.

with the mixture made for hardwoods.

DEFECTIVE PLASTER due to dampness (causing the plaster to perish), or vibration, or the settling of the building, will all be encountered and must be made good. Perished plaster must be cut completely out to the bare bricks, and the cause of the dampness detected and cured at the source. Defects due to vibration take the form of deep cracks with the edges often out of level. This difference can only be made good by cutting out a groove sufficiently wide to disguise that difference when the repair is finished.

Deep patches are made good with a stiff mortar composed of equal parts sand and Keene's cement. The edges are undercut and saturated with clean water to check excessive suction before the new plaster is applied. When hard, a smooth face is obtained by a thin skimming coat of Keene's cement.

FLAT OR SEMI-FLAT OIL PAINTS are already hard, fairly smooth, and after washing down with a weak solution of sugar soap, offer a good key for new paint, but glossy surfaces must in addition be rubbed down with pumice stone, prepared pumice block or waterproof

The decorative value of broken-colour effects is now being more fully realized. The illustration shows the formation of pattern by means of rag-rolling upon the wet paint. Turquoise blue is used upon a cream undercoat.

glass-paper, until a hard, matt surface has been obtained.

Rinse off thoroughly with clean water all traces of the sodium from the pumice block or sugar soap, otherwise the new paint (thinned with equal parts oil and turpentine) may be adversely affected.

BLEEDING COLOURS. Certain pigments, particularly crimson lake and some of the artificial vermilion colours, are capable of bleeding or percolating through superimposed coats of paint. The remedy is to follow the usual procedure of removing completely with pumice stone all painted decoration, or to seal up by coating with white knotting any areas occupied by the doubtful colours.

FOR BLISTERED, CRACKED AND TACKY SURFACES the only remedy is to remove completely the defective paint and make a fresh start. Burning off with a blow lamp is a quicker and more satisfactory method than paint removal by means of chemical solvents, all traces of which must be washed off afterward with turpentine substitute; whereas in the former case, only surface glass papering is necessary to make the work ready for priming.

When burning off, the broad scrape must not be allowed to dig into and damage the underlying surface nor, in the case of woodwork, must the work be badly scorched, or the shavework b permitted to spoil the sharp edges of the mouldings. The treatment of such surfaces is the same as that specified for hardwoods.

FILLING is the application, usuall with the broad scraper, of a semi-stiff rapid-hardening paste, which is afterwards rubbed down perfectly smooth The scraper fills up any further inequalities which may be present after the firs stopping and leaves the high spots quite bare. For interior work "Alabastine" and water make a reliable mixture, bu prepared oil paste fillers prove infinitel more satisfactory for exteriors. Th former is dry glass-papered, and th latter material rubbed down wet, whe finally smoothing off.

Application of Undercoats

As priming alone is insufficient t check completely the porosity of mos surfaces, the application of a finishin coat would under such conditions in evitably result in uneven colour an gloss. Undercoats prevent this and als by bodying-up the surface, increas durability, smoothness, opacity or hid ing power and lastly, accomplish an desired change of colour.

Semi-gloss undercoats (thinned wit equal parts oil and turpentine) are th general rule, although for interior wor where zinc paints are largely employe a mixture of 3 of turpentine to 2 of c is preferable, and proves equally sati factory for both glossy and flat finishe

Brushes, paint and technique are equally important factors throughout the execution of work. Brushes should be of hog's hair, made up by a reputable firm and should be nicely broken in (slightly worn) to obtain best results. A set ranging from 1 in. to 4 in. in width, of the flat type of brush, is adequate for all ordinary purposes. Paint (except gloss finishes) should be thin enough to permit quick and easy spreading and should, of course, be sieved when necessary to remove any coarse particles which may be present.

Laying Off

Undercoats should always be applied rather sparingly, i.e., each brushful of paint spread or brushed out until the brush is almost dry. Except in the case of borders and other narrow widths, the brush strokes will follow a fairly vertical direction until an area of about 3 ft. deep by 2 ft. wide has been coated.

This must be properly completed, first, by lightly crossing, i.e., using horizontal strokes with the object of distributing the paint evenly, and then carefully finished with the lightest possible strokes (an operation known as laying off), again in a vertical direction. All the horizontal brushmarks must be obliterated, otherwise the fault known as ladders will be the result. Other faults due to bad workmanship are ropiness, runs and fat edges.

Cause of Ropiness

Ropiness (coarse brushmarks) may be caused by laying off too heavily, or with an old, coarse brush, by the brush or surface being overloaded with paint, or by extreme slowness in application which permits the paint to become partly set and quite unworkable.

Runs are caused by uneven spreading of the material; and fat edges (sometimes seen on the edges of doors or other sharp

Lining will often give a distinctive finish to the job. A lining fitch and straight-edge, with paint used rather thinly, enable the work to be executed easily and quickly.

angles) could easily have been removed at the time of painting, by one light stroke of the brush.

Finishing Coats, particularly varnishes and high-gloss paints, are applied much more generously than undercoats, yet brush technique follows the same general lines as before, except that the necessary full coat needs a full brush for its application.

Brushmarks quickly disappear as the material floats out to a level surface. A sharp watch must be kept for runs, which are readily checked by a few strokes of the brush.

Paint often begins to set within ten minutes of its application; therefore one must plan the order of painting so as to keep the edges alive, or wet, until the adjoining portion of the work can be coated.

In panelled work, for instance, the order would be panels first, then mouldings, and finally, the stiles.

Large areas, such as ceilings, are

painted in strips about 2 ft. in width, commencing at the lightest edge, i.e., nearest the window and working each strip from right to left without pause (except for moving scaffolding) until the whole area is completed. Ceilings with a span greater than about 15 ft. would require two men or even more, according to the accessibility of the work.

Distempering

The ease and speed of application, coupled with its comparatively low price, is largely responsible for the popularity of distemper. The ready-mixed varieties include: (a) oil-bound, (b) casein-bound, and (c) those in which glue size is the binding agent; (a) and (b) are to some extent washable, whereas (c) has the advantage of being easily removed by washing.

Distemper requires a clean, dry, and equally absorbent surface such as bare plaster, otherwise perfect uniformity of colour cannot be assured. Oil-painted walls do not conform to these requirements unless properly prepared and hung with lining paper; but other surfaces should be treated as previously specified under the heading "Previously Painted Surfaces," omitting the priming

Fig. 5. Method of sieving distemper or oil paint.

coat. Particular attention must be give to any bad stains on ceilings becau these, unless sealed by a thin coat white knotting, will invariably blee through the new distemper.

MIXING DISTEMPER. Size distempe as mixed by the painter, is undoubted the simplest and most economical pr paration. The basic pigment is whitin thoroughly soaked and beaten up stiff in water, then tinted with the appr priate lime-resisting colour also mixe in water. Due allowance must be mac for the alteration in tone which occu when drying.

Sieving through a copper-gau strainer (Fig. 5), will at this stage sa time and produce that smoothne characteristic of the manufacture material. The next ingredient, glue siz is prepared by dissolving 1 lb. conce trated size in $2\frac{1}{2}$ gallons of boiling wate Add 1 part (by bulk) of warm size 2 of colour; any further thinning shou be with water only.

A test on a small sheet of paper w speedily show whether the amount glue size used is sufficient to bind th material properly.

APPLICATION. Size distemper may I applied directly upon lining paper, b other surfaces should first be coated wi " claircolle " (weak jellied size contai ing 20 per cent of the finishing colour) stop excessive porosity and general improve the surface condition.

Applying the Finishing Coat

The finishing coat is applied with 6-in. or 8-in. flat brush, working quick and systematically to keep the ed; alive and taking care not to miss ev the smallest part, because subseque retouching shows up very prominentl Even when all windows are closed, t material dries too quickly to perm crossing and laying off as in oil pai ing; consequently, one is obliged apply a good heavy coat, laying off in all directions. Upon completion, all windows must be opened in order to assist speedy drying, and any splashes removed from the floor.

Natural Wood Finishing

Although French polishers and painters employ diverse methods and materials, both aim to achieve the same result, namely, to bring out the beauty of the natural grain, to disguise faults and to build up a smooth, durable surface. French polishing produces a hard superfine finish but lacks the toughness, weather-resisting qualities and ease of application associated with oil varnishes. Preparatory staining and filling are the same, whatever type of finish is subsequently employed.

The principal stains are: (a) *Water stains*, prepared from semi-transparent pigments such as Vandyke brown, mahogany lake, etc., or from alkaline lyes, decoctions of coffee, saffron, etc., diluted with very weak glue size.

(b) *Chemical stains*, such as limewater, ammonia, solutions of soda, Epsom salts, etc., which, although colourless themselves, darken the softer parts of the grain and so increase contrast.

(c) *Spirit stains* which are prepared by dissolving aniline dyes in methylated spirit. These are notable for their drying speed, clarity and for their richness of colour and deep penetration.

Fig. 6. Panelled work treated in sections, as when graining, spirit staining, etc. Spirit stains require quick brushwork in order to avoid coating any part twice. Panelled work in a door is treated in sections, as shown above.

(d) *Oil stains* are thin washes of oil colour prepared from the translucent pigments mentioned in group (a), thinned with 2 of turps to 1 of linseed oil and containing sufficient liquid driers. Their slow-drying nature ensures easy manipulation, deep penetration and a beneficial preservative action upon the wood itself.

(e) *Varnish stains* are mixtures of either oil or spirit varnish with the requisite amount of pigment. Unless thinned

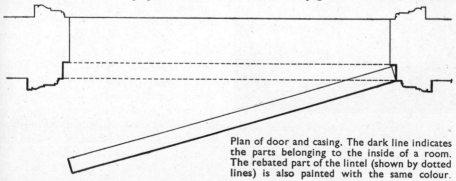

Plan of door and casing. The dark line indicates the parts belonging to the inside of a room. The rebated part of the lintel (shown by dotted lines) is also painted with the same colour.

before use, they fail to penetrate deeply, consequently they are more liable to show early signs of wear.

STAINING. Stain is applied with a full brush, or sponge, the object being to saturate the absorbent parts and so intensify contrast. The colour should be tested upon a scrap piece of timber and allowance made for slight darkening when varnished. Slow-drying stains may, after half an hour, be partially wiped off with clean rag: a particularly useful method for improving the figure of some hardwoods.

Spirit stains call for quick and expert brushwork to avoid coating any part twice.

Panelled work, for instance (Fig. 6), would be treated in sections as when painting, with each rail and stile cut in separately, i.e., painted in with meticulously straight defined edges.

Filling Paste

FILLING is the operation of levelling up any open pores, prior to polishing or varnishing. A reliable composition is made from whiting and turpentine,

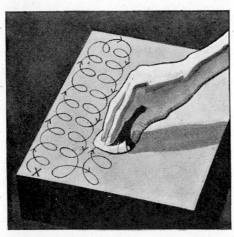

Fig. 7. In French polishing the flow of polish is controlled by pressure on the rubber. In bodying up, the direction followed takes the form of a series of small overlapping circles in order to maintain a level surface.

tinted with the appropriate oil colour. Mix to a cream-like consistency and apply with clean rag, rubbing the paste across the grain until all pores are filled and surplus filler removed. One hour after application, lightly rub down with No. 0 glass-paper.

VARNISHING. The claims of oil, spirit and cellulose varnishes should be investigated when selecting a finish for brush application. High-class cabinet varnishes which dry in two to four hours are probably the best of the interior oil varnishes. Spirit varnishes, including French polish, require a warm, dry atmosphere during application, otherwise loss of gloss and the defect known as blooming (drying with a permanent whitish bloom) may occur. Both spirit and cellulose varnishes are very quick-setting materials, allowing no time for crossing and laying off; therefore, first-time methods and a full brush must be employed.

FRENCH POLISHING. The tools and materials required are: French polish, methylated spirit, linseed oil, spirit-soluble stains, No. 00 sand-paper, a large camel-hair mop, and several rubbers made by wrapping cotton wool inside two layers of clean, soft calico.

The rubber will frequently need re-charging with polish which is fed to the upper surface of the wool, from whence it percolates slowly and evenly to the flat working surface beneath. When in use, the flow of polish is easily controlled by pressure upon the rubber, and, as a coat or rubber of polish should level as well as varnish a surface, the direction followed must take the form of a continuous series of small overlapping circles (Fig. 7).

The operation of polishing embodies the following well-defined stages: (a) staining, (b) filling, (c) oiling in, (d) bodying up, and (e) spiriting off.

Having already dealt with (*a*) and (*b*), he next stage (*c*) involves checking the extreme porosity of the filler, by a paring application of linseed oil. Stage *d*) may be commenced by one coat of polish (either clear or slightly coloured) and brush applied. Then glass-paper and follow with several rubbers of equal parts polish and methylated spirits using an occasional drop of linseed oil on the rubber) until a good surface is obtained.

Stage (*e*), spiriting off, is done with a rubber of 1 of polish to 2 of methylated spirit, applied in the direction of the grain, to even up the gloss generally. Finish off with an almost dry rubber containing only methylated spirit.

Paper-hanging

The fact that the majority of wall-papers are printed in distemper colours should help to explain why surface preparation must be identical with that previously specified for size distemper-ing. In the present case, however, clair-colle is replaced by a coat of jellied size which assists the adhesion of the paper.

ADHESIVES. Paste made from common plain flour, or (for white and very pale papers) from ordinary white starch, still gives absolute satisfaction for general work. The usual method of mixing is to beat up about 1½ lb. of flour—or starch—in cold water, until a smooth batter results. Into this, pour vigorously boiling water and stir briskly until thickening occurs. Allow to cool and then thin to a brushing consistency with cold water.

MEASURING-UP for English wall-paper is based on the assumption that each roll measures 11½ yd. by 21 in. Therefore, given the height of the wall to be papered plus 6 in. or 8 in. for waste and matching of pattern, one can ascertain the number of full lengths of roll required. At the same time, consider the

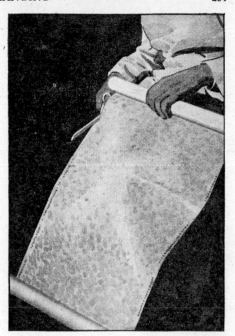

Fig. 8. The usual method of trimming wall-paper.

possibility of making use of short ends, in positions such as those over mantel-pieces and doors.

TRIMMING off the selvedge (Fig. 8) may be done either before or after the lengths are cut, but, in order to avoid damaging the edges, it is advisable to delay the operation until the paper-hanger is actually ready to commence work. Then the various rolls should first be shaded, i.e., carefully examined to see that all are of exactly the same shade of colour. Except for the thinnest and cheapest of papers, both edges are trimmed by scissors or by one of the very efficient mechanical trimmers.

PAPER-HANGING (Fig. 9) should always be commenced at the lightest part—the window side—of a room and finished at a convenient angle, or doorway, away from the light. This helps considerably to disguise joints. It is particularly important to hang the first length abso-lutely straight (a chalk or pencil line is the usual guide) and in the case of walls, the first length on each wall must be checked with plumb-bob and line. The angles of a room are seldom perfect, so a lap of approximately ⅜ in. should be allowed when negotiating angles of both ceilings and walls.

Papering a Ceiling

CEILINGS. In the absence of a straight cornice, strike a guide line 20½ in. away from the wall; face the window when hanging the first length and reverse this position for the remaining lengths. If

Fig. 9. Hanging a length of wall-paper. Paper-hanging should always be commenced near a window for the best light, and finished at a convenient angle farthest from the light, so as to conceal joints as much as possible.

the paper is properly pasted and folded, the bulk can be supported by a roll of paper in the left hand (Fig. 10), leaving the right hand free to attach and slide the loose end into the correct position, and then, as each fold is released, to brush out any wrinkles. It will be found that the course followed by the papering brush will tend to pull the paper in that same direction; it is therefore necessary to brush along the centre, before working outwards towards the edges.

WALLS. Friezes, and sometimes lining paper, are hung horizontally (Fig. 11), and when lengths are over 9 ft., hanging is simplified by folding as for ceilings,

Fig. 10. Papering a ceiling. Note how the length is supported by a roll of paper in the left hand leaving the right hand free to attach and slide the loose end into the correct position and brush out any wrinkles. It is necessary to brush along the centre before working the brush outwards towards the edges.

but without the supporting roll. Strict cleanliness of hands and pasteboard cannot be over-emphasized, otherwise paste and dirt will get out of bounds and soil the surface of the paper. The woodwork, too, will need attention, for paste if not sponged off, has a very damaging effect upon paintwork.

It is equally important to remove immediately with a clean damp cloth any paste which may inadvertently find its way on to the face side of the paper.

Fig. 11. The method adopted when cross lining papering friezes, and hanging borders. These are hung horizontally, and, with lengths of more than 9 ft., hanging is simplified by folding in the same way as for ceilings, without the supporting roll

To hang wall-paper in the usual perpendicular manner (a simple proposition, compared with ceilings) one proceeds as follows: with the paper pasted and folded as per sketch (Fig. 12), mount the steps and place the matching edge against the plumbed line, meanwhile holding the opposite edge about 3 in. away from the wall, so that by raising or lowering the hand, the whole length can be controlled and swung either to left or right as required. The portion in contact with the wall is made to slide into position and the upper 3 ft. or 4 ft. carefully fixed; then brush the full width of paper smoothly to the wall.

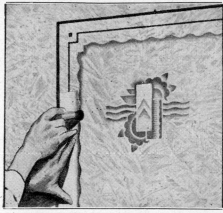

Showing how a shaded edge in wall decoration is obtained by using a mask and stencil brush.

Wall-paper pasted and folded ready for hanging.

Wall-paper pasted and folded ready for cutting.

Wall-paper folded for horizontal application.

Length of ceiling paper ready for hanging.

Fig. 12. METHODS OF FOLDING WALL-PAPERS FOR HANGING IN DIFFERENT POSITIONS

CHAPTER 9

BUILDING MATERIALS

Ingredients of concrete. Portland and other cements. Manufacture of lime. Gypsum plasters. Limestones and sandstones. Granite. Marble. Slates. Bricks and their manufacture. Iron ores. Cast iron and wrought iron. Steel and its properties. Lead. Copper. Zinc. Growth and treatment of timber. Asphalt. Glass manufacture. Plastics and their uses. Miscellaneous materials.

IT is essential that every student of building should have at least an elementary knowledge of the origin, manufacture, properties, and uses, of the various materials used in building operations. A knowledge of these facts will enable him to appreciate more fully why particular materials are, or are not, suitable for particular purposes, and this appreciation will naturally tend to lead to a more intelligent use of the materials.

Importance of Concrete

Perhaps the most important material used in building work in modern times is concrete. It will therefore be given first place in this treatment of materials. One has only to recognize that it is possible to construct almost the whole of the fabric of a large building, i.e., foundations, columns, floors, stairs, roofs, and walls, with concrete, reinforced where necessary with steel rods, to appreciate the importance of this widely used material. Two striking examples of reinforced concrete construction are shown in Figs. 1 and 2.

DEFINITION OF CONCRETE. Concrete, as a rule, is a mixture of coarse aggregate (such as gravel, crushed stone, and crushed bricks), fine aggregate (such as sand and crushed stone), and a suitable binding material (the cement).

The mixture, upon the addition of water, can be formed into a plastic mass and placed into moulds or form-work, where the cement, on setting and hardening, binds the aggregates together, so as to form a stone-like substance of considerable strength and durability. Concrete may be precast into suitable units which are afterwards erected in the building; or, alternatively, as is more usual, may be placed directly in position on the job.

In order to obtain a good-quality concrete, attention must be paid to many factors, the most important being: (1) the cement; (2) the aggregates; (3) proportioning of the materials; (4) the water used for mixing; (5) the mixing, placing, and curing of the concrete.

Main Factors in Concrete

(1) THE CEMENT. The cements used for concrete making are *Portland cements* or, in certain circumstances, *high-aluminous cements*. Lime was formerly used as the cementing material but it is not often used nowadays.

Portland Cements. It must be borne in mind that the importance of Portland cement lies mainly in its combination (as in concretes or mortars) with other materials. The cement is very rarely used neat, as, quite apart from the extra expense involved, it would be inclined to shrink and crack too much.

STRIKING EXAMPLE OF CONCRETE CONSTRUCTION

Fig. I. A reinforced-concrete building of modern design. Note the cantilever construction of the upper corner windows and the absence of traditional ornament.

Portland cement was invented and given its name in 1824, by a Leeds bricklayer, Joseph Aspdin. Since then, as a result of research and alterations in details of manufacture, Portland cement has steadily been improved.

Manufacture of Normal Portland Cement. Chalk (or limestone) is mixed with clay

REINFORCED-CONCRETE BANDSTAND

Fig. 2. A pleasing design with excellent acoustic arrangements. Note the cantilevered roof and monolithic construction, which is only practicable in reinforced concrete.

(proportions about 3 to 1) and water into a creamy liquid or *slurry*. This slurry is heated to a high temperature in a special type of kiln, when it fuses into clinker similar to small coke. The clinker, when cool, is ground into a fine powder, a small amount of gypsum being added to control the setting time. This process is shown in diagrammatic form in Fig. 3.

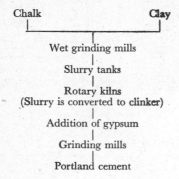

Chalk   Clay

Wet grinding mills

Slurry tanks

Rotary kilns
(Slurry is converted to clinker)

Addition of gypsum

Grinding mills

Portland cement

Fig. 3. Stages in manufacture of Portland cement.

Setting Properties. The heat of the kiln causes the chalk to combine with the clay to form various chemical compounds of cementitious value. The setting action of the cement depends upon chemical combination between the water used for mixing the cement or concrete and the above-mentioned compounds. The action of the atmosphere is not required (compare with limes). Portland cement is a hydraulic cement, i.e., it is capable of setting and hardening under water.

Rapid-hardening Portland cement is more finely ground than normal Portland cement. The finer a cement is ground, the quicker it hardens. Even in the case of the ordinary, or normal, Portland cement, 90 per cent of the cement must pass a sieve having 28,900 holes to the square inch in order to pass the test specified in the British Standard Specification for Portland cement. The set-

ting time of rapid-hardening Portland cement is approximately equal to that of normal Portland cement.

Difference Between Setting and Hardening. Rapid hardening must not be confused with quick setting. *Hardening* means the development of strength, whilst *setting time* refers to the time taken for completion of certain chemical actions between the cement and the mixing water; and, roughly, may be assumed to be the time allowed (about half to one hour) for getting the concrete into position after it has been mixed. This is important and explains why, for instance, any concrete mixed and not used at the time, should not be knocked up with water and used several hours later, but should be discarded.

Advantage of Rapid-hardening Portland Cement. The chief advantage lies in the fact that rapid-hardening Portland cement is approximately as strong three or four days after mixing as normal Portland cement is in twenty-eight days.

Advantages in Rapid Construction

Where speed in erection is essential, therefore, rapid-hardening Portland cement is invaluable. (NOTE: The load-bearing capacity of normal Portland cement concrete is based on its strength at twenty-eight days after gauging with water. The concrete increases slowly in strength over a period of months or even years, but the most rapid development of strength takes place approximately within twenty-eight days after mixing.)

Quick-setting Portland Cement. This is useful for work under flowing water, where normal-setting cement would be washed away before it had set.

Portland blast-furnace cement is a mixture of Portland cement and finely ground slag from iron blast furnaces. It is superior to ordinary Portland cement for both fire-resistant construction and its resistance to erosion in sea work

Type of cement	Setting time	Rate of hardening	Approximate number of days in which working strength is attained
Normal Portland . . .	Normal	Normal	28
Rapid-hardening Portland .	Normal	Rapid	3–4
Quick-setting Portland . .	Quick	Normal	28
Portland blast-furnace . .	Normal	Normal	28
High aluminous . . .	Normal	Very rapid	1

Table I. Summary of comparative setting and hardening qualities of various types of cement.

White and coloured Portland cements are eminently suitable for external decorative finishes.

High-aluminous cement was first marketed in Great Britain about 1923. It is manufactured from a mixture of chalk and bauxite (an ore of aluminium).

Rapid Hardening

Setting time is approximately the same as normal Portland cement, but it hardens very rapidly and is approximately as strong in twenty-four hours as normal Portland cement is in twenty-eight days. High-aluminous cement generates a great amount of heat during this period owing to the speed of the chemical reactions. It is a very useful cement where great speed is essential, such as for road repairs. It is more resistant to sea water than Portland cements and this fact, combined with its rapid development of strength, makes it extremely suitable for harbour works and the like. It is darker in colour than Portland cement, and, other factors being equal, develops greater strength. It should never be mixed with Portland cement, as the latter kills its properties. Table I summarizes the comparative setting and hardening qualities of the various types of cements.

Condition of Cement. Previous to use, the cement should be kept dry. If it becomes damp and lumpy (an indication of partial setting of some of the

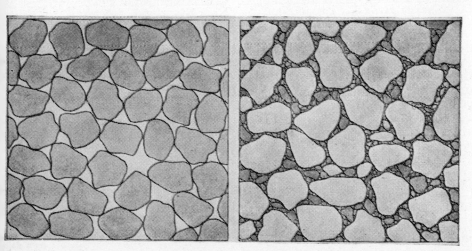

GRADING OF CONCRETE

Fig. 4. The left-hand illustration shows an aggregate with all particles of one size. That on the right shows a graded aggregate, the void spaces being filled with small particles, giving increased density.

P.B.—K*

cement), the resultant concrete will be slower setting and less strong.

(2) THE AGGREGATES. Strong, dense, durable and non-porous aggregates should be used for reinforced-concrete work. The coarse aggregate usually consists of gravel, and the fine aggregate of pit sand which is composed of hard siliceous grains (sea sand contains injurious salts).

Other strong aggregates are crushed granites and sandstones.

For mass, i.e., unreinforced, concrete, in addition to the aggregates mentioned above, broken bricks (for high grade of fire resistance) and coke breeze or pumice (for light weight) may be used.

Graded Aggregate

All aggregate should be clean (clay and dirt form coatings round the aggregate and prevent proper adhesion of the cement) and well graded. A graded aggregate is one which contains many different sizes of particles between the smallest and largest particles; the smaller particles fill up the voids, i.e., empty spaces, between the larger particles so that the cement is not wastefully used in filling up excessive voids.

The more thorough the grading, the denser will be the concrete and hence the greater its strength and watertightness. Fig. 4 illustrates how smaller particles can occupy the void spaces between larger particles, thus increasing the density, and decreasing the amount of cement required.

The size of coarse aggregate depends upon the purpose for which the concrete is to be used. For mass concrete, as in foundations, the larger stones may be up to $2\frac{1}{2}$ in. in diameter. For reinforced-concrete the largest particles are usually $\frac{3}{4}$ in., and the finest should not pass through a $\frac{3}{16}$-in. mesh, the aggregate being well graded between these limits.

Size of Fine Aggregate. The sand should pass a $\frac{3}{16}$-in. mesh, but not more than 5 per cent should pass a sieve having 10,000 holes to the square inch.

(3) PROPORTIONING. The most suitable relative proportions of cement and aggregates depend on several factors, such as the nature of the work, the size of the aggregates, and the required finished appearance of the concrete. For filling in excavations where strength is not required, a concrete consisting of 1 part by volume of cement to 8 to 10 parts of fine and coarse aggregates previously mixed together may be quite sufficient.

For reinforced-concrete work, a common mix consists of 1 part by volume of cement, 2 parts of sand and 4 parts of gravel, i.e., 1 : 2 : 4 mix. This is approximately equivalent to a 1 cwt. bag of cement, $2\frac{1}{2}$ cub. ft. of sand and 5 cub. ft. of gravel. (The materials should be measured separately; a 1 : 2 : 4 mix is *not* equivalent to a mix consisting of 1 part of cement and 6 parts of ready-mixed sand and gravel.)

Avoidance of Surplus Water

(4) MIXING WATER. Provided that a workable mix is obtained, the less water used the better, as any surplus water over and above that required for proper chemical action with the cement will eventually evaporate, leaving voids in the concrete.

Cleanliness of Water. As a rough rule, the water should be fit for drinking, as otherwise it might contain chemicals capable of injuring the concrete.

(5) MIXING, PLACING AND CURING. The mixing platform should be kept clean. Materials should be measured accurately by means of gauge boxes or wheelbarrows of known capacity. If mixed by hand, the cement and aggregates should first be mixed dry to a uniform colour, then mixed again to a

uniform consistency whilst the required amount of water is being sprinkled on. Good machine mixing is better than good hand mixing.

Placing. The concrete should be placed without delay as soon as mixed. It should not be thrown from a vertical height of more than about 4 ft. to 6 ft., or run from long chutes, etc., owing to the tendency for the larger particles to reach the bottom first. This would result in a non-uniform mix. The concrete should be tamped or vibrated to consolidate it.

Curing. The mixing water should not be allowed to evaporate from the concrete as a result of sun or wind action. The concrete may be kept damp by covering it with damp sacks or by periodically spraying it with water (for seven to fourteen days in the case of normal Portland cement).

High-aluminous cement concrete should be kept wet for twenty-four hours after it has been gauged with water. The temperature of concrete should not be allowed to fall below 40 degrees F. during the curing period, as any tendency towards freezing of the mixing water may result in permanent loss of strength of the concrete.

LIME AND GYPSUM PLASTERS. The binding materials used for internal plastering are derived either from chalk (or limestone) or gypsum.

LIMES—MANUFACTURE AND TYPES. After burning in a kiln to drive off carbon dioxide, the chalk or limestone becomes *quicklime*. To produce a putty for plastering (or mortar) purposes, water is added to quicklime, the process being termed *slaking*. The water combines with the quicklime and breaks it up into a powder and then forms a paste, or putty; this process is accompanied by evolution of heat and increase in bulk of the material.

In the case of fat limes the slaking

MASS-PRODUCTION OF ROLLED PLATE GLASS

Even glass is mass produced today. The molten glass is seen flowing out between water-cooled rollers in a continuous band which is then cut into the required lengths.

action is very rapid, the amount of heat generated is great, and there is a very considerable increase in volume of the material. Hydraulic limes slake more slowly, give rise to less heat, and the expansion is not so great. If quicklime is slaked in excess of water, a plastic putty results.

Classes of Lime

The type of lime depends upon the type of limestone used for manufacture, and limes may be classified as (*a*) non-hydraulic; (*b*) moderately hydraulic; and (*c*) eminently hydraulic.

NON-HYDRAULIC LIMES. The principal limes in this class are *fat* or *rich* limes, which are manufactured from white chalk or pure forms of limestone. The quicklime can be purchased either in lump form and slaked to putty on the job—the putty being allowed to mature for three weeks or more before being used—or as a ready-slaked powder (dry hydrate). The latter is suitable for immediate use upon the addition of water, although it is better to make the lime into a putty and allow it to stand for twenty-four to forty-eight hours.

The setting action of fat limes is slow and is due either to the absorption of carbon dioxide from the air, virtually to re-form limestone, or to a very slow formation of silicate of lime. It follows that fat lime is non-hydraulic, i.e., it is not capable of setting under water.

HYDRAULIC LIMES are manufactured from chalk and limestones containing clay impurities.

The setting action is due partly to absorption of carbon dioxide from the air and partly to chemical reactions between the mixing water and the lime-clay compounds formed during burning (compare with Portland cement). Hydraulic limes will therefore attain a certain strength under water; they are stronger than fat limes, the higher the

Gauge box for measuring concrete materials.

proportion of clay, the greater the strength and hydraulic properties.

MODERATELY HYDRAULIC LIMES contain about 12 per cent to 20 per cent clay and are usually referred to as greystone limes.

EMINENTLY HYDRAULIC LIMES contain approximately 20 per cent to 30 per cent clay, blue lias limes (manufactured from blue lias limestones) being one of the most common types. They resemble Portland cement in composition, but are burnt at a lower temperature and are not so strong. Lias limes set quite hard in less than a week after being mixed.

LIME PLASTERING. Fat and moderately hydraulic limes are used for this purpose and the plaster is usually applied in three coats, to a total thickness of $\frac{3}{4}$ in. on a backing of wood laths, metal laths, expanded metal, or brickwork. The first (render or pricking up) coat, is composed of "coarse stuff," which is usually a mixture of greystone lime, sand and water, the proportion of lime to sand being about 1 to 2 or 1 to 3. Ox hair is added to help bind the mixture and to reduce droppings.

The second (floating) coat is of similar composition. The final (setting or skimming) coat—usually known as fine stuff—consists of fat lime slaked to a slurry and mixed with a little sand, and perhaps a small amount of plaster of Paris. The addition of sand to lime plasters increases the bulk of the material and helps to eliminate shrinkage and consequent cracking; it also assists the penetration of carbon dioxide by making the mixture more porous.

Drying of Plaster

The drying and hardening of fat-lime plasters are necessarily slow. As a consequence, a considerable time must elapse before the final decorations (if any) can be applied; for instance, paper should not be hung on lime-plastered walls until about six months after plastering.

Eminently hydraulic limes such as lias limes are chiefly used in mortars and rarely for plastering, as there is a tendency for these limes to contain slow-slaking particles. *See* MORTARS (page 312) for further use of limes.

GYPSUM PLASTERS. Gypsum or hard-

Detail of typical precast concrete sill as commonly used in many modern housing schemes.

wall plasters have superseded lime plasters to a large extent, as they are harder than lime plasters and set much more quickly, thus reducing the time it is necessary to allow between the commencement of the plastering and the application of the final decoration to the walls. As the name "hardwall" plasters suggests, these plasters provide a hard polished surface. Gypsum plasters may be roughly divided into the plaster of Paris type and the hard-burnt (Keene's cement) type.

MANUFACTURE OF GYPSUM PLASTERS. Gypsum is a sedimentary rock (chemically formed) and consists of calcium sulphate containing water in chemical combination. On burning gypsum to about 120 degrees C., three-quarters of the water is driven off and the resulting material, when ground, is *plaster of Paris* which sets very rapidly with water and is much used as an addition to lime plaster to accelerate setting, and for running plaster cornices *in situ.*

Retarded Gypsum Plasters. Plaster of Paris sets too quickly for ordinary plastering purposes, and the set is therefore slowed by the addition during manufacture of a small quantity of retarder such as pulverized glue. This type of plaster, of which there are many brands, is used as wall plaster and for fibrous plaster work (Fig. 5).

Keene's and Other Cements

Hard-burnt Accelerated Plasters (Keene's Type). If gypsum is heated above 300 degrees C. all its water is driven off. The resulting product would be too slow setting for plastering purposes and, in consequence, a small proportion of alum or sodium sulphate is added during manufacture to quicken the set (Fig. 5). These plasters are harder and stronger than the retarded plaster of Paris type.

Keene's cement, Parian cement, Martin's cement, and many proprietary brands, are of this type, and set hard in a few days; they are used for internal plastering and are usually applied as setting coats over an undercoat consisting of Portland cement mortar.

Some types of gypsum plaster, e.g., Sirapite, are used for the two coats, the undercoat consisting of a mixture of sand and plaster, and the finishing coat of plaster only. Gypsum plasters corrode steel and therefore should not be used as undercoats on steel laths or expanded wire lathing. The Keene's type of plaster is also used for the angles, quoins and similar features in lime plaster work in order to give greater strength at these points.

Setting Action of Gypsum Plasters. The setting is due to the chemical combination of the mixing water with the plaster to form interlocking crystals, the plaster virtually re-forming gypsum. Gypsum plaster, however, is not hydraulic, as it is soluble in water.

ANHYDROUS PLASTERS. Some types of plasters are manufactured from natural anhydrite rock, which is a form of calcium sulphate containing no water. When the rock is finely ground and a suitable accelerating salt added, a plaster similar to the hard-burnt type is obtained (Fig. 5).

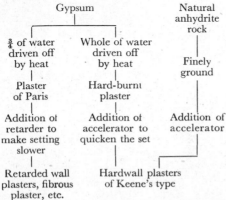

Fig. 5. How plaster, similar to the hard-burnt type, is obtained from natural anhydrite rock.

PLASTER BOARDS are usually composed of two sheets of a special type of paper between which is a layer of gypsum plaster. These boards act as a substitute for laths and the first plaster coat.

When using gypsum plasters, it is essential that mixing boards and tools be kept clean, as even a small amount of previously set plaster may quicken the set of a freshly mixed batch.

Building Stones

The principal stones used for building purposes are limestones and sandstones (sedimentary stones), granites (igneous stones), and marble and slate (metamorphic stones).

SEDIMENTARY STONES were laid down as layers of sediment on sea and lake beds, became consolidated by the increasing weight of further layers of material and by percolation of water containing natural cementing materials, and were subsequently raised above sea level as a result of earth movements.

Fig. 6. Decay in sandstone due to face bedding. (*Reproduced by permission of the Controller of H.M. Stationery Office.*)

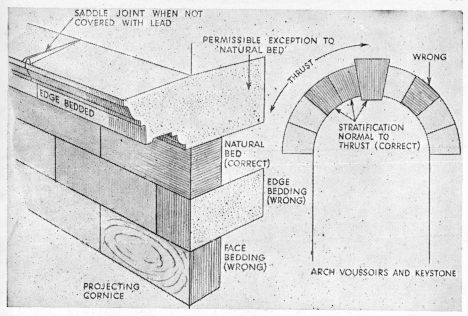

SADDLE JOINT WHEN NOT COVERED WITH LEAD

PERMISSIBLE EXCEPTION TO 'NATURAL BED'

WRONG

THRUST

EDGE BEDDED

NATURAL BED (CORRECT)

STRATIFICATION NORMAL TO THRUST (CORRECT)

EDGE BEDDING (WRONG)

FACE BEDDING (WRONG)

ARCH VOUSSOIRS AND KEYSTONE

PROJECTING CORNICE

METHOD OF LAYING SEDIMENTARY STONE BLOCKS

Fig. 7. Because sedimentary stones were originally deposited in layers they possess natural bedding planes. The correct and incorrect methods of laying these stones are shown above.

The sediments originated as a result of: (*a*) deposition of particles of other rocks carried to the sea beds by rivers, wind, etc. Sandstones, and possibly some limestones, are of this class; or (*b*) the accumulation of vast numbers of shell fragments and the calcareous, i.e., limy, remains of small sea creatures. Some limestones were formed in this way; or (*c*) material deposited as a consequence of chemical action. Gypsum, rock salt and some limestones were formed thus.

It is important to remember that because they were deposited in layers, sedimentary stones possess natural bedding planes. Thus, a block of sedimentary stone may be compared to a book, the leaves of which correspond to the stratified layers of the stone. Although in many limestones and sandstones the bedding planes cannot be detected without the aid of a microscope, never-

theless they do exist; and recognition of this fact must be made when laying the stones. For walling work, a stone should be laid with its natural bed horizontal. In this position, the stone weathers better, as any wearing away of the surface of the stone must take place through all the layers.

If the stone is *face bedded* each layer will tend to flake off in turn and the stone will show signs of weathering much earlier. In addition, the stone will offer less resistance to crushing when its natural bed is not at right angles to the direction of the loading or thrust (Fig. 6).

In the case of projecting cornices, and voussoirs and keystones of arches, the natural bed should not be horizontal, but should be in the positions shown in Fig. 7.

LIMESTONES consist essentially of calcium carbonate. As a rule, only the finer-grained varieties are used as building stones. Limestones, as a class, are not so strong and durable as sandstones and, with the exception of a few notable types such as Portland stone, do not stand up so well as sandstones to the smoke-polluted atmosphere of towns. On the other hand, they are usually easier to carve and work than sandstones and are therefore more suitable for ornamental work.

OOLITIC, i.e., EGG OR ROE STONE, LIMESTONES are much used as building stones; Portland and Ketton stones

LIMESTONES IN GREAT BRITAIN				
Name	*Type*	*Situation of quarry*	*Colour*	*Purpose for which used*
Ancaster	Oolitic	Lincolnshire	Cream to brown	General building
Anston	Dolomitic	Yorkshire	Light cream	Suitable for all building purposes, but stone should be carefully selected
Bath (various types)	Oolitic	Bath district	Cream or light brown	Weathers moderately well. Easily carved. Suitable for internal and external work
Beer Stone	"Chalky"	Devon	Almost white	Soft. Used for interior carvings in churches, etc.
Bolsover Moor	Dolomitic	Derbyshire	Cream to yellowish-brown	Carving, paving, general purposes
Chilmark	Oolitic	Wiltshire	Buff to yellowish-brown	Dressings, general purposes
Clipsham	Oolitic	Rutland	Pale cream to buff	General building
Ham Hill	Shelly oolitic	Somerset	Light brown	Dressings, etc. Weathers moderately
Hopton Wood "Marble"	Crinoidal	Derbyshire	Light grey to light drab	Polishes well. Columns, monuments, decorative work
Mansfield Woodhouse	Dolomitic	Nottingham-shire	Yellow	Poor weathering qualities. Interior carvings
Ketton	Oolitic	Rutland	Yellowish-cream	General building
Portland (Whitbed)	Oolitic	Dorset	White to light grey	Whitbed is strong and durable. Used for all purposes. Other types of Portland stone are softer and are used for interior work
Purbeck "Marble"	Shelly	Dorset	Grey to light brown	General building. Polishes well. Ornamental work

Table II. Names and descriptions of the chief limestones of Great Britain and the purposes for which they are suitable. The situations of the quarries are also given.

Fig. 8. Ketton stone, a type of limestone, in which the egg-like structure is easily discernible.

Fig. 8) are of this class. This type of stone is almost wholly made up of small rounded grains, the appearance suggesting the roe of a fish. In some stones, e.g., Ketton, the egg-like structure is easily observed, while in some others, e.g., Portland, the grains are much smaller.

SHELLY LIMESTONES consist almost entirely of shell fragments and because of this, and of their capability of taking a good polish, are much used as decorative wall linings. These stones are often referred to as marbles, a term which in this instance is geologically quite incorrect.

CRINOIDAL LIMESTONES were formed by the calcareous remains of small sea creatures which are known as crinoids.

DOLOMITIC OR MAGNESIAN LIMESTONES contain a large proportion of magnesian carbonate.

Tabulated information in regard to limestones is given in Table II.

SANDSTONES used as building stones consist of small grains of sand (silica) held together by a natural cementing material. As the sand grains are practically indestructible, it is the nature of the cementing material which frequently determines whether the stone is suitable for building purposes. The best sandstones are those which have a siliceous type of cement. They are strong in compression, extremely durable and are mostly unaffected by polluted atmospheric conditions. Many sandstones split easily into thin slabs suitable for pavings. Sandstones are also often used as padstones for supporting roof trusses and ends of girders.

Table III gives useful particulars of sandstones in Great Britain.

IGNEOUS STONES were formed by the cooling and solidification of molten material, either on the surface of the earth (lava from volcanoes) or at various depths below the surface. True granites originated deep down in the earth's crust. Igneous stones, as a class, are unstratified, i.e., they possess no bedding planes.

GRANITES are hard, dense stones, difficult to work and carve, and consequently are not used to the same extent as limestones and sandstones. True granites have a coarse crystalline texture and are composed essentially of three minerals: (a) quartz, which is generally of a glassy and colourless appearance; (b) felspar, which is sometimes a dull opaque white or grey colour, sometimes pink or of other hues; and (c) mica, which is silvery white, brownish, or black in colour. The felspar crystals are usually the means of imparting the principal colour to granites.

SANDSTONES IN GREAT BRITAIN

Name	Situation of quarry	Colour	Purpose for which used
Bramley Fall .	Yorkshire . .	Light brown . .	General purposes. Engineering work
Corsehill . .	Dumfries . .	Bright pink and dark red	Carvings. General work
Craigleith .	Edinburgh . .	Whitish-grey, white and blue . .	Extremely durable. Used for all purposes
Darley Dale .	Derbyshire . .	Buff and light grey	All purposes
Forest of Dean	Gloucestershire .	Grey to light blue .	Dock walls. General purposes
Heddon . .	Northumberland	Light brown . .	General purposes
Howley . .	Yorkshire . .	Light brown . .	General purposes; also dressings
Pennant . .	Gloucestershire and Glamorgan	Greenish slate. .	General purposes, street paving, etc.
Robin Hood .	Yorkshire . .	Light grey-green .	Pavings, etc.

York stone is a general term which includes all stones from Yorkshire, such as Robin Hood,
Bramley Fall, etc.

Table III. Names and descriptions of the chief sandstones of Great Britain and the purposes for which they are suitable. The Table also gives the situations of the quarries.

Tables IV and V give various particulars of granite and other stones.

METAMORPHIC, i.e., CHANGED, STONES are either sedimentary or igneous, which have been altered from their original forms as the result of great heat or/and pressure.

For instance, marbles are altered limestones, and slates are the result of pressure on clays and shales.

APPROXIMATE WEIGHTS AND CRUSHING STRENGTHS

	Lime-stones	Sand-stones	Granites
Weight per cub. ft. (lb.) . .	125–160	130–180	160–175
Crushing strength tons per sq. ft..	100–500	200–800	1,000–2,000

Name	Situation of quarry	Colour and texture
Correnie . . .	Aberdeenshire . . .	Medium grained, pinkish-red
Creetown . . .	Kirkcudbrightshire .	Light grey, medium grained
Peterhead . .	Aberdeenshire . . .	Red, moderately coarse grained
Rubislaw . . .	Aberdeenshire . . .	Grey, fine grained
Shap . . .	Westmorland . . .	Reddish

Table IV (above, right). Approximate weights and crushing strengths of various classes of stones
Table V. Types of granite suitable for engineering and building works, and situations of quarries

MANUFACTURE OF BLOWN SHEET GLASS

Blowing a cylinder of coloured glass, a delicate operation which requires great skill and experience

MARBLES possess a compact crystalline structure and are employed largely for interior work and monumental purposes. They are obtainable in a large variety of veinings and colours. Carrara white marble comes from Italy, while very considerable marble quarries are worked in Greece, Belgium and France. In Great Britain, small quantities of marble are found in Devon, Anglesey and Ireland.

SLATES of the kind used for roofing, are the result of the metamorphosing, i.e., changing, by great heat and pressure, in the interior of the earth, of clays and shales. The great pressure resulted in cleavage planes being formed obliquely to the original sediment planes, so that the rock when split into slates is not, as might be supposed, split parallel to the original natural bed. Good slates are very durable, the best varieties coming from quarries in North Wales (Bangor, Llanberis, and Blaenau-Festiniog). These slates are purplish-blue in colour. Good slates are also obtained from Cornwall (Delabole) and can be purchased in various colours such as grey-blue, green, and brown. Slates are also quarried in Somerset, Lake District and Scotland.

Causes of Weathering

The chief causes of excessive weathering or decay of building stones are: natural defects in the stone; faulty craftsmanship; chemical agencies, such as effect of atmosphere; various physical agencies, such as expansion due to frost, and movements of salts.

NATURAL DEFECTS. (a) Vents. Some

stones contain small fissures (vents) which tend to open up under the action of the weather. Generally, there is no harmful effect on the stone when it is used for plain ashlar work, but when it is used for a highly ornamented type of building, opening of the vents may lead to excessive decay. This has been the case in the Houses of Parliament, which were built of Anston stone. Extensive stonework repairs have been necessary in recent years.

(*b*) *Soft Beds*. Some stones contain layers of a softer material, such as clay, which wears away more quickly than the remainder of the stone, so that it ultimately presents a furrowed appearance. Fig. 9 illustrates a typical example of this form of decay.

FAULTY CRAFTSMANSHIP. One ex-
ample is the use of iron cramps and dowels which rust and expand and cause damage to the stone. It is preferable to use alloy steels or alloys of copper, nickel, and bronze.

Another example of faulty craftsmanship, viz., placing the stone with its natural bed in the wrong position, has already been referred to.

CHEMICAL AGENCIES. The stones principally affected by the action of smoky atmospheres are limestones. The sulphur gases present in the air dissolve in rain-water to form a weak acid which reacts with the calcium carbonate of the stone. A black skin forms on the surface of the stone and ultimately blisters and falls off, exposing a fresh surface of the stone to the effect of the acid.

PHYSICAL AGENCIES. (*a*) *Frost* is no

DECAY IN STONEWORK

Fig. 9. A typical example of effects of weathering on stonework containing layers of soft material. Note furrowed appearance of the stone. The usual method of repair is to cut out the worst patches and fill in with similar stone. (*Reproduced by permission of the Controller of H.M. Stationery Office.*)

usually a cause of serious decay in this country. Cornices, copings and parapets, are the parts of the building most likely to be affected and the stone should be carefully selected for these positions.

(b) *Movement of Chemicals.* Sandstone and limestone should not be built together in one structure, owing to the fact that chemicals formed in the limestone as the result of the action of polluted rain-water find their way into the sandstone and produce decay in the latter (Fig. 10).

The use of a too strong and dense mortar for pointing (especially in the repair of old buildings) may lead to decay of the stonework for reasons which are given under the heading of "Mortars" on page 312.

Types of Bricks

All bricks, with a few exceptions, such as sand-lime and concrete bricks, are manufactured from brick clays, or shales, which consist essentially of silica and alumina and contain impurities such as oxides of iron, and chalk (or limestone).

As there are many different types of clay used for brick-making, so there are many types of bricks on the market giving a great variety of colours and texture. The colour of bricks is usually imparted by the iron oxides present in the clay, although other impurities, such as sulphur and magnesia also influence the colour.

PLASTIC-CLAY BRICKS. Many of the best types of bricks are made from plastic clays. The clay is dug out in the autumn and mellows throughout the winter, after which it is cut and kneaded into a plastic mass in a pug-mill. In the case of *hand-moulded bricks*, a lump of the clay which issues from the pug-mill is thrown by the workman into a mould resting on a stockboard; this

Fig. 10. Decay in sandstone due to its association with limestone. (*Reproduced by permission of the Controller of H.M. Stationery Office.*)

has a projection in the shape of the *frog*, and the surplus clay is struck off level with the top of the mould.

If the mould and stockboard have previously been sprinkled with sand (*sand-moulded bricks*), the bricks can be turned out of the moulds immediately and stacked either in heated rooms or under a rough-roofed structure in the open air, to be dried. After being allowed to dry for a period ranging from a few days to a few weeks, depending on the method of drying and the type of clay, the bricks are burnt, thus causing the constituents of the clay to fuse together to give a hard compact mass. Burning is usually done in kilns, of which there are various types, as the "Hoffman," "Scotch" and "Tunnel."

WIRE-CUT BRICKS also are made from plastic clays. The clay is pressed or squeezed out through an opening or die in the pug-mill and cut by wire into the correct lengths. If these blocks are placed into steel moulds and then pressed by hydraulic pressure, the brick is termed *machine-pressed* or *re-pressed*. All machine-pressed bricks are not wire cut (*see* Flettons below). In all cases, the raw brick is made larger than the finished article, as bricks shrink about 10 per cent during burning.

SEMI-PLASTIC CLAY BRICKS (FLETTONS) are machine-pressed bricks manufactured from a very stiff clay. After being quarried, the clay is ground to a suitable size and then fed to a mould in a pressing machine, where it receives two thrusts due to the forward and backward stroke of a cam. The brick passes immediately into another pressing machine, which indents the frog and the name, the brick again receiving two thrusts. Each brick, therefore, is pressed four times (Phorpres).

The final process is the burning of the bricks in a kiln. The principal manufacturing districts of this type of brick are Bedfordshire, Buckinghamshire and Northamptonshire. Since there is no expense involved in weathering and preparing the clay, Flettons are cheaper than bricks made from plastic clays.

GLAZED BRICKS (SALT-GLAZED). The glaze is formed by throwing salt into the kiln during the burning process. The colour of these bricks is brown, and they are used in sewer and sanitary work.

ENAMELLED BRICKS are made from a semi-fireclay. The face to be enamelled is dipped into a fine slurry prepared by mixing together china-clay, chalk, and other ingredients such as borax and colouring matter. This film of enamel is fused to the brick by the heat of the kiln.

SAND-LIME BRICKS consist essentially of fine quartz sand bound with a cement consisting of silicate of lime. A small proportion of fat lime is mixed and ground up with the sand, water is added and the mixture is machine pressed into bricks. The bricks are then run on trollies into a steel cylinder, the doors are closed, and the bricks steam heated for a number of hours, the pressure of the steam being over 100 lb. per sq. in.

The lime combines with some of the sand to form a cementing material which binds the rest of the sand to form what amounts to an artificial sandstone. Sand-lime bricks are uniform in shape and possess remarkably sharp arrises which make for ease in building and for more regular bedding. The normal colour is greyish-white, which makes the bricks suitable for light wells, but these bricks can also be obtained in a number of colours, the colour being introduced during the mixing process.

Standard Sizes

The British Standard Specification for Sand-lime Bricks, No. 187—1934, specifies certain tests which the bricks are required to pass.

SIZES OF BRICKS. The majority of brick manufacturers in England and Wales are now making bricks of the standard sizes as given below, which have been agreed upon in collaboration with the Ministry of Works: Length $8\frac{3}{4}$ in., width $4\frac{3}{16}$ in., depth $2\frac{5}{8}$ in. or $2\frac{7}{8}$ in.

A tolerance of $\frac{1}{8}$ in. is allowed on the length, $\frac{1}{16}$ in. on the width, and $\frac{1}{16}$ in. on the depth.

Bricks having a depth of $2\frac{5}{8}$ in. give brickwork rising four courses to the foot. This type is usually known as 9 in. $\times 4\frac{1}{2}$ in. $\times 3$ in., as these are the average dimensions between centres of joints when laid.

Facing bricks of depth 2 in. and $2\frac{1}{4}$ in. are sometimes used.

WEIGHT OF BRICKS. The weight of one brick varies from about 5 lb. (bricks of the Fletton type) to about 9 lb. (dense engineering bricks).

ENGINEERING BRICKS are machine pressed or plain wire cut. They are very hard, strong, dense and durable, and

TWENTY-CHAMBER CONTINUOUS BRICK KILN

The area of each chamber in this brick kiln is 30 ft. x 14 ft. x 9 ft. in height. The kiln is capable of burning 175,000 Staffordshire plastic bricks per week.

are used for carrying heavy loads. They are also used for damp-proof courses, sills and copings. Examples are Staffordshire (blue), Southwater (red), Accrington (red) and Ruabon (red).

FACING BRICKS for external facings of buildings are usually made from plastic clays. The hand-made type, especially the sand-faced varieties, possess most character, their rough texture being usually more pleasing than the more uniform appearance of machine-pressed bricks, although rough-textured Flettons (rustic Flettons) can now be obtained. Examples of facing bricks are Leicester reds, Luton greys, London stocks (yellow), "Multicolours," and rubbers.

COMMON BRICKS are used for general purposes, internal walls, backing to external walls and brickwork which is to be rendered, although some types are also used for facings. Examples are Flettons, stocks.

Some sand-lime bricks are used for facing, others as common bricks, whilst some varieties are used for engineering work.

RUBBERS. These bricks are uniformly fine in texture and are soft enough to be rubbed down and cut easily. They have no frogs and are larger than ordinary bricks, to allow for cutting or rubbing. Rubbers are used for gauged arches, carvings, etc. Examples are Bracknell red rubbers, and Suffolk whites.

FIRE BRICKS are made from special types of clays and are used for fireplaces, furnace linings, and similar purposes.

Weathering Properties of Bricks

The Building Research Station has carried out extensive research on bricks, and the reader is recommended to consult the reports and bulletins issued by the Station. No hard and fast simple tests are capable of being specified, compliance with which would reasonably ensure good weathering durability of the bricks. Even the theory at one time held that, if a brick of one type absorbed more water on immersion in a vessel than a brick of another type, it would be inferior in weathering qualities to the latter, has now been quite discarded.

Keeping the above considerations in mind, it may be stated that a good brick should not contain stones and lumps of unmixed lime (which might eventually slake to the detriment of the brick), it should be free from cracks and flaws, and the interior of the brick

BRICKS AS BUILDING MATERIAL

An experimental example of constructional brickwork in English Garden-Wall bond, using rusti
Flettons. Thick struck joints are shown at C, and thin weathered joints at Z.

should be of uniform colour throughout, indicating uniform burning.

MORTARS FOR BRICKWORK. The choice
of the composition of the mortar should
be guided by the characteristics of the
brick. Modern research indicates that
cracks in the mortar joints, and between
the sides of the joints and the bricks, are
the most usual ways by which rain-
water penetrates through a solid brick
wall. Cement mortars are inferior to
cement-lime mortars in this respect.

MORTAR FOR ENGINEERING BRICKS.
Engineering bricks are generally used
for carrying heavy loads, and a strong,
dense cement mortar, such as 1 part by
volume of Portland cement to $2\frac{1}{2}$ or
3 parts of sand, should be used. If it is
also important that the work should be
waterproof, a suitable mortar which is
more workable and more likely to fill
the joints completely, is $\frac{3}{4}$ cement : $\frac{1}{4}$ fat
lime (putty or dry hydrate) : 3 sand.

MORTAR FOR OPEN-TEXTURE BRICKS.
Weathering properties are generally

more important than strength in th
case of facing bricks, as the loads t
which these bricks are usually subjecte
are well within their capacity. Cemen
lime mortars are preferable to stron
cement mortars. Suitable proportion
are $\frac{1}{4}$ to $\frac{1}{2}$ cement : $\frac{3}{4}$ to $\frac{1}{2}$ fat lime :
sand. (Hydraulic limes should not b
used with Portland cement.)

The bricks should be dipped in, o
sprayed with, water before being laid
to prevent excessive absorption of wate
from the mortar.

Instead of the cement-lime-sand mi
mentioned, hydraulic lime-sand mortar
such as 1 lime : $2\frac{1}{2}$ to $3\frac{1}{2}$ sand may b
used.

The use of strong dense cement mor
tars with certain types of bricks ma
lead to decay of the bricks. Salts con
tained in the bricks themselves or de
rived from other sources, such as th
mortar, will tend—after being dissolve
by rain-water—to take the line of leas
resistance and come out through th

ricks rather than through the dense
ard joints. These salts will tend to
crystallize on the surface of the brickwork and will cause disfigurement and
ossibly decay.

MORTAR FOR STONEWORK. The colour
nd texture of the mortar should har-
onize with the stonework. A typical
ix is $\frac{1}{4}$ part by volume of Portland
ment : $\frac{3}{4}$ part fat lime (putty or
ydrate) : 3 parts fine crushed stone.

Iron and Steel

There are many varieties of iron and
eel, differing from each other in com-
osition and properties, and grouped
nder the two headings "Iron" and
Steel." All varieties are, however,
erived basically from iron ores.

IRON ORES. An iron ore is a com-
ound of iron and oxygen or of iron,
xygen and carbon associated with
her matter such as limestone and
ay, called the gangue. There are
arious types of iron ore, such as
agnetite, hæmatite and clay iron-
ones.

FIRST STAGE IN THE MANUFACTURE
= IRON AND STEEL—PIG IRON. The
on is set free from its ore in a blast
rnace into which weighed amounts of
e, coke and limestone are charged.
he coke is the fuel and the limestone
ts as a flux combining with the im-
urities and rendering them more fluid.
he compressed air (blast) is blown into
e furnace through air pipes. The iron
hich is set free from the ore sinks to
e bottom of the furnace and is run off
to moulds consisting of a network of
annels formed in sand.

The manner in which the smaller
annels branch off from the main
annels once suggested to someone
ung pigs adhering to a sow, hence the
ame *pig iron*.

Alternatively, the iron may be run
f direct into a ladle and immediately
transported to the steel furnace for
conversion into steel.

Pig iron, although mainly iron, contains many impurities and subsequent
treatment in converting it to wrought
iron or steel aims at removing or modify-
ing these impurities. Carbon is a very
important impurity; the greater the
quantity of carbon present, the harder,
stronger and more brittle is the iron or
steel.

Among other impurities which may
be present in iron and steel are manganese (which gives good wearing properties to the metal), silicon (which
increases strength), phosphorus and
sulphur. The two latter are very
undesirable impurities.

CAST IRON. For castings, suitable pig
iron is remelted and poured into sand
moulds shaped according to the article
required. There are various types of
cast iron suitable for various purposes,
but the general properties of the metal
are as follows: Carbon content, 2 per
cent to 6 per cent; weight, 450 lb. per
cub. ft.

Cast iron is brittle, being weak in
tension but strong in compression;
usually, it cannot be forged, i.e., heated
and beaten into shapes. It resists rusting
a good deal better than wrought iron
and mild steel.

Uses of Cast Iron

Cast iron is particularly suitable for
repetition work such as railings, manhole covers, gratings, pipes and stoves.
It was formerly used to a large extent
for columns to transmit compressive
loads in buildings, but has been practically superseded by mild steel. Cast iron
is ideal for engine beds and heavy parts
of machinery, providing that no tension
stresses are induced.

WROUGHT IRON is the oldest form of
iron which has been used by man. It is
obtained by freeing suitable pig iron

"COGGING" OR "BLOOMING" MILL

The steel ingot is passed backwards and forwards between the apertures formed by the roll and it is thus rolled down until its cross-section has been sufficiently reduced. This rough rectangular bar, which is called a "bloom," is afterwards rolled in the finishing mill.

from most of its impurities. Only about ·1 to ·25 per cent of carbon and about 2 per cent of other impurities remain, the rest of the metal being pure iron. The impurities are removed by heating pig iron with iron ore in a puddling furnace.

The oxygen from the ore combines with the carbon in the pigs to form carbon monoxide and carbon dioxide; the metal is stirred or puddled with long rakes pushed through the furnace doors, and at a certain stage in the manufacture the metal begins to set and becomes sticky, when it is worked into balls or blooms. These blooms, weighing about 60 lb. each, are withdrawn from the furnace and hammered and rolled out one or more times, in order to squeeze out the slag and to improve the quality.

PROPERTIES AND USES. Owing to its low carbon content, wrought iron is very elastic, ductile and malleable met. and is very resistant to shock. It can b wrought very easily when heated and the best ferrous metal for smith's wor It weighs about 480 lb. per cub. ft. an will withstand a compressive or tensi load of about 22 tons per sq. in. befor breaking. Owing to its content of sla a fracture of wrought iron exposes fibrous structure. It is less corrodib than mild steel.

Steel Production

The most important methods of ste production are by means of the Siemen Martin or open-hearth furnace (intr duced about 1868) and the Bessem converter (introduced about 1856 Both methods consist of removing th carbon from pig iron and then addir he requisite amount of carbon (and, if ecessary, other materials) to give the ype of steel required.

OPEN-HEARTH FURNACE. Pig iron and crap iron are charged into a furnace eated to a very high temperature by roducer gas (derived from coal). Iron xide, in the form of iron ore, is added 1 small quantities for the purpose of ombining with the carbon, until de-arbonization is complete. Weighed mounts of materials containing carbon, uch as ferro-manganese and anthracite oal, are added to give the exact amount f carbon required.

The molten steel is run into ingot 1oulds, and if the steel is for structural urposes the ingots are subsequently :heated and passed through rollers to >rm rolled steel joists, angle sections, lates and bars.

For forging into guns and for steel astings the composition of the steel ould be different from that of struc-ıral steel. Some open-hearth furnaces re capable of delivering over 200 tons t one tap, the time from charging to ıpping being in the neighbourhood of ght to ten hours.

BESSEMER CONVERTER. Suitable mol-:n pig iron is run into a converter, ʰhich is a kind of cylindrical structure arrowing at the neck and capable of eing revolved from a horizontal to a ertical position. Compressed air enters ırough holes in the bottom and the ɔnverter is swung into a vertical posi-on. The blast roars through the iron, 1e oxygen combining with the carbon, nd decarbonization is complete in bout twenty minutes. The required mount of carbon is added as explained bove, and about 20 tons to 30 tons of eel are obtained from each blow.

CEMENTATION process of manufacture ɔnsists of adding the required amount f carbon to wrought iron to convert it ɪto a high-carbon steel suitable for

tool making. Bars of wrought iron are heated in contact with charcoal in a furnace cemented up to exclude air, for eight to eleven days.

ELECTRIC FURNACES are used for special types of steel and alloy steels, such as chromium steels.

Depending upon the type of steel, the carbon content varies from about ·2 to 2 per cent, steels containing a high percentage of carbon being used for castings and tools, and steel containing a low percentage (mild steel) being used for structural purposes. The higher the percentage of carbon, the greater the toughness, strength and hardness, but the lower is the elasticity. Steel weighs about 490 lb. per cub. ft.

Steel for Building

MILD OR STRUCTURAL STEEL contains about ·2 to ·3 per cent carbon. It is stronger, more uniform and more duc-tile than wrought iron, and its elastic properties render it very suitable for beams and columns in structural work. Mild steel can withstand a compressive or tensile load up to 28 tons to 33 tons per sq. in. before breaking, though in practice it is only subjected to about

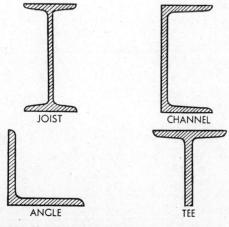

JOIST   CHANNEL

ANGLE   TEE

Fig. 11. Some examples of the various sections commonly used in structural steel work.

one-quarter of the breaking load. It is obtainable in many different sections, including solid round sections used for columns, and bars and rods for re-inforced-concrete. A few of the sections commonly used in structural work are shown in Fig. 11.

HIGH-TENSILE STRUCTURAL STEEL contains copper and chromium. It is stronger than mild steel without being deficient in ductility; it should be re-membered that it is difficult to manu-facture stronger steel than mild steel and at the same time retain the valuable properties of ductility and elasticity. In high-tensile steel the difficulty is over-come by adding copper and chromium. The breaking strength of this steel is between 37 tons to 43 tons per sq. in., and it is a very suitable material where it is necessary to keep the dead weight of the structure as low as possible, since less of this type of steel is required than mild steel.

There are various other types of steels and alloy steels, such as stainless steel, which contains chromium, manganese steel, as used for tram rails; and tung-sten steel, which is used for drills, tools, and similar work.

Manufacture of Lead

LEAD is obtained by smelting lead ores in a furnace. The molten lead is cast into pigs weighing about 80 lb. to 120 lb. each, and this is one form in which it is supplied to manufacturers and plumbers.

PROPERTIES. Lead is very soft and malleable, and durable. It has a much lower strength than steel and possesses no elasticity; it is therefore not suitable for structural work. It is very heavy, weighing about 710 lb. per cub. ft., has a bright surface when freshly cut, but quickly absorbs oxygen from the air to become dull in colour.

USES. Lead is used extensively in buildings in the form of sheets and pipes and is alloyed with tin for soldering both lead and sheet-metal workers' tinplates

SHEET LEAD may be cast or milled In the former case, molten lead is poured on to a prepared bed of sand or a casting bench and smoothed off to the required thickness. In the case of milled lead, several tons are cast into a slab which is subsequently rolled into thin sheets. Most sheet lead used today is milled, although cast lead is reputed to be more durable. Sheet lead is used for flashings, ridges, gutters, rain-water pipes, damp-proof courses, tank linings and similar purposes.

Types of Lead Piping

LEAD PIPING may be seamed, cast or drawn. Seamed pipes are formed from sheet lead, which is folded round mandril, i.e., cylinder, of the required diameter. The seam may then be soldered, although it is now the practice to close the seam by means of a welding operation, the process being termed lead burning. For cast pipes, molten lead cast into sand moulds. Cast pipes are not very common nowadays. Drawn pipes are made by forcing molten lead through a cylindrical die, inside which is a mandril of the required inside dia-meter of the pipe. The piping, as it emerges, is usually wound off into coils

CORROSION OF LEAD. Although lead is one of the most durable of building materials, it is advisable in some cases to take precautions to prevent it corrod-ing. In certain circumstances, timber—especially oak—will corrode lead, and it may be necessary to cover timber boarding with a layer of bitumen felt before laying the lead sheets. Portland cement and limes also corrode lead, and lead damp-proof courses in thick walls and pipes which are laid in cement or lime, should be protected from corrosion by bitumen felt or other suitable means

COPPER. In one method of manufacture copper ore is smelted in a furnace and the resulting material is poured into a converter (similar to the Bessemer converter). Here the impurities are oxidized, the copper being further refined in a refining furnace.

PROPERTIES. Copper is the most ductile and malleable of metals, with the exception of gold, silver and platinum. Working the metal cold has a hardening influence. Its weight is about 580 lb. per cub. ft. The breaking strength of copper in tension depends upon its nature, ranging from about 10 tons per q. in. for cast copper to about 25 tons per sq. in. for drawn wire.

SHEET COPPER may be hot rolled or cold rolled. Hot-rolled copper is soft and is the most suitable material for roofing purposes, i.e., for domes, etc. When exposed to the air, as in the case of roofs, a protective green film (patina) of copper carbonate forms on the copper and is considered to improve the appearance of the roof.

This characteristic green colour is more likely to occur in country districts, where the atmosphere is not so smoky and soot polluted as in cities.

Tempers of Cold-rolled Copper

COLD-ROLLED COPPER is normally hard, but may be annealed soft. It can be supplied in several tempers, "hard," "half hard," and "soft clean." Copper should be "half hard" for purposes such as ridging, where it is required to keep its shape with little or no support.

STRIP COPPER is cold rolled and can be obtained in rolls for damp-proof courses, valleys and gutters.

PIPES may be made by cold solid drawing (giving seamless tubing) or by folding sheet copper around a mandril (seamed tubing).

Other uses of copper are for piping for all types of domestic water services;

mason's cramps and dowels; wall ties; shop fronts; ornamental metal work; covering for timber doors; copper roofing tiles; electric wires, cables, and lightning conductors.

Zinc Manufacture

ZINC ore is "roasted" and then heated with carbon in fireclay vessels. Zinc is formed as a vapour which is converted to liquid metal in condensers. The metal so formed contains about 1 to 2 per cent lead and is known as *spelter*.

Sheet zinc is used for roofing, ridging, and ventilators, but is inferior to lead and copper. It is not very durable in smoky atmospheres, as acids corrode it easily. Zinc is used fairly extensively as a protective coating against rust, on iron and steel, i.e., galvanized iron. The *hot-dip* galvanizing process is the most common, the sheet or other article to be coated being dipped into molten zinc.

ELECTRO-GALVANIZING. In this process the articles are plated with zinc by electrical precipitation. This method is used principally for coating wire, and nuts, bolts and washers used for fixing galvanized sheets.

SHERARDIZING consists of impregnating the surface of the iron or steel with zinc dust, the temperature during the process being about 350 to 400 degrees C. This process is used for springs, scaffolding fittings, chains, aeroplane parts and similar purposes.

In the SPRAYING PROCESS melted zinc is projected by special pistols. This method has the advantage that steel and ironwork such as bridges, pylons and ships can be coated after erection.

Timber Growth

The growth of trees takes place by the addition of a new layer of wood (annual ring) each year. In the spring, sap ascends from the roots to form springwood. During the summer, carbon

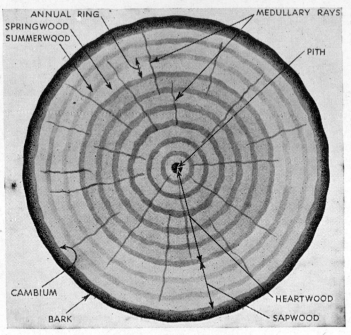

ANNUAL GROWTH OF TIMBER

Fig. 12. The various stages of growth of hardwoods are shown above, and also the medullary rays which are referred to in the text.

dioxide is absorbed by the leaves and thickens the sap, which descends in the autumn to complete the layer. The formation of the annual ring occurs in the cambium layer immediately next to the bark. Each annual ring consists of springwood and summerwood, the latter generally being more dense, harder, and darker in colour, than the springwood (Fig. 12).

HEARTWOOD OR DURAMEN is the inner portion of the tree and is more dense and usually darker in colour than the remainder of the layers (sapwood).

SAPWOOD OR ALBURNUM is of more recent growth than the heartwood and contains more sap. Timber cut from it is not so strong and durable as the heartwood.

PITH is the central core of the tree.

MEDULLARY RAYS are strips or ribbons of cellular tissue running radially from the pith towards the bark; they are only visible in hardwoods (Fig.12).

SEASONING OF TIMBER. All timber should be well seasoned before use, so that as much sap as possible may be removed. If this is not done trouble will be caused by shrinkage of the timber in the finished work.

NATURAL SEASONING. Planks and beams are built in stacks with wedges between the timber to enable free circulation of air to take place. The stacks are protected from the weather by a roof. Two years or more may be required for large sizes of hardwoods (over 2 in. square), the seasoning time being much less for smaller sizes. Softwoods being more porous, season more rapidly.

KILN SEASONING is a much quicker drying process than natural seasoning. Preheated warm air is made to circulate in a steam-heated chamber in which the timber is stacked. Great skill in using the kiln is necessary to avoid cracking and warping.

Causes of Timber Defects

HEART SHAKES are shrinkage cracks starting from the centre of the log. When there are several of these splits, the term *star shake* is used (Fig. 13).

CUP OR RING SHAKES are cracks following the lines of the annual rings.

BURRS are swellings caused by the growth of the tree over a wound, such

might have been caused by the break-
g off of a branch. In woods such as
alnut and oak, burrs are sometimes
nsidered a decorative asset.

KNOTS consist of hard pieces of wood
hich have formed portions of branches
d which have become embedded in
e wood by the natural growth of the
ee.

UPSET refers to the appearance of
res which have been injured by shock
 crushing occurring usually during
owth (Fig. 13).

TWISTED GRAIN is generally caused
 wind action on the tree.

DOATINESS consists of speckled stains
d is a sign of local decay.

DRY ROT is a disease caused by attack
 fungus which feeds upon the timber.
ne common cause of dry rot is lack of
ntilation, combined with warm, damp
nditions. The disease is very infec-
us and other timber may be infected
 spores carried by the wind or vermin,
 even by spores spreading through
ickwork.

Wood attacked by dry rot eventually
comes covered with a network of white

or yellowish grey threads and there is an
unpleasant smell. A cure can be effected
only by removing the cause of the infec-
tion, cutting out the infected wood
(rather more than less being removed),
and treating the adjacent wood with a
disinfectant. Adjacent brickwork should
be treated with a blowlamp.

WET ROT is principally caused by
alternate wetting and drying of timber,
and is not infectious.

DECAY CAUSED BY INSECTS AND
WORMS. Several species of ants attack
woods, some preferring the softwoods
and others the hardwoods.

The death watch and lyctus beetles
usually attack hardwoods such as elm
and oak, whilst the teredo navalis worm
is a common cause of decay in timber
placed in the sea, as in piers and jetties.

CONVERSION OF TIMBER is the term
used for the cutting up of the log into
deals, boards, planks, etc.

ORDINARY SAWN. This is the least
wasteful method, but there is a greater
tendency for warping to take place,
especially in the pieces cut from near
the outside of the log (Fig. 14).

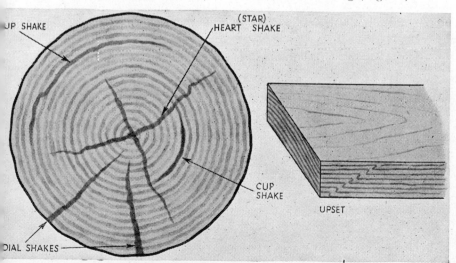

UP SHAKE

(STAR)
HEART SHAKE

CUP
SHAKE

UPSET

DIAL SHAKES

SOME COMMON DEFECTS IN TIMBER

. 13. The effects of heart shakes, cup or ring shakes, and upset are illustrated above

RIFT OR RADIAL SAWN, i.e., sawn at right angles to the annual rings. The logs are first quarter šawn, after which the quarters may be sawn up as illustrated. Method (a) gives planks which are all truly rift sawn, but is wasteful. Methods (b), (c) and (d) are less expensive, but are not truly rift sawn in the same sense as (a) (Fig. 14).

Rift sawing cuts obliquely across the medullary rays and gives decorative figuring (silver grain) in timbers such as oak. This is also the best method of sawing for floor boards or wood blocks.

TANGENTIAL SAWN OR FLAT GRAIN. The boards or planks are cut tangentially to the annual rings. In those woods where there is a strong contrast between the colour of spring and summer woods, as in pitch pine, this method gives attractive figuring. It is not recommended for floor boards, as the heart tends to be kicked up and splintered (Fig. 14).

WANEY EDGES are caused by cutting pieces too large for the size of the log, so that part of the original rounded surface of the tree remains (Fig. 14).

Softwoods and Hardwoods

Trees are divided into two classes, softwoods and hardwoods.

SOFTWOODS are coniferous, i.e., cone bearing, and the trees are evergreen.

HARDWOODS are deciduous and shed their leaves annually.

Although, in general, softwoods are softer and lighter in weight than hardwoods, some softwoods such as pitch pine are harder than hardwoods such as willow and alder.

Generally speaking, softwoods contain resinous matter and hardwoods do not, whilst the former type has wider annual rings than the latter, but no visible medullary rays. The sapwood of the softwoods is usually not much lighter in colour than the heartwood, but in the

case of hardwoods, the difference generally more marked.

It is only possible to mention here few types of timber in common use there is a greater number of hardwood (several hundred species) than sof woods.

NORTHERN PINE (known also Baltic pine, Scotch fir, Baltic fir, yello fir, red or yellow deal). Yellowish reddish-brown. Quality depends c port of shipment, the best timber bein from Archangel. Good timber for a general carpentry and joinery, e.g., ro timbers, stairs, windows, doors, floorin Weight: 30 lb. to 36 lb. per cub. ft.

WHITE DEAL OR FIR (Norway spruc Baltic white deal). Bluish-white yellowish. Soft, easily worked. Be qualities used for shelves, dressers, et Weight: about 34 lb. per cub. ft.

PITCH PINE. Reddish-brown colou very resinous, hard, strong and durabl It takes varnish well, but not pai (owing to resin). The annual rings a wide and strongly marked, giving good figure. Used for heavy structur work, roof trusses, masts, flooring, et Obtained from Canada and U.S.A. Tl weight is about 45 lb. per cub. ft.

DOUGLAS FIR (Oregon pine, Britis Columbian pine). Reddish-brown cc our. Hard, strong and resinous. Tak stain and varnish well. Chief use is fe constructional work, but it is used al for flooring, doors, panelling, et Obtained from North America. Weigh about 36 lb. per cub. ft.

Other softwoods are larch (used fe constructional work, and also telegrap poles, and yew (furniture).

Hardwoods

OAK. There are many varieties, in cluding English, Austrian, America Japanese; English probably being tl best. Oak is strong, tough and durabl and has pronounced medullary ra

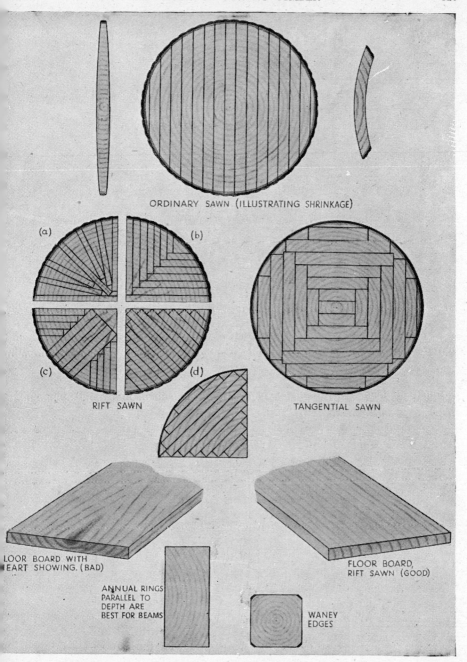

ORDINARY SAWN (ILLUSTRATING SHRINKAGE)

(a) (b)

(c) (d)

RIFT SAWN TANGENTIAL SAWN

FLOOR BOARD WITH
HEART SHOWING. (BAD)

ANNUAL RINGS
PARALLEL TO
DEPTH ARE
BEST FOR BEAMS

WANEY
EDGES

FLOOR BOARD,
RIFT SAWN (GOOD)

CORRECT AND INCORRECT METHODS OF SAWING TIMBER

Fig. 14. Ordinary sawn is the least wasteful method, but there is a tendency to warping. Rift sawn
at right angles to the annual rings. Tangential sawn is tangentially to the annual rings.

B.—L

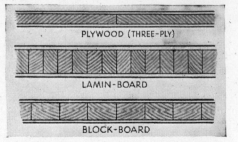

Fig. 15. The three types of plywood. Note that lamin-board has narrower strips for the core than those used for block-board.

which give decorative markings (silver grain) when rift sawn. Hard to work; contains an acid capable of corroding iron and lead. Used for all purposes, internally and externally, including flooring, roof trusses, beams, etc. Weight: about 52 lb. per cub. ft.

MAHOGANY. Red-brown colour. Many types, including Honduras, Cuban, African. Used for decorative work, shop fronts, counters, w.c. seats, etc. Weight: about 36 lb. to 50 lb. per cub. ft.

TEAK. Light brown colour, which darkens with age. Hard, strong, durable and heavy. Difficult to work. Contains an oil which resists insects, and does not warp once it has been seasoned. Used for good-class joinery, e.g., floors, doors, staircases, etc.; also draining boards, laboratory benches, etc. Obtained from India, Burma, etc. Weight: about 38 lb. to 45 lb. per cub. ft.

WALNUT. Dark brown colour; hard and gives good figure. Used for high-class joinery, shop fronts, furniture, etc. Obtained chiefly from Europe. Weight: about 38 lb. per cub. ft.

SYCAMORE. Whitish colour. Used for table tops, etc. Also for panelling. Weight: about 35 lb. to 45 lb. per cub. ft.

BEECH. Reddish-brown. Used for furniture, wood block flooring. Weight: about 40 lb. to 55 lb. per cub. ft.

BASSWOOD. Whitish, soft timber easily worked. Used for joinery, panelling, etc. Tends to shrink and warp. Weight: 30 lb. per cub. ft.

There are many other hardwoods including ash, birch, elm, obechi, iroko, jarrah, greenheart, padauk, chestnut, ebony and maple.

Manufacture of Plywood

PLYWOOD is made by glueing together thin sheets or plys of wood with the grain of each sheet running at right angles to the grain of the sheets immediately next to it. By this means, expansion and contraction due to change of moisture content of the timber are almost eliminated, and this is the great advantage of plywood. When used for decorative work, such as panelling, the top layer may be a veneer of figured wood.

Common plywood sizes are: $\frac{1}{8}$ in. $\frac{3}{16}$ in., usually 3-ply; $\frac{1}{4}$ in., usually sometimes 5-ply; $\frac{5}{16}$ in. to $\frac{3}{8}$ in., usually 5-ply; $\frac{1}{2}$ in. to $\frac{3}{4}$ in., usually 7-ply.

Sheets are obtainable in sizes about 3 ft. × 3 ft. to 7 ft. × 5 ft.

A comparatively recent material is resin-bonded plywood in which a plastic cement (*see* "Plastics") takes the place of glue. Sheets up to 20 ft. long have been used in the U.S.A.

LAMIN BLOCK BOARDS. A laminated board consists of a core of strips of wood the directions of the grain running as shown in sketch, with a layer of wood glued to each side. The core of better quality laminated boards is usually of hardwood, such as Gaboon mahogany. The boards can be obtained in various thicknesses, the thicker varieties being suitable, without any further strengthening, for flush doors (Fig. 15).

METAL-FACED PLYWOOD. Thin sheets of galvanized steel, or copper, bronze, aluminium, stainless steel, are fixed by means of an insoluble cement to best ality plywood. Metal-faced plywood n be cut with metal or wood-cutting ws, and nails can be driven without evious drilling. This material is used r office partitions, shower-bath parti- ons, also for counters, shelves, table- ps, flushed and panelled doors and r shop facings.

Nature of Asphalt

ASPHALT is a natural or artificial mix- re of mineral matter (the aggregate) ound together with bitumen; bitumen elongs to the same family as petroleum. The kind of asphalt used in building ork in normal times is known as *mastic phalt*, which is a mixture of the llowing ingredients: (*a*) finely ground atural asphalt rock, usually a bitu- en impregnated limestone; (*b*) lake phalt, such as that found in the well- nown Trinidad Lake, and which con- sts chiefly of approximately 60 per cent tumen and 29 per cent silica (sand);) a flux consisting of bitumen derived om certain types of petroleum, which added to soften the lake bitumen;) siliceous grit (fine sand) is some- mes added. The manufacturing pro- ss consists merely of mixing together e heated ingredients and running the roduct into iron moulds.

On the building site asphalt blocks e remelted in a cauldron, the asphalt eing brought gradually to the correct mperature and co antly stirred to void local burning; overheating of the ixture, as a whole, should be avoided s important constituents may thus be riven off.

After heating, the hot fluid is placed a its required position. The asphalt is pplied in sections and usually consists f two or three coats, the edges of each oat being made to overlap the edges in e coat below. Fine sand is rubbed into e top coat to act as a lubricant in order o obtain a smooth finish. The sand also neutralizes an excess of bitumen, which tends to occur on the surface.

USES. Asphalt is waterproof and, when properly laid, has no joints. It is there- fore eminently suitable for lining base- ments, tanks, and swimming baths. It is used on flat roofs constructed of timber or concrete, a layer of felt being interposed between the asphalt and the roof; the use of felt reduces any tend- ency towards cracking, due to move- ments in the timber or concrete, and consequent entry of water, and also reduces the tendency towards formation of blisters.

Asphalt is used for footways, court- yards, floors in industrial buildings, and for railway platforms. For situations subjected to heavy traffic, heavy gritted forms of asphalt can be used, and, if necessary, a steel mesh can be incor- porated to act as reinforcement.

Acid-resisting asphalt can be obtained for use in printing works, breweries, pickling factories, etc., and gritless asphalt for floors in explosive factories.

Coloured floors (red, green, brown or grey) can be laid with asphalt which has had pigments incorporated with it, or a coloured surface can be obtained by using asphalt containing coloured marble chippings. The marble chip- pings are brought to view by polishing with carborundum grinders after the floor is laid.

Ingredients of Glass

GLASS is made from sand (silica), chalk, and soda or potash, the principal ingredient being silica. Other ingre- dients such as lead and iron oxides, borax and barium, may be included to give certain results such as hardness, brilliance and colour. The ingredients are fused together in a kiln at a temper- ature of over 1,000 degrees C.

TYPES OF GLASS FOR BUILDING. (*a*) Crown glass (spun); (*b*) blown sheet;

(c) drawn sheet; (d) rolled plate; (e) polished plate; (f) pressed.

CROWN GLASS. Molten glass is gathered on the end of a rod and whirled or spun until it flattens out to a disk about 6 ft. in diameter. The largest economical size of pane which may be cut is about 12 in. × 10 in.; the centre pane contains a bull's eye, owing to the attachment of the rod.

BLOWN SHEET GLASS (HAND-MADE). Molten glass is rotated on the end of a pipe supplied with compressed air. The glass elongates into a hollow "sausage," the ends of which are cut off and the cylinder cut lengthways with a diamond. The cylinder is then reheated and flattened out into a rectangular sheet of glass. If the flattening is done on a patterned bed, a pattern will be impressed on the glass.

FLUTED SHEET consists of a blown glass with corrugated surface to give diffraction of the light rays.

MUFFLED SHEET, used for small panes or leaded work, has a rippled appearance.

SANDED SHEET has a pimply surface caused by scattering sand over the flattening bed.

CATHEDRAL SHEET is made to simulate old glass. It contains bubbles and has an irregular surface.

AMBETTI GLASS, which originally came from Italy, is used in leaded and stained glass work.

ANTIQUE GLASS is used for high-quality stained glass.

Blown sheet glass is only made in comparatively small quantities.

DRAWN SHEET GLASS (MACHINE PROCESS). A heavy trough, containing a slot the same thickness and width of the finished sheet, is set in the surface of molten glass contained in a tank. The weight of the trough forces glass through the slot and the glass is drawn vertically upwards between a series of rollers in a continuous sheet. When it emerges fro the topmost rollers it is cool enough be cut into sheets. Drawn sheet glass obtainable in various qualities a thicknesses and is used extensively f glazing purposes. It is not equal, ho ever, to polished plate glass.

ROLLED PLATE GLASS. Molten gl is poured on to a casting table in fro of a roller, which is then run down t length of the table in order to roll t glass out to the required thickness. using a roller with a pattern incised it a figured glass is obtained; ma patterns are available. For wired gla used for skylights and roofs, wire embedded in the glass during rollin

POLISHED PLATE GLASS is first roll on a casting table to approximate twice its finished thickness. It is th ground flat and polished on both sid iron shoes being used first, the fin polishing being accomplished by f shoes fed with rouge and wat Polished plate glass is obtainable practically any thickness and size a is only used for best-quality work.

PRESSED GLASS. Glass is pressed in moulds; pavement lights and certa types of glass tiles are examples.

PATENT PLATE GLASS is *sheet* gla which has been ground and polished both sides.

SAFETY GLASS is either a toughen glass or a sandwich of two sheets of gl and a sheet of ⸱ nsparent celluloid.

OPAL GLASS is an opaque white gla used for wall linings and shelving.

ARMOUR PLATE is a special toughen plate glass.

COLOURED GLASS. (a) *Pot Colours*. T colour is uniform throughout the thic ness of the glass, which may be rol or drawn. It is obtainable in tra parent and also opaque (opal) colou

(b) *Flashed colours* are only possi with the use of blown glass; the col consists of a thin flash on the surfa

GLASS BRICKS can
: laid in the same
ay as ordinary
icks, with the same
pe of mortar.

Use of Plastics

PLASTICS embrace
wide and extend-
g range of hard
d horny synthetic
oducts, the result
chemical reactions
tween various sub-
ances. They are
aracterized by
aving passed
rough a plastic
te under heat and
essure at some stage
fabrication. While
us plastic, they are
mmonly moulded
form articles both
corative and utili-
rian.

Plastics have re-
aced metal, wood,
ass and porcelain
r many purposes.
astics are used for
lephones, electric-
ght fittings, door
ndles, table-tops,

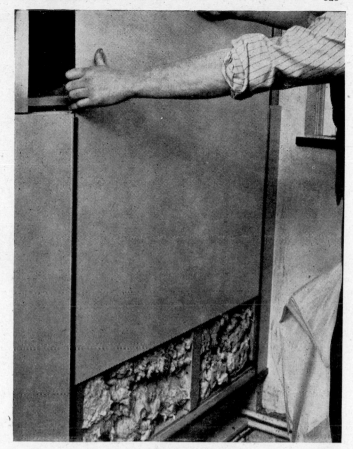

BAKELITE WALL PANEL

Fig. 16. The development of plastics is being made full use of in building. The picture shows the fixing of a Bakelite wall panel between the metal jointing strips which give a neat finish to the wall.

all panelling, and a wide range of
milar articles.

CELLULOID, invented in 1865, is
anufactured by admixing nitro-cellu-
se (obtained by treating cotton with
lphuric and nitric acids) with alcohol
d camphor. Cellulose acetate (non-
flammable celluloid) is similar. Cellu-
id and cellulose acetate, together with
tural plastics such as wax, shellac
sed for gramophone records), pitch
d bitumen products, are thermo-
astic, that is, they are materials which
ll soften as often as they are heated.

The phenolic and urea plastics are
the most important synthetic resins
nowadays from a commercial point of
view. They are thermo-setting materials,
which means that articles made from
them cannot subsequently be softened
after fabrication. These materials are
more recent than celluloid and have
greatly extended the scope and utility
of plastics.

PHENOLIC RESINOID PLASTICS are
manufactured from phenol (carbolic
acid), extracted from coal tar, and
formaldehyde, a gas produced from

PLASTICS AS AN ATTRACTIVE HYGIENIC WALL DECORATION

Fig. 17. A waiting-room panelled with Bakelite veneer which is easily kept clean. The table-t in the foreground is made of wood with a Bakelite finish, which is heat and water resistir

methane, which in turn is produced from coal. (Bakelite, named after Dr. Baekeland, is an example of this type of plastic.) Fillers, such as wood flour (finely ground wood) and colouring matter, may be added during the manufacturing process.

UREA OR AMINO-PLASTICS are manu-

factured from urea (obtained fro ammonia and carbon dioxide) ar formaldehyde, suitable fillers bein added.

CASEIN PLASTICS derive from case (obtained from milk) and formaldehyd

Plastics are available as rods, shee tubes and moulding powders. (Th first moulding powders were marketed in 1916). The former may be cut into finished articles, and moulding powders can be hot moulded in hydraulic presses. One of the largest moulds at the present time is one used for producing plastic coffins. Plastics can be sawn, drilled, turned and carved like wood. Phenolic plastics often resemble polished mahogany or ebony, but may have any dark colour. Urea-formaldehyde plastics can be obtained in many attractive delicate shades.

Methyl methacrylate resins resemble plate glass. These and also cellulose acetate are much used in aeroplane cabins and gun turrets. Some of the synthetic resins are used in the manufacture of paints, lacquers and varnishes.

Laminated Plastics

Apart from the familiar uses of plastics for electric-light fittings, etc., and a fairly recent innovation—plastic ball floats—a product known as laminated or reinforced plastic is likely to be increasingly used in the future. One type is made by impregnating sheets of special paper, cotton or linen, with a resinoid bonding agent, and pressing them together under heat to form a board. A special type of laminated board called Gordon aerolite has a strength of about 22 tons per sq. in., i.e., about three-quarters that of mild steel, with a density of less than one-fifth of the metal!

Laminated plastics can be obtained in sheets of many colours and finishes, ranging in thickness from $\frac{1}{32}$ in. to 2 in. They are also obtainable in rods and tubes. Laminated sheets are admirable for interior wall panellings and ceilings, having an attractive permanent finish, and are light in weight (Figs. 16 and 17).

RUBBER. Raw rubber is obtained from certain tropical trees by tapping the liquid (called latex) which they

contain, adding acetic acid (vinegar is a dilute form of acetic acid) and, when the material is dry, rolling and pressing it. One familiar use of raw rubber is for crêpe soles for footwear.

For the manufacture of rubber flooring material and other products, the raw rubber is crushed and torn between iron rollers, and ingredients such as sulphur and pigments are mixed in. The rubber is then shaped by being forced out of a machine, or, in the case of sheets, by being passed through rollers. Finally, the rubber is vulcanized, that is, heated at a temperature of about 120 degrees to 150 degrees C. to convert the soft plastic material into a hard, resistant product. Rubber for flooring purposes can be obtained in sheets or as tiles, in many colours, plain or marbled.

CORK is the outer layer of the bark of a species of oak, the tree being principally cultivated in Spain and Portugal. For the manufacture of cork tiles for flooring, the cork is subjected to a pressure of about 75 tons per sq. ft. and is baked whilst undergoing the pressure.

TERRA-COTTA is manufactured by burning clays of fine texture, and is used chiefly in the form of mouldings and hollow blocks for the facing of buildings.

CLAY TILES for roofing purposes are made from good-quality brick clays and are available in various colours. Clay flooring tiles are of similar composition.

Properties of Asbestos

ASBESTOS is a mineral, which, after being quarried, is ground and fibreized. It is an incombustible material and is much used for heat-insulating and fire-resisting purposes. It is also acid resistant, the blue variety of asbestos being more suitable than the more generally used white variety.

ASBESTOS CEMENT pipes, roofing tiles, and sheets are manufactured from a mixture of asbestos and Portland cement.

CHAPTER 10

CRAFTSMEN'S TOOLS

Bricklayers' tools: plumb rule and plumb level; trowels. Carpentry an joinery tools: marking and setting out; cutting and planing; boring, drivin and withdrawing. Masons' tools and appliances: hoisting, cutting, and layin stone. Plasterers' tools: mixing, laying, and testing plaster. Painters' tools stopping, paint removing, and applying paint. Slaters' tools. Plumbers' tool.

BRICKLAYERS' TOOLS

THE principal tools of the brick-layer are his trowels (Fig. 1) with which he lays and spreads the mortar on which the bricks are laid or with which he points up the joints at a later stage of the work. The ordinary trowel varies in length from 10 in. to 13 in. and is handed according to whether the bricklayer is left-handed or right-handed.

The *pointing trowel* is one of a much smaller size, varying from 2 in. to 9 in. and is used in conjunction with a *hawk* for pointing and finishing joints or other small work. The hawk is a small square board about 10 in. × 10 in. or 12 in. × 12 in. and 1 in. thick with a handle on the underside of $1\frac{1}{4}$-in. or $1\frac{1}{2}$-in. diameter. It is for holding mortar when pointing.

The *plumb rule* is a piece of pine from 5 ft. to 6 ft. in length by 4 in. wide and $\frac{5}{8}$ in. to $\frac{7}{8}$ in. thick. The sides must be parallel and a centre line marked on the face from top to bottom. The *bob hole* is placed about 9 in. from the bottom and its outline approximately $\frac{5}{8}$ in. wider and $1\frac{1}{2}$ in. longer than the bob.

The *plumb bob* is usually made of lead and in various sizes, varying in weight from 3 lb. for internal work and up to about 10 lb. for external work. The bob string should be of whip cord and passed through an $\frac{1}{8}$-in. diameter

hole at the top and held fast in tw saw cuts. The *plumb level* or *vertical lev* has of recent years almost entirely take the place of the plumb rule. It is fro 42 in. to 48 in. in length, made hardwood, and some are fitted with tw plumbs, a single level and two han holes; others are as shown in sketch.

Line and Pins. The pins are made steel, with flat points to allow for the insertion into a cross joint. The line stretched between the pins in order tha the course of bricks may be laid in the correct position. Where the line is undue length, a small piece of metal copper or zinc, about 5 in. × 2 in., havin two grooves in one end, called a *tingl* is used to take the sag out of the lin

Measuring Rods

The bricklayer uses a *2-ft. rul measuring rod*, and a *gauge* or *storey r* for setting out his work. The gauge usually four courses to the foot in th South of England, but in the North runs four courses to 13 in.

In axed work the tools used are th *tin saw,* with which, after marking th outline, the required shape is cut about $\frac{1}{8}$ in. and then the superfluo material is knocked off with a *boaster,* short broad chisel having a 4-in. cuttin edge which is slightly rounded; and *club hammer* weighing about 4 lb. Th

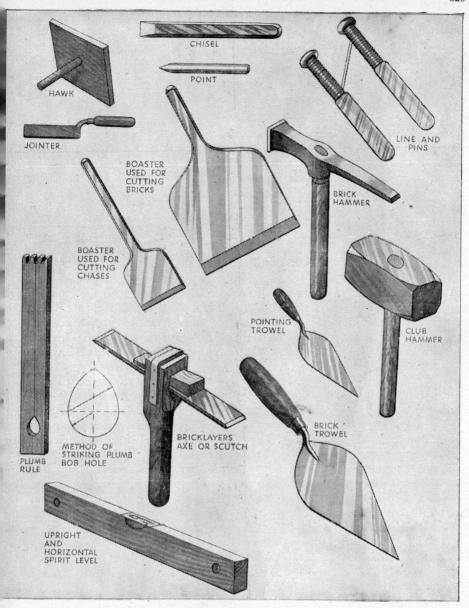

BRICKLAYERS' TOOLS

Fig. I. Illustrating a selection of some of the principal tools which are used by the bricklayer.

brick is placed in a *chopping block* consisting of two blocks of wood secured to a base so as to form an angle in which the brick can be placed for cutting; a

bricklayer's axe or *scutch* which is a double-edged chisel about 1 in. wide, fitted into a stock by means of a wedge.

For the softer qualities of bricks used

for gauged work, an old tenon saw, or a saw which consists of a bow frame and a blade formed of two wires twisted together and strained, is used for cutting the bricks to the required shape. The bricks are then finished on a slab of York stone by rubbing.

The *cold chisel* is used for cutting chases in walls and the *plugging chisel* for cutting holes or for cutting out joints for lead flashings and similar work.

The *jointer* has a steel blade 2 in. to 6 in. long with an edge which is either flat, grooved, concave or convex rounded; used for jointing and pointing brick-

work. Another tool used for jointing i the *pointing rule*, a piece of wood 3 in $\times \frac{7}{8}$ in., bevelled one edge, to which ar fixed $\frac{3}{8}$ in. thick distance pieces. Th *frenchman* is a tool made from an ol table knife cut to a point on each sid at about 30 degrees, filed to a beve edge, and bent at the point about $\frac{3}{8}$ in at right angles to the blade; it is use for tuck pointing. The *square* should b of steel, the blade being about 6 in. lon and the stock about 4 in. The brick layer's *straight-edge* is made of yello pine, usually 3 in. $\times \frac{3}{4}$ in. and 3 ft. 6 in long, parallel and shot both edges.

CARPENTRY AND JOINERY TOOLS

MACHINERY is now extensively used in the preparation of timber of all kinds of woodwork, and this renders unnecessary many tools which were formerly in use.

The various tools used by the joiner may be classified into those used for: (1) marking and setting out; (2) cutting and planing; (3) boring, impelling, etc.

Marking and setting-out tools include rules, marking gauge, straight-edge, try square, mitre square, bevel, compasses, callipers and gauges (Fig. 2).

Rules are made of boxwood, and in a number of varieties, the commonest size being the 2-ft. fourfold. The inches are subdivided into sixteenths.

The *marking awl* and *cutting knife* are used for setting out accurate work. *Straight-edges* are $3\frac{1}{2}$-in. or 4-in. $\times \frac{1}{2}$-in. boards and up to about 8 ft. long, with one edge straight; used for testing surfaces, drawing lines, etc. The *try square* is obtainable in various sizes, used for setting out right angles and for testing whether surfaces are at right angles to each other. The *sliding bevel* has a loose slotted blade which can be secured at any required angle by use of the screw.

Compasses are used for curved work For striking larger arcs or circles a pai of *trammel pins* is needed, consisting o two metal heads which slide along hardwood rod. One point may be re placed by a pencil socket. *Callipers* ar used for measuring the diameter o curved surfaces.

Different kinds of gauges are used the *marking gauge*, which has only on marking point, is used for marking line parallel to the edge of the wood. Th *cutting gauge* is similar to the marking gauge, but differs in having a cutting blade instead of a marking point. It is used for cutting parallel strips from thin stuff. A *mortise gauge* has two adjustable marking points and is used where two parallel lines are to be marked out, as in the setting out of mortises and tenons.

For testing horizontal and vertical surfaces the spirit level and plumb rule are used.

Cutting and *planing tools* comprise saws, chisels, planes, gouges and spokeshaves.

Saws. The blade of a saw is made from best spring steel of uniform hardness and fitted in a wooden handle. The many varieties include the cross-cut saw, rip

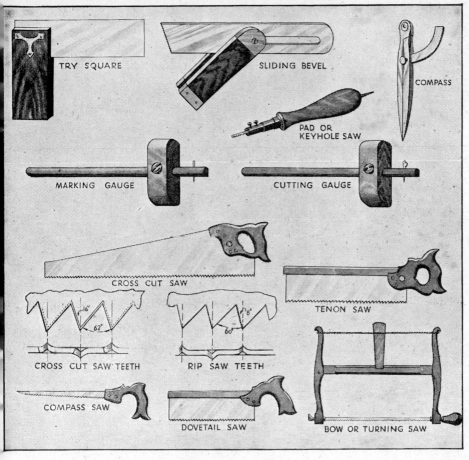

CARPENTERS' TOOLS

Fig. 2. A selection of the marking out and sawing tools in general use by the carpenter.

saw, panel saw, tenon saw, compass saw, dovetail saw and pad saw (Fig. 2).

The *cross-cut saw* is used for cutting across the grain and the *rip saw* for cutting with the grain, that is, in the direction of the fibres, and the *panel saw* is used for fine work. The chief difference in these saws lies in the shape of the teeth. The teeth points in the rip saw are about ⅜ in. apart and those in the cross-cut saw ¼ in. apart.

The panel saw teeth are similar to those of the cross-cut saw but much smaller in size. The teeth are bent or

"set" slightly outwards alternately to the right and left of the blade, to enable the blade to pass through the cut being formed in the timber with the minimum of friction as the sawing proceeds.

The distance which the points project beyond the plane of the blade is called the *set*.

The *tenon saw*, as its name implies, is used for the cutting of shoulders to tenons. The blade is 12 in. to 16 in. long, 3 in. to 4 in. wide, and has ten tooth points to the inch. The blade, being

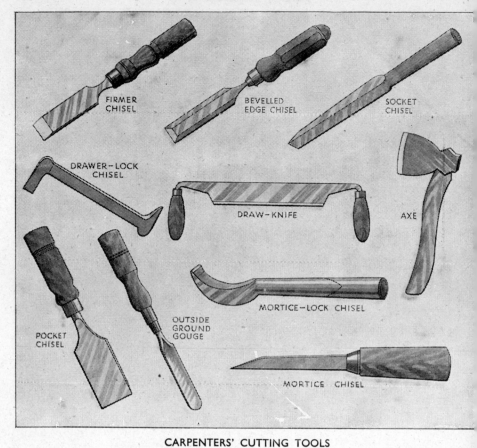

CARPENTERS' CUTTING TOOLS

Fig. 3. There are many types of chisel, the main classes being the firmer, paring and mortising chisels and gouges. These chisels are all sharpened on oilstones.

thinner than the ordinary saw, is stiffened by an iron or brass back. The *dovetail saw* is similar to the tenon saw, but smaller in size with finer teeth. It is used for dovetail joints in drawers and for other fine work.

The *bow* or *turning saw* is used for cutting curved surfaces. It has a thin narrow blade held in tension by a wooden frame and string. The *compass saw* and the *pad* or *keyhole saw* are used for forming keyholes and similar curved work. The blade tapers in width from $\frac{3}{8}$ in. to slightly less than $\frac{1}{4}$ in.

A *two-handled saw* for cutting balk timber is 5 in. to 8 in. wide and from 4 ft. up to 7 ft. long with large teeth.

Chisels (Fig. 3) may be divided into firmer, paring and mortising chisels and gouges. Chisels are made in all sizes from $\frac{1}{16}$ in. up to 2 in. wide.

The *firmer chisel* is the ordinary chisel used by the joiner. The blade is fixed into a wooden handle by a tang, and formed with a shoulder to withstand the blows from a mallet. The *bevelled-edge chisel* has a thinner blade and is used by hand for finer work without the use of the mallet. These chisels are made in varying widths from $\frac{1}{16}$ in. up to 2 in.

Mortise chisels, as the name implies, are used for mortising. They are much stronger and thicker than the firmer chisels, as they have to withstand the leverage necessary in loosening the wood core when mortising.

Socket chisels are used for heavy work. Instead of having a tang, they are provided with a socket into which the handle fits.

The *drawer-lock chisel* is used for forming the mortise in the door rail which receives the bolt of the drawer lock. The *draw-knife* is used for reducing the width of boards where the waste wood is of no value.

Pocket or *sash chisels* have a very thin and wide blade and are used for cutting the pockets in the face of pulley stiles of sash frames.

Gouges are chisels with curved cutting edges; the cutting edge may be ground on the hollow or on the rounded surface. Fig. 3 shows an *outside-ground gouge*.

The *axe* is used for cutting wedges and for rough carpentry work.

Use of Planes

Planes (Fig. 4) are used for the preparation of plane surfaces after the timber has been sawn; they are made either of wood or metal. The planes most in use are the *jack plane*, used for roughing off; the *trying plane*, for trueing up; and the *smoothing plane*, for finishing the surface.

A wooden plane consists of a stock, generally of beechwood, into which is fixed the plane or cutting iron by means of a wedge. To the face of the cutting iron is fixed the *back iron*. This is done by a brass nut fixed to the iron to receive the screw. The back iron stiffens the cutting iron, and also serves to break the shaving as it is cut and bend it over and so prevent choking.

The cutting edge of the jack plane should be slightly convex; for the smoothing and try plane irons the edge should be straight, with the corners slightly rounded. The accuracy and smoothness of planed surfaces will, of course, depend upon the condition in which the plane is kept.

Other planes used by the joiner are the *rebate plane*, used for forming rebates; *plough plane*, used for forming grooves with the grain; *hollow* and *round planes*, used for producing convex and concave surfaces; *router* or *old woman's tooth*, used for cleaning out trenches to the required depth; and the *bead plane*, used for forming a half-round mould with a sinking called a quirk.

The *spokeshave* is used on working circular work having quick curves.

A *fillister* is a rebate plane with an adjustable fence; the depth of the rebate can be regulated by a stop, and a side cutter marks out the rebate in front of the cutting iron.

Metal Planes. Most of the wooden planes described above are also obtainable in metal, or a combination of wood and steel. The advantage of these over wooden planes lies in the fact that the sole does not wear and therefore gives more accurate results, especially on hardwood. Again, in these planes the cutter is held in position by means either of a screw or a lever which gives easier and more accurate adjustment.

Other planes are the metal *smoothing plane*, *bullsnose plane*, and the *block plane*; the latter is used for small work.

Types of Boring Tools

Boring Tools (Fig. 5). The *bradawl* and *gimlet* are the simplest kinds of boring tools. The bradawl has a small steel wedge-shaped cutter and is chiefly used for boring for nails. The gimlet is used for small holes for the insertion of screws.

Brace and *Bits.* The brace is a handle to which is attached a cutter or bit used

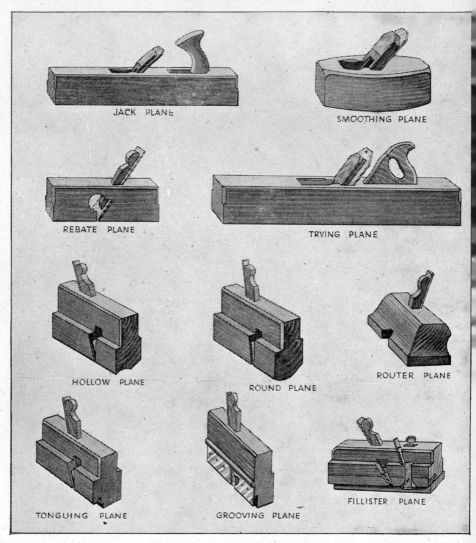

JACK PLANE

SMOOTHING PLANE

REBATE PLANE

TRYING PLANE

HOLLOW PLANE

ROUND PLANE

ROUTER PLANE

TONGUING PLANE

GROOVING PLANE

FILLISTER PLANE

CARPENTERS' AND JOINERS' PLANES

Fig. 4. Some of the types of wooden planes in common use. Most of these planes are also obtainable in metal. The last six planes illustrated here are not as much used as formerly.

for boring holes. Many different types of brace are in use, but the rachet type is perhaps the best, the turning movement being effected by a rack.

There are many varieties and sizes of bits. The *centre bit* varies in diameter from $\frac{1}{8}$ in. to $1\frac{1}{2}$ in. and is one of the tools most frequently employed for boring.

The *spoon* and *nose bits* are very similar; the latter is formed with a projecting nose which assists in clearing the hole. It is especially suitable for holes up to 3 in. deep. The *auger* or *twist bits* exist in many forms and produce holes which are cleaner and more accurate than those formed by the above varieties.

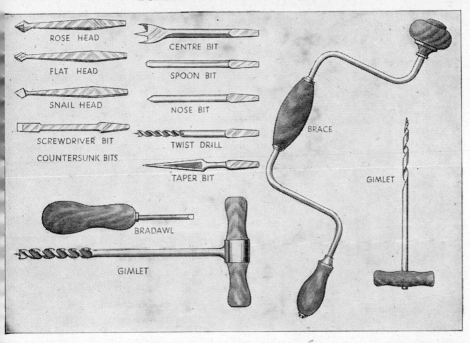

ROSE HEAD

FLAT HEAD

SNAIL HEAD

SCREWDRIVER BIT

COUNTERSUNK BITS

CENTRE BIT

SPOON BIT

NOSE BIT

TWIST DRILL

TAPER BIT

BRACE

GIMLET

BRADAWL

GIMLET

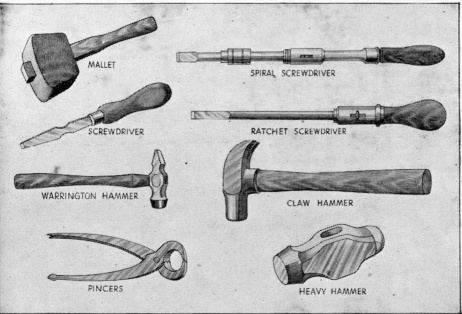

MALLET

SPIRAL SCREWDRIVER

SCREWDRIVER

RATCHET SCREWDRIVER

WARRINGTON HAMMER

CLAW HAMMER

PINCERS

HEAVY HAMMER

CARPENTERS' BORING AND IMPELLING TOOLS

Fig. 5 (above). The bradawl and gimlet are the simplest kinds of boring tools. The brace and various types of bit are also shown ; the taper bit is used particularly for enlarging holes.
Fig. 6 (below). The impelling tools consist of the mallet, the hammer and the screwdriver.

The *forstner bit* has a circular rim instead of a point. It is useful for flat-bottom and angular boring.

Expanding brace bits are provided with adjustable cutters of different sizes within certain limits.

Other brace bits such as *screwdriver bits, countersunk bits,* and *taper bits,* are also used.

Impelling tools (Fig. 6) include mallets, hammers and screwdrivers. The *mallet* is used for driving chisels, as it has greater driving effect and is less liable to injure the handles. The hammer shown in Fig. 6 is called the *Warrington hammer*; the head is made of cast steel weighing about 1 lb. The *claw hammer* is formed with a claw which is used for levering back or withdrawing nails. *Screwdrivers* are of two types: one, the fixed-blade type; and the other the increasingly popular ratchet-driver type.

MASONS' TOOLS AND APPLIANCES

LIFTING AND PLACING STONES. When blocks of stone become too heavy to be lifted by hand various appliances are employed. For lifting rough blocks a *sling chain* is passed round them. The chain has a ring at one end and a hook at the other which is passed through the ring and attached to the lifting gear. Sling chains are not suitable for dressed stones as the arrises are liable to be chipped unless slips of wood or sacking are used.

Dogs or *Chain Dogs.* Dogs are short irons with a bridle chain passing through the rings and are more suitable for lifting worked stone. When the pull of the crane is applied the chain tightens and draws the dogs together. A small hole is punched in each end of the stone to take the point of the dog, and is termed a dog hole. These holes are placed as far from the top as the dogs will allow.

Lewises. The ordinary lewis is an iron wedge, formed in three pieces, which fits into a corresponding hole in the top of the stone. In one design the two outside pieces are wedge shaped, the centre piece having its sides parallel. The wedge-shaped sides are inserted first and the centre piece next. The pieces are holed through the top to a shackle and pin.

In the other design the centre piece is wedge shaped and the two side pieces are parallel. These are connected at the top with transverse pieces to which they are hinged. The lewis should fit tight at the bottom of the hole and allowed a little freedom at the top.

Chain Lewises. For stones of light weight, chain lewises are used, as they are easier to fit. They consist of a pair of curved legs with a top ring. When the chain is drawn tight the legs are pressed against the sides of the hole. The hole is usually slightly undercut.

Lifting Pins. A pair of lifting pins consists of two cylindrical legs inserted into holes which are cut in the top surface of the block at an angle of 45 degrees towards the centre of the stone. The pins are connected up to the lifting gear by a bridle chain, which tends to pull the legs together at the top, causing them to grip the sides of the hole.

A lewising tool is used for cutting lewis holes, and the cutting edge is made slightly wider than the top portion.

Setting-out Appliances. The tools and appliances required for setting out the work are a 2-ft. rule and a straight-edge of wood with splayed edge.

Compasses (Fig. 7) are made in various sizes ranging from 6 in. up to 24 in. long, and formed with a graduated wing

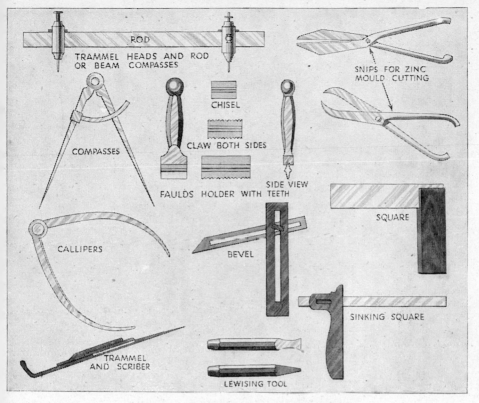

MASONS' TOOLS AND APPLIANCES (1)

Fig. 7. The mason requires many tools specially adapted to his trade. Some of them, chiefly for measuring, testing, and setting out, are shown above and others are seen in Figs. 8 and 9.

and clamp screw for setting the legs to any required opening.

Beam compasses, or *trammel heads,* and *rod* are used for setting out larger circles. *Snips* are used for cutting zinc moulds, together with *bradawls, scribes* and *files* for smoothing the edges of the moulds after cutting.

A *mason's square* is made of thin steel plate of various sizes. The stock is usually about two-thirds the length of the blade. A common size is 24 in. × 18 in. It is most essential that the blade be at right angles to the stock, otherwise serious difficulties will arise.

Sinking squares are used in sinkings where it is not possible to use the ordin-

ary square, and also for measuring depth. The stock is made of brass and is slotted for the blade, which is clamped at any position required.

Bevels or *shift stocks* are made of brass or steel plate. The blade is slotted and fitted to slide between the blades of the stocks, which are double. Fitted with a clamp screw, it can be set at any angle desired.

A *box trammel* consists of a wooden stock and a blade of $\frac{1}{4}$-in. square steel rod with the end turned down; it is used for drawing lines parallel to a circular finished face.

Other appliances are *straight-edges* made of wood with splay edge; *gauges,*

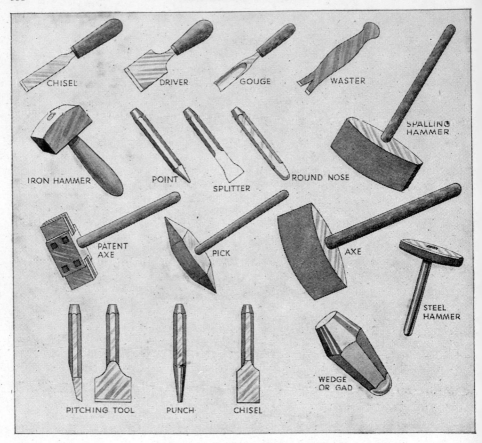

MASONS' HAMMERS AND CHISELS

Fig. 8. The wedge used for splitting blocks of stone, and some of the mason's cutting tools for giving different types of finish to the stones, are shown above.

pieces of wood about 1 in. square to gauge to ensure the height of each course of ashlar being the same; *templets* or *moulds*, usually made from sheet zinc No. 9 gauge, sometimes made in wood or stout paper; *reverses* for testing circular mouldings. *Snips* are used for cutting zinc moulds; and *scribers* are for marking lines on the stone. *Files* are for finishing the edges of moulds, and a *bradawl* for pricking the shape of the drawing through on to the zinc.

Wedges (Fig. 8) are used for coping or splitting blocks of freestone. A groove is cut along the top and two sides of the block of stone. Wedges are inserted at intervals of about 4 in. along the top. The block is then placed on an iron bar and the wedges driven in until the split occurs.

Splitting Granite

Plug and feathers (Fig. 9) are used for coping or splitting granite and are inserted into drilled holes. The hand drill for boring holes to split the granite has a $\frac{3}{4}$-in. bit and is made all in one piece of solid cast steel. The depth of the holes is 3 in. and they are about 4 in. apart. Then the feathers are put in and the plug is driven in until the split occurs.

Cutting Tools (Fig. 8). Masons' tools vary according to the hardness of the stone to be dressed. For hard freestone and granite we have the following:—

The *spalling hammer* is a two-handed tool used for spalling off waste stone previous to using a pitching tool. The head of the hammer is concave, which gives it a cutting edge. It weighs about 16 lb. to 30 lb. If there is only slight waste to be removed the mason would use a pitching tool and a hand hammer.

The *scabbling hammer* is somewhat smaller, weighing from 14 lb. to 20 lb. and formed with one spalling face and one pick or axe face. A *scabbling pick* has two pick faces. The *pitching tool* varies in width from $\frac{1}{2}$ in. for marble up to about 2 in. for the freestones.

Other hammers used by the masons are the *steel hand hammer* and the *iron hammer*. The hand hammer is about 7 in. long and weighs about 5 lb. or 6 lb. and

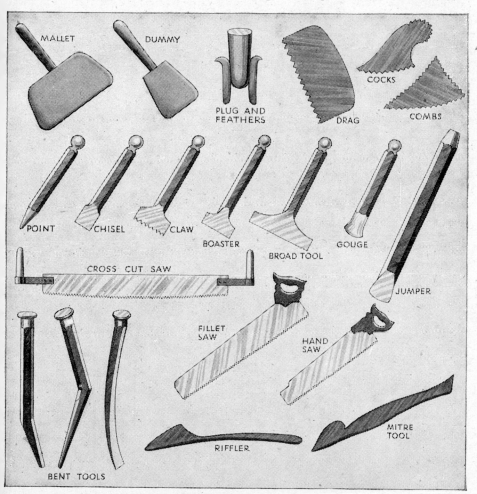

MASONS' TOOLS AND APPLIANCES (2)

Fig. 9. The plug and feathers are used for splitting granite. Various types of mallet and chisel, and several types of saw for use on soft stone, are also illustrated.

is used in conjunction with the pitching tool and punch. The iron hammer is used by marble masons and stone carvers for striking cup-headed tools. It weighs about 3 lb. or 4 lb.

The *axe* has a double-edged head about 8 in. or 9 in. long and is used to chop all round the drafts and to obtain a fairly smooth face.

The *patent axe* is used on granite after using the axe to produce an axed face. A four-bladed axe is used for the roughest patent axe work; a six-bladed axe is generally used for ordinary work, the finest being ten-cut work.

The box of this axe is in two parts, and there are four bolt holes in each for screwing up when the blades are put in.

The *pitching tool* has a flat edge, slightly bevelled, about $\frac{1}{4}$ in. thick by $\frac{1}{2}$ in. wide for marble, up to 2 in. wide for the freestones.

Mallets (Fig. 9) are generally made of beech and sometimes hickory. They are oval in shape and weigh about 5 lb. or 6 lb., and are used for striking mallet-headed tools when working freestone.

The *dummy* is usually made of zinc or lead and weighs about 3 lb. It is used for striking wooden-handled tools in working the softer freestones.

Chisels are classified as hammer-headed, mallet-headed and cup-headed.

The hammer-headed tools have simply a flat head slightly burred over with use. The mallet-headed tools are more common. They are formed with a slender neck and rounded head so as not to damage the mallet in working. These tools include the *drafter* or chisel about $\frac{1}{2}$ in. to 1 in. wide and are used for drafts, fillets, etc.; the *point*, used for removing superfluous material, is followed by the *tooth chisel* or *claw tool*, to reduce further the material to an almost level surface. The surface is then finished off with a *boaster*.

Where a tooled finish is required a *broad tool* is used. *Cup-headed tools* are of small size and are struck with the iron hammer.

Wooden-handled tools are used for the softer freestones, like Bath and Beer stone. They are the *drafting chisel*, about 1-in. cutting edge, and the *driver*, about 2 in. wide, which takes the place of a boaster; *gouges*, formed with a hollow cutting edge for working mouldings, and *drags*, used for finishing the softer freestones.

Cockscombs are similar to drags, but shaped so as to finish mouldings and mitres.

The saws used for softer freestones are the *cross-cut saw*, the *hand saw*, and the *fillet saw*.

PLASTERERS' TOOLS

THE tools used by the plasterer are rather numerous and consist mainly of trowels and rules.

Rules and *floats* (Fig. 10) of various forms and sizes are employed and should be made of well-seasoned pine free from knots. The *Derby* is an elongated float and has a blade 4 ft. to 8 ft. long, 4 in. or 5 in. wide, with two handles so arranged that they can be grasped by one operative; but more often worked by two men. The Derby is used for floating bays between the screeds and for scouring and levelling the surface of wall and ceiling plastering, both in the floating and setting coats as a preparatory labour to the finishing.

A *floating rule* varies from 8 ft. up to 20 ft. long and 4 in. to 6 in. wide; the back is tapered towards each end; it is used for forming screeds and also for

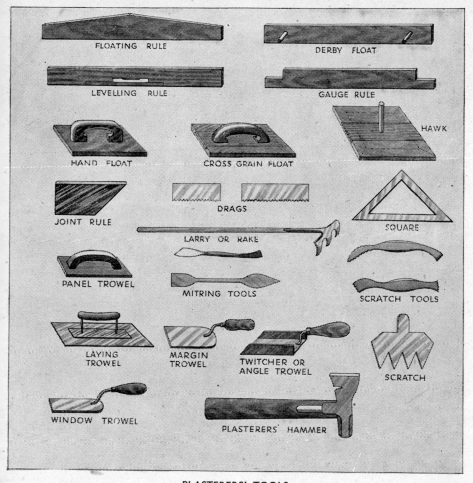

FLOATING RULE

DERBY FLOAT

LEVELLING RULE

GAUGE RULE

HAND FLOAT

CROSS GRAIN FLOAT

HAWK

JOINT RULE

DRAGS

SQUARE

LARRY OR RAKE

PANEL TROWEL

MITRING TOOLS

SCRATCH TOOLS

LAYING TROWEL

MARGIN TROWEL

TWITCHER OR ANGLE TROWEL

SCRATCH

WINDOW TROWEL

PLASTERERS' HAMMER

PLASTERERS' TOOLS

Fig. 10. A selection of the numerous special tools used by the plasterer. The illustration shows tools for applying the plaster, testing the surfaces, and for working the mitres of mouldings.

forming surfaces between the screeds. A *traversing rule* is a similar rule about 6 ft. long used for forming screeds in setting stuff. A *parallel rule* is used for setting out parallel lines. A *levelling rule* is made by fixing a wood fillet above the lower edge of a long parallel rule, on which a level may be placed for levelling soffits.

The *plumb rule* is similar to that used by bricklayers. *Joint rules* are usually made of a strip of steel 3 in. wide and $\frac{1}{8}$ in. thick, mounted in a hardwood stock. One end is cut to an acute angle, and this end and the edge are splayed so as to give a fine edge; these rules are used for forming mitres worked in position.

Hand floats also are in great variety. They are mostly formed in pine, except the panel or margin float. The ordinary hand float is about $10\frac{1}{2}$ in. by $4\frac{1}{2}$ in. and $\frac{3}{4}$ in. thick, with a handle at the back. The *cross-grain float* is similar but a little longer and thicker and cut with the grain across the float. It is formed with a dovetailed groove at the back into which a hardwood key, carrying the handle, is inserted, which keeps the wood from warping. It is used for scouring the setting coat after the work has been ruled off with the Derby.

A *skimming float* is similar to a hand float but 12 in. to 14 in. long and $\frac{1}{2}$ in. thick, and is used for laying the setting coat prior to laying off with the steel trowel; in this case the grain of the wood is parallel to the handle. *Panel* or *margin floats* are usually made of beech about 6 in. $\times$ 3 in. $\times$ $\frac{1}{2}$ in. thick, and, as their name implies, are used for finishing small panels where a larger tool could not be worked.

The *plasterer's hammer*, or *lath hammer*, has a wooden handle with a steel head. In addition to the driving head, the other end is formed as an axe for cutting and fixing laths, and has a slot on the lower edge for withdrawing nails.

The *hawk* is used for gauging small portions of stuff. It is a piece of pine about 12 in. square and $\frac{5}{8}$ in. thick with a round central handle on its underside.

Scratch tools have a shaft with a tool at each end, which are serrated or formed like saw teeth, and are used for carving, working the mitres of mouldings, and cleaning up enrichments. The *scratch* or

birch broom is made from a piece of pine 14 in. long, 7 in. wide and $\frac{1}{2}$ in. thick. One end is shaped, the other cut into teeth about 3 in. long and the points about $1\frac{1}{4}$ in. apart. Sometimes three or four laths are fixed side by side and their ends pointed. The scratch is used for scoring surfaces to provide a key.

The *twitcher* or *angle trowel* is 2 in. or 3 in. wide; its sides stand up at right angles to the blade which allows it to be run up internal angles and smooth both faces of the return at the same time.

Larries or *rakes* are three-prong rakes with a long wooden handle used for mixing hair with coarse stuff.

Trowels for laying and finishing the setting coats are of various shapes and sizes for different classes of work. The *laying trowel* is a rectangular sheet of steel about $10\frac{1}{2}$ in. $\times$ 5 in., the handles being supported either by one or two steel shanks. The *panel trowel* is similar but the blade is very springy. The *gauging trowel* is made in various sizes; it is used for gauging small quantities of stuff on the hawk and for laying stuff on mouldings.

The *steel square* is a triangle of steel having one angle a right angle and the remaining two 45 degrees. Other tools used by the plasterer are brushes, compasses, callipers, drags, planes, gauges, chisels, files, rasps, spirit level, and saws.

PAINTERS' TOOLS

P AINTER's tools (Fig. 11) consist principally of knives and brushes required in preparing the work for distempering and painting, and the repainting of existing paintwork, and those used in connection with betterclass work as stippling, graining, varnishing, lettering and signwriting.

All nail holes are stopped by the use of the *putty* or *stopping knife*, and all

irregularities of surface by using the *filling* or *broad knife* or for scraping if necessary. Paint is removed with a *stripping knife*, or a *blow lamp*, and old paper after wetting, with a *chisel knife*.

Dusting brushes are used for removing dust on the previous coats. *Sand* or *glass paper* is used for rubbing down the work previous to each coat.

Distemper brushes are either a narrow

flat brush, or a two-knot brush about 4 in. to 6 in. wide, and varying in weight up to 12 oz., but 8 oz. may be considered a fair weight. These brushes are either pure or mixed bristle and are held together by copper wire or a flat copper band. Wider brushes, known as Lancashire pattern, are used in the

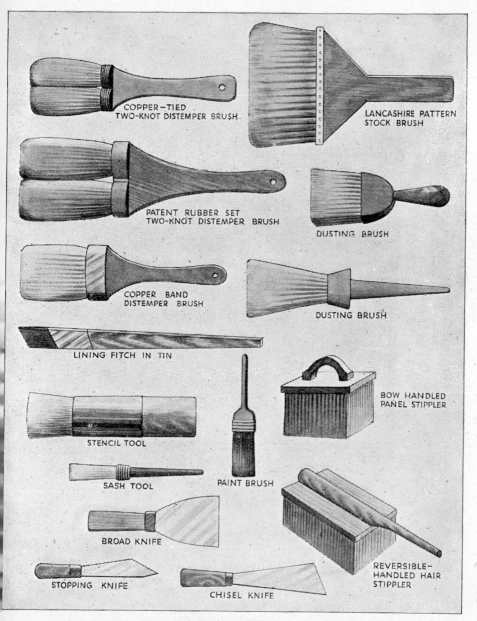

COPPER–TIED TWO-KNOT DISTEMPER BRUSH.

LANCASHIRE PATTERN STOCK BRUSH

PATENT RUBBER SET TWO-KNOT DISTEMPER BRUSH

DUSTING BRUSH

COPPER BAND DISTEMPER BRUSH

DUSTING BRUSH

LINING FITCH IN TIN

STENCIL TOOL

BOW HANDLED PANEL STIPPLER

SASH TOOL

PAINT BRUSH

BROAD KNIFE

STOPPING KNIFE

CHISEL KNIFE

REVERSIBLE-HANDLED HAIR STIPPLER

PAINTERS' TOOLS

Fig. 11. A selection of various types of brushes and other special tools used by the painter.

north. These brushes are about 8 in. in width. Old distemper brushes are known as *stock brushes*.

The *paint brush* is known as a one-knot ground brush; it is made with pure or mixed bristle and bound with copper wire. Similar brushes are the *oval* and *round ground brushes* in various sizes. The *sash tool* is string bound and is used for cutting in paint to sashes.

Lines are run with a *lining* or *angle fitch* flat in section, and bound in tin ferrules, a thin bevelled lath being used as a guide. Fitches in various sizes,

round or flat in section, are used for decorating and signwriting.

Stipplers are brushes with a flat piece of wood to which a handle is attached, and shaped so as to allow the fingers to grip it firmly. The handle may be fixed or reversible, and the brushes are made in a variety of sizes. A new pattern is made of rubber. For small work a *stencil tool* is substituted.

Over-grainer and *graining combs* are used for grained work.

Varnish brushes are oval in section and are made with white bristle.

SLATERS' TOOLS

THE tools used by the slater are few in number. They are required for trimming and fixing slates and for repairing roofs when necessary. The *zax* (Fig. 12) is the tool used for trimming slates; it consists of a blade fixed in a wooden handle. The *cutting* or *dressing*

iron is simply a long iron edge with two spikes at the back so that they can be driven into a wood block.

The slate to be dressed is rested on a *cutting iron* and allowed to overhang by the amount to be cut off. Then with a series of sharp blows the material not

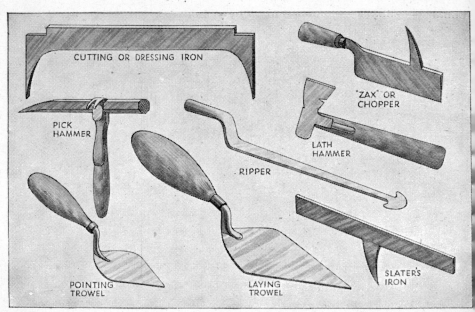

SLATERS' TOOLS

Fig 12. The special tools used by the slater are few in number, and most of these are illustrated above.

required is removed. The size of the slate required is measured with a *gauge stick* or *scantle*. At the back of the zax is a projecting spike which serves to mark the position of the nail holes, and afterwards the holes are made by two sharp blows. Usually the holes are made on the building site by the use of a *holing machine*.

The *hammer* has a broad head for driving nails, a spike at the other end for holing slates if necessary, and a claw at one side by which nails can be withdrawn.

For repairing roofs a tool termed a *ripper* is used; it consists of a long metal arm fixed in a wooden handle at one end, and provided at the other with a cross-piece which forms a hook on each side of the arm and a cutting edge at the back. When a slate has to be removed, the ripper is passed up between the slates and round the nail by which the slate is fixed; on forcibly withdrawing the ripper, it cuts off the head of the nail and so allows the slate to be removed

Other materials used by the slater are the *chalk line* and *rods* and two *trowels*; also *knee caps* and a *deep belt* with a pocket to hold the nails.

PLUMBERS' TOOLS

THE following are illustrations and descriptions of some of the tools used by the plumber (Figs. 13 and 14).

Dressers vary in shape and size and can be obtained in various kinds of wood, the two chief kinds being hornbeam and boxwood; the former is used for general work and the latter for finishing. The handle by which they are grasped should be well pitched to free the knuckles of the user, and the sides and face should not have sharp edges.

The *step setter* or *setting-in stick* is similar, but the underside has a groove, which fits over the lead in setting or bending the top of the steps in step flashings.

Mallets are made in various sizes and usually in boxwood; they are used for bossing lead.

Bending sticks, which are made of boxwood, are broad and slightly rounded on the face in length and width, and are chiefly used for driving lead when making bends in pipes. *Bossing sticks* are similar in shape to a bending stick but they are narrower and more rounded; they are used for working lead round rolls, and into the corners of gutters.

The *plumber's hammer* has a head for driving nails, and the nose is brought to a thin edge, which is used for running between edges that are to be soldered. *Chase wedges* are made in various shapes and sizes, and are known as *side-bent* or *front-bent* according to their shape, whilst *driving wedges* are quite straight.

Dummies are lumps of lead formed on the end of a straight or curved piece of iron, and shaped; they are used for taking dents out of pipes. Where the handle is straight it is usually of malacca cane.

The *drift plate* is a small rectangular steel plate with a curved projecting piece at one end to facilitate insertion and withdrawal, and is used to prevent movement in the working back of overcloaks in lead-covered roofs. This is owing to the fact that lead will not slide on lead.

Mandrils are used for passing through lengths of pipes to remove any indentations, thus leaving the pipe true and cylindrical. They are slightly smaller in diameter than the pipe, and slightly tapered to allow for withdrawal. *Bobbins* are turned balls of boxwood, semi-oval

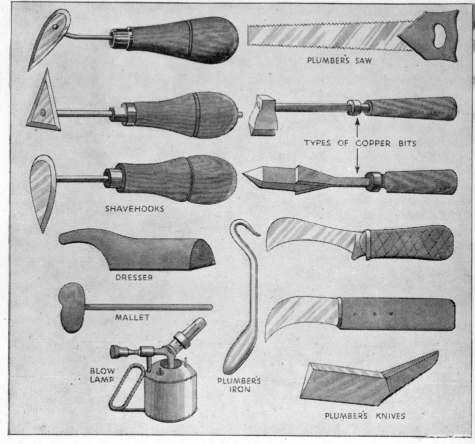

PLUMBERS' TOOLS (I)

Fig. 13. Some of the varied tools used by the plumber are shown above and others are in Fig. 14.

in shape, which are placed in pipes that are to be bent.

To drive the bobbin round a bend a *follower* of the same shape, or a *bobbin weight* is used, a cord passing through the bobbin and fixed in the weight by means of a knot. *Turnpins* are conical pieces of wood used for enlarging the ends of pipes.

Knives are of three kinds: the *clasp knife*, a pocket knife with a single pointed blade hinged to a sheath handle; the *draw knife* with a handle 3 ft. long used for cutting up lead (a cord is passed through the blade as it

requires two men to use this knife); the *hacking knife*, for removing putty. The *bending bolt* or *pin* is a curved piece of wood used in forming openings for branch joints and sometimes for bending. *Shavehooks* are used for taking thin shavings from surfaces of leadwork in preparation for soldering. *Ladles*, of various sizes and formed with a lip on both sides for pouring, are used for carrying liquid lead or solder as required.

The *soldering* or *plumbing iron* is an oval-shaped bulb of iron with a crook handle used for heating solder, but it is now almost entirely replaced by the blow lamp.

Copper bits or *soldering irons* are pieces of copper of various shapes and of suitable sizes fixed to an iron holder which in turn has a wooden handle. Two types generally used are the *straight bit* and the *hatchet bit*. They are used for tinning brass work ready for soldering or wiping to lead pipe.

Plumber's saws are formed tapering with a double edge, the teeth being coarser on one side than the other.

Snips, used for cutting sheet metal.

Step Turner. This useful tool is used for turning the upper edge of step flashings into the brickwork joints. This tool can be made by the plumber himself.

Other equipment includes: rasps, straight-edge, steel square, 2-ft. rule, scribing gauges and solder pot.

Power Tools

In addition to the craftsmen's tools used in the various trades which have been already described, there are many other appliances that could be classed as tools: joiner's cramps, for instance; but they are more in the nature of equipment and are normally the property of the employer. In America, and to a considerable extent in this country, portable machine tools are also used. These are hand-power tools, usually driven off the ordinary electric supply in the same way as a vacuum cleaner. The portable hand circular saw is the most common, but sanding machines and boring tools are also in general use.

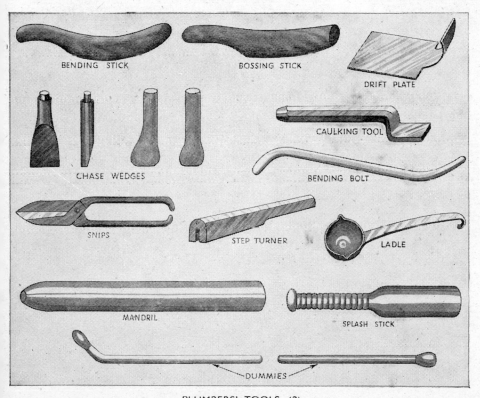

PLUMBERS' TOOLS (2)

Fig. 14. Further selection of the various tools which are peculiar to the plumbing trade.

CHAPTER 11

DRAUGHTSMANSHIP

Reading drawings. Equipment. Using drawing instruments. Drawing to scale. Sketching. Projections: orthographic, isometric. Perspective. Oblique projection. Axonometric drawings. Photography. General instructions. Lay-out plan. Copying drawings. Practical geometry. Plans. Detail drawings. Conventional representation. Lettering. Reproduction of drawings. Reducing and enlarging.

EVERY student of building construction must have a knowledge of draughtsmanship, so that he can thoroughly understand and "read" all types of drawings and, in addition, express his own ideas clearly by freehand sketching or by scale drawings. The ability to draw can be obtained by constant practice and the subject can be extended to cover all types of pictorial representation according to the interest and skill of the draughtsman.

Importance of Reading Drawings

To read drawings correctly demands a sound knowledge of methods of construction and the ability to use a variety of scales. Drawings executed to scale by the aid of instruments must be accurate in detail and clearly defined.

It will be recognized from the examination of first-class plans that each draughtsman displays variation of treatment according to taste, but in all cases the aim is to convey as much information as possible in some easily recognized manner.

PENCILS. Elementary matters in drawing are important and the learner should consider carefully the type of instruments and drawing material. Use good pencils nicely sharpened to a long point. For work completed in pencil an HB is hard enough and suitable for most purposes. Pencils are made in varying degrees from 3B, 2B, B, HB, and F to 6H. Bs indicate softness, Hs hardness, and HBs and Fs are intermediate grades.

DRAWING PAPER. Satisfactory work can be produced on good quality cartridge paper. There is, however, a variation in quality and the main point is to select the grade best suited for the work in hand. "Whatman" is a high-grade paper prepared in a variety of surfaces.

Half Imperial sheets, 22 in. × 15 in., are convenient and suitable sizes for general work. Other standard sizes are named as follows: Antiquarian, 53 in. × 31 in.; Double Elephant, 40 in. × 27 in.; Imperial, 30 in. × 22 in.; Royal, 24 in. × 19 in.; Medium, 22 in. × 17½ in.

TRACING PAPER AND TRACING LINEN. Tracing paper can be purchased in a variety of sizes and grades. Its use is helpful in solving problems by tracing from the original a portion of the work for further correction. Constant repetition of such an act may be required before the best solution of the problem is obtained. Detail paper is not so transparent as tracing paper; it is more suitable for large-size details and quite satisfactory for pen or pencil and colours.

Tracing linen is mostly used for tracing from original work when a negative is required for frequent or constant handling, being much stronger than paper. The surface requires preparing by lightly rubbing with French chalk because of its greasy nature. A rubber will also prepare the surface for the application of pen work, but this method is rather laborious. Colour may be applied quite easily by mixing with a little ox-gall or soap.

DRAWING BOARD AND TEE-SQUARE. Drawing boards are obtainable in standard sizes to suit the various sizes of paper. The tee-square extends across the full length of the board. It is used along the left-hand side for all horizontal lines, whilst set-squares are used in position on the blade of the tee-square (Fig. 1).

When using the tee-square keep the stock pressed firmly against the edge of the drawing board and move up or down with the aid of both hands. Never use a knife against the true edge of the tee-square for cutting paper. Once the edge of the blade is spoilt by such carelessness it is useless for accurate work. For working purposes it is usual to raise the back edge of the drawing board.

SET-SQUARES. The 45-degree and 60-degree types of set-square with 6-in. to 8-in. sides are generally preferred. They are manufactured in hardwood, pearwood or celluloid and with solid or open centres. Celluloid open-type set-squares are nice to work with, but care must be exercised to avoid the ink flooding, which will occur once the ink touches the edge of the celluloid. In use, the edge of the set-square is placed so as to make the best use of the light.

Essential Drawing Instruments

The following drawing instruments are essential: (a) drawing pen ; (b) dividers ; (c) compasses with extension bar for use with pen or pencil.

The drawing pen is the most used instrument and one about 5 in. long

Fig. I. The correct method of using the drawing board, tee-square, and set-square. The tee-square extends across the full length of board.

with ivory handle is a convenient size, although it is entirely a matter of taste. Keep the instruments clean after use and replace them in the case or wallet. The latter is useful for carrying about. Some useful drawing instruments are shown in Fig. 2.

FIXED INKS AND COLOURS. Fixed black Indian ink is indispensable. It is obtainable in $\frac{1}{2}$-oz., $\frac{3}{4}$-oz., and 1-oz. bottles with quill for feeding the pens. By "fixed" is meant the waterproof quality which is so necessary with colour work. Coloured inks can be obtained in all shades, and blue and red colours are essential. Paints are obtainable in many forms, and sticks are a convenient type for use with a nest of saucers.

The most suitable colours are gamboge, burnt sienna, Hookers' green, crimson lake, vermilion, sepia, Vandyke brown, Prussian blue, cobalt blue, ivory black and Payne's grey. It is convenient to remember that the three primary colours, yellow, red and blue, can be used in combination to make purple, green and orange. For instance: red mixed with blue produces purple; blue

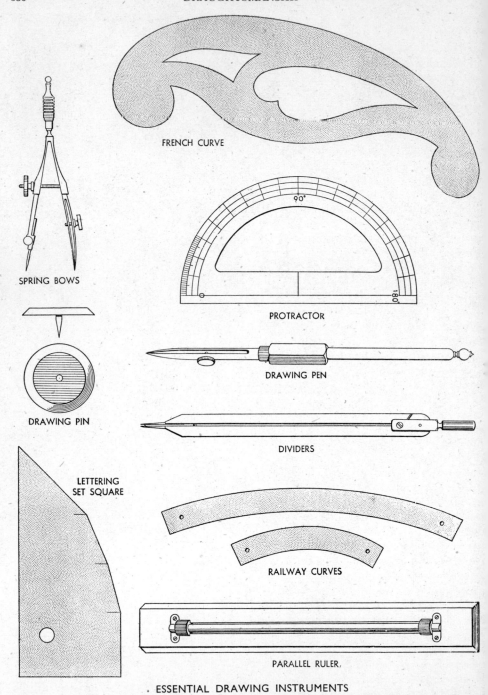

FRENCH CURVE

SPRING BOWS

PROTRACTOR

DRAWING PIN

DRAWING PEN

DIVIDERS

LETTERING
SET SQUARE

RAILWAY CURVES

PARALLEL RULER.

ESSENTIAL DRAWING INSTRUMENTS

Fig. 2. A group of the drawing instruments with the use of which every draughtsman must become familiar. They should always be kept in good condition and cleaned after use

mixed with yellow produces green; red mixed with yellow produces orange; and so on to form other different tints.

BRUSHES. The best brushes are most economical. A good sable or camel-hair brush lasts a long time, and will not pluck, as so often occurs with the cheap type. Thoroughly rinse the brushes after use.

A good soft rubber, a protractor, stencils, a set of scales, and domed-head drawing pins complete the equipment.

Drawing to Scale

Drawings bear some proportion to the actual object, and this proportion is known as the scale of the drawing. Scales are required to construct drawings and those generally adopted for building work are as follows: $\frac{1}{8}$ in. and $\frac{1}{16}$ in. for general building drawings; $\frac{1}{4}$ in., $\frac{1}{2}$ in., $\frac{3}{4}$ in., 1 in., $1\frac{1}{2}$ in. and 3 in. for detail work; 1/500th and 1/2,500th for site plans.

Useful lengths are 6-in. and 12-in. ivory or boxwood scales with the divisions relative to each scale on separate edges. Compound scales with several scales all on one length lead to confusion and error. Good eyesight and care are required to mark off the dimension from the scale in order to produce an accurate and skilful drawing.

Where dimensions are not figured there is an implied undertaking by the draughtsman that the drawings have been made with all proper care; and particularly where figured dimensions are given, the measurements so defined are always accepted in preference to the scaled dimension along the same line, but quite obviously they should agree.

The ability to read plans also requires a knowledge of mensuration and the use of scales for measuring drawings which lack detail. Sometimes the dimensions of joinery, sizes of rooms and openings, are not figured on the plan. Where this

is so, a size can be built up from figured or known sizes. The learner will, however, realize the importance of always stating the scale of a drawing and providing a scale on the plan.

The main object of drawing to scale is to explain to the contractor as clearly as possible the type and construction of a building. The drawings are prepared with a view to showing all the important details fully dimensioned. In addition, the nature of the materials is indicated by special conventional markings of colour, by hatching and by printed notes.

The most widely used scale for small dwelling-houses and similar designs is perhaps the scale of 8 ft. to the inch. A certain amount of *detailing* is usually required to $\frac{1}{2}$-in. and $\frac{1}{4}$-in. scale to simplify the foreman's work (Fig. 3).

Such details as floors, walls, roofs, fittings and pipe ducts can be clearly shown in this manner. The main object is to explain clearly the construction of the building by drawing to a large scale in order to avoid any doubt as to what is required.

It will be appreciated, therefore, that detailed work demands a thorough knowledge of building construction and materials. The draughtsman must adopt dimensions which suit the standard sizes (if any) of the materials to be employed, e.g., bricks, timber and scantlings; otherwise numerous queries will arise while the job is in progress.

Constructing a Scale

Suppose, for example, a scale of $1\frac{1}{2}$ in. to the foot is required. Draw a horizontal line any length (Fig. 3A) and mark off a number of divisions, each $1\frac{1}{2}$ in. long. The first division at the left-hand side has now to be subdivided into twelve equal parts for the purpose of representing the inches.

This is done by drawing a line at a convenient length in a downward

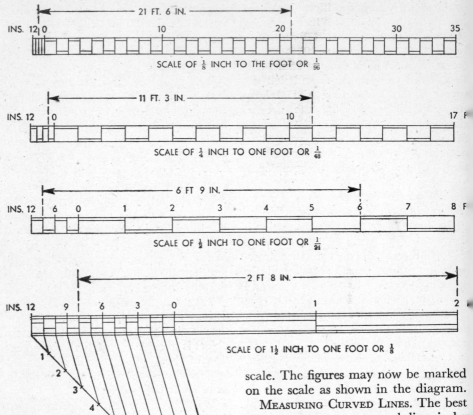

SCALE OF $\frac{1}{8}$ INCH TO THE FOOT OR $\frac{1}{96}$

SCALE OF $\frac{1}{4}$ INCH TO ONE FOOT OR $\frac{1}{48}$

SCALE OF $\frac{1}{2}$ INCH TO ONE FOOT OR $\frac{1}{24}$

SCALE OF 1$\frac{1}{2}$ INCH TO ONE FOOT OR $\frac{1}{8}$

Fig. 3. The scales most widely used in drawing for building work. A certain amount of detailing is usually included in $\frac{1}{4}$-in. and $\frac{1}{2}$-in. scales. **Fig. 3a** (below) shows the method of constructing a scale of 1$\frac{1}{2}$ in. to one foot.

direction from the left-hand end of the horizontal line and making an angle of about 45 degrees. Next divide this line into twelve equal divisions.

Draw a straight line to the end of the first division on the horizontal line, and from all the remaining points draw lines parallel to the first line so that they cut the horizontal line into twelve equal parts to represent the inches on the

scale. The figures may now be marked on the scale as shown in the diagram.

MEASURING CURVED LINES. The best way to measure a curved line is by taking the spring bow dividers set to a small opening, and by stepping along the curved line it is quite a simple matter to transfer the number of steps to a straight line. Next measure the straight line with the scale of the drawing and the distance will represent the length of the curved line.

Another method, although not so accurate, is as follows: Take a length of paper and sweep the edge round the curve by commencing from one end. This is done by fixing the paper by means of a pencil point in various positions along the curved line until the end of the curved line is reached and marked. The length of the line so marked on the paper is measured by the method which is shown in Fig. 4.

FREEHAND DRAWING. The ability to make freehand sketches is most valuable for explanatory purposes (Fig. 5). The sketches may also form the framework around which a finished drawing is to be built. The draughtsman draws a definite plan and makes sure that it is correct in every detail for working purposes.

The difference between the freehand sketch and a true to scale drawing is generally one of finish. A sketch only requires a few minutes' work merely to indicate or suggest the principal features of the object, while a scale drawing

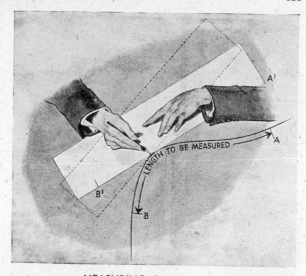

MEASURING CURVED LINES

Fig. 4. The distance on the curve AB is transferred to the straight paper edge A^1B^1 and scaled.

AN EXAMPLE OF FREEHAND DRAWING

Fig. 5. This sketch shows the value of freehand drawing for explanatory purposes

PERSPECTIVE SKETCH

Fig. 6. Another example of freehand drawing, though some lines are put in with drawing instruments for convenience.

orthographic (or right-angled) projection. It is a method most frequently used and represents surfaces with the various points projected at right angles to the planes of projection. The plan is really a horizontal section as it would appear by looking down on the building with the surfaces of all floors, wall thicknesses and other constructional parts exposed to view.

It may be necessary to draw a number of plans if the building contains more than one storey. Plans usually required are those named as follows: Foundation plan, ground-floor plan, first-floor plan, second-floor plan, and so on, to roof plan. In the case of semi-detached houses and terraced houses it is permissible to draw, for example, the first-floor plan adjacent to the ground-floor plan and so utilize the space that would normally repeat the ground-floor information already imparted. The reader should again refer to the plans shown in Chapter 1.

Vertical sections referring to lines on the plans are used to show internal features ; and elevations, to convey external form and design, are necessary to complete the information which a working drawing should convey.

Elevations are either referred to points of the compass, or named front, side, back, etc.

ISOMETRIC DRAWING. This method of drawing is a form of pictorial projection where three straight lines make equal angles to one another, with one line vertical at a meeting point. The length,

indicates particulars in accurate detail.

It is always advisable to carry a small book and a pencil when out of doors. Any object of building interest such as that in Fig. 6 should be jotted down. In addition to giving excellent practice in freehand drawing, these sketches are extremely valuable for future reference. At this point, therefore, the learner should get down to serious practice in sketching, and by observation, individual thought, and initiative, he will acquire competent ability.

ORTHOGRAPHIC PROJECTION. The representation of objects by plans, elevations, and sections is known as

breadth and height are measured along the three axes and it is possible to build an excellent drawing showing clearly all constructional details. As the drawing is not in perspective it will appear a little distorted, but this is a small point compared with the advantages of being able to scale the three dimensions, length, breadth and depth and the ease with which the drawing can be produced.

The three lines, each enclosing an angle of 120 degrees, can be rapidly constructed by the aid of the tee-square and one set-square with angles of 30 degrees and 60 degrees as follows:—

At the selected meeting point o place the set-square in position and draw a line 30 degrees to the left, then turn the set-square over on its same base and draw a line 30 degrees to the right. From o draw a vertical line in a downward direction. It is obvious that the three lines are equally inclined to one another with each pair enclosing an angle of 120 degrees. The height is measured off to scale on the vertical line from point o. Likewise the width is scaled along the line towards the left measured from o and the length is scaled along the remaining lines.

The solid form can now be constructed by drawing the other sides from the new points parallel with the existing. Fig. 7 is an isometric drawing which clearly indicates the main principles of construction. A more detailed drawing is simply an extension of these principles. Learners are advised to study and practise this form of drawing, as it forms part of their equipment in explaining details in a most interesting fashion.

PERSPECTIVE DRAWING. This method of drawing is the art of representing objects as they appear to the eye and in the same way as they would appear in

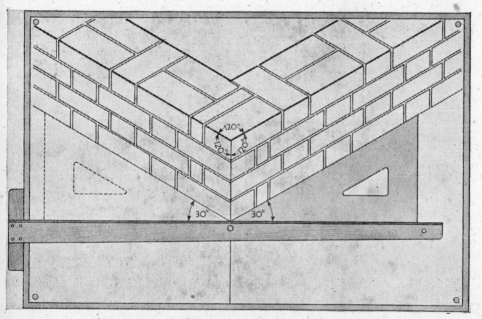

ISOMETRIC PROJECTION

Fig. 7. An isometric drawing by the aid of tee-square and set-square which clearly indicates the main principles of this extremely useful method of projection.

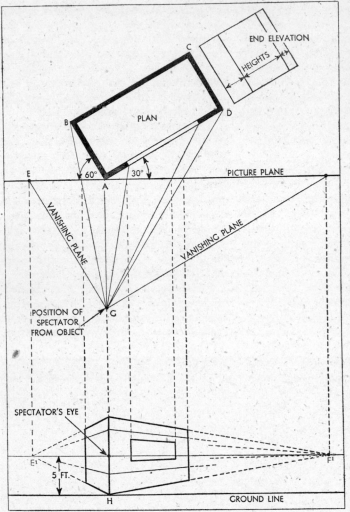

SETTING UP A PERSPECTIVE DRAWING

Fig. 8. The rules of perspective are not difficult to apply, and the method of setting up a perspective is shown above, and explained in the text.

at this position a building extending the whole breadth of the road would so diminish in size as to appear a mere point or line. For practical purposes the observer stands very much closer to the object for making a good perspective drawing. The position greatly depends on taste, but a little drawing practice will soon show that some positions give better perspectives than others.

The rules of perspective are not difficult to apply. The method of setting up a perspective sufficient for general purposes can be followed by reference to Fig. 8. Let $ABCD$ represent the plan of a building. G is the position of the spectator in front of the picture plane EF. Draw EG and GF parallel to the sides of the building AB and AD respectively. Next draw a ground line and then draw another line E^1F^1 parallel to it at about the height of the spectator's eye, which may be taken at 5 ft. The vanishing points E^1 and F^1 are found by dropping lines vertically from the points E and F. The height of the building is set up at HJ. Join H and J to their respective vanishing points E^1

a photograph. For example, if a person stands in the centre of a long road, which is horizontal, perfectly straight and of uniform breadth, the sides appear to approach closer and closer to each other as they recede from the observer at the height of the eye.

On a long road the sides at the farthest end would seem to meet, and

and F^1; then the extent of the sides of the building can be defined by drawing BG and DG to cut the picture plane as shown in the diagram and by dropping verticals from such points on the picture plane to outline the building. Such details as doors, windows, plinths and other features are filled in on similar lines.

For the purpose of a simple perspective drawing it is assumed that the nearest angle of the object touches the picture plane EF. In this case the plan makes angles of 30 degrees and 60 degrees with the picture plane. Many variations may be tried, but the learner is advised to study the principles applied in the diagram which are sufficient to produce a good perspective drawing. Fig. 8a illustrates what is meant by picture plane and point of sight.

OBLIQUE PROJECTION. This is a method used to show three sides of an object in the same drawing. It is a suitable method for rectangular objects, which show the main face as it appears in elevation, and the two adjacent sides at an oblique angle of 45 degrees. These sides appear out of proportion because they are drawn parallel to one another, but the drawing has the advantage of showing length, breadth and thickness (Fig. 9).

Improving the Proportion

A modification of this method of drawing to improve the proportion can be obtained by showing the object to half-scale oblique projection. The elevation is drawn as before to a particular scale and the sides are measured at half the scale. This method improves the appearance of the drawing, but the situation is complicated by the introduction of two scales. Extra care and attention are therefore required if mistakes are to be avoided while working under these more difficult conditions

Fig. 8a. If one looks through a window (picture plane) at an object, then the rays of light joining eye to object penetrate the window; these penetration points define the perspective of the object on the surface of the glass.

AXONOMETRIC DRAWINGS. In scheming the arrangement and appearance of a building and its equipment for the purpose of showing the future work to a client, it is most useful to know how to prepare axonometric drawings. This type of drawing will explain the relative positions of all rooms based on the particulars which the client will already have conveyed to the designer.

The word "axonometric" means a form of pictorial drawing in which the plan of the building is turned through an angle of 30 degrees to 45 degrees, with the horizontal and the vertical lines drawn to scale to show the front and side views (Fig. 10).

PHOTOGRAPHY. The camera and a knowledge of its use can be of immense

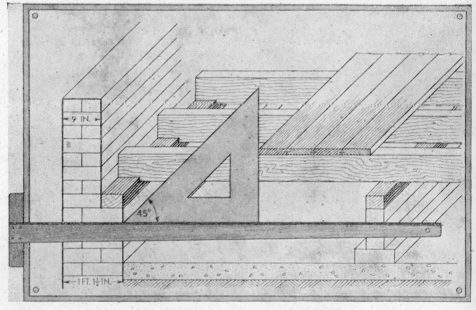

EXAMPLE OF OBLIQUE PROJECTION

Fig. 9. This method shows three sides of an object in the same drawing, i.e., the main face as it appears in elevation and the two adjacent sides at an angle of, say, 45 degrees.

valuc as an aid to the study of architecture and building construction. Many useful details of the various stages of building work can thus be recorded, and every opportunity should be taken of securing such records.

Photography, like sketching, can assist the student in his studies; consequently the camera forms an indispensable part of his equipment. It is not always possible to find time to sketch details of interest, but with the aid of the camera, it will be appreciated that this form of pictorial representation has much to recommend it.

General Drawing Instructions

SECURING THE DRAWING PAPER. The paper can be fastened on the board by drawing pins or by paste. The latter method is done in the following manner: Having cut the paper to the size required, damp the back of it with a sponge soaked in clean water, passing it well over the whole area several times until the water is absorbed. With the paper lying flat apply a rim of paste round the edge, about an inch wide, and then turn the paper upside down and press the pasted border firmly to the drawing board.

The next step is to wet the face of the paper in the centre, taking care not to cover the border. When the material has dried out the surface will be taut and suitable for use. When completed the drawing can be cut over leaving the pasted edge on the drawing board.

USING A PENCIL. In drawing a line hold the pencil almost vertically and move from left to right. Use the pencil lightly along the ruling edge so that a line of regular thickness is produced. Accurate work can only be done with a sharp-pointed pencil. It is useless using a dull point. Finally, touch the drawing up by erasing superfluous marks with the rubber.

USING THE INK. If ready-made Indian ink is used, a few simple hints will not be out of place. Keep the quill attached to the cork in a clean condition and when not in use keep the bottle properly corked.

Do not forget this precaution on each occasion when it is necessary to refill the ruling pen by means of the quill.

Should the quill become damaged it will be found that the ruling pen can be filled easily by the use of an ordinary pen dipped into the Indian ink. If preferred good Indian ink can be rubbed up from a stick in a saucer. It must be sufficiently mixed to produce a dense black colour. As Indian ink thickens when exposed to the air, it is necessary to clean out the ruling pen after use.

USING THE RULING PEN. Before inking

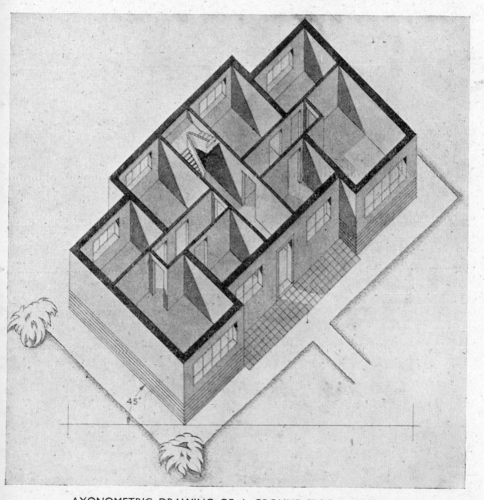

AXONOMETRIC DRAWING OF A GROUND-FLOOR INTERIOR

Fig. 10. This is a pictorial method of showing the general appearance of a building and its equipment; it makes use of the actual plan turned at an angle to the tee-square.

in try the pen out on a piece of spare paper until the pen is set to give neat even lines of the required thickness. The pen must be properly held in the right hand almost perpendicularly, with the forefinger resting outwards on the thumb-screw. Next draw the pen from left to right by sliding against the ruling edge and by using the little finger on the same edge to steady the hand. Curved lines are usually inked in by the aid of French curves which guide the pen along the line. The French curve has to be manœuvred until a portion of its curve coincides with the actual line.

Joining Curved Lines

In joining curved lines with straight ones it is easiest to draw the curved lines first and then to run the straight lines to them. There is less chance of breaking the completed line in this way as compared with the method of constructing the straight lines first and connecting the curved ones to them.

To prevent the pen from clogging take a clean piece of cloth or paper and force the material between the nibs and rub lightly without altering the thumb-screw. A good sharp clean pen is absolutely essential for first - class draughtsmanship.

DIMENSIONS. Inked dimension lines may be drawn in one continuous line or by a broken line with space in the middle for the dimensions. The extent of each dimension is shown by a carefully drawn arrow head. All figures should read in one direction, and should be signified in the usual manner. For example 3 feet 6 inches is shown thus: 3′ 6″.

SECTION LINES are usually drawn across the plans of a building for the purpose of indicating the interior construction. They are placed in a position where the most information can be shown on the sectional drawings and marked with some form of reference. These lines are slightly thicker than the lines of the drawing and marked AB or BC as the case may be.

BORDERS. The border to a plan takes the same relationship as a frame to a picture. A simply executed border may possess much value, inasmuch as it will assist in attracting attention. It is not necessary to draw an elaborate border. The simplest design generally looks the neatest.

Very often a plain line around the plan about ¾ in. from the edge of the paper and a plain bold thick line under the heading will prove helpful. The black line gives emphasis and draws attention to the important heading.

CENTRE LINES. Most drawings have some part of the work which is set out from centre lines. This is often the case with windows, doors, corridors and other similar details. Such lines are very handy for symmetrical measurements.

CORRECTING MISTAKES. Removing pencil lines with indiarubber can be easily accomplished by rubbing out in one direction only. Do not rub both ways otherwise the surface of the paper will be damaged. Dirty drawings on paper or linen can be cleaned with the use of art gum or stale bread. Inked lines are removed by special erasers which can be bought for the purpose.

Preparing the Lay-out

THE LAY-OUT PLAN. A rough pencil draft, termed the lay-out, is the first thing to prepare. Once this has been arranged in a satisfactory manner, the plan can be developed properly on the same lines.

A good deal of skill is necessary in compiling lay-outs. Balance and attractiveness should be the key-note. Arrange the various parts of the drawing in such a manner that it becomes one compact connected design. Do not overcrowd,

WORKING LINE IN PENCIL

INKED BORDER LINE

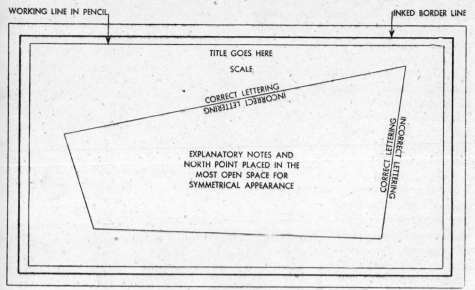

TITLE GOES HERE

SCALE

CORRECT LETTERING

INCORRECT LETTERING

EXPLANATORY NOTES AND
NORTH POINT PLACED IN THE
MOST OPEN SPACE FOR
SYMMETRICAL APPEARANCE

INCORRECT LETTERING

CORRECT LETTERING

TRIMMING LINE OUTSIDE BORDER LINE

LAY-OUT OF LETTERING FOR A PLAN

Fig. 11. The diagram shows the correct and incorrect methods of arranging the lettering on a draughtsman's plan, and also suggests its best general arrangement.

but be certain that no awkward gaps appear.

FINISHING THE DRAWING. The general requirements for all good plans may be given as follows: (1) clean-cut ink lines carefully drawn ; (2) good lettering and plain figures. In this respect the general arrangement of this work should read from left to right or from the bottom up, the words being in straight lines parallel to the side border lines. (3) A neat title placed in a suitable position to give a symmetrical appearance ; (4) the scale of the plan neatly arranged and also given in figures ; (5) a plain border line ; (6) a good arrangement of explanatory notes and conventional signs (Fig. 11).

PREPARATION OF DESIGN. Having obtained all the necessary information, the designer will set to work to co-ordinate all that is required in the intended building. Many attempts may be made before the best solution is found, and the first step towards solving

the problem is to try out a rough drawing indicating a general disposition of the parts of the plan as affected by the character of the building.

The next step is to place a piece of tracing paper over the rough drawing and to try out an alternative solution. This may be repeated again and again, in whole or in part, until the best solution is found.

Constructing the Plan

The designer now proceeds with the construction of the plan, sections, and elevations. A good plan generally gives rise to a good elevation, and so the full picture gradually takes shape. Everything grows from the plan; consequently the time is well spent in the preliminary stages while seeking a solution.

A trained designer must have a thorough knowledge of the various materials required to complete the building. This can be only acquired by

P.B.—M*

a practical training in his early days. He will then be in a position to produce practical drawings of all types.

Having completed the main requirements of his plan it is usual to prepare details drawn to a large scale. Suppose, for example, that it is desired to give a detail of an external 9-in. brick wall from the foundation to the roof, the detail plan should be constructed on the following lines:—

Mark off the brick courses of say four to the foot on a vertical line by using a scale of 1 in. to the foot. Next consider the height of the room and mark this off against the brick courses. The wall plates, thickness of flooring, and joists can now be shown in their relative positions.

Window Openings

The windows are next shown in section having regard to their size and the height of the sill above the flooring. One must have in mind the relation of all the windows throughout the building because, wherever possible, the heads will line with the same brick courses.

The next step is to draw part of the roof at the eaves, and this is represented by drawing a rafter from the wall plate at the required angle or pitch of the roof.

The remaining details at this position are easily built up above and be-

low the rafter. It will be necessary to settle the projection of the eaves from the wall in order to complete the details of the eaves board, soffit board, gutters and other features required. The roof boarding, roofing felt, battens and tiles may now be indicated according to the thickness of these materials. Whatever type of construction is desired may be shown.

At the bottom end of the wall the details of the depth, width and

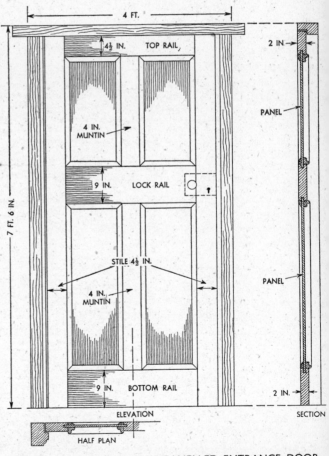

DETAIL DRAWING OF FOUR-PANELLED ENTRANCE DOOR

Fig. 12. In this example the elevation shows the side of a door as it would appear from the outside, and the half-plan is a section above or below the lock rail through the panels.

projection of footings are shown and elsewhere details drawn in until the drawing is completed.

A good example of a detail drawing is the four-panelled, square-framed door shown in Fig. 12. The elevation shows the side of the door as it would appear from the outside, and the half-plan is a section above or below the lock rail through the panels.

There are several methods of copying and transferring technical drawings by the pen or pencil if the draughtsman follows the instructions now given.

Copying Drawings

(1) Secure the plan to be copied on the drawing board over a clean sheet of paper, and prick through on all the points, where change of direction takes place, with a fine-pointed instrument. Be careful not to omit any important points before the upper sheet is removed.

(2) Make a tracing of the drawing on firm tracing paper, and on the reverse side cover all the lines by soft pencil marks. Rub the pencil backwards and forwards until every line is lightly obliterated.

Next turn the drawing over and fix it on the drawing board over a clean sheet and go over all the lines with a sharp-pointed 2H pencil. The moderate pressure of the pencil will leave a faint impression on the clean paper which can be copied over by pencil or pen.

(3) Another device that will be found useful for copying purposes is by means of squares formed on the original drawing. The squares may be ruled any desired size and if the drawing is to be copied to the same size, draw a similar number of squares on a clean sheet of paper and mark off the various points on these squares as they occur on the original. The outline can be completed by linking up the points and, where necessary, the unimportant points may

be judged by the eye and completed in freehand.

(4) A drawing can be copied by placing the original on a strong sheet of glass with a good light underneath. A clean sheet of paper is placed over the original and the reflection of the light from beneath is sufficient to enable the draughtsman to follow the original lines with pen or pencil.

Definitions

Certain definitions will prove of use to the draughtsman as follows:—

A STRAIGHT LINE. When the drawing instrument moves the shortest way between two points it delineates a straight line. The direction is immaterial, but to enable us to represent it in drawings we use a ruler or tee-square.

PARALLEL STRAIGHT LINES are lines in the same plane which are equidistant from each other in every part. The edge of a tee-square can be used to draw such lines on the drawing board by first drawing one line, and then, by moving the tee-square up or down, the other lines can be drawn. Such straight lines on the drawing board are said to be parallel to each other.

ANGLES. Two lines are said to be at right angles when one line stands on another, so that the adjacent angles are equal. For practical purposes a right angle is divided into 90 degrees and can be constructed by drawing a horizontal line with the tee-square and erecting a perpendicular line by means of a set-square used on the tee-square (Fig. 13).

An obtuse angle is greater than a right angle, whereas an acute angle is less than a right angle. In measuring angles on the drawing board it should be remembered that the 45-degree set-square has two anlges of 45 degrees each and one of 90 degrees; the 60-degree set-square has angles of 30 degrees, 60 degrees and 90 degrees. These

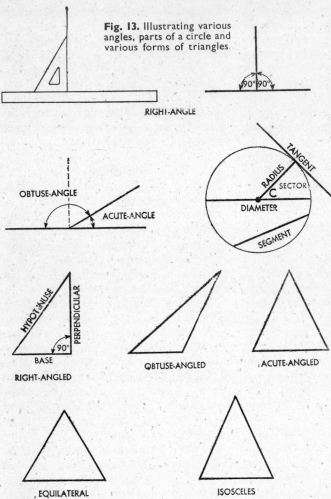

Fig. 13. Illustrating various angles, parts of a circle and various forms of triangles.

Half the diameter is the radius of the circle. A segment of a circle is bounded by part of the circumference and one straight line. A sector is a plane figure enclosed by two radii of a circle and the arc cut off by them. A tangent is a straight line which touches the circumference.

TRIANGLES. A right-angled triangle has one right angle, opposite which is the side called the hypotenuse. The other two sides are known as the base and perpendicular respectively (Fig. 13).

An obtuse-angled triangle has one angle greater than a right angle.

An acute-angled triangle has all its angles less than right angles.

An equilateral triangle has all three sides and angles equal.

An isosceles triangle has two equal sides.

A quadrilateral is a four-sided figure with four angles.

A square contains equal sides and equal angles (Fig. 14).

A rectangle is a four-sided right-angled figure.

A rhombus is a parallelogram with all its sides equal and the opposite angles equal.

A rhomboid is a parallelogram with all its opposite sides equal and the opposite angles equal.

A trapezium is a figure bounded by four straight lines with no two sides parallel.

set-squares held in position on the tee-square are suitable for erecting such angles. The use of a protractor is necessary in the case of other angles.

A circle is a plane figure bounded by a continuous curved line, called the circumference. It is traced by a point moving at a constant distance from a fixed point C, known as the centre. The diameter of a circle is the straight line passing through the centre and bounded by the circumference. It cuts the circle into two equal parts called semicircles.

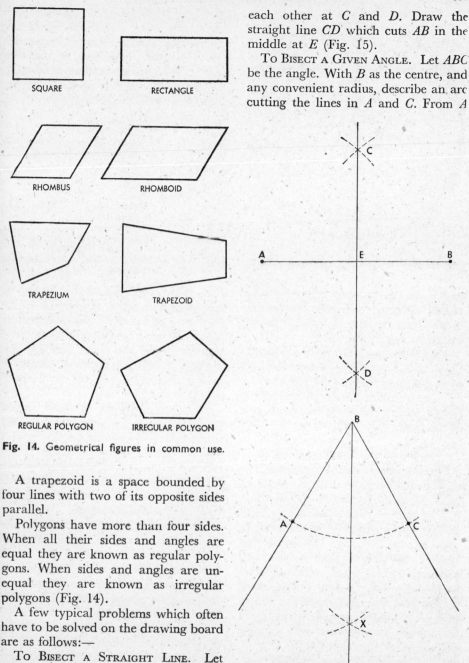

SQUARE

RECTANGLE

RHOMBUS

RHOMBOID

TRAPEZIUM

TRAPEZOID

REGULAR POLYGON

IRREGULAR POLYGON

Fig. 14. Geometrical figures in common use.

A trapezoid is a space bounded by four lines with two of its opposite sides parallel.

Polygons have more than four sides. When all their sides and angles are equal they are known as regular polygons. When sides and angles are unequal they are known as irregular polygons (Fig. 14).

A few typical problems which often have to be solved on the drawing board are as follows:—

TO BISECT A STRAIGHT LINE. Let *AB* be the line. From the centres *A* and *B* with any convenient radius, greater than half *AB*, draw two arcs cutting

each other at *C* and *D*. Draw the straight line *CD* which cuts *AB* in the middle at *E* (Fig. 15).

TO BISECT A GIVEN ANGLE. Let *ABC* be the angle. With *B* as the centre, and any convenient radius, describe an arc cutting the lines in *A* and *C*. From *A*

Fig. 15 (above). How to bisect a straight line.

Fig. 16 (below). How to bisect a given angle.

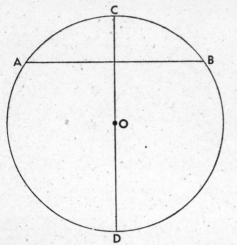

Fig. 17. How to find the centre of a circle.

Here the materials are indicated by means of varied tones according to whether they are in section or elevation. The sectional colouring is usually darker than the elevational treatment and the colours usually adopted for the purpose are detailed below:—

Brickwork	.	Gamboge
Masonry	.	Vandyke brown
Concrete	.	Hooker's green or neutral tint speckled with Indian ink
Cast iron	.	Payne's grey
Wrought iron		Prussian blue
Steel	. .	Purple
Lead	. .	Indigo
Slate	. .	Neutral tint mixed with a little crimson lake
Glass	. .	French blue
Timber .	.	Burnt sienna for joinery; yellow ochre for carpentry
Earth	. .	Burnt umber with irregular edging

and *C*, as centres, and with the same radius, describe two arcs intersecting in *X*. Draw the line *BX* which divides the given angle (Fig. 16).

To Find the Centre of a Circle. Draw any chord *AB* and bisect the line with a perpendicular *CD*. This will be the diameter of the circle. Bisect the line *CD* in point *O* which gives the centre of the circle (Fig. 17).

Conventional Representation

Special conventional markings are used to indicate the different kinds of materials that go to make up the drawing. In addition the markings emphasize the various parts of the drawing in such a way that the composition is readily understood and appreciated almost at a glance. The usual markings for bricks, stone, concrete, metal, wood, plaster and other materials are shown in Fig. 18. These examples are sufficient for general purposes and will improve the value of the drawing to a great extent provided the conventional treatment is not overdone.

Colours. The introduction of colouring also improves the value of the plan.

A few hours should be spent in experimenting with colour, in order that some idea may be gained of colour values. After a while it will be quite easy to obtain the right tone for the work in hand. Always mix plenty of colour and then test on a piece of paper.

Place two tumblers of water beside the table, one to the right and the other to the left. The tumbler on the right is used for mixing colours and the one on the left is convenient for washing the brush. A clean sheet of blotting paper is useful for emergencies and for mopping up any superfluous colour.

The drawing is mounted firmly to the drawing board and the whole placed in a sloping position to allow the colour washes to run downwards. Next prepare the paper surface for the reception of the colour by giving the drawing a clean wash of water all over.

Whilst the preparatory wash is drying prepare the colours to be used by mixing thoroughly. Mix ample supplies for each tone, because if insufficient colour is mixed it is extremely difficult to remix the colours to exactly the same tint.

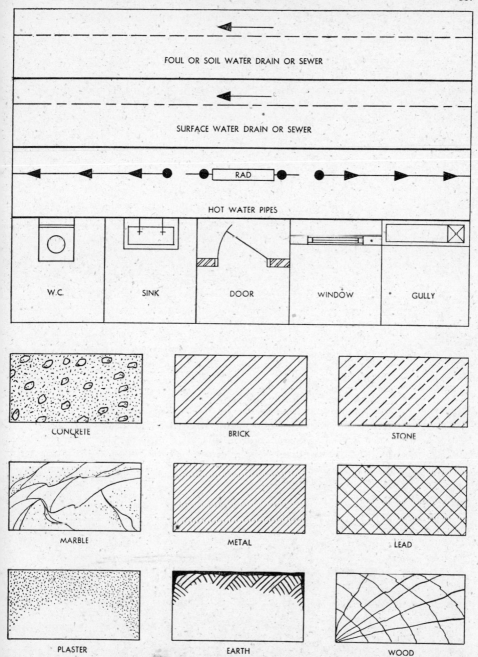

FOUL OR SOIL WATER DRAIN OR SEWER

SURFACE WATER DRAIN OR SEWER

RAD

HOT WATER PIPES

| W.C. | SINK | DOOR | WINDOW | GULLY |

CONCRETE   BRICK   STONE

MARBLE   METAL   LEAD

PLASTER   EARTH   WOOD

CONVENTIONAL REPRESENTATION

Fig. 18. The diagram illustrates the standard symbols most frequently used in plans for building, including drainage, joinery and various types of building material. These should invariably be used by the draughtsman, as their adoption avoids doubts and delay at every stage of the work.

Washes are best applied with a large brush. Flood the portion where it is intended to commence, and work the brush evenly over the drawing. The colour will run freely and will dry evenly without variation of tone and sharp edges, owing to the damp condition of the drawing. After the first colour wash, wait until thoroughly dry. Always allow one portion to dry before tackling another.

It is the best policy to work as direct as possible by making sure that the correct shade is applied at once, instead of having to add tone upon tone. Follow on this system with all the various shades for the elevational work and similar large areas.

Apart from the standard indication of materials it is also necessary to be familiar with standard symbols for representing soil water drains, surface water drains, hot and cold water supplies, sanitary fittings and the like. All these are clearly explained in Fig. 18.

Importance of Lettering

One of the most important phases of plan drawing is the execution of good lettering. Faulty or badly displayed lettering will spoil a drawing, and consequently it is essential that good work should be introduced.

Every drawing needs a title and some description. Such words as plan, elevation, section, scale, etc., frequently recur and the student is well advised to study good examples of neatly drawn lettering, both in headings and in detailed text.

To draw letters, either vertical or sloping, simply rule out an upper and a lower guide line the required distance apart to represent the desired height of the letters. A line running through the centre will allow the centrals to be placed accurately, and afford assistance in aligning the curves in the letters R, P, and B.

A bold, simple, and well-spaced letter is the best. Plain block letters or Roman lettering for headings and main title look well, and italics or small lettering should be made use of for all descriptive notes.

Block Lettering

The design shown in Fig. 19 is an example of well-proportioned block lettering of the solid type. The letters may be left open or filled in. The main features of this mechanical type of lettering are that all the limbs join each other at acute or right angles. The letters for Fig. 19 are drawn to 8 units in height, the width varying from $1\frac{1}{2}$ units for the letter I to 9 units for the letter W. The general width for the limbs of all the letters is taken as $1\frac{1}{2}$ units.

To ensure uniformity in height and alignment, it is essential to draw top and bottom guide lines 8 units high and to draw two inner lines a little less than

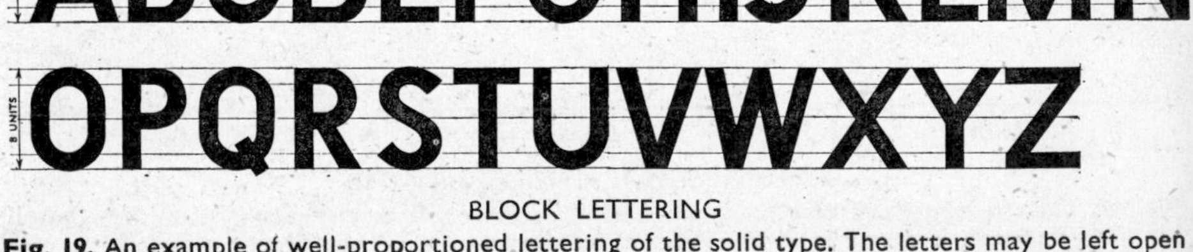

BLOCK LETTERING

Fig. 19. An example of well-proportioned lettering of the solid type. The letters may be left open or filled in. Note the acute or right angles at which the limbs join each other.

ABCDEFG
HIJKLMN
OPQRSTU
VWXYZ

ROMAN CAPITALS

abcdefghijklmnop

qrstuvwxyz

Roman small letters

LETTERING FOR ARCHITECTURAL DRAWING

Fig. 20. The beauty of the Roman letter is well shown in the above examples. Note the proportion, the spacing and the thickness of the strokes. Special care is necessary when drawing the serifs

1½ units wide to aid the construction of the top and bottom horizontal strokes. A centre line is also necessary. These lines are drawn lightly in pencil and should be rubbed out after inking.

ROMAN LETTERING. Fig. 20 shows the main characteristics of all the letters in the alphabet. They have a certain type of beauty brought out by the nature of the serifs and should be copied, letter by letter, until proportion, spacing and the thickness of the strokes has been thoroughly mastered. Special care is required when drawing the serifs at the end of each stroke, and only practice will develop the sweep of the hand so necessary in this type of lettering.

To ensure an even and equal spacing between letters and words a certain amount of thought and care is required. Some draughtsmen draw letters exact distances apart, carefully measuring each letter and allowing so much space to each one. This is no doubt necessary for special headings, but neatness and speed are best obtained by arranging the wording to please the eye.

In drawing curved letters such as R, G, S and O, etc., always take the curve slightly above and below the guide lines; that is, really draw the letters higher and lower than the other letters in the same word. This is necessary so that these letters will appear the same size as the others. If this is not done the curved letters will appear smaller than the others and look out of place owing to an optical illusion.

Letters with cross lines such as F, E and H usually have the cross line placed above the centre to prevent the letter appearing too heavy. It is also a wise policy to draw such letters as R, P, B, X with the upper portions above the central line.

Examples of lettering suitable for general purposes are shown in Fig. 21. The beginner is advised to practise the use of printed letters after a similar style, and later he will develop a style of his own. Avoid the use of too many different types and sizes of lettering on a drawing. Usually three variations are sufficient. Large letters for the main heading, medium-size letters for the sub-titles and small letters for the explanatory notes and conventional signs form the general arrangement.

ABCDEFGHIJKLMNOPQRST
UVWXYZ
PLAN SECTION ELEVATION
PLAN SECTION ELEVATION 65°

NORTH ELEVATION SCALE
NORTH ELEVATION SCALE

LETTERING FOR GENERAL PURPOSES

Fig. 21. This useful sanserif letter is suitable for general purposes in plan work; it has a good appearance both in the upright letter and in the italic, and is easily legible.

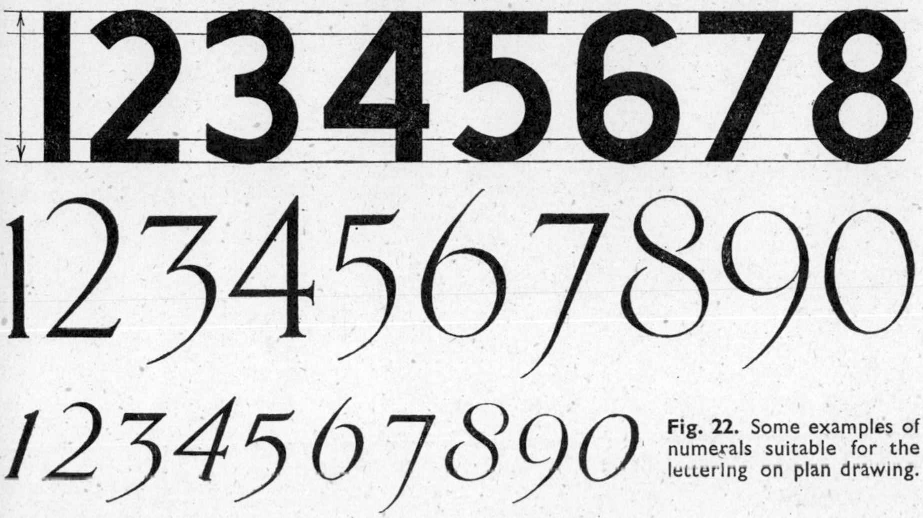

12345678
1234567890
1234567890

Fig. 22. Some examples of numerals suitable for the lettering on plan drawing.

The numerals shown in Fig. 22 explain themselves.

STENCILLING. The stencil method of lettering saves a good deal of time. Naturally the detailed printing cannot be satisfactorily introduced by the stencil method, but it is quite convenient to print the heading of the plan and the more important descriptions by this method. A good set of stencils can be obtained from any specialist firm dealing with drawing materials.

Reproduction of Drawings

PRINTS. It is often necessary to make a number of copies from an original drawing. There are various methods in use, but the most common practice is to use tracing linen, which is placed over the original for the purposes of copying all the lines by the aid of a ruling pen and Indian ink. This tracing becomes a negative suitable for the reproduction of a number of copies which can be reproduced as *black and white prints* on paper or linen. Prints known as *blue prints* show white lines on a blue background. The types of prints required will depend upon their use. Coloured copies call for black and white prints because it is quite a simple matter to colour the paper or linen according to the conventional markings of the original. Plans required for record purposes are best on linen.

Some prints shrink a little during the course of preparation; consequently the need for a scale drawn on the negative is very important.

There are many firms that undertake the reproduction of drawings and it will be found that the cost of providing copies is most reasonable. To undertake the laborious task of making tracing after tracing cannot compare with this cheap and easy method of obtaining prints.

BLACK AND WHITE REPRODUCTION. Frequently the draughtsman is called upon to produce a drawing suitable for reproduction in the Press. In this case the student should understand a little about the process engraver's art, so that the work will reproduce with the best results.

The usual type of reproduction is the line process, which is cheap, simple and very effective. The drawing is prepared with pen and black ink upon white paper of good quality. The original

block, remember to keep the lines open and use dense black colour. Also allow for a reduction in size to about half that of the original. As any lettering will be reduced in size, remember to keep this work large enough in the first place.

A useful way of ascertaining the *pro rata* reduction of a drawing is to draw a divisional line from the left lower corner to the upper right corner. Next take a scale and hold it parallel to the bottom edge of your drawing. Gradually push the scale upwards until the dividing line is met at the width to which it is desired that the drawing should be reproduced. From the position where the scale meets the divisional line down to the lower edge of the drawing will be the height of the reproduction.

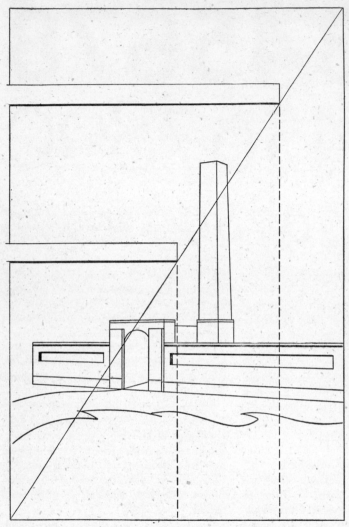

REDUCTION AND ENLARGEMENT

Fig. 23. The diagram shows how, by means of a diagonal drawn from the lower left corner to the upper right corner, the size of an enlargement or reduction of the original drawing may be found.

drawing is placed in front of the process engraver's camera and photographed on a special plate which is not susceptible to any colour but black. In view of this, the lines of the drawing must be dense black and not flimsy. Faint lines do not reproduce.

In preparing a drawing for a line

This method enables the draughtsman to visualize what the drawing will be like after reduction. If the area of space allowed for reproduction is known it is quite easy to enlarge the size by the same method for the purpose of the original drawing. Fig. 23 shows clearly how to make use of this simple method.

CHAPTER 12

ESTIMATING

Main classes of estimating. Bills of quantities and their lay-out. General principles. Prices and quantities. Labour rates and output. Hardcore. Concrete. Proportions. Bricklayers', masons' and other tradesmen's costs. On-costs and profits. Preliminaries. Tabular information.

ESTIMATING ranks high as one of the responsible duties of the senior staff of a building contractor's organization. Although there has been a marked improvement in estimating principles and organization during the past one or two decades, there are many estimators who follow unscientific methods which do not give the best results.

Competitive Tendering

Much estimating is done in connection with competitive tendering, and it must be realized that any of the following results may occur:—
(1) Over-estimating, even by a small amount, will probably lose the contract.
(2) Being a little below a *competent* competitor will probably get the contract.
(3) Being much below a *competent* competitor who is *not* estimating "high" to lose the contract because he does not want it; or, too frequently, being much above a competent competitor indicates faulty estimating.

Stress has been laid on *competent*, for the special reason of showing that competency in estimating is all-important. Estimating calls for exceptionally good knowledge of building construction, costs of materials, labour output and organization, conduct of works, costing, obtaining prices and placing orders for materials, sub-contract work, etc., and many other items which are quite apart from the knowledge which is necessary to allow estimating to be conducted on scientific lines.

Many master builders, and practically all general foremen (the author prefers the designation of works managers) advance from the ranks of practical craftsmen, who are much interested in estimating, and often have to settle down to its problems. The professional estimator is usually an office man, and a surveyor. As such he comes very frequently in contact with the work of all classes of craftsmen, and with the men themselves; he contacts building owners, architects, surveyors, quantity surveyors, officials of local authorities, sub-contractors, specialists, works managers, all kinds of staff members, suppliers and many others.

Main Classes of Estimating

The subject of estimating may be divided into the following main classes:
(1) Pricing bills of quantities prepared by a quantity surveyor employed by the building owner.
(2) Pricing bills of quantities prepared by the builder's surveyor.
(3) Pricing schedules of prices or rates which form the basis of paying for work which is eventually measured.

(4) Estimating the percentage addition to or deduction from standard schedule of prices which form the basis of payment for work which is eventually measured.

(5) Spot pricing.

(6) A combination of any two or more of the above.

(7) Approximate estimating, such as cubing, cubing plus approximate quantities, combined quantities, etc.

For the purpose of this chapter it is necessary to keep rather rigidly to the subject of estimating, and it is not advisable to discuss the varying merits of the above seven classes as they open many viewpoints. However, it may be stated that estimating on the basis of bills of quantities prepared by a quantity surveyor employed by the building owner is recognized as the fairest to a builder. Classes (2), (3) and (4) entail builders bearing the cost of preparing quantities and/or measuring works.

No better way of explaining the principles and details of estimating can be chosen than firstly, to consider the general lay-out of proper bills of quantities, and secondly, to give typical examples of how to estimate some of the chief items in them.

General Lay-out

The general lay-out usually consists of separate bills or sections devoted to:—

Preliminaries (and work on site).
Excavator.
Concretor.
Bricklayer.
Mason.
Drainlayer.
Asphalter.
Pavior.
Slater, tiler and slate mason.
Carpenter, joiner and ironmonger.
Ironfounder, smith and structural engineer.
Plasterer and wall tiler.
Plumber and gas fitter.
Electrician.
Glazier.
Painter and decorator.
The summary.

There are variations to the above lay-out; but these will not affect the explanations.

PRELIMINARIES refer to the general conditions of contract and many other items; but those which are of particular importance to the estimator relate to the following items which have to be priced either in the preliminaries, or elsewhere, as will be explained: (1) all insurances—health and unemployment, employer's liability, third party and fire; (2) water for building purposes; (3) plant; (4) general foreman (works manager) and/or other works staff; (5) contractor's temporary buildings; (6) other items which have a monetary value, often including an amount for contingencies.

THE VARIOUS TRADES, giving quantities and descriptions of the various works, follow the preliminaries.

The Summary

THE SUMMARY completes the bills, and is, as its name implies, a summary of all the separate bills. It also usually contains abstracts from the preliminaries, of items such as insurances and water which are intended to be priced in summary.

COMMENTS ON THE LAY-OUT can be limited to a suggestion that, in addition to insurances and water being taken to summary for pricing, it would be equally advantageous if other items, such as plant and general foreman, which are by old custom given in preliminaries, are also included in summary. There is a very good reason for this: the modern estimator never prices these items until every other item in the bills has been settled. By the time the trades bills have been priced, the estimator has the best knowledge of the general and detailed character of the many works and is then, and not before, in a position to decide as to what class of works manager shall

BILL No. 1: PRELIMINARY AND GENERAL ITEMS

Item No.			£	s.	d.
9	Allow for paying all liabilities incurred by the National Health and Unemployment Insurance Acts, the Widow's, Orphan's and Old Age Pensions Acts, the Workmen's Compensation Acts, Employer's Liability and any other Acts of Parliament of like nature or any subsequent amendments thereto (*see* Summary)				
10	The contractor is to insure against damage by fire his own plant, scaffolding, temporary buildings and equipment .				
	(*Many other items are included in this bill*)				
	Carried to Summary . .	£			

BILL No. 3: CONCRETOR

Yd.			£	s.	d.
	The concrete for foundations to be composed of 1 part of Portland cement to 6 parts of clean approved ballast of 2-in. gauge and with sufficient washed sand to fill the interstices				
80	Cube	Concrete (1–12) in filling to old vaults to be done from the front of the vaults (after pulling down front wall and the pavement to be left undisturbed) (upholding pavement, etc., measured separately)			
	(*Many other items are included in this bill which is followed by the other bills shown in Summary*)				
		£			

SUMMARY

Bill No.			£	s.	d.
1	Preliminaries and general items				
2	Excavator				
3	Concretor				
4	Bricklayer				
5	Mason				
6	Drainlayer				
7	Asphalter				
8	Pavior				
9	Slater, tiler and slate mason				
10	Carpenter, joiner and ironmonger				
11	Ironfounder, smith and structural engineer . . .				
12	Plasterer and wall tiler				
13	Plumber and gas fitter				
14	Electrician				
15	Glazier				
16	Painter and decorator				
	The contractor is to allow for the following items in preliminaries bill:—				
	(*Here would be described the items*)				
Add	Surveyor's fees, 2 per cent, to be paid out of the first certificate				
Add	For lithography, typing, etc.				
	Amount of estimate. Carried to form of tender . . .	£			

Fig. 1. The above three Tables give some typical extracts from bills of quantities.

control the works, the time it will be necessary to allow to complete the works, the nature of plant required, and insurances to allow for the works and labour of the main contractor and sub-contractors.

Fig. 1 shows extracts from the preliminary and general items bill, the concretor bill, and the summary.

Gross versus Net Estimating

It is now advisable to consider two methods of estimating, one, the gross method, being hopelessly out of date, but still used by some old-fashioned estimators, and the other, the net method, used by modern estimators.

The *gross method* includes the addition to every item in the bills of quantities or estimates of a percentage addition to cover on-costs and profit. Not only is this method a waste of time in adding a percentage to each of the oft-times thousands of items, but it is fundament-

ally wrong in view of modern conditions, as will be understood from the following explanations of the net method.

Study Figs. 2 and 3. The *net method* is exceptionally simple, and it is used by a great number of estimators in this country as practical, sound, and giving far better results than the gross method. Briefly, it is:—

(a) That every item is estimated or priced at net cost of material and/or labour; net specified allowance or cost of all prime cost, provisional sum and provisional amount items, and then a percentage is added in summary to cover on-costs and profit.

(b) Although every (1) prime cost, (2) provisional sum and (3) provisional amount item is priced in the main bills, a separate schedule is made of each of these three important sections for very particular reasons as explained below. Fig. 2 gives a practical idea of how the schedules are compiled on these lines.

CONTRACT............................

SCHEDULE OF P.C., P.S., AND OTHER ITEMS

Page of bills	Items	P.C. items			Provisional sum items			Provisional amounts, etc.		
		£	s.	d.	£	s.	d.	£	s.	d.
7	Amount for contingencies							200	0	0
15	10,000 facing bricks at £6 M.	60	0	0						
20	Artificial stone	250	0	0						
27	Asphalter				175	0	0			
41	50 doors at £2	100	0	0						
50	Ironmongery	75	0	0						
57	Structural engineer				550	0	0			
58	Lantern lights				125	0	0			
61	Wall tiling				80	0	0			
67	Sanitary fittings	110	0	0						
72	Heating engineer				275	10	0			
	Builder's work							20	0	0
80	Electrical work				100	0	0			
83	Patent glazing				114	10	0			
87	Wall papers	15	0	0						
		£ 610	0	0	1,420	0	0	220	0	0

Total is £2,250

Fig. 2 Abbreviated example of prime cost, provisional sums and other items.

SUMMARY

Bill No.			£	s.	d.
1		Preliminaries and general items	560	0	0
2		Excavator	156	15	0
3		Concretor	382	10	6
4		Bricklayer	1,076	4	3
5		Mason	371	0	0
6		Drainlayer	97	13	0
7		Asphalter	210	0	0
8		Pavior	63	11	2
9		Slater, tiler and slate mason	410	2	1
10		Carpenter, joiner and ironmonger	1,171	0	6
11		Ironfounder, smith and structural engineer	942	9	6
12		Plasterer and wall tiler	391	0	0
13		Plumber and gas fitter	567	8	3
14		Electrician	115	0	0
15		Glazier	201	13	0
16		Painter and decorator	107	12	9
			6,824	0	0
	Less	P.C., P.S., etc., as schedule	2,250	0	0
			4,574	0	0
	Add	On-costs and profit 15 per cent	686	2	0
	Add	P.C. items 610 0 0			
		5 per cent . . 30 10 0			
		£640 10 0	640	10	0
	Add	P.S. items 1,420 0 0			
		7½ per cent . . 106 10 0			
		£1,526 10 0	1,526	10	0
	Add	Provisional amounts, etc.	220	0	0
			7,647	2	0
	Add	Surveyor's fees, 2 per cent, to be paid out of first certificate	152	19	0
	Add	Lithography, typing, etc.	20	4	0
		Amount of estimate. Carried to form of tender	£7,820	5	0

Fig. 3. The modern summary sheet presents a clear view of the various trades included in an estimate.

(c) It is, or should be, a general principle with estimators to allow different on-cost and profit percentages for the following four main financial sections of building contracting. (1) A certain percentage, usually the highest, for all ordinary works (instances are ordinary excavating, concrete, carpentry, etc.) which carry the greatest financial risk to the contractor because he has to stand by his rates. (2) A percentage, usually much lower than (1), on P.C. items, which are supplied only by a nominated supplier, and fixed by the main contractor. P.C. items carry no financial risk to the main contractor, as they are costs which are instructed to be allowed, and any variation in the cost is adjusted in the final accounts.

Under the R.I.B.A. form of agreement a contractor is entitled to 5 per cent discount on such P.C. items which discount with the lesser financial risk than (1) permits consideration of a reduced profit on such items. Also there are other sections of the percentage allowed for on-costs which can be reduced as explained later. (3) Another percentage usually a little higher than (2) and still much lower than (1) is permissible on provisional sum items which briefly consist of sums specified to be allowed by the contractor for work or materials which are *supplied and fixed* by a nominated specialist or sub-contractor, and for which the main contractor is entitled to $2\frac{1}{2}$ per cent discount. (4) Usually no percentage at all is added to what are known as provisional amounts, which include such as " amount for contingencies "; amounts for work which will be measured and paid for at rates as, or analogous to, those in the main estimate with the appropriate on-cost and profit percentage. Manifestly the last percentage is all that is necessary.

(*d*) Again study Figs. 2 and 3 and it will then be seen that the estimator, together with the chief of technical staff, and the principals of the business, have before them a clear view of the general works comprised in the work being tendered for; they can see at a glance the different totals of ordinary works in which there is the greatest financial risk, and sub-contractor's work; they are in a good position to gauge with reasonable accuracy the time which will be required to carry out the work, the finance required for operational purposes, the best works manager for the work; they can then discuss the various percentages for on-costs and profit, and alter them if advisable; and they will have the knowledge that every item in the main bills has been priced net, which is best understood as the basis for comparing costs on job.

They will also know that the rates in bills do not divulge to works staff the percentages allowed for on-costs and profit, and there is the great saving of time by having to make only three accurate percentage computations instead of a very considerable number which would be necessary if the gross method were adopted.

Finally it will be realized that percentages which are practically accurate cannot be added to a great many of the low-priced items in bills of quantities—as an instance, adding say 15 per cent to 2d. makes a rate of $2\frac{3}{10}$d. which is so impracticable as to cause most estimators to call it $2\frac{3}{8}$d. or even $2\frac{1}{2}$d. causing, if quantities are considerable, an appreciable financial difference.

The general principles of practically all estimating are based on ascertained prices of materials which are wanted, quantities of materials, information and knowledge of the quantities of materials which make up the components of finished work which consists of more than one material (such as concrete), and labour rates and output.

Variation of Prices

PRICES OF MATERIALS. It is essential to understand that prices of many similar materials vary to a rather great extent, depending on locality, transport and labour rates. There are, of course, many, but not a great many, materials which are standardized for certain regions; cement and stoneware drainage goods are two good examples.

Some manufacturers have printed schedules of prices which are subject, in some cases, to percentage additions or deductions according to quantities, transport and other factors. Whatever method is adopted by suppliers of materials it is absolutely essential for the estimator to be completely up to date with prices, and, although records of prices and quotations for recently estimated work may often be used, it will be found in practice that there are usually conditions which make it very prudent to obtain many quotations for each job as it is estimated. Discounts for payment within a stipulated period should be sought.

COMPUTATION OF QUANTITIES for obtaining prices or quotations should be done with reasonable care; but, in this respect, it should be realized that the work is being estimated and it is not certain whether the estimate will be successful. There is a difference between computing quantities for obtaining quotations when estimating and preparing requisition quantities for a contract which is obtained; the latter must be exact, whereas the former may not call for anything more than an approximation within reasonable limits.

If, however, there are items which will not be varied if the contract is obtained, then it will certainly save time in the future if quantities for estimating purposes are so specified and prepared as to make them suitable for placing orders. With regard to various components in finished work, such as the different materials to make concrete, it will be found that the tabular information is useful. As a guide, bills of quantities give so many yards cube of finished concrete; it is necessary to allow more yards cube of aggregate than the bills of quantities show because the aggregate loses bulk when mixed with water.

LABOUR OUTPUT is a very important matter and requires handling by the estimator with the utmost care. The fundamental basis of estimating output is the *unit* or *constant* method, which is as follows: The use by the estimator of tabular information which sets out the times which operatives should require to do certain works.

Such times are based on usually accepted units of work, such as 1 yd.

cube of excavating, 1 yd. cube of concrete in bases, 1 yd. super of surface concrete, 1 square of flooring and 1 ft. cube of timber in floor joists. The times or constants for units must be treated as a standard for normal conditions and quantities of work, and it is essential to modify them for small and exceptionally large quantities of work or units.

Tables of data, of which a few (of the many hundreds) are given in this chapter, will enable a sound practical knowledge to be gained of how to estimate the cost of the chief items of all trades. Once the principles are mastered it will be found comparatively easy to augment the knowledge by the accumulation of data on many other items. For ease of computing, 2s. and 1s. 6d. an hour has been allowed for mechanics and labourers.

The first trade described is that of the excavator. The other trades are also briefly dealt with, but most of these are specialists' work.

EXCAVATOR (TABLE I) gives typical labour constants, and the following examples will show how easy it is to estimate for the various kinds of excavation:

EXAMPLE 1. Excavate common ground over surface average 6 in. deep, throw out, and afterwards fill into barrows, remove material not exceeding 50 yd. and deposit.

Estimate at *yard cube* and convert to *yard super*, therefore:—

	Hours Labourer
Surface excavation as col. 2	1·25
Fill into barrows (not done at time of excavating) as col. 7 . . .	0·50
Removing N/E 50 yd. and depositing as col. 10	0·50
	2·25 at 1 6=3 4½

(*s. d.* and *s. d.* appear above the last line)

As rate of 3s. 4½d. is for 1 Y.C. and the surface work is 6 in. deep, divide by 6= 6¾

Add one-tenth to 1·25 hr. for levelling ground, etc., therefore 0·125 at 1s. 6d.= 2¼

Cost per Y.S. . . . 9d.

TABLE I — **EXCAVATOR**

LABOUR CONSTANTS—HOURS OF LABOURER PER CUBI
YARD ALL IN SOLID UNLESS OTHERWISE STATED

WORK TO BE DONE

Class of earth (1)	*Surface excavation not exceeding 12 in. deep and throwing out into heaps; or into barrows* (2)		*Excavating over areas exceeding 12 in. deep and bulk excavations such as to basements and throwing out into heaps or into barrows* (3)	*Trench excavating not exceeding 5 ft. deep and throwing out into heaps or into barrows* (4)	*Extra thro not exceedi 5 ft. hig* (5)
Loose soil or sand	0·75	All plus one-tenth hour per YARD SUPER See footnote	0·50	1·00	0·50
Made ground or light soil	1·00		0·75	1·25	0·50
Common grounds, loams, vegetable earth	1·25		1·00	1·75	0·67
Stiff clay, gravel, hard earth	1·50		1·25	2·00	0·75
Earth mixed with coarse gravel and stony earth	1·75		1·50	2·25	0·75
Hard ground where picking is necessary as road surfaces	2·50		2·00	—	—
Soft chalk with pick work	2·75		2·50	3·00	0·75

FOOTNOTE. Surface excavation is to have one-tenth hour labourer per YARD SUPER to co cost of levelling bottom and general preparatory work.

Table I. Tabular information is of great value in obtaining a sound practical knowledge of how to estimate the cost of the chief items in the building trades, and in recording information and data of

EXAMPLE 2. Excavate common ground over areas exceeding 12 in. deep, and throw out and afterwards fill into carts.

	Hours Labourer		
Excavate as col. 3 .	1·00		
Fill into carts as col. 7	0·50		
		s. d.	*s. d.*
	1·50 at	1 6=Y.C.	2 3

HARDCORE to be laid under concrete floors and similar work should be estimated as follows:—

To the cost of the hardcore delivered to site, add for any filling into barrows, and removing to situation where the material is to be laid. Allow that the hardcore is equal to common ground for the lighter types of materials, such as

ᴏᴛᴇs. The whole of the constants allow for work being in solid, i.e., measured before excavation, being the state that usually exists in most building works. If constants are required for excavated ᴇrial allowing for increase in bulk after excavation, for labour as columns (7), (10) and (11), ᵢ reduce the constants shown in such columns, as follows:—

    Sand, gravel and ballast .   .   10 per cent reduction of labour constant
    Ordinary earth and clay .   .   20 per cent reduction of labour constant
    Chalk .   .   .   .   25 per cent reduction of labour constant

the items (excepting surface excavation as column (2) which is measured in yards super) are ᴇred in yards cube.

WORK TO BE DONE

ading and ᵈling from ᵥated heap ᵥithout ᵣwing) in ᵧers not ᵪceeding in. deep	Filling into barrows or carts	Returning and filling to trenches, etc.	Ramming around foundations in 12-in. layers	Removing in barrows and depositing (not including filling barrows) not exceeding 50 yd. run and returning empty	Every 25 yd. extra run
(6)	(7)	(8)	(9)	(10)	(11)
0·25	0·50	0·50	0·50	0·50	0·25
0·25	0·50	0·50	0·50	0·50	0·25
0·25	0·50	0·50	0·50	0·50	0·25
0·33	0·50	0·67	0·67	0·50	0·25
0·33	0·50	0·67	0·67	0·50	0·25
0·33	0·50	—	—	0·50	0·25
0·33	0·50	0·67	0·67	0·50	0·25

ᴇe items which have to be estimated. The above Table gives the chief typical labour constants ᵣr the excavator, and is of great assistance to the estimator in compiling excavation costs.

ᵈinker used as hardcore, and as gravel ᵣ hard earth for the heavier types such ᵴ broken bricks, and use the appro-riate labour constants as Table I for ᵈling barrows and removing. Then use ᵢllowing data:—

Hardcore is usually laid from 3 in. to ᵢin. thick *after consolidation*, and this ᵣakes it necessary to allow about 25 per cent to the consolidated thickness in computing the quantity of hardcore required. Then allow that a labourer will take the following times to spread, level and consolidate by rolling:—

3 in. thick .   .   .   ⅟₇ yd. super
4 in. thick .   .   .   ⅛ yd. super
5 in. thick .   .   .   ⅙ yd. super
6 in. thick .   .   .   ¼ yd. super

SPECIFICATION OF CONCRETE. Specifications vary, and are often not well
considered from points of view of construction and costs. A specification
should be clear as to proportions of
cement, fine and coarse aggregates, and
should clearly state whether the proportions are by volume or otherwise.
Cement is the most costly component
in concrete, and as its volume can vary
by its looseness or tightness it is good
practice to specify cement by weight
(usually 1-cwt. sacks) and other materials by volume; this method is adopted
in the L.C.C. by-laws.

Concrete Specifications

Concrete may be specified as (1) 1
part of Portland cement to so many
parts of combined fine (sand) and
coarse aggregate (pit or river ballast
as raised unscreened and therefore containing sand are examples); (2) 1 part
of Portland cement, so many parts of
sand, and so many parts of coarse
aggregate, such as gravel free (and
screened) of sand. (1) and (2) are
known as proportions such as 1 : 6 and
1 : 3 : 6 respectively.

PROPORTIONS AFFECT ESTIMATING to
a rather great extent. When the proportions are such as 1 : 6, 1 : 8 and
1 : 12 the estimating is usually ruled by
the price of the aggregate, which will
vary according to the requirements of
grading of the coarse material and proportion of sand in the combined fine
and coarse aggregate. Unscreened aggregate is generally much cheaper than
coarse aggregate free of sand, to which
aggregate must be added the specified
proportion of sand which is purchased
separately. Also the labour constants
are a little lower for a proportion such
as 1 : 6, etc., than for 1 : 3 : 6 because
it takes more time to dry-mix the latter
than the former.

In such mixes as 1 : 3 : 6 it is intended that the proportion of sand
should be sufficient to fill, or a little
more than fill, the voids in the coarse
material, and if the voids are about 45
per cent then the above proportions will
cause the 10 parts of material when *dry-
mixed* together to equal *about* 6 parts by
volume. If the proportions are 1 : 3 : 5
the resulting dry-mixing of the 9 parts
would be about $5\frac{1}{2}$ parts. This must, of
course, considerably affect estimating,
as will be understood a little later.

VOIDS IN AGGREGATES vary with
different classes; but for practical purposes the following rules may be accepted: Reasonably well-graded coarse
aggregates without sand contain 45 per
cent voids, and very well graded 40
per cent; 45 per cent is normal for
ordinary concrete work.

A very important matter has now to
be considered. If a quantity of sand
exactly equal in volume to the voids in
the coarse material is added to the
latter the sand will *not* exactly fill the
voids, but there would be sand over
which would increase the bulk of the
mixture. The reason of this is that there
would be a quantity of voids in the
coarse material which the sand could
not get into owing to the shape, grading
and fineness of the sand.

Filling the Voids

Therefore, another rule may be used
with confidence: The amount of void
in coarse aggregate which will be filled
by sand or fine aggregate will be equal
to the percentage of voids minus 10.
Therefore, if voids equal 45 per cent, the
sand will only fill 35 per cent and there
will be an increase in volume of the
dry-mix aggregates.

Losses due to mixing together the
separate dry materials are very considerable as the foregoing explanations make
clear. The proportion of cement is
often lost in the voids of the aggregate

TABLE II — **BRICKWORK. QUANTITIES OF BRICKS PER ROD WITH STANDARD BRICKS ($8\frac{3}{4}$ in. × $4\frac{1}{4}$ in. approx.)**

Thickness of brick in inches	*Thickness of joints and quantities of bricks*		
	$\frac{1}{4}$ in.	*$\frac{3}{8}$ in.*	*$\frac{1}{2}$ in.*
2	5,800	5,500	5,220
$2\frac{5}{8}$	4,540	4,350	4,180
$2\frac{3}{4}$	4,350	4,180	4,010
$2\frac{7}{8}$	4,180	4,010	3,870
3	4,010	3,870	3,730

NOTE. The 2-in. thick bricks are seldom used throughout the thickness of walls more than $\frac{1}{2}$ brick thick, but are used as facings and backed by thicker bricks. These quantities must be adjusted to suit this condition.

TABLE III — **BRICKWORK. QUANTITIES OF MORTAR IN CUBIC YARDS PER ROD ALLOWING FOR COMPRESSION AND WASTE**

Thickness of brick in inches	*Bricks with single frogs*			*Bricks without frogs*		
	Thickness of joints			*Thickness of joints*		
	$\frac{1}{4}$ in.	*$\frac{3}{8}$ in.*	*$\frac{1}{2}$ in.*	*$\frac{1}{4}$ in.*	*$\frac{3}{8}$ in.*	*$\frac{1}{2}$ in.*
2	$3\frac{3}{4}$	$4\frac{3}{4}$	6	3	4	$5\frac{1}{4}$
$2\frac{5}{8}$	$2\frac{3}{4}$	$3\frac{1}{2}$	$4\frac{1}{2}$	$2\frac{1}{4}$	3	4
$2\frac{3}{4}$	$2\frac{3}{4}$	$3\frac{1}{2}$	$4\frac{1}{2}$	$2\frac{1}{4}$	3	4
$2\frac{7}{8}$	$2\frac{1}{2}$	$3\frac{1}{4}$	$4\frac{1}{4}$	$2\frac{1}{4}$	$2\frac{3}{4}$	$3\frac{3}{4}$
3	$2\frac{1}{2}$	$3\frac{1}{4}$	4	2	$2\frac{3}{4}$	$3\frac{1}{2}$

NOTE. Quantities are to nearest $\frac{1}{4}$ yd. and will vary a little according to bond and thickness of wall. Two-inch thick bricks are generally used for facing work only with backings of thicker bricks. Such facings are usually measured as feet super extra over common brickwork, and the extra mortar required should be computed as an extra over, allowing for work in facings as $\frac{3}{4}$ brick thick to cover headers, etc.

'ables II and III. Two very useful Tables in connection with the estimating of brickwork, showing quantities of bricks and of mortar for bricks and joints of various thicknesses.

BALLAST AS RAISED which contains and does not need the application of he rules governing separate fine and oarse aggregates. Cement, of course, is ›st in the voids and does not, with good ›roportioning, increase volume.

Losses due to mixing the various naterials with water is another matter vhich affects volume of finished concrete and, manifestly, estimating as well. A good practical rule is: When coarse and fine aggregates, which are reasonably well graded, and cement are mixed dry together they become a certain volume, and when they are mixed with water and placed in position as finished concrete they reduce in volume, which necessitates adding $12\frac{1}{2}$ per cent or one-eighth to the dry-mix to make a cubic yard of concrete. If the aggregates are very well graded 10 per cent should be added.

BULKING OF SAND, an important element which affects concrete, is not well known to many. A builder who can buy *dry* sand is in a more favourable position than if the sand were wet.

If otherwise dry sand contains about 5 per cent water content by weight of dry sand which is enough to make it moist, it swells by 20 to 25 per cent. Under average conditions moist or wet sand should be considered as bulking 20 per cent.

It may be thought that this bulking does not affect estimating or the concrete, but it does because of the peculiar phenomena that sand, although it swells with a little addition of water, at once goes back to its original dry volume when it is absolutely saturated with water. Any of the following conditions' may arise by using bulked sand:—

(1) According to the data given above under "Voids in Aggregates," if there is a calculated increase in volume of dry-mixed materials due to sand more than filling the voids in the coarse aggregate, then, when the materials are mixed with water the wet sand will reduce considerably in volume.

(2) If there is no such excess of sand then nothing much happens to affect the estimator, as the wet sand will simply shrink and leave more voids for the cement to fill.

(3) If it is the intention of the architect or engineer to use proportions based on *dry sand*, then this should be definitely stated, or a mention made that if wet sand is used the specified volume must be increased by 20 per cent.

(4) If ballast as raised is used, and it is wet, as many river ballasts are, and it contains an abnormal proportion of sand, then due allowance for the shrinkage of sand must be made. This is why it is usual to allow an addition of 25 per cent to the dry-mix to make 1 cub. yd. of concrete.

ESTIMATING COST OF CONCRETE. It is first necessary to compute the quantities of materials to make 1 Y.C. concrete, and then to use labour constants.

EXAMPLE 3. Estimate the cost of concrete in trenches 12 in. thick and not less than 24 in. wide composed of 1 part Portland cement, 60s. a ton, and 6 parts ballast as raised containing about 50 per cent sand, 10s. Y.C.

	s.	d.
1 Y.C. ballast at 10s. . . .	10	0
⅙ Y.C. (equals ⅛ ton) cement at 60s. .	10	0
	20	0
Add for shrinkage, etc., 12½ per cent .	2	6
4-hr. labourer at 1s. 6d. . . .	6	0
Cost Y.C. . .	28	6

EXAMPLE 4. Estimate the cost of concrete, in trenches as above, composed of 1 part Portland cement, 3 parts dry sand 8s. Y.C., and 6 parts gravel 10s. Y.C.

	s.	d.
1 Y.C. gravel at 10s.. . . .	10	0
½ Y.C. sand at 8s.	4	0
⅙ Y.C. cement at 60s. . . .	10	0
	24	0
Add for shrinkage 12½ per cent . .	3	0
Labour, say as before, but it should be slightly more	6	0
	33	0

Now compute as follows the effect of the sand increasing the volume:—

1 Y.C. gravel	27·00 F.C.
½ Y.C. sand . 13·50 F.C.	
Less 45 per cent voids in gravel—10=35 per cent of 27·00 = 9·45	4·05
	31·05

In this case shrinkage must be deducted and adding 12½ per cent means that about 11 per cent must be deducted from 112½ to reduce to 100, say 10 per cent . . . 3·10

Quantity of concrete made . 27·95

Therefore the cost of 1 Y.C.

$$= \frac{27 \cdot 00 \times 33/\text{-}}{27 \cdot 95} = \quad s. \quad d. \\ 31 \quad 10$$

TABLE IV	BRICKWORK. QUANTITIES OF MATERIALS IN CUBIC YARDS TO MAKE ONE CUBIC YARD OF MORTAR					
Proportions	Portland cement, lime-putty, or hydrated lime	Sand which is		Unslaked lump lime ★	Sand which is	
		Dry	Moist and bulked		Dry	Moist and bulked
1 : 1	0·70	0·70	0·84	—	—	—
1 : 2	0·50	1·00	1·20	0·40	0·80	0·96
1 : 3	0·37	1·10	1·32	0·33	1·00	1·20
1 : 4	0·28	1·10	1·32	0·28	1·10	1·32
1 : 5	0·22	1·10	1·32	0·22	1·10	1·32
1 : 6	0·19	1·10	1·32	0·19	1·10	1·32

NOTE. ★ Allowances have been made for increase in bulk of unslaked lime after slaking and quantity necessary to fill voids in sand.

CEMENT-LIME (OR COMPO) MORTAR. This consists of 1 part of cement, so many parts of hydrated lime or lime-putty to so many parts of sand. For practical purposes the quantity of cement and lime in the proportions specified should total the quantity shown in column 2.

EXAMPLE. If a specification calls for 1 part cement, 2 parts lime and 9 parts sand, this is equal to 1 to 3 proportion requiring 0·37 Y.C. of matrix (of which ⅓ would be cement and ⅔ lime) and 1·10 or 1·32 Y.C. of aggregate of dry or moist sand respectively.

TABLE V	BRICKWORK. LABOUR CONSTANTS FOR COMMON BRICKWORK. Assisting in unloading bricks, mixing mortar, laying bricks and erecting and striking scaffolding			
Storeys of brickwork	In cement mortar		In lime, or cement-lime mortar	
	Bricklayer hours	Labourer hours	Bricklayer hours	Labourer hours
Average for buildings not exceeding three storeys	66	50	60	45
Average for buildings not exceeding five storeys	72	60	66	55
If work is taken separately for each storey, allow:—				
Foundations up to damp-course level . .	40	20	36	18
Ground storey	66	44	60	40
First storey	70	58	64	53
Second storey	72	60	66	55
Third storey	74	74	68	68
Fourth storey	76	76	70	70

CAVITY WALLS. With two ½-brick walls, add 25 per cent to above times; with one ½-brick wall and one 1-brick wall add 16 per cent.

HALF-BRICK WALLS. Add 10 per cent to above times.

BRICK-ON-EDGE WALLS. Add 20 per cent to above times.

FACTORIES, ETC., AND VERY PLAIN WORK. Deduct 10 per cent from above times.

NOTE. The constants refer to ordinary work in reasonable quantities and include all rough cuttings, etc. They do not include pointing or jointing or any of the usual items of labour which are measured separately to the common brickwork.

Tables IV and V. Two tables dealing with quantities and time constants for brickwork

Example 5. As Example 4, but using bulked moist sand for which an allowance is made. This will affect the cost as follows:—

	s.	d.
1 Y.C. gravel at 10s.	10	0
½ plus 20 per cent = ⅗ Y.C. sand at 8s.	4	10
⅙ Y.C. cement at 60s.	10	0
	24	10
Add for shrinkage 12½ per cent . .	3	1
Labour as before	6	0
	33	11

The principle of increase of volume is the same, so $\frac{27\cdot00 \times 33/11}{27\cdot95}$ = Y.C. 32 9

Bricklayer. The bricklayer's trade represents a considerable proportion of the total cost of many classes of buildings, particularly housing work, and, therefore, it is vitally important to master the correct methods of estimating. Once the main principles are understood, and the assistance of tabular information appreciated, it will be found easy to estimate successfully.

Tabular Information is given in Tables II to V, and the following examples will show how to estimate the cost of some of the main items.

Example 6. Estimate the cost per rod of common brickwork as specified below in a building three storeys high with materials costing, delivered to site, as follows: common bricks, 70s. per 1,000; Portland cement, including bags, 62s. ton; sand, 8s. Y.C. Labour is to be 2s. and 1s. 6d. for bricklayers and labourers respectively. The brickwork is to be of common bricks standard 2⅝ in. thick with single frogs, ⅜-in. joints, built in Flemish (or English) bond in cement mortar proportioned 1 part cement to 4 parts bulked sand.

	s.	d.	£	s.	d.
4,350 bricks (Table II) at 70s. 1,000			15	4	6
3½ Y.C. mortar (Table III) which requires per Y.C. (Table IV) 1·32 Y.C. sand at 8s. = .	10	7			
0·28 Y.C. cement at 62s. = ...	17	4			
at	27	11	4	17	9
66 hr. bricklayer (Table V) at 2s. .			6	12	0
50 hr. labourer (Table V) at 1s. 6d.			3	15	0
Cost, exclusive of on-costs and profit, per rod			£30	9	3

Example 7. If standard-sized facing bricks are 130s. 1,000 and common bricks 70s. 1,000, what is the cost E.O. common brickwork for facings in English and Flemish bonds, including neat struck-weather pointing? Estimate at per square of 100 F.S. and afterwards convert to F.S.

	£	s.	d.
Facing bricks	6	10	0
Common bricks	3	10	0
Difference in cost per 1,000	£3	0	0
English bond 800 bricks at £3 1,000 .	2	8	0
9 hr. bricklayer at 2s. . . .		18	0
3 hr. labourer at 1s. 6d. . .		4	6
	100)3	10	6
F.S.			8½
Flemish bond 700 bricks at £3 1,000 .	2	2	0
Pointing as above . . .	1	2	6
	100)3	4	6
F.S.			7¾

Example 8. Estimate the cost per Y.S. of 3 in. thick breeze slab partition in cement mortar with 18 in. × 9 in. slabs costing 3s. Y.S. delivered site.

	s.	d.
1 Y.S. slabs at 3s.	3	0
5 per cent waste		1¾
¾ hr. bricklayer at 2s. . . .	1	6
⅜ hr. labourer at 1s. 6d. . . .		6¾
Y.S.	5	2½

Mason. It is customary to employ specialist sub-contractors for this work, whether it is for natural or artificial masonry. All the work, excepting such small items as York stone pads, are often supplied and fixed by the sub-contractor and the cost is usually covered by provisional sums.

Drainlayer. The bulk of drainlayers' work consists of stoneware drains, their various fittings, and inspection chambers.

Example 9. Estimate the cost of 4-in. diameter stoneware drain per Y.R.

	s.	d.
1 Y.R. 4-in. stoneware pipe at list price	2	6
Jointing material 4 in. at ½d. . .		2
$\frac{3}{10}$ hr. drainlayer and labourer at 3s. 2d.		11½
Y.R.	3	7½

ASPHALTER. The work under this trade is usually done by specialist sub-contractors from whom prices should be obtained if the work is not covered by provisional sums.

PAVIOR. There are many classes of paving such as quarry tile, terrazzo, mosaic, asphalt and various composi-tions, all of which are usually laid by specialists from whom prices should be obtained if provisional sums are not allowed. Cement and sand and grano-lithic pavings may be laid by the main contractor.

ROOF SLATER. Although slating to roofs is most usually entrusted to a sub-contractor, it is advisable for the esti-mator to have knowledge of the funda-mental principles of estimating for the work. The architect should specify with care not only the size and lap of slates, but whether they are to be centre or head-nailed and full particulars of the nails to be used. There is an appreciable difference in the number of slates re-quired per square depending on whether they are centre-nailed or head-nailed, the former requiring less than the latter.

THE NUMBER OF SLATES PER SQUARE is given by various tables and is easily calculated by the following formula:—

$$\frac{14,400}{\text{width of slate in in.} \times \text{gauge in in.}} + 5 \text{ per cent waste.}$$

ALLOWANCES FOR CUTTINGS, ETC. After the basic cost per square has been estimated, the costs of cuttings, waste, etc., are computed by:—

Allowing, extra over the ordinary slat-ing, the following additional widths per F.R.:—

Square abutments, top edges and verges . . .	6 in.
Raking cuttings and ditto to hips and valleys . .	9 in.
Double course at eaves .	12 in.
Ditto, but with raking eaves and slate and half at verges	18 in.

SLATING NAILS. Use two nails to each slate: $1\frac{1}{2}$ in. long to slates less than 20 in. long; $1\frac{3}{4}$ in. long to slates over 20 in. long. The nails should be:—

Least weight per 1,000

	$1\frac{1}{2}$ in.	$1\frac{3}{4}$ in.
Copper . .	6 lb.	8 lb.
Zinc . .	$5\frac{1}{4}$ lb.	$7\frac{1}{2}$ lb.

Galvanized nails should not be used in lieu of zinc.

ROOF TILER. Estimating is done very similarly to slating, with allowances made for the following variations in details: most tiles are nibbed and only nailed with two nails to each tile every fourth or fifth course, with nailing to each course at abutments, verges, hips, valleys, and, of course, at top edges and eaves. The nails should be $1\frac{3}{4}$-in. copper or zinc, weighing 8 lb. or $7\frac{1}{2}$ lb. per 1,000 respectively.

The gauge equals: $\dfrac{\text{Length of tile} - \text{lap}}{2}$.

Number of tiles per square equals:—

$$\frac{14,400}{\text{width of tile in in.} \times \text{gauge in in.}} + 5 \text{ per cent waste.}$$

The number of nails per square equals double the number of tiles com-puted by above formula divided by number of courses nailed (plus 15 per cent for top edges, abutments, etc., if not allowed elsewhere).

SIZE OF TILES AND LAP. Standard tiles are $10\frac{1}{2}$ in. $\times 6\frac{1}{2}$ in. and 11 in. $\times 7$ in., and the usual laps are $2\frac{1}{2}$ in., $2\frac{3}{4}$ in. and 3 in.

ALLOWANCES FOR CUTTINGS, ETC. As E.O. ordinary tiling, additional widths per foot run are as follows:—

Square abutments, top edges and tile and half at verges	6 in.
Raking cuttings and ditto to hips and valleys . .	9 in.
Double course at eaves .	8 in.
Ditto raking . . .	14 in.

CARPENTER AND JOINER. These are two of the most important trades in building, and there are a considerable number of tables available which give information to enable the costs of the works to be estimated. Very few builders nowadays have a joiner's shop as they know that it is impracticable to try to compete with specialist joinery manufacturers who quote economic prices for the items of joinery work required under present-day conditions.

IRONFOUNDER, SMITH AND STRUCTURAL ENGINEER. Practically all materials for these trades are supplied and fixed by specialist contractors, or supplied only by them and fixed by the main contractor.

PLASTERER AND WALL TILER. These two trades are usually sublet to sub-contractors, or carried out complete by specialist contractors from whom rates should be obtained.

PLUMBER AND GAS FITTER are two closely related trades which contain many hundreds of items, and estimating the cost of them comes under the category of advanced estimating. The items are covered by a considerable number of tabular data. It is becoming customary for even large contractors to entrust plumbing work to specialist sub-contractors, who undertake plumbing, hot-water and heating engineering, and gas-fitting work.

ELECTRICIAN'S WORK is almost invariably done by electrical engineers, from whom prices should be obtained if the work is not covered by a provisional sum.

GLAZIER. Prices for glass and glazing should be obtained from a glazing contractor.

PAINTER AND DECORATOR. This trade is a very interesting subject, and the keen estimator will soon find it a comparatively simple matter to master the many classes of painting and decorating work, the various surfaces, conditions and situations to which the work has to be applied, the covering capacities of the many materials, and labour constants for executing the work.

ON-COSTS AND PROFIT should be the final and exceptionally important computations made by the estimator in conjunction with the appropriate control officer of the firm or company. On-costs may be defined generally as all items of expenditure which cannot be allotted to a definite job.

Table VI depicts an on-costs and profit computation sheet suitable for comparatively small contracts, and should be read in conjunction with the following comments, in which the index figures in brackets correspond with those shown in this Table.

(1) *Insurances.* These must include health and unemployment, employer's liability, third party risks and any necessary to cover sub-contractors.

(2) *Water.* The percentage sometimes varies with nature of job, and whether supplied by meter or otherwise.

(3) *Ordinary plant* includes such items as scaffolding, barrows, running planks, hoists, etc.; machinery such as concrete mixers, mechanical excavators, dumpers, etc., are usually allowed separately and included in cost of work in which they are used.

(4) *Works Manager* (proper name for general foreman). The salary may be percentaged to ordinary work only, or if desired may be spread over P.C. and P.S. items as well. As a rule it is good practice to confine the percentage to ordinary items.

(5) *Other Works Staff.* For contracts of large value there are usually several staff members, such as agent, sub-agent, works manager, surveyors, accountants, etc., and for such contracts the form of on-cost and profit computation sheet is varied a little.

(6) *Attendances re Provisional Sum Items.* A specification and/or bills of quantities call for attendances on sub-

TABLE VI — **ON-COSTS and PROFIT COMPUTATION SHEET**

....194...

CONTRACT.. E/No...........................

Details of on-costs and profit	*Ordinary items per cent*	*Prime cost items per cent*	*Provisional sum items per cent*
(1) Insurances	$1\frac{1}{4}$	—	$\frac{1}{4}$
(2) Water for building purposes	$\frac{1}{2}$	$\frac{1}{4}$	$\frac{1}{2}$
(3) Ordinary plant, etc.	1	$\frac{1}{2}$	$\frac{1}{2}$
(4) Works manager (general foreman), 10 weeks at £8 $=£80=\frac{£80\times 100}{£4574 \text{ cost of ordinary items}}=$	$1\frac{3}{4}$	—	—
(5) Other works staff	—	—	—
(6) Attendances re provisional sum items . .	—	—	1
(7) Establishment charges	$2\frac{1}{2}$	$1\frac{1}{4}$	$1\frac{1}{4}$
Total on-costs . .	7	2	$3\frac{1}{2}$
(8) Profit on ordinary items	$7\frac{1}{2}$	—	—
(9) Profit on P.C. items:— $7\frac{1}{2}$ per cent less 5 per cent discount . . .	—	$2\frac{1}{2}$	—
(10) Profit on P.S. items:— $7\frac{1}{2}$ per cent less $2\frac{1}{2}$ per cent discount	—	—	5
(11) Profit on on-costs:— $7\frac{1}{2}$ per cent of $7\frac{1}{2}$ per cent	$\frac{1}{2}$	ignore	ignore
Totals	15	$4\frac{1}{2}$	$8\frac{1}{2}$
Totals used . . .	15 per cent	5 per cent	$7\frac{1}{2}$ per cent

Table VI. On-costs and profit computation sheet, suitable for comparatively small contracts. Each numbered item corresponds with the numbered paragraphs given in the text.

contractors; the cost may be added to each item, or it may be included as an on-cost item.

(7) *Establishment charges* are exceptionally important, and can be very costly to a contractor if not regulated properly. They include the cost of the head office staff, rent or equal, rates, telephone, stamps, stationery, auditor's and bank charges, etc. Sometimes establishment charges are not included as an on-cost item, but placed below the "total on-costs" line, in which case they will not rank for profit as (11).

(8) *Profit on ordinary items*, which are the ordinary risk items of contracting, needs very careful consideration.

(9) *Profit on P.C. items* may be governed according to the cash discount permitted or obtained on items which are supplied only by nominated suppliers. The discount is usually 5 per cent.

(10) *Profit on P.S. items* is regulated similarly to (9), but the discount is usually $2\frac{1}{2}$ per cent on work which is supplied and fixed by a nominated sub-contractor.

(11) *Profit on on-costs* is sometimes ignored entirely.

PRELIMINARIES, usually included in bill of quantities No. 1, invite the estimating of such special items as office for clerk of works, and making good damage to roads and adjoining property.

CHAPTER 13

BUILDERS' BUSINESS ADMINISTRATION

Builders' varied operations. Business organization. Maintenance and repair. Superintendence. Departmental divisions. Estimating. Costing. Contract key plans. Materials. Transport. Schedule tallies. Clerk of Works.

GOOD administration should normally help the builder to achieve success, but even good administration is not a complete guarantee against some risk factors such as, for example, losing invested and working capital by having to meet heavy establishment charges during quiet business periods, or loss due to carrying idle plant, unprofitable contracts or bad debts. To guard against these hazards, it is essential that the builder's business is organized and conducted efficiently.

Business Comparisons

The manufacture of a speciality, or merchanting a group of materials, is much simpler than the work of a builder. The builder's case may involve:—

(a) Undertaking contract work, which binds him to obtain labour and materials, provide plant necessary to assemble and complete a given building project in a certain specified manner to client's, architect's, engineer's or other proxy's satisfaction.

(b) Undertaking on a priced schedule unknown specific building work where the extent of the final operations cannot be anticipated.

(c) Undertaking work for a client on a net cost plus lump-sum profit charge.

(d) Undertaking work for a client on a day-work basis or priced schedule for the supply of labour, materials, scaffolding and other necessary plant.

In addition, to ensure retaining a nucleus of workmen, it is quite a common practice for a builder to run up dwelling-house property in order to find occupation for regular workmen during slack periods. These differing business features cannot be separately catered for in business administration; they have to be dovetailed into a composite business procedure that accommodates the whole group.

Although we are concerned with builders' administration, it is not proposed to deal with the up-and-down fluctuations of the builder's business; but rather to describe the work undertaken by sectional members of the builder's office staff—the workshop and building-site labour associations—as a business team, because by that method builders' business procedure can best be illustrated.

The general public want dwelling-houses, churches, institutes, schools and hospital buildings; public bodies and professional men want offices; business men want shops, stores, workshops, warehouses and mills.

Maintenance and Repair

Maintenance and repair work is another phase common to all buildings. The builders' organizations must be sufficiently elastic to undertake all these types of constructive and repair work; equal, on the one hand, to undertake the

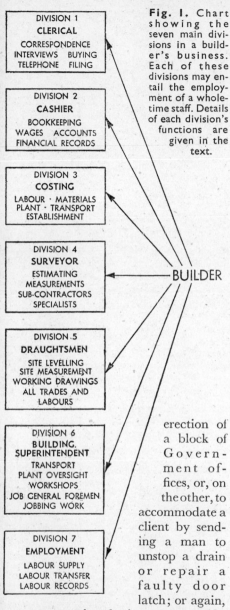

Fig. I. Chart showing the seven main divisions in a builder's business. Each of these divisions may entail the employment of a whole-time staff. Details of each division's functions are given in the text.

DIVISION 1
CLERICAL
CORRESPONDENCE
INTERVIEWS   BUYING
TELEPHONE   FILING

DIVISION 2
CASHIER
BOOKKEEPING
WAGES   ACCOUNTS
FINANCIAL RECORDS

DIVISION 3
COSTING
LABOUR · MATERIALS
PLANT · TRANSPORT
ESTABLISHMENT

DIVISION 4
SURVEYOR
ESTIMATING
MEASUREMENTS
SUB-CONTRACTORS
SPECIALISTS

DIVISION 5
DRAUGHTSMEN
SITE LEVELLING
SITE MEASUREMENT
WORKING DRAWINGS
ALL TRADES AND
LABOURS

DIVISION 6
**BUILDING.
SUPERINTENDENT**
TRANSPORT
PLANT OVERSIGHT
WORKSHOPS
JOB GENERAL FOREMEN
JOBBING WORK

DIVISION 7
EMPLOYMENT
LABOUR SUPPLY
LABOUR TRANSFER
LABOUR RECORDS

BUILDER

to the builder, as an estimate for a contemplated building, or an actual commission to execute. The work may reach the builder through goodwill, competition, finance or jobbing connections. Commissions undertaken may have to be executed under the direction of the client and paid for directly by him; or under conditions in which the builder agrees to satisfy his client through a third party, for example, an architect, an estate agent, or a civil or mechanical engineer.

Superintendence

The policy, direction and supervision of a builder's business are matters that concern the owner, who organizes business procedure and supervises the clerical and workers' staff in his employ.

He seeks to co-ordinate office and works records and methods, and to build up good standard routine practice, equal to maintaining vital business principles, without overlapping of duties.

Although direction and supervision are rightly the preserves of the employer it does not follow that these are always retained by him, as the subsequent review of staff duties will reveal; the multitudinous matters passed up to the chief for directional instructions automatically delegates the control and supervision of the junior staff and workers to those in charge of the various business sections.

Business Divisions

In a medium builder's business there are recurring business duties which entail whole-time staff service in each of the seven chief business divisions, which are charted in Fig. 1.

DIVISION 1. Chief clerk and general office, where the pulse of the business can be gauged:—

(a) Receipt, copying and distribution of correspondence to all concerned.

erection of a block of Government offices, or, on the other, to accommodate a client by sending a man to unstop a drain or repair a faulty door latch; or again, to carry out a hundred or more specific jobs, on constructional work in progress, in all stages from digging foundations to elaborate fittings and finishing of board-rooms and council chambers.

Administration must include the channels by which business is introduced

BUILDING CONTRACT OR WORKS ORDER	*No.*......................
To..	*Date*..
Charge materials and manufacturing costs to { Firm's Order No................................ / Contract Order No...............................	
(wavy rule line)	
A separate sheet to be used for each order	
	Authorized..

Fig. 2. Building contract or works order form for general business purposes. One copy serves as authority to workmen for obtaining materials, etc.; one copy serves costing department for collating charges for labour and materials; one copy is retained at source. For method of allocating numbers see page 398, where the system of parent job numbers is explained and examples are given.

(*b*) The receiving centre of all job foremen's returns of materials (Fig. 3) received, and requisitions for all and sundry materials, plant and labour.

(*c*) The clearing station for all incoming telephone calls, and link with principal or other member of staff.

(*d*) Attendance to callers who may be clients placing an order (Fig. 2), enquiring about unfinished work, requiring some modification of work in progress, enquiry for an estimate; delivering messages or plans required at scattered work centres; sub-contractors, travellers, specialists, consultants, architects. All or any of these may require contacting with some member of the business specially versed in their requirements.

(*e*) During the day will be interviews with the principal; transport, stores, office staff and foremen's enquiries; the preparing and dispatch of orders for material, all fully specified for quantities, delivery dates and transport directions; telephoning or telegraphing to firms whose material deliveries are behind time and delaying process work; and following up letter references which are out of date.

(*f*) Daily return sheets of materials received by job foremen (Fig. 3), firm's invoices and advices for delivered or dispatched goods with requisitions for workshop and merchant supplies.

(*g*) Other items dealt with are those of petty cash for fares, carrier charges, telegrams, postages, special minor supplies obtained by direct messenger.

The foregoing do not exhaust the business service items that are negotiated under the direction of the chief clerk, but they indicate the trend of matters negotiated in this important clearing centre, and the builder in choosing his staff officer realizes the need for employing an active practical chief clerk with a retentive mind able to switch over quickly from any business in hand to negotiate a more urgent call or telephone matter, returning later to the unfinished work in hand.

The stationery used in this business department is largely for correspondence, that is, letter heads, post cards, order forms, invitation-to-quote forms, comparison of quotations, invoice register form, stock letters for urging delivery, tracing whereabouts and reporting

FOREMAN OR STOREKEEPER'S RETURN OF GOODS RECEIVED, OR DISPATCH OF PLANT, etc.

NOTE TO FOREMAN.—Report all goods received on site, whether unpacked or left in crates, how signed for, shortages, breakages; also use this return for recording dispatches, transfers of material, plant, tools, etc. Foreman to retain carbon or other copy for site reference.

Transport medium	Suppliers	Order No.	Description of goods	Quantity					Advice No.	Distribution	
				Count	tons	cwt.	qrs.	lb.		Stock	Job No.

Fig. 3. A typical method of collecting records of goods received or released from every business centre of the firm in connection with work in hand in each department.

damage of materials in transit, catalogues and cross-index cards scheduled under: (a) material names stating supplying firms; (b) firms' names stating material supplied (Figs. 4 and 5).

DIVISION 2. Cashier's office business procedure and records. The chart (Fig. 1) allocates four chief headings of office work, each one of which embraces a very considerable amount of detail in record work that must be kept up to date.

It is from debit and credit records maintained in the books of this sectional business office that the builder frames his policy, as to incurring or reducing his business commitments, and if balance of the whole or part has to be struck at short notice the book records must be kept up to date, for these reveal the financial strength or weakness of the business.

These books record assets like working capital, debtors, capital locked up in buildings, machinery and plant, work in progress, etc., as well as liabilities for

LETTER OF ALPHABET...............			
Name	Address	Shelf	Catalogue No.

NAME OF MATERIAL OR ARTICLE..........			
Supplier	Address	Shelf	Catalogue No.

Fig. 4 (top) **and Fig. 5.** How catalogues are filed to ensure the recording of the name of the supplying firm or the name of the material.

rent, rates, taxes, materials, bank over-draft or balance, and the like, providing thereby a gauge by which to measure the condition of the business.

The cashier's department collects asset and debit data for record from all sources of the business. It is the department from which all moneys are distributed as well as received, where claims for wages of staff and employees generally, whether at headquarters or on building site, are checked and prepared.

It is also the office to which all invoices, travelling (Fig. 6), advertising expenses and payments for materials are distributed after being fully investigated and checked (Fig. 7), also foreman's daily diary sheet (see page 395).

PETTY CASH EXPENSE VOUCHER

Week ending Friday...194....

N.B.—Receipts to be attached for purchases and other expenses if possible.
All charges to be initialled by departmental head and check-initialled by management before payment.

Date	Particulars	Job or Code No.	Site, Job, and other charges			Direct Works charges		
			£	s.	d.	£	s.	d.

Signature..................................... SITE WORKS TOTAL

Authorized for payment .... GENERAL AND WORKS DEPOT TOTAL

Fig. 6. Petty cash voucher for general business use. It is passed to the costing department, after payment has been completed, by the cashier or chief clerk.

INVOICE RETURN SHEET OR REGISTER · FOLIO...............

Invoice No.	Date	Firm supplying	Material description	Amount			Shortage, break-age, discount claims			Passed to cashier		Remarks
				£	s.	d.	£	s.	d.	Date	Initials of clerk	

Fig. 7. Method of collecting and scheduling the invoice debits that are later to be cleared by the cashier

FOREMAN'S DAILY DIARY SHEET

....194...

WEEK.................................

TIME LIMIT—WEEKS.............................

.... WEATHER.....................................

Firm's workmen employed on site	Charge-hands	No. of men	Name of sub-contractors	Fore-men	No. of men	Visitor
Foreman and staff . .						
Plumbers						
Do. mates. . .						
Steel benders . . .						
Fitters, etc.						APPROXIMATE WORK DONE:—
Do. mates. .						
Electricians. . . .						Excavating, cub. yd.
Scaffolders						
Do. mates. . .						Concrete, cub. yd.
Carpenters and joiners .						
Do. do. labourers .						No. of bricks
Plasterers						
Do. labourers . .						Stone, cub. ft.
Painters and glaziers . .						
Do. labourers . .						Steel, tons
Masons						
Do. labourers . .						Timber, bulk
Bricklayers . .						
Do. labourers . .						„ boards
Slaters.						
Tile layers . . .						
Steel erectors . . .						
Concretors						PROGRESS
Navvies						Record work in hand and state of building. Commencement or completion of any section should be here noted.
General labourers . .						
Off-loaders						Particulars of drawings received on site.
Crane Drivers . .						
Mess-room attendants .			TOTAL .			
Messengers						
Miscellaneous . . .			CLERK OF WORKS AND ARCHITECT'S VISITING STAFF			
TOTAL . . .						
TOTAL ON SITE . . .			TOTAL .			

MEMORANDA

General remarks of interest. Likely memo. for guidance and reference. Delays—cause and duration. Accidents—circumstance and action taken. Work delayed or material rejected, and by whom, etc., etc.

....Building Foreman.

A useful method by which the general foreman keeps head office in touch with progress on the site. See text reference on the opposite page and on page 408.

| Date | Invoice No. | SUPPLIES | MATERIAL | QUANTITY | | Ledger Folio | Package | Am |
				Number	Weight			

THE MONTH

| | Direct charges | | | EXPENSE ACCOUNTS | | | | | |
Repairs and maintenance	Job Order No.	Amount	Rent, rates and taxes	Insurance	Laboratory and experiment	Motor lorries and cars	Fuel, gas, water and electricity	C

Fig. 8. Illustrates how the chief items and charges of purchased goods and materials are recorded in purchase ledger for easy reference by the builder and his staff. The result analyses not only the

The information is compiled under headings that allow of full and separate values being available, as illustrated in Fig. 8, which shows suitable headings for a purchase ledger.

Accounts compiled in this manner in loose-leaf ledgers under job numbers (provided by the costing department), provide ready information to the other interested members of the staff, who are saved the trouble of abstracting their requirements or having separately to compile them.

Should the builder, survey or cost clerk want to compare the quantities of bricks, cement, stone, or timber delivered to a building site with the amounts stated in the quantities for the job, the information is provided in the systematic entries of the receipts under its respective head in the purchase journal.

Similar advantage accrues when the builder is preparing a certificate claim statement from an architect on a building contract. The purchases journal records costs and quantities of material delivered, and a site visit supplies, by measurement or check, the amount of the unfixed or stock parcel; a calculation can then be made to establish a fair claim for reimbursement of the value of the amount built into the fabric.

This method of compilation provides a ready factor figure for up-or-down checking of an estimate in priced quantities, when coupled with the value of the trade labour cost, of the trade or labour concerned. The advantages referred to do not exhaust the values of this method, for the record may become a useful one later, should a repeat contract for a replica building be given.

PURCHASES FOR

		CAPITAL EXPENDITURE			STOCKS AND STORES					
g	Fixed plant	Loose plant and tools	Cores, dies, and special tools	Motor lorries and cars	Sawdust	Cement	Hydraulic lime	Material	Pigments	Sundry stores

)ING................. 194......

	EXPENSE ACCOUNTS—continued						
ries ffice ses	Printing and stationery	Carriage and cartage	Travelling expenses	Advertising, including samples	Telephone	Local and audit	Head office

full costs but also the debits of sectional charges which are useful for certificate claims and check of job quantities. The form should be read from left to right as a loose-leaf ledger sheet.

The cashier's department includes all the regular routine maintenance services connected with bank, petty cash, insurance and wages books; workmen's compensation and employer's liability records, register forms, and invoice, purchase, nominal, contract and jobbing journals; machinery and plant, with accepted tenders, labour registers; employees' income tax record sheets and quarterly return sheets; payment of headquarters and building-site wages, receipt and banking of incoming cheques, preparing and dispatch of merchants, sub-contractors, specialists and other creditor payments.

The labour clerk although scheduled as in a separate group in the chart (Fig. 1), is subordinate to, but a staff member of, the cashier's department. His duties include: entering and maintaining up-to-date records of all employees in the firm's labour register, as name, address, identity card number, clock number, insurance book records, including weekly stamp maintenance; contract on which engaged, whether started on site or transferred.

The labour clerk acts as intermediary between foremen of contracts in progress for the temporary or permanent transfer of workmen, and in directing applicants to work on jobs where there is a labour shortage.

He also keeps records of compensation claims, obtains particulars of accidents, and checks for being in order, the data required by the medical officer, insurance company, head office, etc.; he maintains the supply of Government, Home Office and other forms that are necessary on all jobs where power plant is in commission; receives, files and submits (as and when required to H.M. Inspector) the accident register, insurance company's boiler and other certificates of inspected, checked and tested plant and machinery units.

DIVISION 3. Sectional administrative work provides records which reveal profit or loss on every physical item of the business transactions. The staff of the costing department analyses all business costs of materials purchased, wages paid, plant employed, power consumed, rateable value of areas occupied by stores, workshops and machines.

Costing Abstracts

Costing abstracts are a simple means of classifying and allocating all business expenses to the actual item of work for which they have been incurred. In practice, definition by the use of numbers has proved satisfactory, being simple, effective and elastic in accommodating the varying classes of work undertaken. The following lay-out illustrates the method in principle and provides a range free from overlapping:—

Jobbing and repair work   *Numbers*
    at day work rates, say   1/01 to 1/999
Contracts for which esti-
    mate has been given, say 2/01 to 2/999
Schedules of prices based
    on measured work, say   3/01 to 3/999
Cost plus percentage sys-
    tem, say   .   .   .   4/01 to 4/999
Lump sum profit work,
    say   .   .   .   .   5/01 to 5/999

Parent Job Numbers

The foregoing comprises a system for parent job numbers, to which can be added specific trade, labour, expense or material charges that link its character by the added tail number, as follows:—

Preliminary site lay-out charges for Contract No. 2/01 are automatically defined when they are coded as follows:—

2/01/0   Site surveying draughtsman and labour in attendance
2/01/1   Charges for architect's drawings and photo prints
2/01/2   Watching, lighting and first-aid supplies and attendance

and so on, leaving a group of say 50 unit tail numbers to define and accommodate these and similar charges like insurances, mess-rooms, stores, water, electricity, hoarding, etc., common to all contracts.

Carried to the next stage:—

2/01/50   Soil stripping
2/01/51   Bulk excavation and grubbing out old foundations
2/01/52   Trench excavating
2/01/53   Trench timbering material and labour
2/01/101 Common brickwork in foundations
2/01/102 Common brickwork above damp courses, etc.

Systematic Coding

Regular systematic coding of this nature serves for workmen recording: (*a*) time engaged on any given piece of work in workshop or on the site; (*b*) material requisitioned for use on the job; (*c*) transport service in supplies.

Building organization on these lines simplifies the work of the costing clerks in the abstract of labour, material, machine, transport and all other business charges, and the results provide useful comparisons between work of similar nature being undertaken on a dozen or more contracts, revealing efficient or inefficient control; providing reliable cost figures for subsequent estimating; showing the net value of work executed relative to governing conditions; showing the capital locked up in work in progress; showing the capital locked up in stores and the material stock which is awaiting the time when it will be built into the fabric.

Date....................	JOBBING AND DAYWORK						
Day.................... Job No. 1/924 Name of building... N.B.—Materials used record on back of form.	WORKMAN'S DAILY TIME SHEET RETURN Workman's name...................... ,, Clock No.........................						

Transferred from Job No.	Particulars or description of work	Time		For Cost Office			
		Hrs.	Mins.	Rate	£	s.	d.
	Hanging sash windows with new cords, correcting door and window furniture and making good prior to repainting this property	7	30				
Signed:	Foreman or Charge Hand...............................						
	Client's signature for service and correct hours..						

Fig. 9. Costing department form, recording time and material chargeable to the client on jobbing or day-work services. Every item of expense must be recorded by the costing department.

The cost department functions in abstracting all time, material, transport, plant, machine and running expense accounts, under job number headings, and compile weekly returns that act as indicators in revealing strong, weak and delayed operating centres.

The costing department requires feeding with the information of every business expense, every item of which must indicate the job number to which the charge must be debited. In this way it is possible to liquidate the separately abstracted workmen's time sheet (Figs. 9 and 10) returns with the grouped wage totals (Fig. 11) received from workshops or general foremen for site labours. Stores requisitions (Figs. 12 and 13) showing issued items should balance stocks in hand less extract values for the week, and invoice amounts clear the entries of goods re-turned by foremen on building sites (Fig. 3) and stores collection sheet (Fig. 14).

When a builder's business includes a fleet of motor lorries or other vehicles it is customary to requisition for service by job numbers. In these cases wages and service hours are returned to the costing department for abstract, the weekly totals of which serve a dual purpose: revealing chargeable wages against specific contracts and void standing or non-service periods to be a charge to the establishment, thus showing shortage or excess transport facilities.

The costing department prepares and fixes the hourly service charge for costs of fuel, oil, and running and repair expenses for each vehicle, including capital cost and depreciation with profit.

The rate charges are similarly compiled for workshop machinery and portable plant units by this department, which analyses the capital cost, the

CHARGE HAND'S DAILY TIME SHEET RETURN
FOR GANGS OR GROUPS OF WORKMEN EMPLOYED
IN A BODY ON SIMILAR WORK

Day.................................

Date...........................194

Trade { ....
        ....

Rate of pay per hour ☞																
All tally numbers on board ☞																Total hours
Job No.	Description															

〰〰〰〰〰〰〰〰〰〰〰〰〰〰〰〰〰〰〰〰〰〰〰〰〰

															Total	
Number working	Hours paid for per day															
....	Note exceptions, late starters, etc.														Total	

Tally No.

Signature...Charge Hand ....

Checked by...Foreman

Abstracted by...Cost Clerk

Fig. 10. Costing department return form of labour charges for grouped labour, such as a ganger controlling a group of navvies, or a foreman bricklayer in charge of a section of brickwork.

estimated life of useful commission, the cost of power with repair and maintenance charges, and the rental and rateable values of space occupied whether fixed on foundation bed or stored during non-service periods. Labour in setting up machines, and cleaning and wear of parts, are separately included as charges to the work in hand, grouping all business charges in Fig. 15.

DIVISION 4. The builder's surveyor's department embraces the business ser-vices of estimating, obtaining measurements of executed work, and negotiations between sub-contractors and specialists undertaking portions of contract work which are under the control of the builder.

The general character of the surveyor business service starts with the preparation of an estimate based on the priced items of an architect's bill of quantities for a given project, but before the surveyor spends his time and experience on pricing the quantities he submits to his

WAGES SHEET

NAME OF BUILDING SITE............................. JOB NO.............

Week ending.....................................194.. SHEET NO...........

Check No.	Name	Thur. O.T. after 5 p.m.	F.	S.	S.	M.	T.	W.	T.	Time pay-able	Total hours	Rate	Wage total	Wage* trans-fer	Fares	Gross wages	Income tax deduc-tion	Insur-ance firm	Insur-ance men	Net wages
													£ | s. | d.	£ | s. | d.	£ | s. | d.	£ | s. | d.	£ | s. | d.			£ | s. | d.

Workmen's transfer record when dividing service between building sites, for payment where engaged on pay day.

Fig. II. Method by which the general foreman advises his firm of wages due to building site workers each week. The collated hours on time sheets (Figs. 9 and 10) are checked by the costing department for balancing before the wage of each workman is made up.

REQUISITION FORM FOR STOCK OR MATERIAL ON STORES

DEPARTMENT... DATE.....................194....

Position or Job No. requiring	Material	Description	Stores physical Number	For allocating cost use only

Signature.. DEBIT TO STORES STOCK CARD

Officer requiring ....Storekeeper or Clerk

Date ....

Checked by .... ADJUSTED IN COST RECORD LEDGER

Person receiving ....Clerk

Date ....

NOTE.—If quantity detailed not received amend figures in red ink to agree with actual amount received.

Fig. 12. Costing department, showing the type of form recording withdrawal of material from stores and linking it up with the job on which it is used as well as providing check on stocks.

MATERIAL STOCK-LEDGER CARD

Description or Name..

Size..

Bin No. ....

RECEIVED

Order No.	Date	Supplier	Weight				Quantity	Rate	Amount		
			tons	cwt.	qrs.	lb.			£	s.	d

Fig. 13. Costing department stock-ledger card which records under physical or vocabulary numbers the materials purchased in bulk, and links issues by recording all requisitions withdrawn as in Fig. 12.

chief certain of its main features, for example:—

(a) The cubic contents with an approximate cubic feet value; for, should the size, value or scope be outside the range of the builder's business capacity, there is no object in facing the expense of preparing the estimate.

(b) The quantity items to allow of comparison with the business lay-out. A firm with large joinery and masonry equipments are more interested in work in which these trades dominate, rather than in a heavy brickwork or reinforced-concrete building. Additional items, including exceptional time-limit clauses, extra risk to workers with increased insurance charges, as, for instance, on works where live electricity, railway, or acid dangers are evident, cramped sites involving heavy transport, or night labour dispatch and receiving, owing to police restrictions, with all the extra negotiations to insure railway or merchants' supplies being accessible.

(c) Danger of liabilities to adjoining buildings, shoring settlements, risky underpinning, etc.

The foregoing and similar items that a preliminary consideration of each job throws into the limelight, are first reviewed by the surveyor and then submitted in précis form to his chief, for a ruling about action to prepare and submit a tender.

On works executed on a schedule basis, the surveyor is engaged measuring up for checking measurements of sub-contractors to insure agreement in claims, keeping an accurate check of all schedule items of buried work, in excavating, brick, stone, damp courses and timberwork. He also takes out building insurances in joint names of builder and owner, or the latter alone, maintaining and increasing such policies with added value as the work proceeds,

PHYSICALLY NUMBERED

PEAK QUANTITY AMOUNT...

RE-ORDERING QUANTITY AMOUNT.............................

ISSUED

Stock hand	Date	Requisition No.	Job allocation	Weight				Quantity	Rate	Amount		
				tons	cwt.	qrs.	lb.			£	s.	d.

This card allows the builder to obtain a theoretical stock balance at any time independently of the quarterly, half-yearly, or yearly practical stocktaking periods, besides being a check on leakages.

together with sundry other services in which he can serve in clearing items connected with site work that arrive at headquarters instead of the site, and other items that, while they may be vitally required on a building site, are also in the nature of information wanted for record purposes at head office.

Estimating is sectional work of the surveyors' department. It is essentially an expense department of any business from the fact that a 10 per cent return of accepted tenders for estimates compiled is generally considered fairly satisfactory.

By the time a builder has obtained all the initial information he requires for estimating, a very considerable amount of basic office work has been undertaken.

A wide experience of all building-trade labours and good judgment are vital for estimating efficiently. In the main all the items of the quantities are separately considered, but there are exceptions in such items as: labour in excavating over the building site area per cubic yard; labour and materials common brickwork per rod; labour and materials 1-in. T. & G. flooring laid and cleaned off per square. These and similar standard items can be dealt with on an up-or-down price on reliable basic values.

The sections of the quantities for which outside firms are invited to quote require typed copies from the original for forwarding to two or more sub-contractors with conditions of contract particulars.

DIVISION 5. The headquarters of the draughtsman are in the drawing office at head office, where original drawings are received, registered and copied to requirements. The signed contract drawings are vital for reference between architect and builder, but usually print copies are multiplied for use at head office as well as for use on the site.

The draughtsman provides print or tracing copies to requirements for the use of the firm's staff as well as other interested parties, after having first entered the original in the register of drawings.

When a contract building scheme lends itself for division, the draughtsman prepares and circulates a small key plan, dividing the scheme into lettered blocks, A, B, C, D, etc., as sketch, with or without the north, south, east and west directions, to use during construction by all interested parties.

	West			
L	J	F	D	A
M	Light well	G	Light well	B
N	K	H	E	C

South (left side), North (right side), East (bottom)

The introduction of this simple medium simplifies communication by letter, telephone or sketch, because it conveys to the receiver in a moment, the precise point about which a query is being raised, always, of course, providing that the query links up the floor level with the block letter.

Building cube contents are measured and calculated by the drawing office staff. Building-site services of the drawing office are specially valuable to the rank and file as well as to the general foreman. The draughtsman's services are semi-professional in character; they are not directly concerned with finance or the direct control of labour.

The vital initial site work which the draughtsman undertakes in the survey, with theodolite and dumpy level, includes:—

(a) Setting out from a fixed building line

the building outline and boundaries.

(b) Fixing datum levelling block with auxiliary datum pegs about the site.

(c) Checking at intervals the foundation, damp course, step floor sill and similar levels on all sides and on site interior.

(d) Marking datum levels above inserted floors on stanchions and walls (Chapter 1, Fig. 38).

(e) Fixing peg levels for drain manhole channel inverts before and after connecting.

(f) Preparing subsidiary working drawings for submission for licences from authorities, for encroachment on footways, gantrys, shoring, etc.

(g) Setting out roads, sweeps gradients, as well as plotting best positions for installing derrick universal jib, gantry, and other cranes, with plant and machines, narrow-gauge track, concrete mixers, mortar mills, hoists.

Maintenance Charges

Buildings that require years to erect often carry maintenance charges throughout the building years and for a specified period after completion. In these and similar practices the builder's administration provides references through the sectional drawing office staff records.

DIVISION 6. The builder administers his business in the work's superintendent's section through the experience of a well-qualified practical tradesman, who has not only reached a high standard in one of the building crafts, but is qualified by his wide building experience to direct building operations in a sound, safe, and efficient manner. An architect will often call for building features without knowing the practical steps required to execute requirements.

The superintendent, as far as practical building work is concerned, is a works manager for the builder, who is execut-

Order or Job No.	Ironmongery		Plumbing		Paints and glass		Bulk material		Timber		Stores Collection
	Page	Amount	Page	Amount	Page	Amount	Page	Amount	Page	Amount	
		£ s. d.		£ s. d.		£ s. d.		£ s. d.		£ s. d.	

Form No. 4/14 ....
STORES COLLECTION
Week Ending ....

Fig. 14. Costing department stores collection form for compiling all supplies either grouped together or serving from the various stores or any of the building site works.

ing contracts beyond the range of personal attention to all building work; his duties include a combination of practical, theoretical and administrative services which may be summed up as follows:—

(1) Visit to sites for which an estimate is in preparation, for reporting later to estimating clerk information about the proposed building requirements in demolition, shoring, propping, site fencing, footpath or gantry licences, conditions normal or abnormal for material transport, labour supplies, public services, water, gas, electricity, introduction of stock plant, cranes and machinery equipment or special hire or purchase items, not common for re-use on other contracts.

(2) Selection of general foremen to take charge of job, with regular contact during construction of administrative and practical policy procedure in the lay-out and process operations, to ensure the firm's labour and plant being employed to the best advantage. Arranges plant, tools and materials and transport facilities in the unit job and firm's interest, keeps a watchful eye on costly labour operations, and encourages foremen to aim at the greatest efficiency of organization.

(3) Consultation and oversight of work programme at headquarters, as in joinery manufacture, stone masonry yard work, plant store fitting and repairs to equipment.

(4) Care of scaffolding, working tools for excavating, scaffolding, shoring, propping and trenching timbers, including transfer between works in progress to save handling labours and transport charges.

(5) Oversight of plant erection, checking the erectors' work and ensuring that conditions and equipment comply with Home Office regulations, including periodic chain testing with register and certificate records. Assists foreman in trade union difficulties.

(6) Personally supervises the expediting of material or manufactured supplies to ensure building works proceeding with regularity.

(7) Obtains stationery supplies for general foreman on outside work, and informs foremen of business routine about which they lack information.

The job foreman is responsible for keeping time records of all labour employed and for returning weekly wage sheets (Fig. 11), including petty cash

MANAGEMENT CONSOLIDATED WEEKL

"F" JOB No............................

DESCRIPTION..

DEMONSTRATION SHOWING METHOD OF COMPILING ALL CURRE

N.B.—*Blank space to be left at the close of each month for monthly totals.*

Date			Site wages				Depot wages				Grouped stores				Transport				Credits including empt...	
Wk. end. month	Day	No. sheet	Amount			No. sheet	Amount			Page	Amount			Page	Amount			Page	Amou	
(Estimated amounts in red ink figures)			£	s.	d.		£	s.	d.		£	s.	d.		£	s.	d.		£	s.
Job No. 140/1			313	10	4		73	4	8	04/5	151	8	10	04/	2	2	4½			
142/1			264	5	7		95	3	5	,,	123	12	3	,,	3	9	2			
142/4			293	14	4		24	7	4	,,	126	10	2	,,		15	9			
145/1			262	7	9		41	10	2	,,	220	17	1	,,	2	4	8			
150/4			427	16	9		37	14	2	.,	134	3	6	,,	1	8	9			
150/7			193	10	5		49	4	10	,,	157	12	6	,,	5	6	8			
151/4			213	4	10		72	5	0	,,	158	11	7	,,	4	9	5½			
154/1			305	3	7		17	4	3	,,	279	6	3	,,	7	6	4			
			£2,273	13	7		£410	13	10		£1,352	2	2		£27	3	2			

Fig. 15. Costing department form, showing collection of charges under specified heads collating all the charges under sectional headings that allow of check balance with duplicate records. The

items (Fig. 6), arranging payment for back days, certifying overhead charges, collecting insurance cards and numbering workers to an agreed code.

A further duty of the foreman is to anticipate material requisitions (Figs. 16 and 17), reserves, stocks and returns particulars of all materials required for building purposes under the direction of the visiting superintendent; and to supply sub-contractors' workmen with the materials they require.

Requisitions for transport, motor lorry, horses and carts, to job, requirements for material supplies to and from headquarter's workshops, railway station, or merchants' depots, for actual site work, are all part of the foreman's work. The preparation of site plant for insurance inspection, the maintenance of hoist or crane ropes, lighting, heating and cooking requirements, are all subject also to the foreman's direct arrangement and superintendence.

When a clerk of works is engaged by the architects for whole-time service on the same building site, considerations and agreements have to be reached on many matters not fully anticipated by the quantities and specification, but which require settlement to maintain regular process work. These difficulties are readily cleared when both minds seek to reach agreement in the spirit of the whole contract.

Day-work items are inevitably introduced on some of the revisions, in which case the foreman applies for the usual order, and on receipt arranges to keep time and material separately recorded to submit to clerk of works for certifying signature as correct record. Measurements of depths of footings, manholes, trench and other items—which process work demands should be filled in as executed—call for joint agreement between foreman and clerk of works.

Besides returns already indicated, the

B COST AND REVIEW SHEET

No.............................

COSTS FOR WEEKLY OR MONTHLY REVIEW AND BALANCE

age	Sundries Amount			Ledger folio	Purchases Amount			Page	Sub-contractors Amount			Totals			Charges			Work in progress totals		
	£	s.	d.		£	s.	d.		£	s.	d.	£	s.	d.	£	s.	d.	£	s.	d.
8/8		7	2	04/9	210	15	0					751	8	11½						
,,		14	3	,,	315	7	6		320	0	0	1,121	12	2						
,,	3	2	10	,,	23	4	5					471	15	2						
,,		5	8	,,	7	4	9		100	0	0	624	10	1						
,,			6	,,	118	3	8					719	7	3						
,,		2	3	,,	472	4	10		150	0	0	1,028	6	6	As	sum	o			
,,			9	,,	156	15	0					605	6	7½	Flat	Rat	e			
,,	1	4	6	,,	19	7	9		240	0	0	869	12	8	sa	y 2½	%			
	£5	17	11		£1,323	2	11		£810	0	0	£6,191	19	5	£155	0	0	£6,346	19	5

same sheet can be used as a unit job cost sheet retaining the same heading costs, but limited to revealing loss or profit in separate trade work—information which is of exceedingly great value.

SCHEDULE TALLY NUMBERS OF CRAFTSMEN, SEMI-SKILLED, AND LABOURERS FOR ISSUE AS DETAILED (*see* page 408)

	Numbers start at	Numbers finish at
Craftsmen		
Carpenters and joiners	1	50
Bricklayers	51	100
Plumbers and pipe fitters	101	125
Masons	126	175
Plasterers	176	200
Painters	201	250
Semi-skilled		
Gangers	251	260
Winch and crane drivers	261	280
Scaffolders	281	310
Ironworkers—all sections	311	350
Labourers		
Carpenters' labourers	351	375
Bricklayers' labourers	376	425
Plumbers and pipe fitters' labourers . .	426	450
Masons' labourers	451	500
Plasterers' labourers	501	525
Painters' labourers	526	550
Timbermen	551	575
Navvies and timbermen	576	675
General labourers	676	725
Miscellaneous	726	775
Watchmen	776	800

FOREMAN'S OR DRAUGHTSMAN'S WINDO[W]

JOB NAME..

SCHEDULE (

N.B.—0/1=Below ground floor; G=Ground floor; 1/1 upwards=1st floor, etc.

Position as block letter	Floor level	Position	Room No.	Win- dow No.	Kind of window			Size		Reveals		
					Sash frames	Steel case- ments	Lava- tory pivoted	Height ft. in.	Width ft. in.	9-in. rebate	2¼-in. rebate	4½-i reba
Block A	L.G. floor	Front area	0/1	0/1	1	—	—	5 0	3 0	—	—	√
Block C	Gd. floor	Side elevation	G/14	G/14	1	—	—	6 4	3 0	—	—	—
Block E	2nd	Light well area	2/9	2/9	—	1	1	5 0	2 6	—	√	—

Fig. 16. Method by which ready and useful information is compiled by the general foreman or

JOB NAME............................

JOB NUMBER............................

DATE............................

TYPICAL EXAMPLE (
FURNITUR[E]

Block letter position	Floor level	Room No.	Door			Locks										Kicking plates	Doo check
			No.	Description	Size	Dead		Latch		Rebate		Box		Special			
						R.	L.	R.	L.	R.	L.	R.	L.	R.	L.		
Block A	Gd.	G 1	G 1	Entrance door	7′ × 3′ × 2¼″	—	1	—	—	—	—	—	—	—	—	—	—

Fig. 17. A form similar to that in Fig. 16, but giving particulars with regard to doors instead of

foreman prepares a daily or weekly report with sundry information about the work in progress to keep his firm and colleagues in touch with the work (*see* the form on page 395).

Foresight and good management are expressed by the foreman in a hundred ways if his ability is equal to opportunities provided by every unit job.

All sections of business departments reap the benefit of specializing workmen's numbers in consecutive order somewhat on the lines of the classification in the schedule tally on the previous page, where separate time and wage returns carry the indicating job number.

When a clerk of works is engaged on a building contract, his services closely link the architect and his professional assistants with the builder's foreman in

DER, FIXING AND RETURN RECORD

NDOW OPENINGS

JOB No....................................

DATE ....

Description	Furniture and fittings						Glazing			
	Sash fastener	Sash lifts	Sash eye openers	Hopper catches	Balance weights		26 oz.	Polished plate	Flemish glass	Vita glass
					Lead	Iron				
...l throughout excepting ...nglish oak sill . . .	1	2	1	—	2-18lb. 2-20lb.	— —	√	—	—	—
...l outside; mahogany ...nings inside; oak sill .	1	2	1	—	2-20lb. 2-24lb.	— —	—	√	—	—
...l casement with opening ...opper.	—	—	1	1	—	—	—	—	√	—

builder's draughtsman in regard to the building project he controls, and for ordering various fittings.

...OR FITTING AND
...HEDULE

Reference for pull handles and locks { L.=Large / S.=Small / R.=Right han / L.=Left hand

...or ...hes	Door furniture								Hinges					Bolts		
	Room No. plates	Pitts	Escutcheons	Finger plates			Pull handles		Steel washered			Floor, spring and check hinges		Monkey tail	Tower bolts	Flush bolts
				Single	Double	Special	L.	R.	4 in. butts	5 in. butts	Rising butts	Single spring	Double spring			
	—	½	1	—	—	1	—	—	—	1½	—	—	—	1	1	—

windows. It introduces method into requisitioning and keeps a check on issues during fixing

all matters appertaining to the material specified for use and employed in the fabric, together with the manner in which the workmen perform their work.

For instance, he checks the thickness of the brick bedding to insure the brick courses rise in correct level and regular height dimension, satisfies himself that concrete aggregates are to specification requirements, keeps check records of foundation depths, drain trenches, and other buried or modified work which are not as described on the plans and in the quantities and specification.

The clerical side of his duties includes reporting to the architect any matters about the building in progress, such as dates and results of drain tests, cement and steel consignments, and the number and nature of workmen employed

PULLMAN COURT, STREATHAM

These blocks of flats were designed by Frederick Gibberd, F.R.I.B.A., and comprise one of the first examples of modern flat construction in Britain. They are built of reinforced concrete, and are designed to give a maximum of daylight, fresh air and convenience. Flat dwelling is a new form of living which is still insufficiently understood in this country, in comparison with other countries.

MODERN COUNTRY HOUSE IN SURREY

This house was designed by Maxwell Fry, F.R.I.B.A., one of the leaders of modern architectural design. It is of concrete construction. Note the horizontal treatment and the balcony arrangement on the top floor. Flat roof construction is becoming increasingly popular in country houses.

CHAPTER 14

TECHNICAL TRAINING

Future developments and opportunities. Technical colleges. Apprenticeship. Junior schools. General education. Technology and drawing. Craftwork. Evening classes. Examinations. Administration and estimating. Architecture.

IT is generally realized that the building industry will be required to play a vital part in the new world developments, not only in the replacement of buildings destroyed by enemy action, but in the erection of the many kinds of buildings which are essential to the proper advancement of civilization.

The demands which will be made on the industry and associated professions will be on a scale without precedent; their magnitude, complexity and urgency will provide far greater and more numerous opportunities for individual skill and collective effort than ever before. But there will be difficulties, not the least of which is the training of the necessary architects, surveyors, engineers, building administrators and organizers, supervisors and craftsmen, and it is the last-named category that is likely to present the greatest problems.

New Materials

The many recent changes in building technique are not likely to displace these craftsmen, but there will undoubtedly be a great increase in the number and types of new materials and prefabricated units of construction which may, in due course, result in the creation of new classes or categories of craftsmen.

It is not here intended to speculate on the precise nature of these new trades, but it is reasonable to assume that a craftsman who has a sound educational foundation, general and technical, in addition to his craft skill and experience, is not likely to find exceptional difficulty in dealing with new methods and materials.

It is important, however, that a man who has not this educational advantage, and whose efficiency depends solely on his practical experience, should consider this aspect of building activity; it is rarely too late to study, and technical colleges in most towns offer excellent facilities in evening classes for adult workers as well as juniors.

Entering the Building Industry

It is not possible to refer in detail to courses suitable for senior craftsmen, nor for those older men who may be attracted from other occupations into the building industry; their problems will be largely individual, which can only be solved by consultation with the heads of technical colleges and others experienced in education.

At present, entry to the craft may be direct—on leaving the elementary school—or after a pre-entry training of two or three years in a junior technical school. In either case apprenticeship is necessary, but the boy who has had full-time education in a junior technical school obtains an extended fundamental education. All boys with ambition should attend part-time classes for the purpose of supplementing their experience and obtaining varied training in both theoretical and practical building.

The good craftsman, whatever his trade and however he is trained, must not only be well skilled in the use of tools, but he must also have a thorough theoretical knowledge, so that his ability is not limited to the particular kind of experience his daily work may provide.

Success for the student depends very largely upon the nature of the business undertaken by the employer. Where the work is of a high standard and carried out locally, the apprentice may not only gain valuable experience, but also is able to attend regular part-time classes. If, however, the work is of poor quality or has to be carried out in conditions of great urgency, and is some distance from the apprentice's home, he may have little opportunity of gaining and developing craft skill, and none of attending evening classes.

The difficulties of present-day apprenticeship are appreciated by employers, and under the rules of some organizations, they are expected to allow or require apprentices to attend a technical college on two half-days in each week.

Junior Technical Schools

Full-time schools for boys destined to become craftsmen were introduced in a few centres before the last war; since that time others have been established and have trained many boys who have found successful careers in the building industry. The number so trained, however, has at no time represented the major source of supply of craftsmen, and it is already recognized that post-war requirements will involve the opening of schools in all important centres of building activity.

Junior schools of building may vary somewhat in different parts of the country, but they generally provide a two-year or three-year course, the age of entry being thirteen to fourteen years. In some cases the whole course is of a general character with little emphasis on any individual craft; but the type of school most likely to be established is that which aims at a sound basic training in the general work of the building industry.

Workshop study taught in schools may provide for some or all of the following: bricklaying, carpentry and joinery, plumbing, painting and decorating, masonry, plastering, and woodcutting machinists' work.

The subjects of the curriculum fall generally into three main categories: (1) general education; (2) building technology and drawing; and (3) craftwork.

General Education

The age of entry is such that a boy's general education is by no means complete, and it is essential to his future progress that it should be continued throughout the whole course of his technical training.

English subjects, including history and geography, may not appear to have a direct vocational value, but besides enabling a student to express himself clearly and intelligently, these subjects are now taught in such a way as to encourage a better understanding of the cultural, social, and economic structure within which every craftsman must live and work.

Mathematics and science are first taught on general lines, but their application to simple technical problems soon reveals a close connection with building technology, and some degree of specialization may be possible in respect of each of the trades. Mathematics, which includes arithmetic, algebra, geometry, and perhaps elementary trigonometry, leads naturally to the study of mensuration and builders' quantities, and also to the application of scientific principles to those problems of structural and mechanical design which may be encountered by the craftsman.

Science, which comprises elementary chemistry and physics, enables a student to study intelligently the properties of building materials, and the principles which underlie the engineering practice which forms part of the industry, such as heating and ventilating.

It will, however, be clear that a junior student cannot devote sufficient time to chemistry and physics to be able to study exhaustively the scientific problems related to his craft, but it is important that he should be made aware of the nature of those problems so that he can recognize them and appreciate the principles of both traditional and modern technical processes.

Technology and Drawing

All craftsmen must have a sound knowledge of the materials they use: many of these materials have been used for hundreds of years; their characteristics are well known and their use in craft processes is based on rule of thumb methods evolved by long experience. Students are taught that those methods will not always apply in connection with new materials intended to serve a similar purpose; hence the need for a knowledge of the properties and uses of materials, based on the scientific laws which govern the behaviour of those materials.

It is also important that students should appreciate the general scope of other trades to which their own craftwork is related, so that in the setting out of work in the shop or on the site, they may make adequate provision for other trades and avoid unnecessary cutting away and making good.

This general knowledge of building is known as building construction, a subject which is usually taught to all students in each year of the course. It is not to be expected that the subject can be studied to an advanced stage; indeed it is better to restrict teaching to the general characteristics of simple typical examples of traditional and modern methods of construction.

Importance of Draughtsmanship

It will be appreciated that the study of building subjects and the practice of building crafts involve at all times a sound knowledge of technical drawing, while in some cases considerable skill in draughtsmanship is an essential qualification. Drawing is, in effect, the language by means of which technical details and instructions can be most effectively communicated.

Technical drawing is developed from simple geometrical principles which are usually taught in the first year. During the second and third years, the study of geometry may be continued by students in some trades with special reference to practical problems in masonry, plastering, etc., while ability in making and reading technical drawings is developed with the study of building construction.

Freehand drawing is usually taught to all students in order that they may be able to make clear and accurate sketches, but in some trades the subject is of considerable importance.

Craftwork

As we have already stated, most technical schools are likely to give a boy the opportunity to select and to work in the craft which attracts him. This is no doubt a very desirable procedure, but the choice of trade must be made carefully in the knowledge that it may well be the most important decision in his life.

This may best be achieved by arranging for all first-year students to spend a period in each of the workshops, where they may attempt simple characteristic exercises in order to discover whether they have the aptitude and interest which are so essential to a successful and happy career. From the second year onwards a boy may specialize in workshop practice and in those other subjects which are specially related to his craft.

It is highly important to distinguish clearly between workshop practice in a school of building, and manual training in an elementary or secondary school. While the junior technical school is not intended to produce a fully trained craftsman, it is essential that the teaching and practice of craft processes should be related, as far as possible, to shop and site conditions. Tools, equipment and materials ought to be identical with those in normal use, while exercises should, wherever possible, be carried out to full size.

Evening Classes

There are few towns which do not provide some form of evening education for those engaged in the building industry and certain of the closely allied trades and professions. The number and grades of classes must depend upon the number of students to be provided for. In some cases, for example, it may only be possible to provide one course or group of classes in each of the first, second and third years, students in various occupations being required to study collectively such subjects as mathematics and calculations, geometry, technical drawing and building construction.

In some of the larger towns, however, it is possible to provide complete and specialized courses for each of the important trades, for persons engaged in building organization, management and supervision, and for technical assistants in the offices of architects and surveyors.

The objective in every class, however general or specialized it may be, must be to provide the fullest possible training in the basic principles which govern practical work. It is essential for teachers and students alike to bear in mind that day-to-day experience in an office or on the site is often very limited in scope: technical education must fill in the gaps, and enable—and encourage —a student to advance his knowledge systematically so that he may ultimately become proficient in all branches of his calling, and qualify himself for the more responsible, more interesting, and better paid posts which are always open.

It is neither possible nor necessary to set forth the various kinds of evening courses which are available, but the following is a four-years' course which has been planned for apprentices and improvers in the plumbing trade.

First Year

PLUMBING THEORY LECTURE. Tools and materials in common use; simple details of sheet-lead work and pipe work; fittings in general use.

CALCULATIONS AND DRAWING. Calculations of areas of pipes and capacities of tanks, etc.; measurement of temperatures, and elementary science in relation to plumbing practice; geometry and drawing to scale of simple plumbing details.

PRACTICAL WORK. Simple exercises in sheet-lead and pipe work.

Second Year

PLUMBING LECTURE. More advanced details of sheet-lead work and the introduction of sheet-copper work; elementary principles of hot and cold water supply systems and materials and fittings used; sanitary fittings in general use and methods of fixing and jointing.

CALCULATIONS AND DRAWING. The use of duodecimals and more advanced calculations; more advanced science in relation to the properties of water, water and air pressures, and the measurement of heat; drawing to scale of more advanced technical details studied in second-year lectures.

PRACTICAL WORK. More advanced exercises in sheet-lead and pipe work; sheet-copper work; simple light-gauge copper pipe work; lead burning.

Third Year

PLUMBING THEORY LECTURE. The further consideration of the principles and practice of hot and cold water supply for domestic and industrial purposes; drainage details; sanitary fittings and connections to drains; materials and joints for industrial and other special purposes.

PLUMBERS' WORKING DRAWINGS. The setting out of sheet-lead work from plans and measurement of quantities of material required; the setting out of groups of sanitary fittings and the arrangement and detailing of all waste, soil and ventilating pipes; the lay-out of drains.

PRACTICAL WORK. The development of skill in sheet-lead and pipe work, and in sheet-copper and copper pipe work; bending of wrought-iron pipes; lead burning and ornamental lead work.

Fourth Year

PLUMBING THEORY LECTURE. Water supplies, storage, treatment and distribution; the principles of practice and design of hot water heating systems; other methods of heating; ventilation of rooms, sanitary fittings used in hospitals, hotels and public buildings; by-laws; drainage schemes; sewage disposal; drain testing.

PLUMBERS' WORKING DRAWINGS. Calculations and lay-out of systems of heating by hot water; methods of taking off quantities; drawing to scale of typical examples of equipment taught in theory lectures.

PRACTICAL WORK. More advanced lead burning; brazing and welding; bending and jointing of lead pipes up to 4-in. diameter; exercises in the installation of various types of W.W.P.s and other fittings.

This course, although not set forth in complete detail, illustrates the progressive nature of study which should be characteristic of the evening training of junior craftsmen in all of the crafts. The student is first of all given a basic training in elementary mathematics and science and simple technical drawing, a knowledge of the tools of his trade, and is required to carry out simple practical exercises intended to teach him the feel and properties of the materials in common use. From this basic training develops the study of all branches of his trade, in theory as well as in practice, so that however limited his opportunities in his daily work, the student is given the widest knowledge of his craft.

The relationship between education and examinations is a matter about which there is a great deal of controversy, but it is generally conceded that a sound system of examination has definite educational advantages. Students of the building crafts are fortunate in the existence of the City and Guilds of London Institute, whose examinations are recognized throughout the country by teachers, employers, and the various institutions whose registration is an important qualification. Examinations are conducted annually in the following subjects: carpentry and joinery, woodcutting machinists' work, brickwork, masonry, plasterers' work, painters' and decorators' work, plumbers' work, sanitary and domestic engineering in relation to plumbers' work, builders' quantities, and heating and ventilating engineers' work.

Examinations for Craftsmen

In each subject there are intermediate and final stages, and each examination usually includes a practical and theory test. The whole system is under constant review by advisory committees, each of which includes representatives of technical education and employers' and operatives' associations.

Candidates usually have the advantage of being able to take the City and Guilds examinations at their own technical colleges. In conclusion it may be pointed out that the examination syllabuses are drawn up by the advisory committees, and are so arranged that they constitute an invaluable guide to progressive study over a period of years.

Most large technical colleges provide excellent facilities in evening classes for those employed in the offices of building contractors, but it is to be regretted that although the building industry is one of the largest and most important in the country, little advantage has been taken of the long-standing opportunities of organizing large and important full-time senior schools of building.

It appears to be a popular view that the industry does not offer sufficiently attractive careers to young men of secondary school education to justify full-time technical training for a period of two or three years. There is also some evidence that most firms have a definite preference for taking boys straight from school and providing training for them in their own offices.

Senior Schools of Building

There are, however, a few senior schools of building throughout the country which have trained a number of men who now occupy posts of responsibility and whose careers are a complete justification of this form of education. These schools provide a two or three years' course, and the curriculum includes those subjects referred to in some detail under junior technical schools, but with a general training in all of the crafts, and advanced study of building construction, including steel-framed buildings and reinforced concrete construction. Builders' quantities and estimating are introduced at appropriate stages when students have a sufficient knowledge of constructional details and mensuration, while drainage and sanitation, land surveying, specifications, building law and accountancy are also included.

Building Diplomas

National building diplomas and certificates were introduced some years ago by the Board of Education in conjunction with the Institute of Builders, and provide for a system of examination by the schools in relation to a course of instruction previously approved. The courses are more or less uniform throughout the country, having building con-struction as the principal subject.

The Ordinary Certificate is awarded at the end of three years evening study, and the Higher Certificate at the end of a further two years. Diplomas are awarded to full-time students who complete satisfactorily a more or less similar programme of study.

Perhaps the most appropriate qualification by examination for the builder is Licentiateship, Associateship or Membership of the Institute of Builders, followed in due course by election to Fellowship after approved experience as a master builder. The Institute examination syllabus is closely related to the professional qualifications of a master builder and his administrative staff, and requires of candidates a sound business experience as well as school training, although the Licentiateship or first examination may be considered to mark the completion of a three-years' full-time course.

Architecture

During the last twenty-five years, many architectural schools have been established in many parts of the country, and a large proportion of those who enter the profession do so after a three or five years' full-time course of study. Schools which reach and maintain a sufficiently high standard, and fulfil certain other requirements, are recognized by the Royal Institute of British Architects, and the school examinations are accepted as a qualification for election, in due course, to Associateship of the Institute.

Most of the schools offer free places and scholarships, while a large number of maintenance scholarships is offered annually by the Architects' Registration Council.

Those who desire further information should write to the Secretary to the Board of Architectural Education.

CHAPTER 15

BUILDING LAW
.

Public Health and other Acts. Model by-laws. Contracts and their conditions. Warranty and Negligence. Accidents. National Health Insurance. Unemployment Insurance. Workmen's Compensation. Apprenticeship. Fire Insurance.

PRE-EMINENTLY amongst Building Acts, the Public Health Act, 1936, concerns the builder operating outside the Metropolis.

Those operating within the Metropolis are mainly concerned with the Public Health (London) Act, 1936, the London Building (Amendment) Act, 1935, the London Building (Amendment) Act, 1939, and the Metropolitan Water Board Act, 1932.

Those operating either outside or within the Metropolis are concerned also with the Housing Act, 1936, the Shops Act, 1934, and Factories Act, 1937.

Section 61 of the Public Health Act, 1936, requires local authorities to make by-laws with respect to buildings and sanitation, including temporary buildings. Local authorities are under an obligation to pass the plans of a building within one month of the date of these being submitted, if they conform to the by-laws.

A local authority has power under the Act to require houses to be supplied with water (Sections 137–141).

Section 3 of the London Building (Amendment) Act, 1935, requires the construction of every building or shelter existing on August 2, 1935, to be in accordance with the London Building Act, 1930 (*see*, now, the London Building (Amendment) Act, 1939), the Act of 1935, and any by-laws under the latter Act. (Section 4 of the Act of 1935 empowered the London County Coun-

cil to make by-laws in respect to nineteen matters affecting buildings; and Section 97 of the Act of 1939 increased the number of these matters very considerably.)

Section 16 of the Metropolitan Water Board Act, 1932, empowers the Metropolitan Water Board to make certain classes of by-laws. These are to deal with the construction of pipes, materials to be used, joints, taps, valves, cisterns, testing and stamping of fittings, and similar matters.

The Housing Act, 1936, is mainly concerned with making provision for securing the repair, maintenance and sanitary condition of houses; the clearance of areas and redevelopment; abatement of overcrowding; and the provision of housing accommodation for the working classes.

Model By-laws

Alterations and additions to buildings and the construction of new buildings, for the most part, are regulated by local by-laws.

Section 68 of the Public Health Act, 1936, provided that outside the Metropolis all by-laws in force at the date of the passing of the Act should expire on July 31, 1939; and that by-laws made under Part 2 of that Act should cease to have effect on the expiration of ten years from the date on which they were made, unless either period should be extended by the Minister of Health.

By Section 61 of that Act every local authority may, and if required by the Minister must, make by-laws regulating the construction of buildings within its area, and the materials used for the purpose; the space about, and the lighting and ventilation of, buildings and the dimensions of rooms intended for human habitation; the height of buildings, and of chimneys above the roofs; sanitary conveniences, drainage, cesspools and ashpits; stoves and other fittings (but not electric stoves and fittings) in so far as these affect the health of the community, and fire prevention; private sewers and communication between drains and sewers.

By-laws may require the giving of notices to, and the deposit of plans with, the local authorities; and when plans are deposited the local authority must, within four (or in certain circumstances five) weeks, give notice of their acceptance thereof; or in the case of rejection their reasons for this.

If work to which plans relate is not commenced within three years, the local authority may declare the deposit of the plans to be of no effect.

An appeal from a local authority's decision lies to a court of summary jurisdiction. By Section 67, questions between local authorities and persons who have executed, or are proposing to execute work may, on joint application by the parties, be referred to the Minister of Health for determination.

Contracts

All business firms at some time enter into contractual relations with others, so that a working knowledge of the law of contracts is essential to assure the legality of business dealings.

A contract is a mutual promise enforceable at law. The contract creates obligations for all parties thereto; and each party has the right in law to the performance by the others of their obligations in his interest. There are promises which are not enforceable by law, and the term "contract" should not be applied to these.

Essentials of a Contract

(1) OFFER AND ACCEPTANCE. In a simple contract, whether oral or written, offer and acceptance must be intercommunicated by writing, actual words or conduct; mere moral, social or honorary obligations cannot create a contract. Words or writing create an express contract; but a contract inferred from the promisor's act or conduct is termed an implied contract, that is, implied in law. In all cases it must be clear that the parties intended that the offer and acceptance should be certain, and establish legal relations between them; and the acceptance must be in the same terms as the offer.

An offer can be withdrawn by notice at any time before it is accepted. A letter of acceptance is effective as soon as it is posted; unless, of course, the notice of retraction has already been received by the party accepting.

(2) CONSIDERATION. Simple contracts are only valid when some consideration is expressed showing that the agreement made is not for gratuitous services or things. But a promise made by the solemn form of a deed in writing—signed, sealed and delivered—is a valid contract in absence of any consideration.

(3) CONTRACTUAL CAPACITY OF ALL PARTIES. To make a contract binding, all the parties must have the capacity to enter into it. For instance, a corporation must contract under its seal. A contract is not required to be under seal when the matter is of trifling importance or of daily necessity, or where the work to be done was included among the general objects for which the contracting corporation was created.

(4) GENUINENESS OF CONSENT. In all contracts there must be evidence that the parties were of the same mind when contracting.

(5) LEGALITY. Some contracts are illegal by the rules of Common Law or by Statute.

AN ENEMY ALIEN cannot make a valid contract with a British subject.

A contract may become invalid by reason of the following:—

(1) MISTAKE. A contract made under a mistake may be avoided.

(2) MISREPRESENTATION. If misrepresentation is innocent, that is, if it consists of an untrue statement made without knowledge of its untruth, the contract so made is voidable; if the misrepresentation is fraudulent the contract is voidable, and, further, the wronged party may claim such damages as he can prove. Fraudulent misrepresentation is that made with knowledge of its untruth, and with intent to deceive and to cause the other party to act on the misrepresentation.

(3) COERCION. A person may be coerced and his consent to a contract extorted by duress or undue influence; these circumstances may make a contract voidable.

CONTRACTS IN WRITING. Certain contracts are not valid unless in writing, e.g., bills of exchange and promissory notes. Certain contracts must be evidenced in writing: (a) those coming under Section 4 of the Statute of Frauds, as agreements which are not to be completed within one year from the contract date; (b) those contracts which come within the scope of Section 40 of the Law of Property Act, 1925, as transfer of land. In this instance there must be a memorandum setting out the terms of the contract for sale, the consideration, and the names of the parties, and it must be signed by the party who is to be charged or by his agent.

CONTRACTS BY DEED. Some contracts are only valid when made by deed, e.g., when a corporation is one party, when there is no consideration, and again when leases covering three or more years, or sales of sculptures (with the copyright thereto), are involved.

VOID CONTRACTS. This is really a misnomer. They are not real contracts. The parties acquire no contractual rights or liabilities.

VOIDABLE CONTRACTS. These are contracts which may be held valid or rendered void at the option of one of the parties.

IMPOSSIBILITY OF PERFORMANCE OF THE CONTRACT. This is not really a substantial ground for avoiding contracts. If a person binds himself unconditionally to do something which eventually proves to be impossible, he will still be held to his bargain and have, in addition, to pay damages. As to this, see the Law Reform (Frustrated Contracts) Act 1943, which adjusts the rights and liabilities to parties to frustrated contracts.

DISCHARGE OF CONTRACT. This may be effected by: (a) agreement of the parties before the contract has been performed; (b) performance; (c) breach of the contract; (d) in some instances the operation of law.

BREACH OF CONTRACT may occur by prevention, refusal, or default of the parties severally.

Building Contracts

Building contracts are governed by the general rules applying to all contracts, but they have been held to be specially complex. The parties to a building contract are the building employer and the general contractor.

Other persons who may be concerned with the contract, though not parties to it, are: architect, surveyor, clerk of works, contractor's agent or foreman;

in some instances there may also be a consulting engineer or other specialists.

Nowadays, much of the work is delegated to sub-contractors and suppliers; but none of these is party to the main contract, and the building employer has no privity of contract with any of them.

MEASUREMENT CONTRACTS. These are of two types:—

(a) A schedule is prepared of all the items likely to be required in the contract work, and a unit price is put to each. A copy is issued to the contractor, and his tender is in the form of an average percentage on, or off (or it may be that he accepts) these prices; this percentage is added to, or taken from, the total sum for the work done, calculated on the unit prices of the schedule.

(b) A similar schedule is provided, but the contractor is asked to tender by the putting of his own unit price to each item. In either method, payment is made by measuring up the work.

PRIME-COST-PLUS-PERCENTAGE CONTRACTS. The contractor agrees to do the work and to keep a prime-cost book. He is paid on the total shown in the book plus a percentage agreed upon as his profit. The tender is in the form of this percentage. Overhead charges are included in the prime-cost.

TARGET CONTRACTS. In inviting tenders for a target contract the employer, or his agent, prepares a rough estimate of the proposed work based on similar work already executed. This figure is put to contractors who are asked to tender in the form of a percentage they would require on this figure for their services (or fees), on the basis of the rates for labour and prices of materials prevailing at the end of the first four weeks of work on the proposed building. These are the target prices. Subsequently, if any of these vary the contractor receives, in addition to his fees, an agreed percentage of any sum

by which admissible costs are less than target costs; and forfeits an agreed percentage on the amount by which they have increased. In calculating bonus or penalty, variation in increased labour and materials costs are allowed for.

DEFINITIONS. Section 42 The London Building (Amendment) Act, 1939, defines a builder as "the person who is employed to build, or to execute work on a building or structure; or, where no person is so employed, the owner of the building or structure."

No statutory definition of a building appears to be extant; though the Courts have given many legal definitions. For instance, that it is a block of brick or stone work covered in by a roof. A bay (or bow) window or an addition to an existing building has been held to be a building, as has also a structure of wood to be used permanently as a shop.

Where an architect is employed, there is no implied warranty, i.e., a contract collateral to the main contract, that his plans and specification can be carried out. When a quantity surveyor is employed to prepare bills of quantities, there is no implied warranty that his bills of quantities are correct.

Architect's Responsibility

An architect is chargeable with negligence if he neglects to examine the site before completing the contract documents; he must decide on the practicability of carrying out the proposed work on the site. It seems to be a duty laid on the contractor also to acquaint himself with the conditions of the site before tendering. In some contracts, only the drawings and specification, with the formal contract, are involved. In this case, all work which can reasonably be said to have been contemplated must be done, and at whatever cost, in order that the contractor may claim payment for the whole work. This holds for items not shown in the drawings or specially named in the specification.

APPROVAL OF WORK. Sometimes the contract provides for the approval of the work: (a) by the employer alone; (b) by the architect alone; (c) by both the employer and the architect. However it be, approval must be given without unreasonable demands on the contractor. It is the duty of both employer and architect to give all facilities to the contractor to enable him to carry out his contract with advantage to himself.

COMPLETION. Most building contracts include a clause providing for the work to be completed at a stated date, and for penalties by way of liquidated damages (agreed damages) if the time is exceeded. Further, what is called a maintenance period is provided for, during which the contractor has to maintain, that is, to make good defects in, the contract work. The end of this period limits the contractor's liability for any patent defects, though he may be liable for defects which appear afterwards (up to six years) if it can be proved that they are latent defects; that is, defects due to defective work carried out by the contractor during the contract period.

CERTIFICATES. As previously stated, where an architect is employed, he is usually the certifier under the contract in respect to payments to be made to the contractor. The certificates are of three kinds: (1) interim, for payments on account during the progress of the works; (2) penultimate (or completion) certificates, when the work is virtually completed; (3) final certificates.

Provision is made for an amount, usually 10 per cent, to be held back on each certificate. These amounts are called retention moneys; they are paid in full on the final certificate and serve to insure that final adjustment of accounts may be made before final payment.

Some contracts provide for the final certificate to be conclusive and binding on both parties, leaving no opportunity for review or redress for either in such matters as claims for extras, delay in completion, defective work, over- or under-certifying of the final account, or other things about which one or other considers himself aggrieved.

But the usual form of contract preserves a way for redress by an arbitration clause. Then the final certificate is reviewable by an arbitrator.

Accidents

Every artisan or workman employed by a building contractor has the legal status of a servant, and it is his duty to obey the lawful instructions of, and to serve, his master faithfully.

The contractor is not a servant. His status is that of a person carrying on an independent business.

An architect or surveyor is the agent of the building owner, but he must meet the building owner's wishes and not act arbitrarily or capriciously.

On employment, an artisan or workman implicitly warrants that he possesses, and will exercise, reasonable skill and competence in his craft or labour. He must take due and proper care of property entrusted to him; and, if he does not, and any accident or damage results, he becomes liable for negligence unless he can prove that such damage was due to accident or to other circumstances beyond his control.

On an accident being caused to building works by an employee, the loss falls primarily on the contractor for the works; for the tendency is to absolve an employee from any liability. Special circumstances such as gross carelessness may modify this general rule.

A building contract usually provides that the contractor shall indemnify the building owner against liability for damage or injury to the works on the part of the contractor and his workmen. A sub-contractor is liable to the general contractor in his turn.

If the building owner lends men to the contractor, or a contractor lends men to a sub-contractor, then the person under whose control any workman causing damage was, at the instant of his default, is liable. A person accepting the loan of a workman and yet not actually paying for the loan, is still liable, because the real employer of the workman has handed over the control of him *pro tem*.

National Health Insurance

With few exceptions, all employed persons over the age of sixteen years are insurable compulsorily by their employers against sickness under the National Health Insurance Act, 1936, the National Health Insurance, Contributory Pensions, and the Workmen's Compensation Acts, 1941 to 1943. They are known as "employed contributors." Persons of the same age, but not employed, may insure themselves voluntarily under the Act. They are known as "voluntary contributors."

Medical benefit is also payable to every person who becomes employed between school-leaving age and the age when insurance becomes compulsory (sixteen).

The total weekly sum payable by an employed contributor is, for a man 11d. a week, and for a woman 10½d. Of these amounts the employer contributes 5½d. A man therefore contributes 5½d. and a woman 5d. The employer pays, in the first instance, the whole amount; but he recovers the contributions paid by him on behalf of the contributors, by deduction from wages.

A voluntary contributor contributes at the employed rate if he is entitled (or when his total income from all sources does not exceed £420 a year) to receive medical benefit.

BENEFITS. In general all insured persons are entitled to the following benefits: (*a*) medical treatment and attendance, including proper and sufficient medicines, etc.; but medical treatment and attendance in respect of a confinement is not included (*see* below); (*b*) sick benefit; that is, a series of weekly periodical payments commencing on the fourth day of incapacity, and continuing for twenty-six weeks; (*c*) disablement benefit; that is, periodical payments after the determination of sick benefit. This is not available until 104 weeks after the contributor's entry into insurance, and at least 104 weekly contributions have been paid. This benefit ceases at the age of sixty-five.

Unemployment Insurance

Under the Unemployment Insurance Act, 1935, all persons of either sex, whether British subjects or not, if employed in insurable employment, must be insured against unemployment.

In order to receive benefit a claimant must prove: (*a*) his payment of thirty contributions under the general scheme of insurance, and twenty under the agricultural scheme; (*b*) that he has applied for benefit, and that since the date of his application he has been continuously unemployed; (*c*) that he is capable of, and available for, work; (*d*) that when required to attend at authorized or approved courses he attended such, or that he had good cause for non-attendance.

Workmen's Compensation

The employer has a liability to pay compensation to workmen who sustain injuries during the time of, and as a result of, their employment. The law relating to this is contained in the Workmen's Compensation Acts, 1925 to 1943. Since 1925, many amendments have been made to this Act.

By Section 3 (2) (a) of the Act, persons whose remuneration exceeds £350 a year (made up of monetary remuneration or other things of pecuniary value) are expressly excluded from the provisions of the Act. This limit was, however, increased (as from January 1, 1942) to £420, by Section 13 of the National Health Insurance Contributory Pensions and Workmen's Compensation Act, 1941.

No compensation is payable unless the injury disables the workman from earning full wages for more than three days. If it can be proved that the accident is due to the workman's serious and wilful misconduct, compensation is only payable if the injury results in death or serious and permanent disablement. Also, where a workman is incapacitated for more than four weeks, no compensation is payable in respect of the first three days.

Juvenile Training

The National Federation of Building Trades Operatives recommend, amongst other things, that boys on leaving school should be under the supervision of local advisory committees; that juvenile unemployment centres should be set up; that juveniles should be absorbed in the building industry immediately on leaving school; and that vocational training should be given locally throughout the period of apprenticeship.

APPRENTICESHIP SCHEMES. There are many and varied apprenticeship schemes existing in Great Britain. In Scotland, the number has been reduced to two; one general scheme operating south of Dundee only, and another agreed between the Aberdeen master builders and the Aberdeen branch of operative masons. In Ireland the apprenticeship schemes consist of local agreements.

APPRENTICESHIP IN LONDON. It might be useful to outline the model scheme in London. The minimum entry age is fifteen, and the leaving age twenty-one; the maximum period five years, minimum four years. If a boy satisfactorily completes a three-years' course at an approved technical school prior to apprenticeship part of this counts in the apprenticeship period, and he starts practical work at the third year wage with other special privileges.

Other apprentices must, in lieu, attend a day technical school during the first year for one whole or two half-days per week, which is done in their employer's time. All apprentices must attend technical classes on two evenings a week.

Insurance

FIRE INSURANCE. The contractor of a new building is liable to the building owner if the building is damaged or destroyed by fire prior to completion. When, however, the contractor is carrying out alterations, additions or repairs to an existing building and it is destroyed or damaged by fire, the owner of the building bears the loss.

A contractor for a new building usually insures against fire, and most forms of building contracts include a provision that he shall do so. He should also see that all sub-contract work is covered by insurance. In this way, the building owner is protected against damage by fire if it occurs prior to completion.

A fire policy is a contract of indemnity. The insurers usually reserve to themselves the right or option of reinstating damage by fire as an alternative to the payment of the insurance money.

No person can insure a property against loss by fire or otherwise, unless he can prove beyond doubt that he has a definite financial interest in it.

CHAPTER 16

SCIENCE AND BUILDING

New materials. Building Research Station: tests and experiments. Damp. Use of plastics. Alternative methods of construction. Future possibilities. Prefabrication methods. American methods. The house of the future.

SCIENCE is playing a more and more important part in modern building. It is greatly increasing the number and variety of methods and materials. Today there are many synthetic materials, cements, plastics, plasters, building boards, partition and nailing blocks and various types of paints all developed by scientists. Some combine strength and light weight. Some are designed to deaden sound; others to resist damp; others to protect against fire.

For over twenty years the Building Research Station at Garston, near Watford, has been studying all aspects of building, and it has been of great service to the building industry. Some of its many activities are mentioned in this chapter.

Hundreds of cases of smoky chimneys have been referred to the Building Research Station, where examination found that generally the root of the trouble lay in the fireplace design. Builders often try to abate the nuisance by providing more ventilation, by adding various chimney pots and cowls and by reconstructing flues. But scientific tests have proved that usually reconstruction of the fireplace in accordance with proper plans can alone provide a complete cure.

In recent years the volume of normal building has been largely reduced, but the large programme of construction for war purposes has brought up fresh problems. An example of a war problem is that of fire resistance. For a number of years scientists have been testing the fire resistance of the structural elements of buildings. The knowledge accumulated has been of great value in providing for air raid protection.

Vertical Fire Stop

There is no doubt about the effectiveness of a vertical fire stop. Fig. 1 shows an actual test of setting a timber roof on fire, and any damage, or even the charring of the timber beyond the stop, being effectively checked. As shown in the photograph, the fire stop consists of a screen of fire-resisting material fixed at right angles to the roof surface from eaves to ridge.

Progress has also been made under wartime conditions in the building of factories and economizing in building materials and labour. Examination of such materials as steel, timber, cement and bricks, has made it possible to cut down quantities very considerably below normal peace-time standards. In the design of steel-frame factories particular care has been taken to minimize damage from bomb explosions.

The following are some interesting examples of research recently carried out. Until a short time ago we had little practical knowledge of the strength of bridges. We knew that certain bridges would carry certain weights, from

VERTICAL FIRE STOP TEST

Fig. I. General view of a timber roof immediately after a fire test, showing how the vertical fire stop, which is fixed at right angles to the roof surface, has effectively prevented damage or charring of the timber beyond it. (Reproduced by permission of the Controller, H.M. Stationery Office.)

centuries of experience, and we could calculate bridge designs theoretically. But to what extent certain bridges were necessarily strong or weak in practice was doubtful.

The decision of the Ministry of Transport to pull down seventeen bridges, and replace them by new and wider bridges, provided the opportunity to carry out tests on the dispersion and distribution of an applied load and the extra strength contributed by the parapet walls. Laboratory tests were made on some of the specimens of cast iron, brick and stone, which had been removed from the bridges.

The actual tests were made at night when the traffic was at its minimum. The results were of great value to the Ministry of Transport. Fig. 2 is a picture of the Alcester Road South

Bridge, Birmingham, erected in 1795. This was tested so as to determine (*a*) the dispersion and distribution of an applied load and (*b*) the strength contribution of the parapet wall and filling. In one test a load of eighty tons was applied. From these and other investigations on highway bridges much is being learnt of real value for the future.

Damp Problem

Another subject of general interest is that of damp. Many thousands of house owners have complained bitterly in their new homes of damp coming through brickwork. In some cases it appeared that the rain penetrated through brick. In order to test this out in a laboratory a small rain machine (Fig. 3) was constructed. This enabled 1 sq. ft. of wall to be exposed to a wind blowing at 30 m.p.h., accompanied by an artificial rain of a desired intensity. Tests were made on various types of brick panels.

In some cases the panels were penetrated by the wet in forty minutes, while others remained dry at the back after treatment for four hours. Inquiries into damp buildings showed that not all the cases were due to the brickwork failing to resist rain penetration. In many the cause of dampness was condensation, the presence of salts in plaster, or the misplacing or absence of damp courses.

All these experiments have increased our knowledge of the strength and weathering properties of bricks. With a

BRIDGE USED FOR LOAD TESTS

Fig. 2. Erected in 1795, this bridge of stone and brick construction stood up to a load test of over eighty tons before collapsing. (Reproduced by permission of the Controller, H.M. Stationery Office.)

ARTIFICIAL RAIN MACHINE

Fig. 3. Machine for producing the effect of driving rain on 1 sq. ft. of brickwork panel and used in the preliminary study of resistance of brick walls to rain penetration. (Reproduced by permission of the Controller, H.M. Stationery Office.)

vastly increased demand for building in the near future it is of vital importance that we shall have proper standards for such common building materials as stones and bricks.

Not only the outside of a home, but also the inside, can be greatly improved in comfort and convenience by the application of the results of scientific research.

An example of this is heating and ventilation. We do not wish to spend unnecessary money upon fuel, and at the same time warmth is essential for good health. Tests have been made in relative advantages of hot water radiators, tubular heaters and plenum heating. Much valuable information has been learnt on this subject and also on the kindred subject of ventilation of a warm room. Fig. 4 shows the Eupatheoscope used for measuring the equivalent temperature of a warmed room and thus helping to investigate the various physical factors influencing human comfort.

Comparisons were made of the ventilation of a room heated by an open coal fire or stove ; by a normal gas fire ; by a radiant electric fire on the hearth ; and a unit electric heater in the corner of the room and a hot water radiator under the window. Special attention was directed to the following points: the circulation of the air in the room; whether there was any stagnation or if there were any pronounced draughts; and how frequently the air in the room was changed.

These and many other experiments will help to ensure better and more comfortable homes in the future. It is anticipated that upwards of 4,000,000 new houses will be required during the next few years, as well as offices, factories and public buildings.

Clearly new methods and new materials will have to be used if the losses are to be made good within a reasonable

Fig. 4. The Eupatheoscope Mark II used for measuring the equivalent temperature of a warmed room and thus helping to investigate various physical factors in human comfort. (Reproduced by permission of the Controller, H.M. Stationery Office.)

period, as well as the design and equipment meeting modern needs.

We must therefore expect to see the use not only of brick, stone and cement, but of new and untried systems. Fortunately scientific research has now been developed so that the householders of the future may be more protected against damp and insecure homes. We must always remember that the criterion of design in a home is warmth and weather resistance. The illustrations which are shown in this chapter will give every reader, whether he has scientific training or not, some idea of the importance of science to building.

Fig. 5 shows, for example, an experimental roof. All builders have had experience at one time or another of the leaking roof. Investigation by scientists shows defects to be due to wetness of roof timbers, or damage to tiles from frost or faults in construction. On the experimental roof the behaviour under artificial weathering conditions of tiles laid at different pitches was observed.

Figs. 6 and 7 illustrate the effect of chemicals on a house. Sulphates derived from brickwork by moisture entering at the exposed parapets, caused the cement rendering of the wall to crack and lift away. An upward movement of the wall followed, due to the expansion of the outer leaf of cavity brickwork. This caused a crack inside the building extending horizontally for a distance of about 30 ft. As a result of this and similar investigations, builders can be advised on the composition of stuccos that resist the penetration of water.

With the extensive use of concrete

ARTIFICIAL WEATHERING OF TILES

Fig. 5. Experimental roof for observing the behaviour under artificial weathering condition of tiles laid at different pitches. (Reproduced by permission of the Controller, H.M. Stationery Office.)

now and in the future, it will be more necessary to avoid defects. The ageing of the concrete makes these defects all the more apparent.

As, generally speaking, greater care is taken on the Continent to ensure a well-finished structure, special study was made before the war of the exposed surfaces of many concrete buildings in Continental countries. A series of specimens have been exposed to natural weathering in South Kensington and elsewhere, and Fig. 8 shows a place of exposure at Sheffield. These and many other tests will influence future standard specifications for cement and building regulations.

A new and ingenious method of construction devised by the Building Research Station is shown in Fig. 9. This method enables an arched structure to be built without the use of centering. Thus, in view (*b*), the next block to be fixed will be held up, owing to its semicircular ends resting on the concrete dowels; and in the centre of this block will be another projecting dowel to support the adjoining ends of two subsequent blocks.

Possibilities of Plastics

Perhaps the most important modern building development is the range of materials known as plastics. These are synthetic resins, of which there are many varieties, phenol formaldehyde being the best known. This synthetic resin is the chief constituent of Bakelite.

The unique property of synthetic resins is that they are thermo-setting; that is, when the resin powder is compressed and heat applied, the plastic sets, and when further heat is applied it has no effect. Plastics can thus not only be conveniently moulded to any shape, but they are highly heat and water resisting. Usually the resin is mixed with a filler, such as wood flour. An important use of plastics is for glues, and the best plywoods are now bonded with synthetic resin adhesives. These plywoods are so water resistant that they can be used for outside work.

Probably in the near future plastics will be used in the manufacture of windows, doors, door frames, window sills, lintels, skirtings, staircases, floor slabs, roof slabs, and sheeting. Indeed it may be possible to establish a new structural method of plastic building technique, but all this must be subject to costs, and, of course, durability and weathering. Plastic materials are light and can be easily handled. It may be possible to manufacture in workshops sections of the new homes of the people.

Fig. 6. How sulphates, derived from the brickwork by moisture entering at the exposed parapets, have caused the cement rendering of the wall to crack and lift away from the brickwork, is shown in the above photograph. (Reproduced by permission of the Controller, H.M. Stationery Office.)

Fig. 7. The crack inside the building extended horizontally for a distance of about 30 ft. and was caused by an upward movement of the wall due to expansion of the outer leaf of cavity brickwork and arising from sulphate action. (Reproduced by permission of the Controller, H.M. Stationery Office.)

TESTING CONCRETE WEATHERING QUALITIES

Fig. 8. Specimens of various concrete mixes, made up into thin slabs, exposed on roof to determine their weathering qualities. (Reproduced by permission of the Controller, H.M. Stationery Office.)

and then transport them direct to building sites. At present, however, the cost of plastics is too high, and the supplies are too limited for them to be used as structural building materials. It is for the future to show that they can be effectively used in combination with other materials, and a new building technique evolved.

Plastics can be coloured both in gloss and matt. Our future houses may be brightly coloured and do much to cheer up drab neighbourhoods. We may even see the colours of Italy in our industrial towns. These are the hopes of the advocates of plastics, but hopes may prove to be illusory when tested scientifically.

In all these and many other ways the scientist is enabling the architect and the builder to be free from out-of-date limitations. Although science moves slowly it moves surely. Those who wish to study its developments as applied to building should read the various publications of the Building Research Station, details of which can be ob-

tained from H.M. Stationery Office.

Apart from pure scientific research for which the Building Research Station, at a cost of some £80,000 from public funds, as well as the laboratories attached to private firms, are responsible, there is also the important question of economic research aimed at improving building efficiency. Waste of labour, materials, and manufacture have imposed unnecessary burdens in the past on the community.

Several years ago a Committee of the Federated American Engineering Societies estimated that 53 per cent of building operations represented waste. In Great Britain, out-of-date regulations, thoughtless demands made by owners, bad organization by clerks of works and foremen, and slackness by the operatives, have admittedly slackened the pace of building. Every day's delay means that capital is unproductive for an unnecessary period.

In the United States, as well as in Europe, there has recently been an

enormous advance in both mechaniza-
tion and standardization. By the use of
labour-saving devices, including electric
handsaws, planes, hammers, screwdrivers, mortisers, drills, grinders and
polishers, much time has been saved.
There has been a quickening up in
certain service centres. The influence of
American and Canadian technical
soldiers and airmen doing constructional
work will be considerable upon British
workers. But it is still true to say that the
actual process of assembling various
materials so as to form a building has
lagged behind other industries.

There will be a very great demand
for new homes in the future, and
economic science will have to be allowed
to play its part in order to bring the
house-building industry up to date.
This has already been recognized by the
Ministry of Works, which recently sent

to the United States several experts
who have studied American building
methods, which in some respects are
ahead of Great Britain.

Prefabrication

Of particular interest is what is known
as the prefabricated house. The walls,
windows, floors and roofs of small
houses are built in factories, and then
carried in sections to sites, where they
only require to be bolted together. In
the United States thousands of such
houses have been erected in workshops
and carried on trucks. In this country
our scientists may be able to discover
new ways of treating timber and its
derivatives such as plywood and wood-
fibre board, and using these as suitable
material for prefabricated houses.
Already the Forest Products Research
Laboratory has been carrying out

NOVEL METHOD OF CONCRETE ARCH CONSTRUCTION

Fig. 9 (*Left*). View taken during the construction of the curved roof of a 20-ft. span arched structure,
showing arrangement of the concrete blocks and dowels to dispense with centering. (*Right*) Detail
of concrete dowel block showing the use of wooden wedges to adjust the curve of the arch. (Reproduced by permission of the Controller. H.M. Stationery Office.)

interesting experiments on home-grown timbers, such as beech, birch and poplar, and it has been found that these woods can be used for the manufacture of excellent plywood.

Future Building Materials

For example, in place of the ordinary brick or stone house, we may see in the future many thousands of homes for ex-Service men and others built of a mixture of plywood and synthetic resins.

It has, however, to be remembered that whatever advances science may make in the laboratory, the results have to be applied to the building. This necessitates knowledge on the part of the men actually doing the work. Technical education will be the handmaid of scientific advance. It is therefore hoped that we shall see a development of technical schools for the building industry, which have suffered much during wartime, and which go far to meet post-war needs. The training given should form part of a definite apprenticeship.

Junior Technical Schools

The Ministry of Works experts are responsible for a circular recently issued by the Board of Education, urging the importance of greatly increased provision in junior technical schools for the training of recruits to the building industry. But higher education must start with the architects, and it is satisfactory to know that the Royal Institute of British Architects is reconsidering and revising its own views. During the past fifty years architectural education has passed from a training influenced by the *beaux arts* to a greater appreciation of scientific and technical developments.

We shall, in fact, in the future, have to take every possible advantage of

science in order to rebuild quickly the bombed cities, which will be the tragic legacies of war destruction in so many countries. We shall have to avoid the mistakes made in Great Britain after the last war, and welcome every possible improvement in materials, machinery and methods which may eliminate waste and improve production.

Mass Production of Houses

Although there is much prejudice against mass production of houses, it may well be that good houses, well designed, and equipped with such amenities as refrigerators, thermostatic controls, central heating, which have, up to now, been mainly confined to the wealthy, will be made available for the many. Rationalization, based on the more recent discoveries of science, may well provide the 4,000,000 houses needed in a reasonable time.

The advocates of mass production and prefabrication do not want all houses to be built alike, but that the houses shall be built of layer preassembled sections of many designs, so that building operations will be greatly speeded up. A rich variety of form, colour and texture can be made available if only prejudiced influences can be put on one side. The advance that can be made by making the fullest possible use of science will have immense social possibilities. With a greater efficiency and speed in building, more convenient homes at less cost can be provided; and there is little doubt that the building trade will meet all the demands made by the acute housing shortage.

It needs no Utopian vision to see that soon there may be created in this country new domestic and civic forms of building construction which will have a lasting and beneficial effect on the present and future generations.

CHAPTER 17

BUILDING AND ARCHITECTURE

Three conditions. Evolution. Periods in architecture : Prehistoric, Egyptian, Greek, Roman, Byzantine and Early English, Gothic, Renaissance, and the Transitional Period. The Great Hall. Town and country houses. Use of new materials. Twentieth-century development. Present and future.

"THE end of architecture is to build well. Well building hath three conditions: commoditie, firmness and delight," wrote Sir Henry Wotten in 1624. These three conditions are timeless: Commodity: the arrangement of the plan units to satisfy the social requirements; firmness: the disposition of the structure to give shelter and stability; delight: the ability of combining firmness and commodity to give visual and sensual pleasure.

Creating Architecture

This book is mainly concerned with the second of these conditions, "firmness." The number of trades and techniques discussed in the many chapters reveal how complex has become this side of building. At the same time the growth of civilization has produced an increase in the number of uses for which building is required. The vast amount of information in these two fields needs to be organized so that out of it all can emerge buildings which are both stable structurally and convenient for use.

This is where the architect comes in. The architect's task is to co-ordinate building needs with the resources of science and industry—and to create architecture.

Throughout history architecture has evolved naturally in this way—by a blending of existing techniques and

materials with the social requirements of the times. And throughout history the third requirement, delight, has been present at this blending through the skill and knowledge of the blender.

From earliest times new social demands and new materials have ever led to continual adjustments in building and thus to a continuous series of new styles. Wherever in the past we have found a bad period of building, it has always taken place because the co-ordinator—the architect—has lost touch with one or other of these aspects. The chaotic flounderings of style in the Victorian era, for instance, were the result of the architect failing to adjust himself to the new materials of the time—iron and glass. This failure to adjust technique to new circumstances and materials has occurred in varying degrees through history, but always, inexorably, in the end the far-seeing man is justified; and out of chaos a new building era begins and a new style is founded. This is how history is created.

Prehistoric

At the beginning of life on this globe the separation between human and beast was comparatively slight, and men and women lived in conditions similar to the animals. But a primitive desire for shelter soon arose and caves probably formed the earliest homes. Then the use of wood was discovered together with methods of cutting it. This led to a primitive tent form in which boughs were leant against each other, bound at the apex and covered with brush and moss to keep out the weather. Later a simple post and lintel system was evolved by making use of the same materials.

THE PYRAMIDS

Fig. I. The pyramids are one of the earliest building forms, and were erected by means of an unlimited supply of slave labour. They are built of massive rough blocks of stone.

Egyptian

The Egyptians with their early civilization took this post and lintel a stage further by the discovery of new materials—stone and, to a lesser and less successful extent, mud bricks. Life was still primitive, and the priests, who did most of the building, took care to keep the people in ignorance and subjection. Their slave labour, therefore, was completely unskilled, and buildings were formed from massive rough blocks of stone used vertically as columns and horizontally as beams. Little decoration was used and the scale was huge, as can be seen from the Pyramids (Fig. 1) still standing in Egypt today.

Greek

With the advent of the power of Greece came a new mode of life. Greek culture and philosophy reached a very high standard, and more than any race before or since, the Greeks evolved a philosophy of life based on simplicity. The post and lintel form of construction was still in use and continued throughout this era, in spite of the fact that the arch form (Fig. 2) had been discovered and rejected as being too complicated.

The Greeks approached building as they approached life. They were artists rather than architects; and the incredible subtleties and refinements which

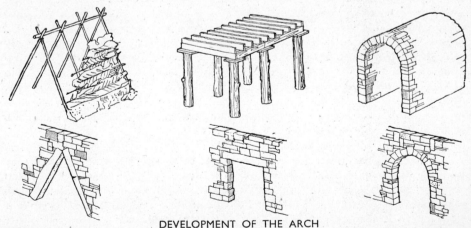

DEVELOPMENT OF THE ARCH

Fig. 2. (*Left*) Lean-to. (*Centre*) Post and lintel. (*Right*) Arch and barrel vault. These sketches show the development of methods of spanning a compartment and of forming an opening in a wall. All building construction is dependent upon these two simple requirements.

THE PARTHENON, ATHENS

Fig. 3. All that remains of the Parthenon. The small scale and direct simplicity of the Grecian form of construction are in strong contrast to the complicated grandeur of Roman architecture.

they managed to produce from their simple building forms were revealed by the brilliancy of the Mediterranean sun.

Their buildings became largely backgrounds to their sculpture, and the layout of these was governed more by aesthetic reasons than by reasons of circulation and accessibility. This is shown in the Parthenon, Athens (Fig. 3).

Roman

With the ascendancy of the Roman Empire came a completely new form of planning and structure. The simplicity of Grecian life was supplanted by a very highly-developed civilization. Rome's conquests and trade gave her new interests, new visions and new wealth. As the centre of a vast Empire her life became more complicated and complex, and her buildings and towns became more magnificent and splendid. Out of Roman Imperialism came the "grand plan." The ruins of many examples of huge amphitheatres, baths and temples may still be seen in Italy today.

The Romans were helped in their new ideas of building by the discovery of pozzolana, out of which was made a strong form of concrete. With this homogeneous jointless material they developed the arch form, the barrel vault (the arch over a long cell), and the dome (the arch over a circular cell).

With their structure the Romans were, for their times, incredibly daring, with their aesthetics absurdly timid. They were fascinated by the aesthetic perfection of the Greeks, and used Greek motifs and decoration merely to mask their new structural forms. In consequence the detail in their buildings became coarse and meaningless.

With the defeat of her armies abroad and the inability to replenish her supplies of wealth and slave-power began the fall of the Roman Empire. Inexorably the greatness of Rome faded and the extent of her achievements was lost. Her greatest contribution to architecture, her essays in grand planning with large-scale buildings, were forgotten for centuries until the Renaissance brought new interest in Classical design.

Byzantine and Early English

With the rise of Christianity came a new religious belief to the people, and a demand for new types of buildings. The first Christian churches were very simple and consisted of a nave and aisles. Columns, many of them from Classical

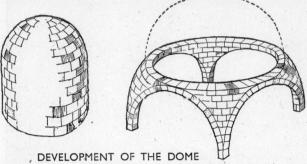

DEVELOPMENT OF THE DOME

Fig. 4. (*Left*) Dome over circular cell. (*Right*) Dome on pendentives. Earlier domes developed directly from the barrel vault and were constructed over circular compartments. The discovery of the pendentive permitted the use of a dome over a square compartment.

temples, were used to line the nave, and spans and openings were bridged with stone or wood lintels, the outside walls being solid. Later the arch was extensively used, and then the dome (Fig. 4), not only over a circular cell, but, on discovery of the pendentive, over a square.

With the end of slave labour, concrete construction was found to be uneconomical, and light volcanic stones and small bricks took its place. The lightness of the new material helped considerably in reducing sideways thrusts and thus diminishing the massive thickness of walls necessary to withstand them. At the beginning, domes were even formed in regular diminishing rings of hollow earthenware urns bedded in mortar.

With the rise of the power of the Church its influence spread and its doctrine and its building increased throughout Europe. In each country the buildings adapted themselves to the peculiar circumstances governed by local climate and materials. In England this developed into the Norman style.

Gothic

It was soon found that it was possible to interpenetrate two similar barrel vaults to form what is called a cross vault. When this is done the curved

surfaces intersect to form sharp edges known as groins, each edge being straight on plan. Later, perhaps as emphasis, projecting ribs were used along these groins, and also directly across the barrel vault from pier to pier. These ribs finally became the structural members, and the spaces filled with stone slabs.

This form of construction was only possible over a square cell, and the width of a nave and the distance between wall piers had of necessity to be equal. If barrel vaults of different radii were intersected the top of the narrower one must be lower than that of the wider one, and a satisfactory simple penetration cannot be achieved

Pointed Arch

Many attempts were made to solve this problem, but none were satisfactory until the discovery of the pointed arch. This form of arch (Fig. 5) can be any height in relation to its width, and vaulting over a rectangular space can be achieved by using two arches of differing widths but of the same height. The pointed arch marked the beginning of what we now know as the Gothic style —although the term Gothic was not invented until Renaissance times, when it was used as a term of disparagement about what was then considered an impure form of Romanesque architecture.

Gothic architecture lasted in this country from the twelfth century to the fifteenth century. It is largely an ecclesiastic form of architecture and finds expression in a host of great churches and cathedrals. There was now complete unity of religious belief in Europe and the Roman Catholic Church was all

DOME OF ST. SOPHIA, ISTANBUL

This new Byzantine form of church construction was brought about and made possible by the advances in dome and pendentive design, as shown in Fig. 4.

powerful. Medieval life centred around the cathedral and in building it king and serf did more than provide a place for worship: through it they erected a monument to their beliefs.

Gothic is an architecture of small stones. Stone was less easily obtained and transported in Western Europe than it had been in the Mediterranean cradle of the world. With the increase in the number of stone joints came a reduction in scale and a gradual disuse of Classical detail, which relied mainly for its effect on a monolithic appearance. The reduction of the size of the building unit and the new scale produced a lightness of structure in direct contrast to the heavy mass construction of the Romans.

A Gothic cathedral, unlike a Roman building, is a frame structure. Its weight

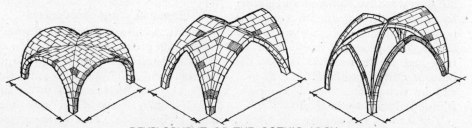

DEVELOPMENT OF THE GOTHIC ARCH

Fig. 5. (*Left*) Cross vault. (*Centre*) Gothic cross vault. (*Right*) Gothic rib-barrelling structure. The cross vault formed by the intersection of two barrel vaults can only be formed over a square compartment. The pointed arch obviates the necessity for this, as it can be any height relative to its span. Final development was to use the ribs as structural members to support stone slabbing.

WESTMINSTER ABBEY

Fig. 6. Note the complicated detail and the dynamic flying buttress system of this fine example of the later development of Gothic architecture. Buttresses assimilate the sideways thrusts of the walls.

is brought down to the ground at a number of isolated points rather than on continuous walls. The wall areas between these points of support now served no other purpose than to be weather-resisting screens. The discovery of stained glass provided an ideal material for these wall areas, and the size of windows grew until they finally occupied almost all the space between the supporting piers. Built with a multitude of small stones, each transmitting thrusts on to each other, this form of building was alive, dynamic and elastic. In direct contrast to the inherent stiffness of the Roman concrete vault, each arch and rib produced sideways thrusts that had to be resisted. It was the buttress that assimilated these thrusts, and by virtue of its own dead weight transferred them to the ground (Fig. 6).

The story of the evolution of Gothic architecture is the story of the craftsman's mastery over the complicated series of thrusts that these ribs and arches produced. It was an architecture

of craftsmen, and it was this craftsmanship which brought about its charm.

With each new cathedral and church the builders grew more daring. The ribs became more numerous and smaller, and the columns thinner and more widely spaced. The windows became larger and interlaced with intricate patterns of stone tracery. Buttresses became narrower, and, as the buildings grew in height, the outward thrust of the complicated roof vaulting was counteracted by flying buttresses.

Beginning of the Renaissance

Gothic architecture passed through three main phases which are known as "Early English," "Decorated" and "Perpendicular." By the time the last phase had been reached in the fifteenth century, the style had come to its logical conclusion. The wiriness and thinness of the design and the enthusiastic daring of the masons caused a series of structural collapses which convinced builders that they had reached the limit of their material. Even if there had been no new stimulus to encourage design into other directions, there could have been no further development here. But there was this stimulus. The Renaissance had begun.

With the decline of the feudal system in Western Europe, power shifted from the Church to a new land-owning class. Travel became easier, and there was a revival of interest in the antique. The invention of printing brought about a new access to ancient learning, and admiration for the literature of Rome led to admiration for its buildings. The Classical influence first showed itself in the design of the mouldings and detail on Gothic buildings; then these buildings lost the traditional informality and irregularity of Gothic architecture, and became much more formal both in plan and in elaboration of detail.

Classic Architecture

Finally, Gothic construction was largely superseded by the more rigid Classic approach to form. These changes were very gradual and spread over a number of years. It was in Italy that this new style started, the Renaissance style based on the Classic architecture of ancient Rome. Classic Roman detail was used again, but with more refinement; and the "grand plan" was reintroduced and developed with a freshness which the Romans had lost.

An important advance was in the design of domes. Whereas the Romans had built a number of domed buildings, externally they had hidden the dome by their roof structure. Renaissance architects, however, gave prominence to the dome as an architectural feature by raising it on a cylindrical drum, usually encircled by a colonnade. There was now no unlimited slave labour and these new fine buildings were erected slowly and laboriously by a team of craftsmen.

These were the craftsmen who produced the fine detail for which Renaissance architecture is famed.

In England the change between Gothic and Renaissance occupied what is called the "Transitional Period." Tudor and Elizabethan England also experienced a great change. In the middle of the sixteenth century Henry VIII dissolved the monasteries, assumed the title of the "Supreme Head of the Church of England," and distributed the wealth and lands of the Church to the people. This new land-owning class started at a time when enterprise was being encouraged by new world exploration and discoveries. Trade of all kinds increased, and wealth was now beginning to enrich merchants and traders.

This was, in fact, the birth of the Middle Class. With it came a general increase in learning and education and a desire for houses to suit the new needs. Life had become more secure, and the necessity for castles built for defence had disappeared.

The evolution of the house plan sprang from the great hall of the medieval castle. In medieval times this hall was a multi-purpose room which served as shelter to the whole household. In it the lord and his family and their retainers lived. The hall was heated by an open fire in the middle, and smoke escaped as best it could through a hole in the roof. The walls were of rough stone and the roof was of timber covered with thatch. Windows were small both for defence reasons and because glass, when it was obtainable, could only be used in small sizes. Kitchen quarters were added later, and an entrance gallery formed by placing a screen between these and the hall. Then sleeping accommodation for the family, often two storeys high, was added at the other end of the hall. These changes came gradually until,

BLICKLING HALL, NORFOLK

Fig. 7. A beautiful example of the development of the country house in Renaissance times, when a more general appreciation of good design in architecture and building began to develop.

with the Renaissance in the sixteenth century, the retainer became the servant and now had his own quarters, while the accommodation for the family had been extended to include a series of new living-rooms in addition to the private sleeping apartments.

Brick came in as a building material and houses were built on several floors. With the new Classical approach these plan units were assembled in a more formal manner. Plans became symmetrical and balanced about a central axis. With the increase of cultural knowledge design became all important, and buildings tended to become visual works of art. To gain this, function was often forfeited and the service rooms inefficiently placed in relation to their use. There was, however, a more universal appreciation of good design, and the arts now held a high place in the social structure (Fig. 7).

This period produced many fine architects such as Inigo Jones and Wren. The Classical influence also spread to lay-out, garden design and town-planning. Many fine examples of these remain today in our London squares, and the formal gardens attached to such great houses as Blenheim.

Towards the end of this Renaissance period there came a gradually increas-ing demand for town houses. The extent of the overseas trade gave a new prominence to towns and many more people came to live in them. This new town dweller now developed into a new land-owning class who possessed a very pronounced cultural education and a keen civic sense. The design of a town house was a completely new problem.

Whereas the country house was usually surrounded by many acres of land, the town house had of necessity to be near to its neighbour. Architects therefore were now confronted with a new factor—the design of a street.

The Georgian town house of the eighteenth century was a natural solution to this problem. Here the house is used as a unit in the general street design. Selfish individual preferences are sublimated to the advantage of the community, and through this good taste on the part of those responsible for building a high degree of design reigned.

Nineteenth Century

Meanwhile, however, other influences were at work. The Industrial Revolution was gradually changing Britain from an agricultural into an industrial country. The invention of steam power produced a stream of inventions for speeding up all forms of manufacture.

With it came a demand for labour in the coal mines and in the now growing industrial centres. Britain's facilities for overseas trade increased these demands, for the strength of her navy ensured deliveries of her commercial undertakings abroad. This expansion and drift of population did not spread itself evenly through the whole of the country, but concentrated in areas where cheap power made manufacture and commerce easier.

The uncontrolled and rapid growth of these towns produced a whole series of new requirements for building types which had never existed in the past. The old factory buildings became unsuitable for the new machinery, and the existing houses quite insufficient to house the growing new army of workers. The invention of the railway brought a new need for bridges and railway stations; increased inland traffic demanded better roads; and the growing merchant service required new docks and dock buildings. The new large and ever-increasing communities created an unprecedented demand for hospitals, schools, shops and other public buildings.

New Materials

Along with these new demands came new materials. Iron, steel, and glass provided untold possibilities for new ways of providing shelter for the new activities. They also provided builders of the times with countless troubles. The architect of those times was still engrossed by the artistic side of his profession. Returning from his travels in Rome and Greece he was exercising his talents by scholarly handling of Classical detail. The type of clients for whom he built encouraged this, and from it came fine houses for the wealthy and an occasional church and civic building.

Now the new and different social requirements and the newly available materials produced problems which could not satisfactorily be answered in this way. It took a long time for this fact to sink home both to the architects and to those for whom they built. It is not universally appreciated even to this day.

To start with, the architect continued to mask his buildings with a veneer of classical detail. The absurdity of this grew with the complications of the buildings' requirements. The newly obtainable building heights, and demands for good natural lighting, were quite incompatible with correct classical proportions and the solid monumentality of heavy classical masonry. The cost and labour involved in providing this inefficient and complicated face to a building were great and unjustified. Through this false vision architecture was becoming separated from its natural function of building, and degenerating into a mere decorative art. This degeneration led to the Classic and Gothic Revival styles for which the Victorian Age became infamous.

Structural Engineers

Now that the architect had become interested only in decoration the development of structure was being handled by a new professional man—the engineer. The engineers were responsible for the advances in the use of the new materials. Progress was necessarily slow but while the public were blinded by the writings of John Ruskin and William Morris into accepting the self-conscious pseudo-art of the time as the beginning and end of architecture, the engineers were too intrigued by the possibilities of the new materials and techniques to be affected by these negative consequences of the Industrial Revolution. With calm deliberation they examined and experimented with the possibilities and limitations of these new materials.

The strength of steel and iron in relation to its size was soon appreciated and many original new structures appeared, mostly in the form of road and railway bridges. Soon, slender iron columns were used to support the new iron arch forms, and the spans of the arches became bigger, giving grand opportunities for large buildings with an uninterrupted floor space.

The full effects of this change were first very forcibly revealed in the Crystal Palace designed for the Great Exhibition of 1851. The designer of this interesting building was neither an architect nor an engineer, but a gardener. Joseph Paxton, head gardener to the Duke of Devonshire, based his design on his previous experience.of greenhouses. His building was an iron skeleton sheathed in glass. The weight of the glass and of the supporting arches was transferred to the ground by a grid of uniformly spaced cast-iron columns.

The building units were carefully designed and standardized throughout. Every sheet of glass in the building, for instance, was the same size.

This type of construction was adapted with great success to the now rapidly growing railways, and examples of its use may still be seen today at many of the great railway termini, such as King's Cross, St. Pancras and Paddington.

But, whereas the engineers at this time produced by their detachment and experimentation logical forms of structure using the new materials, they did not necessarily produce fine architecture. The training of an engineer does not include a knowledge of the use of form and masses to produce beauty. A well-trained engineer will produce a sound building, but not necessarily good architecture. The nineteenth century was fortunate in having a few great engineers gifted with a sense of form.

Famous Engineers

Among these, such men as Telford, Brunel (Fig. 8) and Barlow distinguished their work by using this aesthetic sense. Apart from these brilliant exceptions and their great influence on the future, the buildings of the time had little to offer. The separation of the architect and engineer had split up the three basic requirements of commodity, firmness and delight, and architecture suffered accordingly. The design of a

CLIFTON SUSPENSION BRIDGE

Fig. 8. Brunel's famous bridge near Bristol shows the new approach to building design brought about by the discovery of the many varied possibilities of iron and steel in building construction.

MODERN DESIGN IN SHOP CONSTRUCTION

This striking design for Messrs. Peter Jones' Stores introduces many original ideas. Note how the maximum of daylight is introduced; also how skilfully a heavy mass effect is avoided. (Architects: Messrs. Slater, Moberly & Uren, associated with Mr. W. Crabtree and Prof. C. H. Riley.)

building can never be disassociated from its structure.

Twentieth Century

Many of the troubles arising from the Industrial Revolution are with us today. In addition, the speed of modern civilization has given us many other problems. The new materials of the nineteenth century, still not completely mastered, have been supplemented by a growing new list.

Today, while we are still in the process of perfecting the use of steel and glass, we are confronted with the new possibilities of reinforced concrete, and of light-metal alloys and the rapidly developing field of plastics.

In addition, new factors have altered the whole course of our lives. The motor car, the aeroplane, wireless, television and the many other inventions and discoveries of the twentieth century have changed our whole mode of living.

From these new social conditions and the new materials, must come a new architecture. At present we are in the midst of growing pains. Progress has come too fast for us to keep up. Nevertheless now, as throughout history, arising out of the confusion is a band of pioneer architects who are continually striving to find a new expression to satisfy the new conditions and materials. It is upon the work of these men that the new architecture will be founded, an architecture firmly based still on "commodity, firmness and delight."

INDEX

(Figures in italics refer to illustrations)

ACKNOWLEDGMENTS

We are indebted to the following for kind permission to make use of illustrations :—
Holland & Hannen and Cubitts, Ltd.; Imperial Chemical Industries, Ltd.; The Grand Secretary, Freemasons' Hall, London; Kerner-Greenwood, Ltd. (Pudlo Waterproofing); Dudley Foundry Co. Ltd.; The Proprietors of "Building"; Scaffolding (Gt. Britain), Ltd.; Colthurst, Symons & Co. Ltd.; Cement and Concrete Association; Chance Brothers & Co. Ltd.; Mr. Gordon Smith, Kiln Specialist; Dorman Long & Co. Ltd.; Bakelite, Ltd.; The British Council; Messrs. Slater, Moberly & Uren, Architects.